SCIENTIFIC AMERICAN | **Resource Library**

Life Sciences 6

SCIENTIFIC AMERICAN

Resource Library

READINGS IN THE

Life Sciences   VOLUME **6**

OFFPRINTS 1029–1073

W. H. FREEMAN AND COMPANY   San Francisco

Each of the articles in this volume is available as a separate Offprint. For a complete listing of Offprints available in the Life Sciences, Chemistry, Physics, Technology, Psychology, the Social Sciences, the History and Philosophy of Science, and the Earth Sciences, write to W. H. Freeman and Company, 660 Market Street, San Francisco, California 94104 or to W. H. Freeman and Company, Ltd., Warner House, Folkstone, Kent.

Printed in the United States of America.
Library of Congress Catalog Card Number: 71-87739
Standard Book Number: 7167 0989-9

Organization of the  Resource Library

Subject Series:

The *SCIENTIFIC AMERICAN Resource Library* is a multi-volume compilation of more than 700 articles selected from the magazine. These are organized under five subject classifications.

Readings in Earth Sciences (2 volumes)
Readings in Life Sciences (7 volumes)
Readings in Physical Sciences and Technology (3 volumes)
Readings in Psychology (2 volumes)
Readings in Social Sciences (1 volume)

Numbering System:

Each article is numbered and the articles in the volumes are arranged in numerical order. The numbers assigned to each series are:

Earth Sciences, 801–999.
Life Sciences, 1–199 and 1001–1999.
Physical Sciences and Technology, 201–399.
Psychology, 401–599.
Social Sciences, 601–799.

Topic Index:

This index classifies the Readings in Life Sciences by topic. Note that articles from other subject series that are relevant to the topic are also listed.

Author Index:

The authors of the articles in all five subject series are given. The numbers after the authors' names are the article numbers, not page numbers.

Scientific American Offprints:

Every article in these volumes is published separately in the SCIENTIFIC AMERICAN Offprint Series and may be purchased in any quantity. Order by article number and title.
The number of each offprint corresponds to the number on each article in the Resource Library.
A catalog of SCIENTIFIC AMERICAN offprints may be obtained from the publisher.

Additions to the Series:

New titles are added to the SCIENTIFIC AMERICAN Offprint Series every month and when enough new articles on a subject are available, a new bound volume will be added to the *SCIENTIFIC AMERICAN Resource Library*.

W. H. Freeman and Company
660 Market Street, San Francisco, California 94104
Warner House, Folkestone, Kent, England

Contents

VOLUME **2**

Topic Index
Author Index

VOLUME 3

Topic Index
Author Index

VOLUME **4**

Topic Index
Author Index

VOLUME 5

Topic Index
Author Index

VOLUME **6**

Topic Index
Author Index

Topic Index

(This index includes not only the articles in Readings in the Life Sciences
but also relevant articles from other subject series.)

Author Index

(The authors of the articles in all five subject series are given here.)

A Abelson, P. H.   101
Adams, E.   1081
Adams, R. M.   606
Adolph, E. F.   1067
Alder, B. J.   265
Alfvén, H.   311
Allen, R. D.   182
Allfrey, V. G.   92
Allison, A. C.   1065, 1085
Amerine, M. A.   190
Amoore, J. E.   297
Anderson, D. L.   855
Andrew, R. J.   627
Arditti, J.   1031
Arnon, D. I.   75
Asch, S. E.   450
Astin, A. V.   326
Axelrod, J.   1015

B Bailey, Jr., H. S.   830
Baker, P. F.   1038
Bales, R. F.   451
Bandura, A.   505
Barnes, V. E.   802
Barnett, S. A.   1060
Barron, F.   432, 483
Bartholomew, G. A.   1120
Bascom, W.   828, 845
Baserga, R.   165
Bass, A. M.   263
Bassett, C. A. L.   1021
Bassham, J. A.   122
Batra, L. R.   1086
Batra, S. W. T.   1086
Beadle, G. W.   1
Bearn, A. G.   150
Beermann, W.   180
Benzer, S.   120
Benzinger, T. H.   129
Beranek, L. L.   306
Berelson, B.   621
Berger, H.   287
Berkowitz, L.   481
Berlyne, D. E.   500
Bernal, J. D.   267
Bernstein, J.   829
Beroza, M.   189
Best, J. B.   149
Bethe, H. A.   201
Bettelheim, B.   433, 439
Biale, J. B.   118
Biddulph, S. & O.   53
Bilaniuk, O.   284
Billingham, R. E.   148
Bitterman, M. E.   490
Blackler, A. W.   94
Blough, D. S.   458
Boehm, G. A. W.   258
Bogert, C. M.   1119
Bonner, J. T.   164, 1051
Botelho, S. Y.   194
Bower, T. G. R.   502
Boycott, B. B.   1006
Brachet, J.   90

Brady, J. V.   425
Bragg, L.   325
Braidwood, R. J.   605
Braude, A. I.   177
Braun, A. C.   1024
Brazier, M. A. B.   125
Brett, J. R.   1019
Brindley, G. S.   1089
Broadbent, D. E.   467
Bronowski, J.   291
Broom, R.   832
Brown, H.   102
Brown, Jr., J. F.   280
Brues, C. T.   838
Buchhold, T. A.   270
Bullen, K. E.   804
Bunnell, Jr., S.   483
Burbidge, G.   202, 203, 305
Burbidge, M.   203
Burnet, M.   2, 3, 78, 138
Buswell, A. M.   262
Butler, R. A.   426
Butler, W. L.   107
Butterfield, H.   607

C Cairns, J.   1030
Calhoun, J. B.   506
Calvin, M.   308
Caplan, N. S.   638
Carey, N.   4
Carr, A.   1010
Carter, A. P.   629
Cattell, R.   475
Ceraso, J.   509
Champagnat, A.   1020
Changeaux, J.   1008
Chapanis, A.   496
Chapman, C. B.   1011
Chew, G. F.   296
Clark, B. F. C.   1092
Clark, J. D.   820
Clarke, C. A.   1126
Clements, J. A.   142
Clevenger, S.   186
Clever, U.   180
Cobb, W. C.   109
Cockrill, R.   1088
Cohen, J.   427, 489
Colbert, E. H.   806
Cole, L. C.   144
Collier, H. O. J.   132, 169
Comer, J. P.   633
Comroe, Jr., J. H.   1034
Constantinides, P. F.   4
Cooper, C. F.   1099
Coopersmith S.   511
Corey, R. B.   31
Crary, A. P.   857
Crawford, Jr., B.   257
Crick, F. H. C.   5, 54, 123, 1052
Crombie, A. C.   184
Crow, J. F.   55
Csapo, A.   163
Cuff, Jr., F. B.   204

D Darrow, K. K.   205
Davidson, E. H.   1013
Davis, H. M.   206
Dawkins, M. J. R.   1018
De Benedetti, S.   207, 271
de Duve, C.   156
Deering, R. A.   143
Deevey Jr., E. S.   608, 811, 834, 840
de Heinzelin, J.   613
Delbrück, M.   1104
Delbrück, M. B.   1104
Denenberg, V. H.   478
Derjaguin, B. V.   266
DeVore, I.   614
Dietz, R. S.   801, 866
Dilger, W. C.   1049
Dirac, P. A. M.   292
Dobzhansky, T.   6, 609
Doty, P.   7
Doumani, G. A.   863
Dowling, J. E.   1053
Downs, R. J.   107
Dulbecco, R.   1069
Dyson, F. J.   208

E Eaton, J. W.   440
Ebert, J. D.   56
Eccles, J. C.   65, 1001
Echlin, P.   1044, 1105
Edgar, R. S.   1004, 1079
Edwards, R. G.   1047
Eglinton, G.   308
Ehrenberg, W.   317
Ehrlich, P. R.   1076
Eibl-Eibesfeldt, I.   470
Einstein, A.   209
Eiseley, L. C.   108, 846
Ellison, W. D.   817
Elsasser, W. M.   825
Emerson, R.   115
Emiliani, C.   815
Emlen, J. T.   1054
Epstein, R. H.   1004
Ericson, D. B.   856
Esch, H.   1071
Etkin, W.   1042
Eysenck, H. J.   477

F Fairbridge, R. W.   805
Fantz, R. L.   459
Feder, H. S.   281
Fender, D. H.   187
Ferster, C. B.   484
Festinger, L.   472
Field, W. O.   809
Fieser, L. F.   8
Fischberg, M.   94
Fisher, A. E.   485
Fisher, R. L.   814
Flyger, V.   1102
Fowler, W. A.   210
Fraenkel-Conrat, H.   9, 193
Franzini-Armstrong, C.   1007
Fraser, D.   59
Freedman, L. Z.   497

SCIENTIFIC AMERICAN | Resource Library

Life Sciences 6

SCIENTIFIC
AMERICAN   December 1965, Vol. 213, No. 6, pp. 76-84   OFFPRINT 1029

HEAT TRANSFER IN PLANTS

by David M. Gates

Plants, like animals, must regulate their temperature in order to function at optimum physiological efficiency. This is accomplished through three mechanisms: radiation, transpiration and convection.

There is an old Iowa saying that on a hot summer night one can hear the corn grow. This is no tall tale. Many physiological processes in plants depend primarily on temperature rather than on light, and among them is the enlargement and elongation of cells; if the weather is warm enough, corn will grow at night. A plant's temperature can also affect its photosynthetic activity, even though photosynthesis is primarily dependent on light. The photosynthetic process will slacken or halt if the plant's temperature gets too high or too low; it will reach an optimum at some intermediate temperature level. Evidently the temperature of a plant is a major factor in determining how efficiently the plant functions. But what determines the temperature of a plant?

The answer is that a plant's temperature is determined by its total environment. If the plant gives up more energy than it receives, it will become cooler; if it receives more energy than it gives up, it will become warmer. If the inward and outward flows of energy are equal, the plant is in thermal balance with its environment. Three separate phenomena govern the transfer of energy: radiation, transpiration and convection. In this article I shall first describe each of these processes and then consider some of the means by which they work together to regulate plant temperatures.

Radiation is quantitatively the most important of the three processes. In this connection it has two distinct forms. The first is solar radiation, the primary external source of energy for all physical and biological processes on the earth; this radiation is broadcast over a wide range of wavelengths [see top illustration on page 2034]. Second is thermal radiation; this is the energy emit-

ted by any object that is warmer than absolute zero. Thermal radiation is broadcast within a much narrower band than solar radiation; objects with temperatures between zero and 50 degrees centigrade, for example, radiate only at infrared wavelengths, and their peak output is at a wavelength of about 10 microns.

Solar energy falls on the earth's upper atmosphere at an average rate of two calories per square centimeter per minute; this energy flow is known as the solar constant. Minor constituents of the atmosphere absorb portions of the sun's radiation at each end of the visible spectrum. The ozone in the upper atmosphere screens out ultraviolet radiation at wavelengths shorter than 2,900 angstrom units (.29 micron); water vapor and carbon dioxide do the same for infrared radiation at wavelengths longer than 22 microns. Although the resulting "window" in the earth's atmosphere is only a narrow band of the sun's entire radiant spectrum, the sun emits most of its energy at these visible wavelengths; consequently a large fraction of the solar constant reaches the earth's surface.

In summer the surface of the earth in the Temperate Zones receives solar energy at a rate of between 1.2 and 1.4 calories per square centimeter per minute; mountains and deserts, which are often free of cloud cover, may receive as much as 1.6 calories. The solar energy that impinges on a tree or a stalk of corn includes not only direct sunlight but also sunlight that has been scattered by the atmosphere and sunlight that is reflected up from the earth's surface or down from clouds. On high mountains, on which intense direct sunlight and sunlight reflected from clouds occasionally fall at the same time, radiation values go as high as 2.2 calories—higher than the solar constant.

Solar radiation affects the earth's surface only between sunrise and sunset; thermal radiation, on the other hand, is always present. Every part of the environment steadily broadcasts energy at infrared wavelengths. If human eyes were sensitive to infrared radiation, the daytime sky would not be blue. Instead broad shafts of different hues (the "colors" of different infrared wavelengths) would be seen extending from the sky to the ground and from the ground to the sky. Even during the day the total amount of thermal energy radiating from the ground and from the atmosphere can equal or exceed the sun's radiation.

If a plant continuously absorbed energy without dissipating any, its temperature would increase steadily until it had suffered heat death. In actuality plants dispose of considerably more than half of the radiant energy they absorb by reradiating it. Plants also transpire; this second process of energy transfer further helps to rid a plant of surplus heat.

Transpiration converts the water in the leaves of a plant from a liquid to a gas; the water vapor then passes from the leaf into the surrounding atmosphere. The process of evaporation consumes energy and the transpiring leaf grows cooler. The water vapor is emitted through the pores in the leaf called stomates; there can be as many as 20,000 of these openings in one square centimeter of leaf surface. Specialized sausage-shaped cells of the leaf epidermis, which are known as guard cells, control the opening and closing of the stomates. Normally the stomates are closed during the night and open during the day.

The effectiveness of transpiration in transferring energy can be judged by the fact that a transpiration rate of only five ten-thousandths of a gram of water per square centimeter per minute gives rise to an energy loss of approximately three-tenths of a calorie. This is enough to lower the temperature of a transpiring leaf by as much as 15 degrees C. The process of transpiration can nonetheless be halted under circumstances that seem to threaten the plant with imminent heat death.

As the morning passes on a warm summer day a plant's sunlit leaves steadily rise in temperature and their photosynthetic activity approaches the optimum rate. At midday, when the heat load is at its peak, each leaf's transpiration rate is also at its highest and produces the maximum cooling effect. In spite of this energy transfer, the temperature of the leaf now rises above the optimum level and the photosynthetic process slows down. The concentration of carbon dioxide in the leaf's guard cells increases; the cells react and close the leaf's stomates. This puts an end to further transpiration; the leaf's temperature rises even higher and photosynthesis stops. At this point the leaf wilts and the plant appears to be on the verge of thermal catastrophe.

Fortunately wilting changes the leaf's orientation with respect to direct sunlight, so that the heat load is reduced. A cooler leaf temperature may allow photosynthesis to resume, thus reducing the concentration of carbon dioxide in the guard cells and causing the stomates to reopen. Normally, however, once the leaf temperature has gone too high the leaf will remain wilted until the sun has fallen low in the sky and the air has cooled.

I witnessed a remarkable example of temperature control by transpiration in August, 1963, when I accompanied W. M. Hiesey, Harold W. Milner and Malcolm A. Nobs of the Carnegie Institution of Washington on a visit to the institution's botanical study area near Yosemite National Park in California's Sierra Nevada range. Our purpose was to record the leaf temperatures of native species of the monkey flower, *Mimulus,* at various altitudes. The day was dry and cloudless. As we climbed the slopes above the tree line, where the alpine species *Mimulus lewisii* grew at an altitude of 10,600 feet, the sunshine was brilliant and the sky had a clarity that is seldom seen at lower altitudes. There was no wind; the air temperature was 19 degrees C. We found that the temperature of the alpine species' sunlit leaves was warmer than the air; it

WARM PINE BRANCH is cooled by rising convection currents. Each needle yields some of its heat conductively to the cooler air in contact with the needle surface. As the air is heated it rises (*shadows above the branch in this schlieren photograph*). Cool air replaces it and repeats the process. The rising current is somewhat turbulent because of a slight wind.

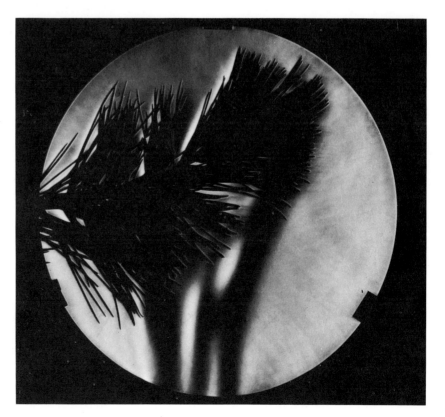

COOL PINE BRANCH that has lost heat by radiation to the night sky is warmed by falling convection currents. Each needle now absorbs heat from the warmer air in contact with its surface. As the air is cooled it sinks (*shadows below the branch in this schlieren photograph*). In both examples the heat transfer helps to stabilize the plant's temperature.

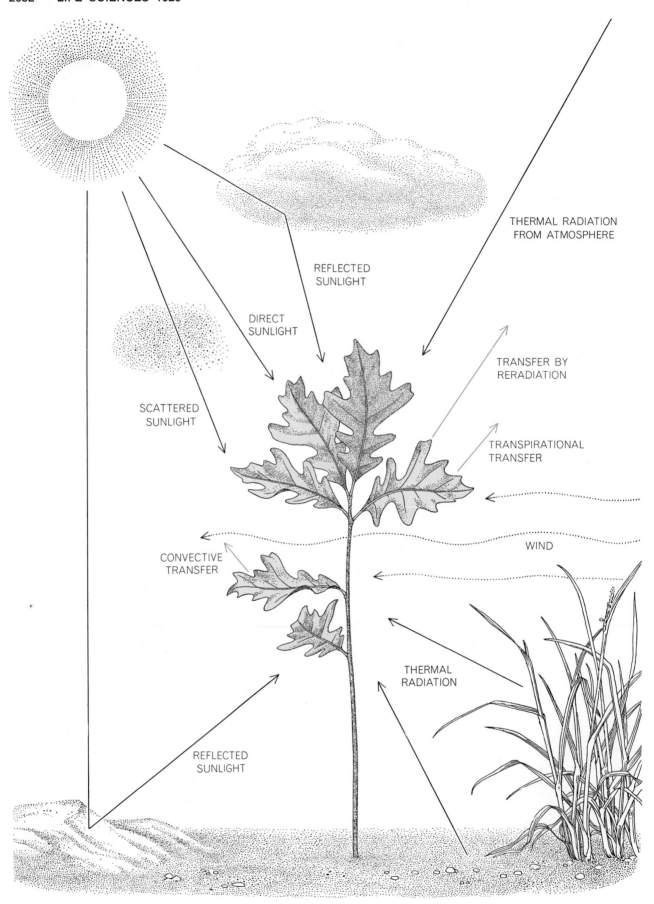

THERMAL RADIATION
FROM ATMOSPHERE

REFLECTED
SUNLIGHT

DIRECT
SUNLIGHT

TRANSFER BY
RERADIATION

SCATTERED
SUNLIGHT

TRANSPIRATIONAL
TRANSFER

CONVECTIVE
TRANSFER

WIND

THERMAL
RADIATION

REFLECTED
SUNLIGHT

EXCHANGE OF ENERGY between a plant and its environment is shown schematically. Of the two inputs, solar radiation reaches the plant as direct, scattered and reflected sunlight. The second input, the thermal radiation, is emitted at infrared frequencies by the atmosphere, the ground and other plants and animals. A plant would die of heat if most of this energy were not dissipated (*color*). The bulk of the heat load is reradiated; evaporative cooling by transpiration and heat transfer by convection removes the rest.

ranged between 25 and 28 degrees C. We returned to our jeep and quickly set off to check the temperatures of other monkey flowers growing at lower altitudes. On the edge of the San Joaquin valley, at an altitude of 1,300 feet, the sky was just as clear as it had been above the tree line and the air temperature was 37 degrees C. We examined some flowers of another species, *Mimulus cardinalis*, growing at this comparatively low altitude. I was quite prepared to predict that these sunlit leaves, which had a higher heat load than the alpine species, would yield temperature readings between 42 and 47 degrees C.

Instead the lowland leaves were cooler than the air surrounding them; their temperature ranged from 30 to 35 degrees C., not much warmer than the leaves above the tree line. This finding, contrary to all my previous experience, made me suspect that transpiration was involved. Monkey flowers are water-loving plants. Even the alpine species favor damp soil, and the plants we were examining in the valley grew along the border of a drainage ditch. When we measured the leaf temperatures of other species of plants growing in the same well-watered zone, they proved to be equally low. Then we tested the leaves of a live oak that was growing a few yards away in drier soil; their temperature was above the air temperature, ranging from 40 to 43 degrees C. It seemed likely that an abundant water supply, allowing liberal transpiration, accounted for the other plants' cooler temperatures.

This raised the question of whether the observations could be duplicated with monkey flowers raised in a growth chamber in which the temperature could be varied to match the range of natural conditions from valley to tree line. We placed monkey flower plants in a growth chamber under even and constant illumination and raised the air temperature successively from a low of 10 degrees C. to a high of nearly 60 degrees. The plants' leaf temperatures almost exactly duplicated those measured at various altitudes in the Sierras. It soon appeared that some kind of threshold effect was operating. When the air temperature was about 30 degrees C. or lower, the monkey flower leaves were warmer than the surrounding air; when the air temperature was raised above 30 degrees, the leaves remained cooler than the air.

As the leaf temperature rose, the plants' transpiration rate slowly increased until another kind of threshold

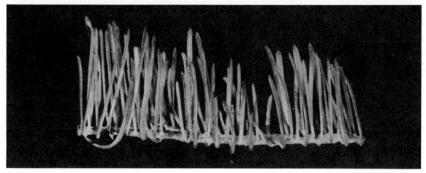

SILVER REPLICAS of conifer twigs were among the casts of various plants that the author made to determine which leaf shapes were the most efficient for heat transfer by convection. The conifers' cylindrical needles proved to be far superior to the flat leaf surfaces.

was reached at 41.5 degrees C. Just below that temperature the transpiration rate was about .0005 gram of water per square centimeter per minute. At the threshold temperature the rate jumped to .0022 gram, an increase of more than 400 percent. It was evident that a dramatic increase in leaf permeability took place at this temperature; the additional cooling effect was enough to prevent the monkey flower leaves from becoming warmer than 42 degrees C. even when the air temperature in the growth chamber was raised nearly 20 degrees higher than that.

A number of other plants—including species of cactus, agave, rhododendron and oleander—were included in these experiments. Their leaves also remained cooler than the air when the temperature was 30 degrees C. or higher, as long as the plants were watered abundantly. None of them, however, performed as dramatically as the monkey flowers.

These experiments clearly demonstrate that transpiration is an efficient mechanism for heat transfer in plants. Independent confirmation of this conclusion came recently from an experiment conducted at Purdue University. There G. D. Cook, J. R. Dixon and A. Carl Leopold painted the leaves of

tomato plants with a substance that prevented the stomates from opening. This treatment of course suppressed transpiration. When the experimenters then measured the temperature of treated and untreated leaves, they found that the transpiring leaves were cooler than the nontranspiring ones by 5 degrees C.

Convection, the third mechanism that allows energy transfer between a plant and its environment, has an important feature not shared by the other two. Radiation raises a plant's temperature and transpiration lowers it; convection will warm a cool plant or cool a warm one with equal facility, depending on whether the air is warmer or cooler than the plant. Convection acts across a thin atmospheric zone, known as the boundary layer, that surrounds all surfaces in still air. The rate at which energy is transferred across the boundary layer depends on the thickness of the layer and on the difference in temperature between the object and the atmosphere.

In still air the boundary layer is often about one centimeter thick. By means of schlieren photography, sometimes called shadow photography, the boundary layer and other regions of small variations in air density can be made

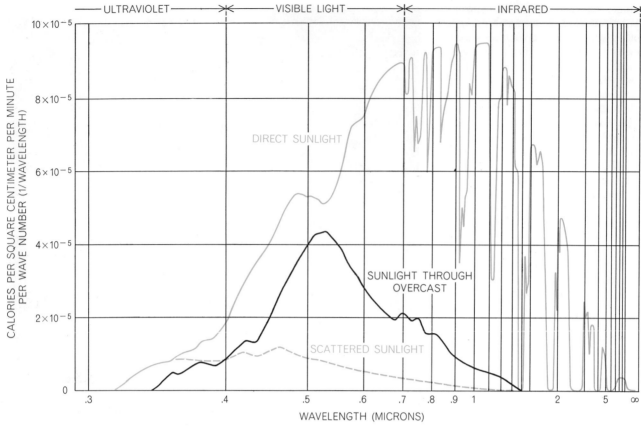

SOLAR RADIATION is not of equal intensity in all parts of the spectrum. Three curves show the variations from ultraviolet to infrared in the case of direct sunlight, of sunlight diffused through an overcast, and of sunlight scattered in the atmosphere. Divisions of the horizontal scale are proportional to frequency of radiation because the energy per quantum is similarly proportional. On this basis direct sunlight reaches peak intensity in the near infrared; how plants escape this heat load is shown in the illustration below.

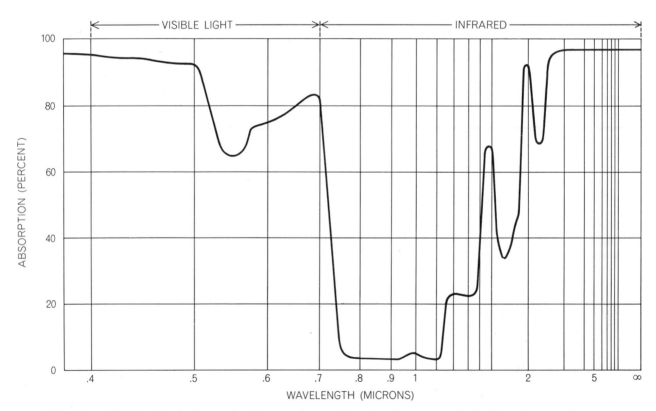

ABSORPTION OF ENERGY by the leaves of a plant averages nearly 90 percent of solar radiation in the spectral range from ultraviolet through visible frequencies. At near-infrared frequencies, however, absorption falls off sharply and stays at a low level throughout the range at which solar radiation is the most intense (*see illustration at top of page*). The curve shows absorption by a leaf of the poplar *Populus deltoides*; as at top, the divisions of the horizontal scale are proportional to the frequency of the radiation.

visible. Schlieren photography soon taught me that the air near the surface of a leaf is never really still. Consider a sunlit leaf becoming warm from solar radiation. If the air is cooler than the leaf, the molecules of gas in physical contact with the leaf's surface will be warmed by conduction and gain energy. The increase in the molecules' energy causes the mass of air to expand and rise like smoke going up a chimney [*see top illustration on page 2031*]. As warm air rises, cooler air replaces it along the leaf's surface; this air in turn is warmed, rises and is replaced, and thus the process of draining heat from the warm leaf continues.

At night, or whenever a leaf is cooler than the air, the situation is reversed. In darkness a leaf may emit more energy than it receives and become cooler than the surrounding air. Convection now forces the warmer air to give up energy to the cooler leaf. As the gas molecules lose energy the air sinks and streams downward to form a cool mass around the base of the plant [*see bottom illustration on page 2031*]. This reverse transfer warms the leaf and tends to stabilize its temperature at a point near the temperature of the surrounding air.

A decrease in the efficiency of this energy transfer, which may occur on clear and still nights when the air temperature falls to near the freezing point, can bring disaster to a citrus grove. The leaves and fruit, radiating to the cold sky, can fall several degrees below air temperature and freeze. One way to combat this result is to use wind machines that create strong air currents among the trees. The airflow increases the rate of energy transfer from the warmer atmosphere to the cold trees and keeps them above the freezing temperature.

As the example of the citrus grove suggests, even a small amount of air movement rapidly destroys the boundary layer and thereby increases the rate of conductive heat transfer. As long as the flow of air over the surface of a leaf remains laminar, or unturbulent, the rate of heat transfer remains proportional to the square root of the wind velocity. The flow of air through vegetation, however, quickly becomes turbulent, and when this occurs the transfer rate becomes almost proportional to the actual wind velocity.

In a study of comparative convection efficiencies Frank Kreith, Cam Tibbals and I made precise silver casts of leaves and branches at the University of Colorado and measured the proper-

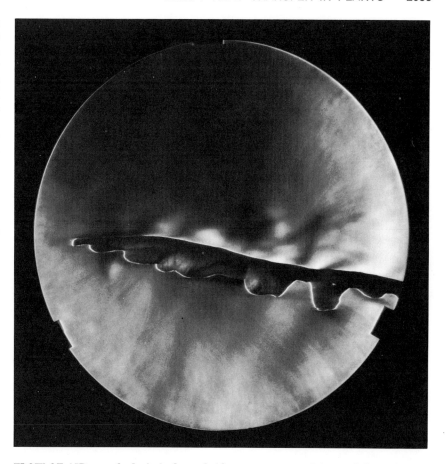

FLOW OF AIR over the leaf of a bur oak (*Quercus macrocarpa*) is revealed in schlieren photograph. Laminar near the leaf tip (*left*), the flow becomes quite turbulent farther along the leaf surface. This accelerates convection and also carries away transpired water vapor.

ties of the casts in a wind tunnel. It soon became clear that, as leaf size increased, the amount of heat transferred to the air by convection per unit of surface area became smaller. The air flowing across the surface of a leaf cast quickly approached the temperature of the surface; as the gradient between the temperature of the air and the temperature of the surface decreased so did the air's capacity for energy transfer over the downstream remainder of the surface.

The wind tunnel studies of silver casts showed that, per unit of surface area, the rate of energy transfer by convection would be many times greater for a pine needle than for a poplar leaf. Moreover, when the pine needle cast and poplar leaf cast were exposed to equal amounts of radiation, the temperature of the pine needle cast remained much closer to the air temperature than did that of the poplar leaf cast. These studies obviously could not account for cooling effects that would have been operated if our silver casts had been capable of transpiration.

The roles that radiation, transpiration and convection play in the life of

a plant during the daylight hours are quite different from the roles they play at night. In daylight, for example, the energy budget for a horizontally oriented leaf exposed to the noonday sun in still air has the following breakdown. Direct sunlight and sunlight scattered in the sky irradiate the leaf's upper surface at the rate of 1.4 calories per square centimeter per minute. In addition, perhaps 20 percent of the sunlight that strikes the ground nearby is reflected upward and irradiates the lower surface of the leaf; this adds another .28 calorie per square centimeter per minute to the leaf's potential absorption of solar energy. Actually the leaf absorbs only 60 percent of the solar radiation impinging on it, so that the total load of absorbed heat attributable to solar radiation is 1.01 calories per square centimeter per minute. In addition to this the leaf is exposed to thermal radiation. The flow of energy at infrared wavelengths down from the atmosphere and the flow up from the ground respectively add to the leaf's heat load at the rate of .5 and .6 calorie per square centimeter per minute. The leaf absorbs 100 percent of this radiation, bringing the total input of radiant energy up to a rate of 2.11 calories per square centimeter per minute.

Assuming a leaf temperature of 36 degrees C. and a transpiration rate of .00054 gram per square centimeter per minute, the leaf will start to balance its energy budget by reradiating 68 percent (1.44 calories) of the radiant energy it is absorbing. Transpiration will dissipate an additional 29 percent (.62 calorie) of the load. Only 3 percent of the total (.05 calorie) remains to be disposed of by convection cooling. This is quite a small figure, but we have been assuming that the leaf is in still air; given a wind, convection would account for a much larger part of the energy transfer and might even play a larger role than transpiration.

At night a different series of transfers is required to keep the energy budget in balance. First, with the leaf stomates closed, transpiration is negligible. Second, as the leaf temperature drops below the temperature of the surround-

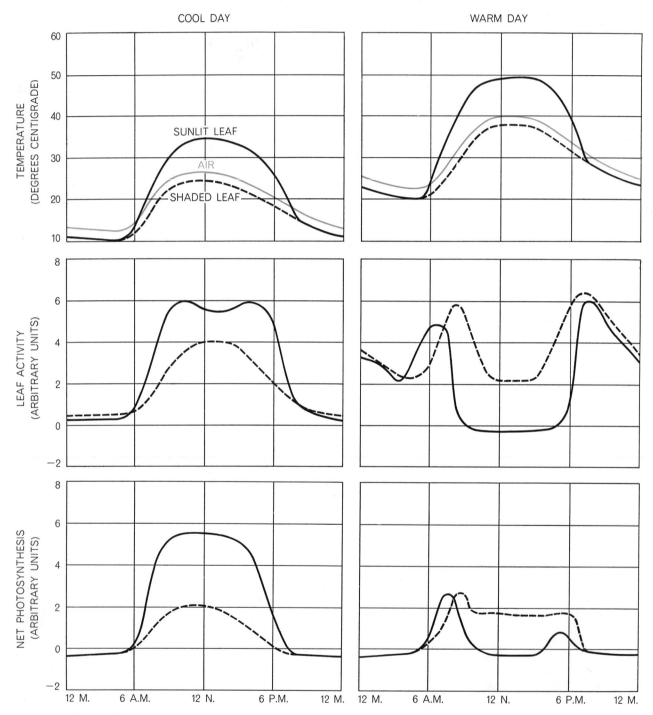

COOL DAY — WARM DAY

COOL SUMMER DAY produces sharply contrasting performances by a sunlit and a shaded leaf. Between sunrise and sunset the sunlit leaf is much warmer than the air (*top*). Its warmth favors physiological activity (*center*); net photosynthesis during the hours of daylight (*bottom*) attains a high level. The shaded leaf never gets enough light to engage in strong photosynthetic activity.

WARM SUMMER DAY produces the opposite effect by bringing the sunlit leaf to the brink of thermal catastrophe. As the leaf temperature rises during the forenoon it soon reaches the level at which biochemical activity is inhibited; photosynthesis stops (*bottom*) and cannot resume until late afternoon. In contrast, the shaded leaf is near optimum temperatures during most of the day.

ing air the convection process ceases to extract energy from the leaf and adds energy instead. Third, between sunset and sunrise the leaf has no solar radiation load to cope with. Although thermal radiation continues throughout the night, even the output of this energy source is somewhat reduced. The night budget has the following breakdown.

Thermal radiation from the atmosphere reaches the leaf at a rate of .4 calorie per square centimeter per minute, compared with the daylight rate of .5 calorie. Thermal radiation from the ground adds .55 calorie per minute, compared with the daylight rate of .6 calorie. The total night heat load from radiation is thus only .95 calorie per square centimeter per minute. Assuming still air, an air temperature of 15 degrees C. and a leaf temperature of 10 degrees, an additional .04 calorie per minute (4 percent of the total heat load) will be supplied to the leaf by convection. The energy input from radiation and convection combined comes to less than one calorie per square centimeter per minute. Reradiation suffices to dispose of this small input and balance the energy budget.

In nature, of course, matters are by no means as simple. There are cool days and warm nights; there are winds, clouds and overcast skies. The variations in energy transfer and fluctuations in leaf temperature under such changing circumstances are evident from a few examples of leaf-temperature readings I made during the summer in the yard of my former home in Boulder, Colo. I found that on overcast days all leaf temperatures remained below the temperature of the air. On cloudy days the leaf temperatures shifted rapidly from 6 to 8 degrees C. above the air temperature to 2 to 4 degrees below it as the clouds alternately exposed and obscured the sun. In the middle of a sunny summer day leaves that were exposed to the sun were warmer than the air by 5 degrees or more; the highest leaf temperature I recorded at Boulder—51 degrees C.—was 22 degrees warmer than the air. Leaves that were in the shade on the same kind of day, however, ranged from close to air temperature to as much as 5 degrees below it.

Each such variation naturally affects the plant's physiological activities. A sunlit leaf's approach to thermal catastrophe was described earlier; the midday heat load broke the leaf's photosynthetic activity into morning and afternoon intervals. A leaf that had been in shade throughout such a day would easily outdo the sunlit leaf in total photosynthetic

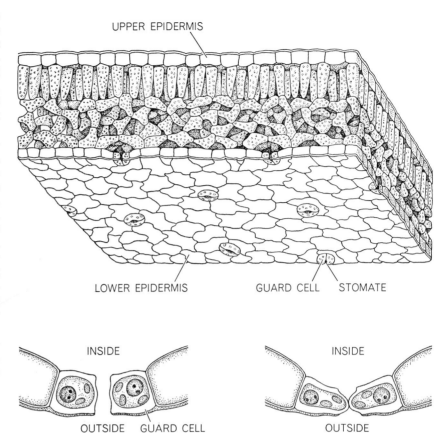

UPPER EPIDERMIS

LOWER EPIDERMIS   GUARD CELL   STOMATE

INSIDE   INSIDE

OUTSIDE   GUARD CELL   OUTSIDE

LEAF CROSS SECTION shows the paired sausage-shaped guard cells that control the opening and closing of the stomates, through which water vapor is emitted during transpiration. Stomates are normally closed at night and open during the day. Details show how guard cells bend to form an opening when turgid with moisture (*lower left*) but straighten to close when less turgid (*lower right*). An excess of carbon dioxide also closes the cells.

production. By the same token the pattern of energy transfers during a cool summer day would favor the sunlit leaf and prevent the shaded leaf from reaching the optimum temperature range for photosynthesis.

In spite of such variations there appears to be a balance of factors working in favor of overall plant efficiency. First, the energy transfers we have noted—which tend to keep leaves warmer than cool air but cooler than warm air—serve to maintain the leaves reasonably near the temperature range for optimum physiological activities. Second, taking photosynthesis as an example, the optimum temperature range for the process varies a great deal. For many plants in temperate regions the optimum ranges from 25 degrees C. to 30 degrees; the optimum for arctic and alpine plants can be as low as 15 degrees. One indication of how such optimums may have evolved has been discovered by H. A. Mooney of the University of California at Los Angeles. Mooney and his associates have found that the optimum temperature for photosynthesis depends

at least in part on a plant's own life history. When they were raised under conditions of moderately low temperature, Mooney's experimental plants achieved optimum photosynthesis at one temperature level. When they were acclimatized to warmer temperatures, optimum photosynthesis occurred at temperatures as much as 5 degrees higher than before. This kind of adaptability would be vitally important to plant populations that were extending their range into extreme environments.

In summary, it has been shown that one of the key interactions between a plant and its environment is transfer of energy between the two; the transfers determine the plant's temperature and the plant's temperature affects its physiological efficiency. A question that remains unanswered is why it is that different plants show optimum efficiency at different temperatures. The eventual answer to this question will probably involve the catalytic activity of plant enzymes; when it is found, it should open the door to the understanding of a fundamental mechanism in the ecological system of our planet.

The Author

DAVID M. GATES is director of the Missouri Botanical Garden in St. Louis and professor of botany at Washington University. "As a boy," he writes, "I walked in the footsteps of my father, an eminent ecologist and botanist, as we studied the forests, dunes, bogs and beaches of northern Michigan." He found, however, that "biology then was not sufficiently quantitative or analytical, and physics captured my imagination." He obtained bachelor's, master's and doctor's degrees at the University of Michigan, thereafter teaching physics and doing research in atmospheric physics for several years. But he "could not forget biology" and eventually returned to it because "to understand the natural ecosystems is the greatest challenge to man today," since "we are rapidly eroding the natural ecosystem from the surface of the earth and soon it will be too late to understand."

Bibliography

CONVECTION PHENOMENA FROM PLANTS IN STILL AIR. David M. Gates and Charles M. Benedict in *American Journal of Botany*, Vol. 50, No. 6 (Part I), pages 563–573; July, 1963.

ENERGY EXCHANGE IN THE BIOSPHERE. David M. Gates. Harper & Row, Publishers, 1962.

HEAT TRANSFER BETWEEN THE PLANT AND THE ENVIRONMENT. K. Raschke in *Annual Review of Plant Physiology*, Vol. 2, pages 111–126; 1960.

RADIATION AND CONVECTION IN CONIFERS. E. C. Tibbals, Ellen K. Carr, David M. Gates and Frank Kreith in *American Journal of Botany*, Vol. 51, No. 5, pages 529–538; May–June, 1964.

SCIENTIFIC
AMERICAN January 1966, Vol. 214, No. 1, pp. 36-44

OFFPRINT 1030

THE BACTERIAL CHROMOSOME

by John Cairns

When bacterial DNA is labeled with radioactive atoms, it takes its own picture. Autoradiographs reveal that the bacterial chromosome is a single very long DNA molecule and show how it is duplicated.

The information inherited by living things from their forebears is inscribed in their deoxyribonucleic acid (DNA). It is written there in a decipherable code in which the "letters" are the four subunits of DNA, the nucleotide bases. It is ordered in functional units—the genes—and thence translated by way of ribonucleic acid (RNA) into sequences of amino acids that determine the properties of proteins. The proteins are, in the final analysis, the executors of each organism's inheritance.

The central event in the passage of genetic information from one generation to the next is the duplication of DNA. This cannot be a casual process. The complement of DNA in a single bacterium, for example, amounts to some six million nucleotide bases; this is the bacterium's "inheritance." Clearly life's security of tenure derives in large measure from the precision with which DNA can be duplicated, and the manner of this duplication is therefore a matter of surpassing interest. This article deals with a single set of experiments on the duplication of DNA, the antecedents to them and some of the speculations they have provoked.

When James D. Watson and Francis H. C. Crick developed their two-strand model for the structure of DNA, they saw that it contained within it the seeds of a system for self-duplication. The two strands, or polynucleotide chains, were apparently related physically to each other by a strict system of *complementary* base pairing. Wherever the nucleotide base adenine occurred in one chain, thymine was present in the other; similarly, guanine was always paired with cytosine. These rules meant that the sequence of bases in each chain inexorably stipulated the sequence in

the other; each chain, on its own, could generate the entire sequence of base pairs. Watson and Crick therefore suggested that accurate duplication of DNA could occur if the chains separated and each then acted as a template on which a new complementary chain was laid down. This form of duplication was later called "semiconservative" because it supposed that although the individual parental chains were conserved during duplication (in that they were not thrown away), their association ended as part of the act of duplication.

The prediction of semiconservative replication soon received precise experimental support. Matthew S. Meselson and Franklin W. Stahl, working at the California Institute of Technology, were able to show that each molecule of DNA in the bacterium *Escherichia coli* is composed of equal parts of newly synthesized DNA and of old DNA that was present in the previous generation [*see top illustration on page 2041*]. They realized they had not proved that the two parts of each molecule were in fact two chains of the DNA duplex, because they had not established that the molecules they were working with consisted of only two chains. Later experiments, including some to be described in this article, showed that what they were observing was indeed the separation of the two chains during duplication.

The Meselson-Stahl experiment dealt with the end result of DNA duplication. It gave no hint about the mechanism that separates the chains and then supervises the synthesis of the new chains. Soon, however, Arthur Kornberg and his colleagues at Washington University isolated an enzyme from *E. coli* that, if all the necessary precursors were provided, could synthesize in the test tube

chains that were complementary in base sequence to any DNA offered as a template. It was clear, then, that polynucleotide chains could indeed act as templates for the production of complementary chains and that this kind of reaction could be the normal process of duplication, since the enzymes for carrying it out were present in the living cell.

Such, then, was the general background of the experiments I undertook

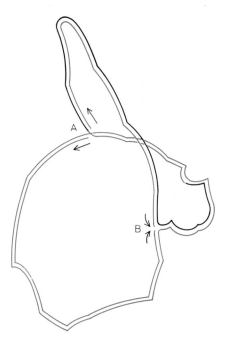

INTERPRETATION of autoradiograph on the next page is based on the varying density of the line of grains. Excluding artifacts, dense segments represent doubly labeled DNA duplexes (*two colored lines*), faint segments singly labeled DNA (*color and black*). The parent chromosome, labeled in one strand and part of another, began to duplicate at *A*; new labeled strands have been laid down in two loops as far as *B*.

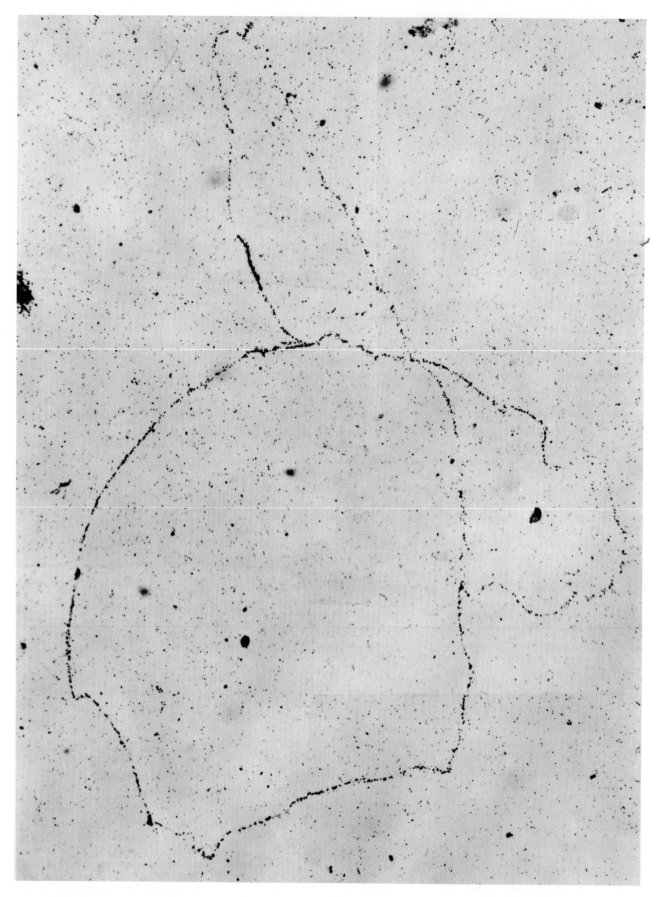

AUTORADIOGRAPH shows a duplicating chromosome from the bacterium *Escherichia coli* enlarged about 480 diameters. The DNA of the chromosome is visible because for two generations it incorporated a radioactive precursor, tritiated thymine. The thymine reveals its presence as a line of dark grains in the photographic emulsion. (Scattered grains are from background radiation.) The diagram on the preceding page shows how the picture is interpreted as demonstrating the manner of DNA duplication.

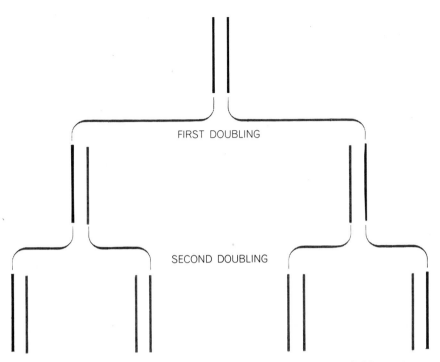

SEMICONSERVATIVE DUPLICATION was confirmed by the Meselson-Stahl experiment, which showed that each DNA molecule is composed of two parts: one that is present in the parent molecule, the other comprising new material synthesized when the parent molecule is duplicated. If radioactive labeling begins with the first doubling, the unlabeled (*black*) and labeled (*colored*) nucleotide chains of DNA form two-chain duplexes as shown here.

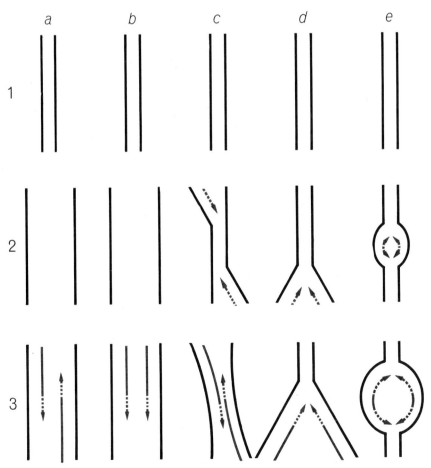

DUPLICATION could proceed in various ways (*a–e*). In these examples parental chains are shown as black lines and new chains as colored lines. The arrows show the direction of growth of the new chains, the newest parts of which are denoted by broken-line segments.

beginning in 1962 at the Australian National University. My object was simply (and literally) to look at molecules of DNA that had been caught in the act of duplication, in order to find out which of the possible forms of semiconservative replication takes place in the living cell: how the chains of parent DNA are arranged and how the new chains are laid down [*see bottom illustration on this page*].

Various factors dictated that the experiments should be conducted with *E. coli*. For one thing, this bacterium was known from genetic studies to have only one chromosome; that is, its DNA is contained in a single functional unit in which all the genetic markers are arrayed in sequence. For another thing, the duplication of its chromosome was known to occupy virtually the entire cycle of cell division, so that one could be sure that every cell in a rapidly multiplying culture would contain replicating DNA.

Although nothing was known about the number of DNA molecules in the *E. coli* chromosome (or in any other complex chromosome, for that matter), the dispersal of the bacterium's DNA among its descendants had been shown to be semiconservative. For this and other reasons it seemed likely that the bacterial chromosome would turn out to be a single very large molecule. All the DNA previously isolated from bacteria had, to be sure, proved to be in molecules much smaller than the total chromosome, but a reason for this was suggested by studies by A. D. Hershey of the Carnegie Institution Department of Genetics at Cold Spring Harbor, N.Y. He had pointed out that the giant molecules of DNA that make up the genetic complement of certain bacterial viruses had been missed by earlier workers simply because they are so large that they are exceedingly fragile. Perhaps the same thing was true of the bacterial chromosome.

If so, the procedure for inspecting the replicating DNA of bacteria would have to be designed to cater for an exceptionally fragile molecule, since the bacterial chromosome contains some 20 times more DNA than the largest bacterial virus. It would have to be a case of looking but not touching. This was not as onerous a restriction as it may sound. The problem was, after all, a topographical one, involving delineation of strands of parent DNA and newly synthesized DNA. There was no need for manipulation, only for visualization.

Although electron microscopy is the

obvious way to get a look at a large molecule, I chose autoradiography in this instance because it offered certain peculiar advantages (which will become apparent) and because it had already proved to be the easier, albeit less accurate, technique for displaying large DNA molecules. Autoradiography capitalizes on the fact that electrons emitted by the decay of a radioactive isotope produce images on certain kinds of photographic emulsion. It is possible, for example, to locate the destination within a cell of a particular species of molecule by labeling such molecules with a radioactive atom, feeding them to the cell and then placing the cell in contact with an emulsion; a developed grain in the emulsion reveals the presence of a labeled molecule [see "Autobiographies of Cells," by Renato Baserga and Walter E. Kisieleski; SCIENTIFIC AMERICAN Offprint 165].

It happens that the base thymine, which is solely a precursor of DNA, is susceptible to very heavy labeling with tritium, the radioactive isotope of hydrogen. Replicating DNA incorporates the labeled thymine and thus becomes visible in autoradiographs. I had been able to extend the technique to demonstrating the form of individual DNA molecules extracted from bacterial viruses. This was possible because, in spite of the poor resolving power of autoradiography (compared with electron microscopy), molecules of DNA are so extremely long in relation to the resolving power that they appear as a linear array of grains. The method grossly exaggerates the apparent width of the DNA, but this is not a serious fault in the kind of study I was undertaking.

The general design of the experiments called for extracting labeled DNA from bacteria as gently as possible and then

mounting it—without breaking the DNA molecules—for autoradiography. What I did was kill bacteria that had been fed tritiated thymine for various periods and put them, along with the enzyme lysozyme and an excess of unlabeled DNA, into a small capsule closed on one side by a semipermeable membrane. The enzyme, together with a detergent diffused into the chamber, induced the bacteria to break open and discharge their DNA. After the detergent, the enzyme and low-molecular-weight cellular debris had been diffused out of the chamber, the chamber was drained, leaving some of the DNA deposited on the membrane [see illustration below]. Once dry, the membrane was coated with a photographic emulsion sensitive to electrons emitted by the tritium and was left for two months. I hoped by this procedure to avoid subjecting the DNA to appreciable turbulence and so to find

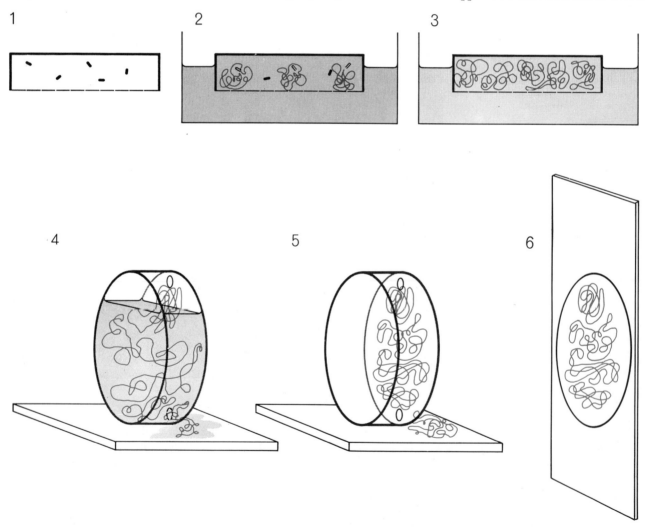

AUTORADIOGRAPHY EXPERIMENT begins with bacteria whose DNA has been labeled with radioactive thymine. The bacteria and an enzyme are placed in a small chamber closed by a semipermeable membrane (1). Detergent diffused into the chamber causes the bacteria to discharge their contents (2). The detergent and cellular debris are washed away by saline solution diffused through the chamber (3). The membrane is then punctured. The saline drains out slowly (4), leaving some unbroken DNA molecules (color) clinging to the membrane (5). The membrane, with DNA, is placed on a microscope slide and coated with emulsion (6).

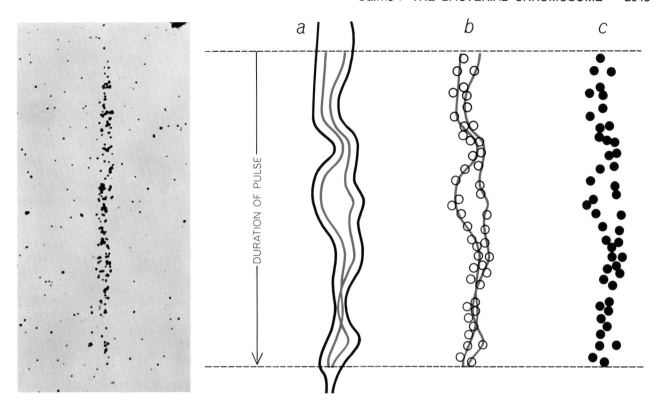

DNA synthesized in *E. coli* fed radioactive thymine for three minutes is visible in an autoradiograph, enlarged 1,200 diameters, as an array of heavy black grains (*left*). The events leading to the autoradiograph are shown at right. The region of the DNA chains synthesized during the "pulse-labeling" is radioactive and is shown in color (*a*). The radioactivity affects silver grains in the photographic emulsion (*b*). The developed grains appear in the autoradiograph (*c*), approximately delineating the new chains of DNA.

some molecules that—however big—had not been broken and see their form. Inasmuch as *E. coli* synthesizes DNA during its entire division cycle, some of the extracted DNA should be caught in the act of replication. (Since there was an excess of unlabeled DNA present, any tendency for DNA to produce artificial aggregates would not produce a spurious increase in the size of the labeled molecules or an alteration in their form.)

It is the peculiar virtue of autoradiography that one sees only what has been labeled; for this reason the technique can yield information on the history as well as the form of a labeled structure. The easiest way to determine which of the schemes of replication was correct was to look at bacterial DNA that had been allowed to duplicate for only a short time in the presence of labeled thymine. Only the most recently made DNA would be visible (corresponding to the broken-line segments in the bottom illustration on page 2041), so it should be possible to determine if the two daughter molecules were being made at the same point or in different regions of the parent molecule. A picture obtained after labeling bacteria for

three minutes, or a tenth of a generation-time [*at left in illustration above*], makes it clear that two labeled structures are being made in the same place. This place is presumably a particular region of a larger (unseen) parent molecule [*see diagrams at right in illustration above*].

The autoradiograph also shows that at least 80 microns (80 thousandths of a millimeter) of the DNA has been duplicated in three minutes. Since duplication occupies the entire generation-time (which was about 30 minutes in these experiments), it follows that the process seen in the autoradiograph could traverse at least 10 × 80 microns, or about a millimeter, of DNA between one cell division and the next. This is roughly the total length of the DNA in the bacterial chromosome. The autoradiograph therefore suggests that the entire chromosome may be duplicated at a single locus that can move fast enough to traverse the total length of the DNA in each generation.

Finally, the autoradiograph gives evidence on the semiconservative aspect of duplication. Two structures are being synthesized. It is possible to estimate how heavily each structure is labeled (in

terms of grains produced per micron of length) by counting the number of exposed grains and dividing by the length. Then the density of labeling can be compared with that of virus DNA labeled similarly but uniformly, that is, in both of its polynucleotide chains. It turns out that each of the two new structures seen in the picture must be a single polynucleotide chain. If, therefore, the picture is showing the synthesis of two daughter molecules from one parent molecule, it follows that each daughter molecule must be made up of one new (labeled) chain and one old (unlabeled) chain—just as Watson and Crick predicted.

The "pulse-labeling" experiment just described yielded information on the isolated regions of bacterial DNA actually engaged in duplication. To learn if the entire chromosome is a single molecule and how the process of duplication proceeds it was necessary to look at DNA that had been labeled with tritiated thymine for several generations. Moreover, it was necessary to find, in the jumble of chromosomes extracted from *E. coli*, autoradiographs of unbroken chromosomes that were disentangled enough to be seen as a whole. Rather than retrace all the steps that led, after many months, to satisfactory pictures of the entire bacterial chromosome in one piece, it is simpler to present two sample autoradiographs and explain how they can be interpreted and what they reveal.

Autoradiographs on page 2040 and at the right show bacterial chromosomes in the process of duplication. All that is visible is labeled, or "hot," DNA; any unlabeled, or "cold," chain is unseen. A stretch of DNA duplex labeled in only one chain ("hot-cold") makes a faint trace of black grains. A duplex that is doubly labeled ("hot-hot") shows as a heavier trace. The autoradiographs therefore indicate, as shown in the diagrams that accompany them, the extent to which new, labeled polynucleotide chains have been laid down along labeled or unlabeled parent chains. Such data make it possible to construct a bacterial family history showing the process of duplication over several generations [see illustration on next page].

The significant conclusions are these:

1. The chromosome of E. coli apparently contains a single molecule of DNA roughly a millimeter in length and with a calculated molecular weight of about two billion. This is by far the largest molecule known to occur in a biological system.

2. The molecule contains two polynucleotide chains, which separate at the time of duplication.

3. The molecule is duplicated at a single locus that traverses the entire length of the molecule. At this point both new chains are being made: two chains are becoming four. This locus has come to be called the replicating "fork" because that is what it looks like.

4. Replicating chromosomes are not Y-shaped, as would be the case for a linear structure [see "d" in bottom illustration on page 2041]. Instead the ends of the Y are joined: the ends of the daughter molecules are joined to each other and to the far end of the parent molecule. In other words, the chromosome is circular while it is being duplicated.

It is hard to conceive of the behavior of a molecule that is about 1,000 times larger than the largest protein and that exists, moreover, coiled inside a cell several hundred times shorter than itself. Apart from this general problem of comprehension, there are two special difficulties inherent in the process of DNA duplication outlined here. Both have their origin in details of the structure of DNA that I have not yet discussed.

The first difficulty arises from the opposite polarities of the polynucleotide chains [see illustration on page 2046]. The deoxyribose-phosphate backbone of one chain of the DNA duplex has the sequence $-O-C_3-C_4-C_5-O-P-O-C_3-C_4-C_5-O-P-\ldots$ (The C_3, C_4 and C_5 are the three carbon atoms of the deoxyribose that contribute to the backbone.) The other chain has the sequence $-P-O-C_5-C_4-C_3-O-P-O-C_5-C_4-C_3-O-\ldots$

If both chains are having their complements laid down at a single locus moving in one particular direction, it follows that one of these new chains must grow by repeated addition to the C_3 of the preceding nucleotide's deoxyribose and the other must grow by addition to a C_5. One would expect that two different enzymes should be needed for these two quite different kinds of polymerization. As yet, however, only the reaction that adds to chains ending in C_3 has been demonstrated in such experiments as Kornberg's. This fact had seemed to support a mode of replication in which the two strands grew in opposite directions [see "a" and "c" in bottom illustration on page 2041]. If the single-locus scheme is correct, the problem of opposite polarities remains to be explained.

The second difficulty, like the first, is related to the structure of DNA. For the sake of simplicity I have been representing the DNA duplex as a pair of chains lying parallel to each other. In actuality the two chains are wound helically around a common axis, with one complete turn for every 10 base pairs, or 34 angstrom units of length (34 ten-millionths of a millimeter). It would seem, therefore, that separation of the chains at the time of duplication, like separation of the strands of an ordinary rope, must involve rotation of the parent molecule with respect to the two daughter molecules. Moreover, this rotation must be very rapid. A fast-multiplying bacterium can divide every 20 minutes;

COMPLETE CHROMOSOME is seen in this autoradiograph, enlarged about 370 diameters. Like the chromosome represented on pages 2039 and 2040, this is circular, although it happens to have landed on the membrane in a more compressed shape and some segments are tangled. Whereas the first chromosome was more than half way through the duplication process, this one is only about one-sixth duplicated (from A to B).

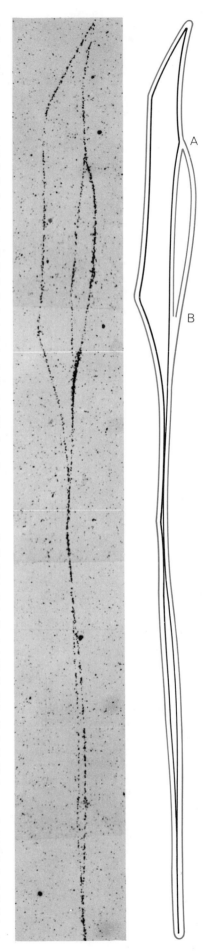

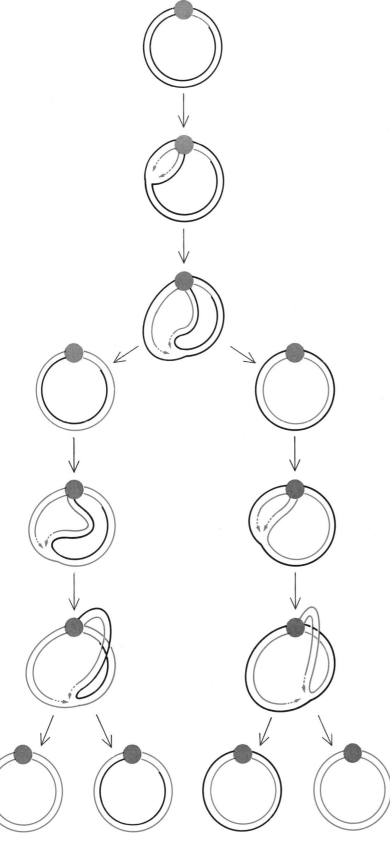

BACTERIAL DNA MOLECULE apparently replicates as in this schematic diagram. The two chains of the circular molecule are represented as concentric circles, joined at a "swivel" (*gray spot*). Labeled DNA is shown in color; part of one chain of the parent molecule is labeled, as are two generations of newly synthesized DNA. Duplication starts at the swivel and, in these drawings, proceeds counterclockwise. Arrowheads mark the replicating "fork": the point at which DNA is synthesized in each chromosome. Drawing A is a schematic rendering of the chromosome in the autoradiograph on page 2040.

during this time it has to duplicate—and consequently to unwind—about a millimeter of DNA, or some 300,000 turns. This implies an average unwinding rate of 15,000 revolutions per minute.

At first sight it merely adds to the difficulty to find that the chromosome is circular while all of this is going on. Obviously a firmly closed circle—whether a molecule or a rope—cannot be unwound. This complication is worth worrying about because there is increasing evidence that the chromosome of *E. coli* is not exceptional in its circularity. The DNA of numerous viruses has been shown either to be circular or to become circular just before replication begins. For all we know, circularity may therefore be the rule rather than the exception.

There are several possible explanations for this apparent impasse, only one of which strikes me as plausible.

First, one should consider the possibility that there is no impasse—that in the living cell the DNA is two-stranded but not helical, perhaps being kept that way precisely by being in the form of a circle. (If a double helix cannot be unwound when it is firmly linked into a circle, neither can relational coils ever be introduced into a pair of uncoiled circles.) This hypothesis, however, requires a most improbable structure for two-strand DNA, one that has not been observed. And it does not really avoid the unwinding problem because there would still have to be some mechanism for making nonhelical circles out of the helical rods of DNA found in certain virus particles.

Second, one could avoid the unwinding problem by postulating that at least one of the parental chains is repeatedly broken and reunited during replication, so that the two chains can be separated over short sections without rotation of the entire molecule. One rather sentimental objection to this hypothesis (which was proposed some time ago) is that it is hard to imagine such cavalier and hazardous treatment being meted out to such an important molecule, and one so conspicuous for its stability. A second objection is that it does not explain circularity.

The most satisfactory solution to the unwinding problem would be to find some reason why the ends of the chromosome actually *must* be joined together. This is the case if one postulates that there is an active mechanism for unwinding the DNA, distinct from the mechanism that copies the unwound

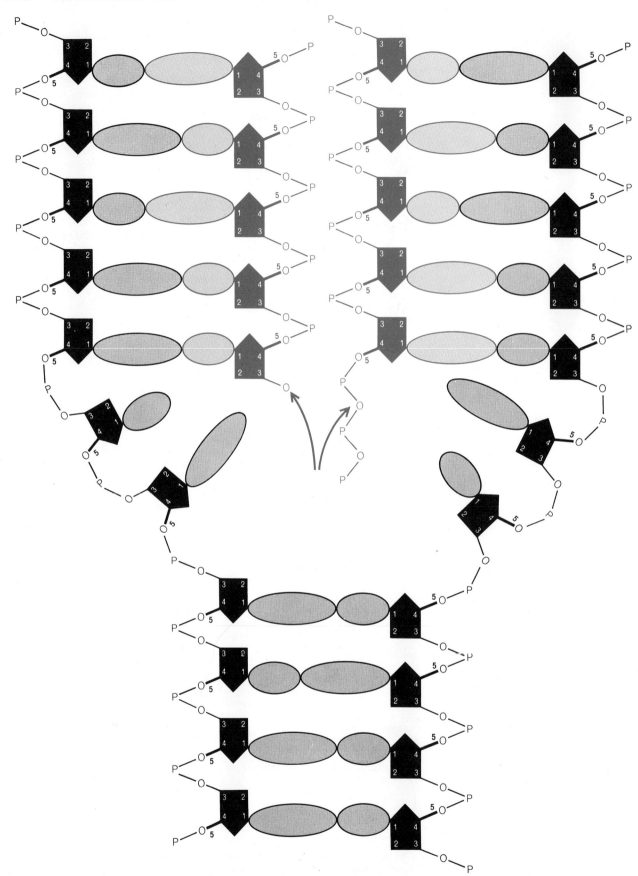

OPPOSITE POLARITIES of the two parental chains of the DNA duplex result in opposite polarities and different directions of growth in the two new chains (*color*) being laid down as complements of the old ones during duplication. Note that the numbered carbon atoms (*1 to 5*) in the deoxyribose rings (*solid black*) are in different positions in the two parental chains and therefore in the two new chains. As the replicating fork moves downward, the new chain that is complementary to the left parental chain must grow by addition to a C_3, the other new chain by addition to a C_5, as shown by the arrows. The elliptical shapes are the four bases.

chains. Now, any active unwinding mechanism must rotate the parent molecule with respect to the two new molecules—must hold the latter fast, in other words, just as the far end of a rope must be held if it is to be unwound. A little thought will show that this can be most surely accomplished by a machine attached, directly or through some common "ground," to the parent molecule and to the two daughters [*see illustration below*]. Every turn taken by such a machine would inevitably unwind the parent molecule one turn.

Although other kinds of unwinding machine can be imagined (one could be situated, for example, at the replicating fork), a practical advantage of this particular hypothesis is that it accounts for circularity. It also makes the surprising —and testable—prediction that any irreparable break in the parent molecule will instantly stop DNA synthesis, no matter how far the break is from the replicating fork. If this prediction is fulfilled, and the unwinding machine acquires the respectability that at present it lacks, we may find ourselves dealing with the first example in nature of something equivalent to a wheel.

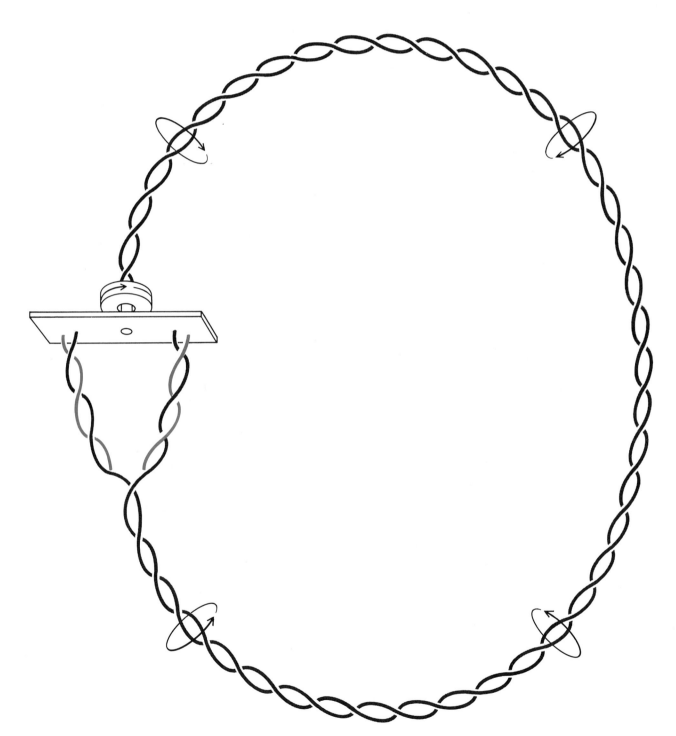

POSSIBLE MECHANISM for unwinding the DNA double helix is a swivel-like machine to which the end of the parent molecule and also the ends of the two daughter molecules are joined. The torque imparted by this machine is considered to be transmitted along the parent molecule, producing unwinding at the replicating fork. If this is correct, chromosome breakage should halt duplication.

The Author

JOHN CAIRNS is director of the Cold Spring Harbor Laboratory of Quantitative Biology. He was born in England and obtained a medical degree at the University of Oxford. For several years he did research in Australia on the multiplication of influenza virus and vaccinia virus. Later he worked on the visualization of DNA molecules by autoradiography, a project he describes in part in the present article. Cairns writes that since assuming his present position he has found himself "mainly occupied with fiscal problems," although he has done some work "on the effect of breaking the bacterial chromosome on the replication of the chromosome."

Bibliography

THE BACTERIAL CHROMOSOME AND ITS MANNER OF REPLICATION AS SEEN BY AUTORADIOGRAPHY. John Cairns in *Journal of Molecular Biology,* Vol. 6, No. 3, pages 208–213; March, 1963.

COLD SPRING HARBOR SYMPOSIA ON QUANTITATIVE BIOLOGY, VOLUME XXVIII: SYNTHESIS AND STRUCTURE OF MACROMOLECULES. Cold Spring Harbor Laboratory of Quantitative Biology, 1963.

MOLECULAR BIOLOGY OF THE GENE. James D. Watson. W. A. Benjamin, Inc., 1965. See pages 255–296.

SCIENTIFIC
AMERICAN   January 1966, Vol. 214, No. 1, pp. 70-78   OFFPRINT 1031

ORCHIDS

by Joseph Arditti

There are more than 20,000 species of them, comprising the largest
family of plants. Not all of them bear the ornate flowers used for
corsages, but their evolutionary adaptations are remarkably diverse.

Late in the 17th century a German botanist named Jacob Breynius undertook to gather information on plants that were unfamiliar to Europeans at the time. When he published his compendium *Exoticarum Aliarumque Minus Cognitum Plantarum,* he commented in particular on the extraordinary diversity of orchids. "If nature ever showed her playfulness in the formation of plants," he wrote, "this is visible in the most striking way among the orchids.... They take on the form of little birds, of lizards, of insects. They look like a man, like a woman, sometimes like an austere sinister fighter, sometimes like a clown who excites our laughter. They represent the image of a lazy tortoise, a melancholy toad, an agile, ever-chattering monkey. Nature has formed orchid flowers in such a way that, unless they make us laugh, they surely excite our greatest admiration."

The plants Breynius was describing are now classified under the family name Orchidaceae. They comprise the largest of all plant families; it contains, according to various estimates, 500 to 600 genera and 20,000 to 35,000 species. Orchids are herbaceous (nonwoody and grasslike) perennials that occur as shrubs, vines and even grasses. They may bear a single flower or many flowers. They are found from the Arctic to the borders of the Antarctic. They grow in tropical rain forests, subtropical plains and alpine meadows; in bogs, moors and deserts; in deep valleys and on high mountains. Most of the tropical and subtropical species are epiphytic, that is, they grow on the trunks and limbs of trees and shrubs as independent nonparasitic plants. It is not uncommon, however, to find normally epiphytic species growing on rocks. I have also seen them perched on top of utility poles and wires. Some orchids, particularly those of regions outside the Tropics, are called terrestrial: they grow in the ground Some orchids are saprophytic: they subsist on decaying organic matter.

Orchid flowers range in size from less than a sixteenth of an inch to more than a foot. Some give off a pleasant odor, some an unpleasant one, and some are odorless. As Breynius wrote, the shapes of the flowers are so fantastically varied that many of them inevitably seem to be mimicking something else. *Habenaria blephariglottis* of North America is commonly called monkey face. The genus *Cycnoches,* which is native to Central America, is known as the swan orchid because of its resemblance to a swan's neck. In Israel *Ophrys sintenisii* is called the velvet bee orchid. The tropical genus *Stanhopea* is often called *torrito* (little bull) in parts of Latin America because of a structure that resembles two horns. The shoelike form of the genus *Cypripedium* is reflected in such names as lady's slipper, Venus's-shoe, *Frauenschuh, pantofella* and *scarpa della Madonna.*

Among other noteworthy characteristics of orchids are resupination, a twisting of the bud that occurs as the bud becomes a flower, and a fungus infection that is necessary for the germination of the orchid seed. Orchids also have some unusual mechanisms for pollination. Of all these matters I shall have more to say later.

The evolutionary steps that brought orchids to their present state of development are largely conjectural. The late Oakes Ames of Harvard University, who was one of the foremost American orchidologists, accorded the orchids a special place in the plant kingdom by suggesting that they represent a culmination of evolution, at least among the monocotyledonous plants—plants that have a single cotyledon, or embryonic leaf, in each seed. His suggestion, with which most other students of the family agree, is based partly on the complex structure of orchid flowers.

The term "orchid" goes back to classical Greek times. The scholar Theophrastus, who was one of Plato's students and is often called the father of botany, described a plant with paired roots that looked like testicles; he gave it the name *orchis* from the Greek word for testicle. Whether or not he was actually describing an orchid is uncertain, because his statement was rather vague, but the later Greek botanist Dioscorides interpreted the description as referring to an orchid. Carolus Linnaeus adopted the name in *Species Plantarum,* the monumental work of botanical classification that he published in 1753, and in 1836 the British botanist John Lindley introduced Orchidaceae as the name of the family.

The odd shapes of the flowers and other parts of orchids have suggested to many peoples that they have magical and medicinal powers. Medieval European herbalists collected what they called "dog stone roots" (apparently again in reference to the resemblance of some orchid roots to testicles) for the preparation of aphrodisiac potions. It was also thought that a married couple could predetermine the sex of a child by means of orchid roots. As a work of 1640 put it: "The roote thereof being boyled is eaten as other sorts of bulbes are, and ... if men eate the greater, they shall beget men children, and if women eate the lesser they shall bring forth women children." On the Indonesian island of Amboina a paste made from an orchid of the genus *Grammatophyllum* is used as a remedy for sores, and in

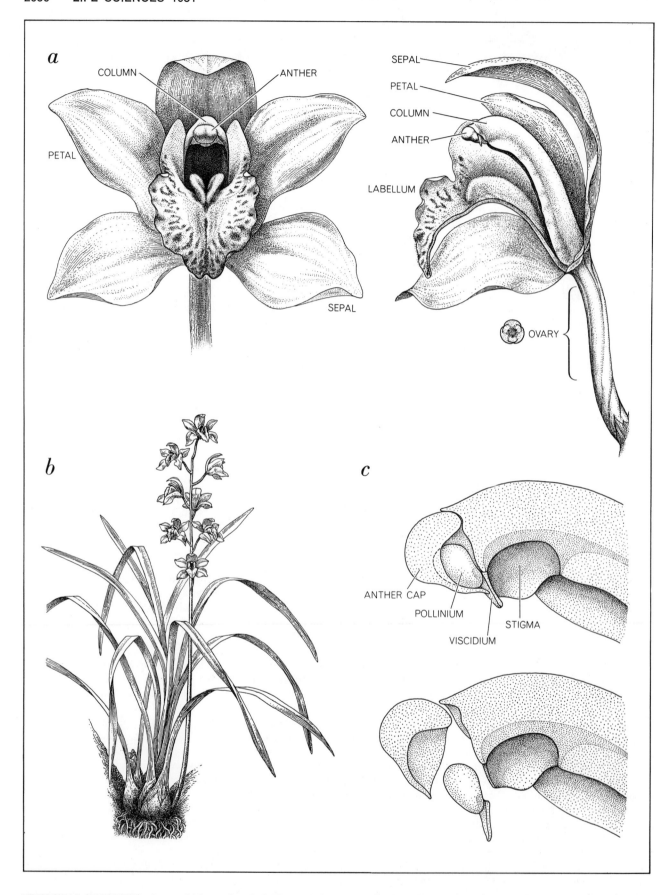

PRINCIPAL FEATURES of an orchid are identified. The orchid depicted is a species of the genus *Cymbidium*. At *a* the flower is shown in a front view and in a sectional view from the side. At *b* the full plant is depicted in a typical habitat, the crotch between the trunk and a limb of a tree. This species of orchid also grows in the ground. Details of the column are portrayed at *c*. The column is a structure that distinguishes orchids from other monocotyledonous plants; it includes the stamen, which is the male organ carrying the pollen-bearing anther, and the stigma, which is the part of the pistil, or female organ, that receives the pollen.

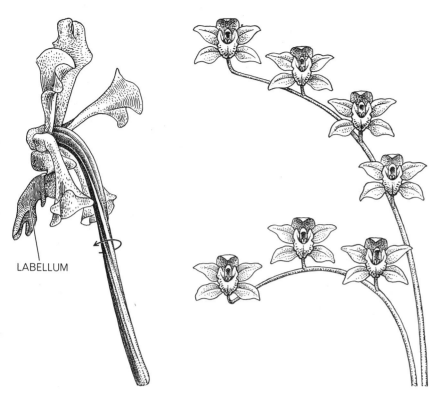

TWISTING MOVEMENT characteristic of orchid flowers is portrayed. The process is called resupination. At left an orchid of the genus *Vanda* is shown twisting so that the lip, which is on the top in the budding stage, is on the bottom in the flower. In a *Cymbidium* with several flowers (*right*) each flower twists enough to cause its lip to hang downward.

TWO FORMS OF GROWTH occur in orchids. The plant at left, an orchid of the genus *Cattleya,* is showing sympodial growth: the main stem stops growing at the end of a season and a new stem appears in the next season. Often the old stem forms a fleshy structure called a pseudobulb. At right a *Vanda* has monopodial growth: the main stem grows indefinitely.

Malaya a preparation from *Dendrobium* is applied in the treatment of skin infections. In Africa the Zulus employ *Habenaria* as an emetic, and the Swagi treat a children's disease with *Lissochilus.* In South America *Epidendrum bifidum* is used to expel tapeworms and *Spiranthes* as a diuretic.

How effective these medicinal uses of orchids are I do not know. It can be said, however, that orchids have a significant place in modern commerce beyond their use in corsages and other floral displays. True vanilla comes from the beanlike fruit of the orchid genus *Vanilla,* which is a tropical and climbing group of orchids. By far the most important vanilla orchid is *V. planifolia,* a plant that is cultivated widely throughout the Tropics.

The detailed features of orchids are no less diverse than their more obvious ones. The roots of orchids occur in several colors and many sizes and shapes. They are usually fleshy. In certain terrestrial orchids the roots are bulbous, but most tropical epiphytic species have elongated greenish or white roots that adhere tenaciously to the surface on which the plant lives, often forming a thick mat. This trait enables the plants to anchor themselves in somewhat improbable positions; *Cattleya citrina,* for example, is usually found hanging upside down. In several saprophytic orchids the entire plant consists mainly of red, purple or yellow roots that produce a flowering stem at appropriate times. A special characteristic of orchid roots is the velamen, a multilayered epidermis consisting of several tiers of spongelike cells. The function of this tissue is still being debated; it may be to provide space for water storage.

The stems of orchids grow in two different ways. Some species exhibit what is known as sympodial growth: the growth of the main stem ceases at the end of one season and does not resume in the next; instead a new stem develops. The old stem may become thick, short and fleshy, forming a structure known as the pseudobulb. In other species the form of growth is monopodial: main-stem growth continues indefinitely and no pseudobulbs are formed.

The most definitive characteristics of the orchids are undoubtedly to be found in their flowers. Some of the flowers are Lilliputian; for instance, the flower of *Platystele ornata* measures about a millimeter in diameter. Others, exemplified by certain hybrids of the genus *Cat-*

tleya, average 30 centimeters or more. Orchid flowers are borne either singly or in clusters of various forms and sizes. I once had a specimen of *Oncidium carthaginense* that produced a stem some 12 feet long with several hundred flowers. I am sure that this is by no means a record length.

The orchid flower has certain structural features in common with most other flowers, but these can be greatly modified and are often unrecognizable. Looking at the outer parts of the flower, one sees the sepals—the leaflike structures that are usually green in most other flowers but may be almost any color except black in orchids. Next come the petals. They too may be any color except pure black and are not necessarily the same color as the sepals. Inside the petals is one or both of two structures: the stamen, which is the male organ and carries the pollen, and the pistil, the female organ containing the ovules. Most orchid flowers contain both structures, with some of the parts united and highly modified to form a "column" [*see illustration on page 2050*].

Orchid flowers are bilaterally symmetrical: they have distinct but similar

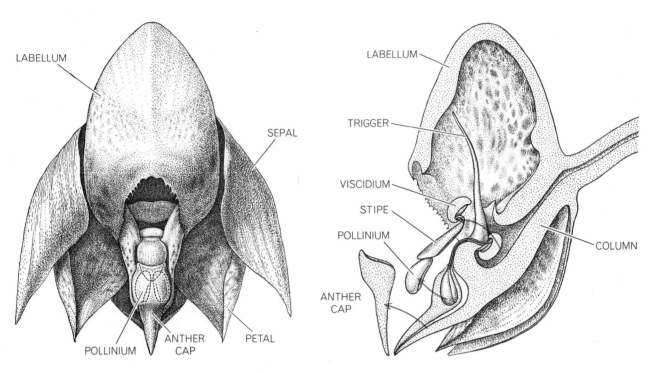

TRIGGER MECHANISM that begins the process of pollination in an orchid of the genus *Catasetum* is depicted. At left is a frontal view; the broken lines show the position of the pollen-bearing pollinium under the anther cap. At right is a sectional view, from the side, of the interior of the flower. The trigger, when touched by a bee, releases the sticky viscidium, which twists as indicated by the upper arrow and lodges against the bee's abdomen. Hence the departing bee carries the pollinium. The anther cap falls away.

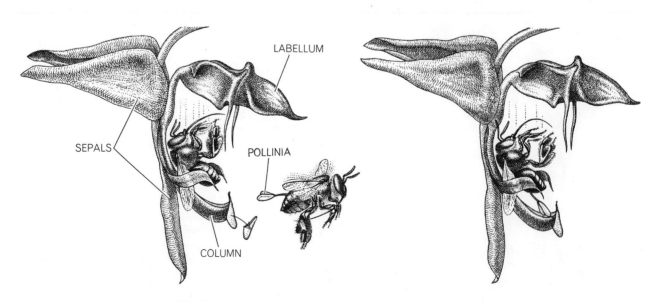

POLLINATING DEVICE of an orchid of the genus *Gongora* is a slippery column. At left a bee, having penetrated the flower, encounters the slippery surface and gets a toboggan-like ride down the column. There the bee strikes the viscidium, which adheres to the insect's abdomen, so that when the bee flies off it carries the pollinia. At right the bee, still carrying the pollinia, enters another flower and gets another ride down the column. On this visit the pollinia adhere to the stigma and the flower is pollinated.

left and right sides. The sepals and petals are borne in threes; it is a characteristic of monocotyledonous plants to bear such structures in threes or multiples of three. Some orchids are unisexual, which is to say that they have either stamens or pistils but not both, and some are bisexual.

One of the sepals in the orchid flower—the one on the upper side of the flower's base—may differ from the other two. It may be larger or fleshier than the other sepals; it may also be richly colored and decorated. This type of dorsal sepal appears prominently in the lady's slipper orchids.

Usually one of the three petals in the orchid is also much different from the others. It forms the distinctive feature called the labellum, or lip. This structure assumes strikingly handsome shapes and may be further distinguished by spots of color in splashes, blotches or more intricate designs. The labella of many *Cattleya* species and hybrids are surely among the most beautiful objects in nature.

In most fully opened orchid flowers the labellum hangs below the other two petals. In the unopened bud, however, it is above them. The change in position is brought about by the phenomenon of resumation that I have mentioned. The entire bud twists on its axis, usually about 180 degrees, as it opens [see top illustration on page 2051]. This twisting movement is one of the hallmarks of the Orchidaceae. In some species the twisting facilitates pollination by placing the labellum at the bottom as a perch for visiting insects, and that presumably is the evolutionary reason for the phenomenon.

Although the beauty of the dorsal sepal and the labellum is the most spectacular feature of orchid flowers, the most unusual feature from the botanical standpoint is the column, or gynandrium. This is a structure not found among other monocotyledonous plants. It represents a fusion of three structures: the stamen, the stigma, which is the part of the pistil that receives the pollen, and the style, which provides a pathway for the pollen to reach the ovules. The anthers—the pollen-bearing parts of the stamen—are also borne on the column. The pollen grains occur separately or are compressed into masses known as pollinia.

As their diverse forms suggest, orchid flowers are pollinated by a multitude of agents. Among the reported pollinators are not only bees and a variety of other insects but also birds, bats, frogs and snails. Not all these reports have been fully substantiated. C. H. Dodson of the University of Miami found in a series of detailed observations that in the American Tropics he could confirm only insects and hummingbirds as pollinators of orchids.

The pollinating mechanisms of many orchids are remarkably intricate. The late Paul H. Allen, who worked as a botanist in Latin America, investigated the pollination of the orchid *Gongora maculata*. He suggested that the fragrance of the orchid attracts males of the bee *Euglossa cordata*. A bee lands on the flower in search of nectar. There, because parts of the flower are slippery, the insect loses its footing and gets a toboggan-like ride down the curved column. In the process it dislodges the pollinia, which become attached to its back [see lower illustration on preceding page]. The insect gets another ride on the next flower, but here the pollinia it is carrying are deposited on the sticky stigma.

Some orchids enlist the sexual behavior pattern of an insect to meet their own reproductive needs. In the early part of this century the French investigator A. Pouyanne, working in Algeria, noted that the orchid *Ophrys specu-*

LIQUID IN A TRAP facilitates pollination in the orchid *Coryanthes speciosa*. The colored line, followed from right to left, shows the path taken by the bee as it arrives at the flower and falls into the bucket, which contains a liquid produced by the gland at top center. The only way out for the bee is through a narrow opening that forces the bee against the pollinia.

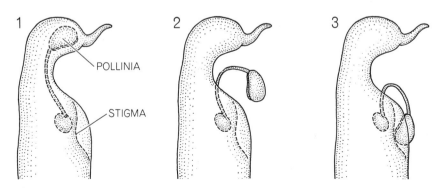

SELF-POLLINATION is shown in an orchid of the genus *Ophrys*. Before pollination (1) the column stands upright. As a result of autolysis, or self-digestion of certain tissues by the plant, the stipe bends (2), carrying the pollinia downward toward the sticky stigmatic surface. When the pollinia reach the stigma and adhere to it (3), pollination is complete.

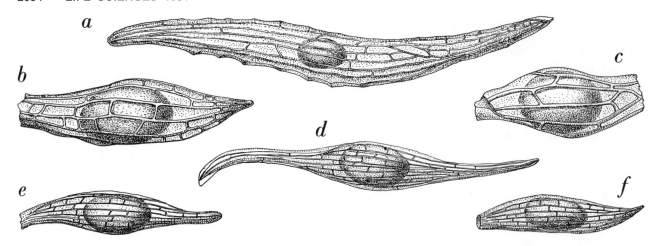

ORCHID SEEDS are shown in relative scale but much enlarged. They include: *a, Paphiopedilum curtisii; b, P. specierum; c, P. parishii; d, Cattleya labiata; e, C. trianaei,* and *f, Odontoglossum pescatorei.* A single orchid flower produces a large number of seeds.

lum, like a legendary temptress, has assumed the shape and odor of an insect to facilitate its pollination. Its flowers resemble the female of the insect *Scolia ciliata.* Male insects attempt to copulate with the flowers; thus pollination is achieved. This phenomenon, called pseudocopulation, is reportedly responsible also for the pollination of the orchid *Ophrys sintenisii,* which is found in Israel.

In the male flowers of the orchid *Cycnoches* a visiting insect of the species *Centris fasciata* trips a trigger mechanism that causes forceful ejection of the pollinia, which become attached to the rear portion of the insect's abdomen. When the insect visits a female flower, the pollinia are caught by two notches on the stigma (which in this instance is not sticky). A similar but more powerful ejection mechanism operates in the orchid genus *Catasetum.*

Orchids of the genus *Coryanthes* have a bucket-like lip filled with a liquid that is apparently somewhat intoxicating. Visiting insects fall into the "bucket" and can get out only by crawling through a narrow opening just below the pollinia [*see top illustration on preceding page*]. As the insects crawl out they pick up the pollinia and may eventually transport them to other flowers. Still another mechanism employed by orchids is self-pollination. The late Lewis Knudson of Cornell University observed that self-pollination can occur in older flowers of *Cattleya aurantiaca* as a result of the self-digestion of certain parts of the flower [*see lower illustration on preceding page*].

The depositing of pollen on the stigma triggers a series of profound changes in the form of the pollinated orchid flower. Within hours the flower begins to wilt and change color. The column sometimes turns dark red. The petals and sepals may swell. They may become fleshy and develop a pigmentation that is green or red or both.

The physiological changes induced by the pollen, although subtler, are no less striking. Pollination stimulates the production of the plant hormone indoleacetic acid. In many orchids the ovules are not fully developed by the time of pollination; in these species pollination induces final development.

After the pollen grains have been deposited on the surface of the stigma, they germinate by forming thin tubes that grow toward the ovarian cavity. This growth proceeds slowly; there may be a considerable lapse of time between pollination and fertilization. In *Gastrodia elata* fertilization may occur after four days; in *Vanda suavis* the period between the two events may be six to 10 months.

When an orchid pollen grain is first deposited on the stigma, it contains two nuclei. On germination one of these divides to form two sperm nuclei. During fertilization one of the sperm nuclei may fuse with the egg nucleus inside the embryo sac. The third nucleus may disintegrate just before or immediately after fertilization. Alternatively it may combine with the "polar" nuclei, two of the eight in the embryo sac, in a process known as triple fusion, to produce the primary endosperm nucleus. In most plants this nucleus gives rise to the endosperm, which is the food-storage tissue of the germinating plant. In the Orchidaceae, however, the endosperm nucleus disintegrates either immediately or after a few divisions. Accordingly orchid seeds do not have an endosperm or any other specialized tissue for food storage. Knudson found that their food reserves are located within the embryo and contain about 32 percent fat and 1 percent sugar but no starch.

The development of the embryo in the Orchidaceae has been described by Carl L. Withner of Brooklyn College and his associate Michael Wirth as being complex and confusing. The reason for their statement is that they have found a large number of variations in the relatively few species they have studied so far. It can be said, however, that as the young embryo develops, its cells do not differentiate, or specialize. As a result the mature orchid seed is a cluster of undifferentiated cells enclosed in a flimsy and often transparent seed coat. The seeds are tiny. According to Hans Burgeff of the University of Würzburg their weight ranges from .3 microgram to 14 micrograms. Their average length is about one millimeter; their diameter probably averages from half a millimeter to three-quarters of a millimeter [*see illustration above*]. The cells in some embryos have been estimated to number as few as 120.

The exceedingly small size of orchid seeds is more than balanced by their vast numbers. Published counts range from 1,330 seeds per capsule in *Coeloglossum viride* to some four million per capsule in a variant of *Cycnoches ventricosum.* Orchids with 750,000 to a million seeds per capsule and three or more capsules per plant are not at all uncommon. Charles Darwin estimated that if the viable seeds produced by a single *Orchis maculata,* an English orchid with 6,200 seeds per capsule and 186,300 per plant, were to germinate and grow to maturity, they would cover an acre. He also estimated that the fourth-generation descendants of the

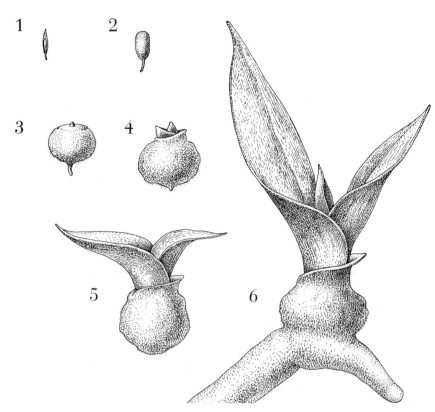

STAGES IN GERMINATION of a *Cattleya* seed begin (*1*) with a swelling of the embryo inside the seed coat. Succeeding steps are: *2*, embryo growing after it has burst out of the seed coat; *3*, embryo forming a protocorm with a pointed vegetative apex; *4*, the protocorm becoming disklike and showing leaflets; *5*, the protocorm forming a plantlet with two spreading leaves, and *6*, the plantlet forming larger leaves and the start of a root system.

plant would cover the entire globe. Obviously most orchid seeds fail to germinate.

An orchid seed that lands on a suitable growing surface and begins to germinate undergoes several structural changes [*see illustration above*]. It swells and its cells may divide a few times. It acquires a green color. It also develops a tiny structure that resembles a corm, or underground stem with rootlike functions; the structure is called a protocorm. The seed may remain in this condition for as long as 24 months. What it is waiting for, and what in most situations it must have before it can develop further, is the fungus infection I have mentioned.

If the young protocorm does become infected by any one of several species of fungus, it immediately resumes growth and forms a larger, disklike protocorm. This soon develops an apical meristem, a dome-shaped mass of cells that are rapidly dividing. The meristem gives rise to one leaf and later to more leaves. The appearance of roots completes the formation of a miniature orchid plant.

The fungus that penetrates the seed or young protocorm is eventually local-ized in the roots. It has therefore acquired the name mycorrhiza, from the Greek words for "fungus" and "root." Mycorrhizas are not limited to the Orchidaceae; they are found in many forest shrubs and trees. As knowledge of the subject expands it becomes apparent that such symbiotic relations between different kinds of plants may be the rule rather than the exception.

The existence of mycorrhiza in orchids was apparently first noted in 1824 (by the German naturalist Heinrich Link), but the role of the fungus infection in the germination of orchid seeds remained obscure. In fact, until 1804, when the English botanist Richard Salisbury reported having observed germinating orchid seeds, it was generally believed that these seeds were incapable of germination. In spite of strenuous efforts by horticulturists to induce orchid seeds to grow, the cultivation of orchids remained for many years a haphazard undertaking.

The discovery early in this century that a fungus plays a critical role in the germination of orchid seeds is said to have been made almost accidentally. Noël Bernard, a young French botanist, apparently discovered a clump of germinating seeds of the European bird's-nest orchid (*Neottia nidus-avis*) during a stroll in a forest. On examining the seedlings he noted that all of them were infected with a fungus. Bernard advanced the idea that the infection was not parasitic or pathogenic but symbiotic and in fact a necessity for germination of the seed. Supplementing his shrewd insight with imaginative experimentation, Bernard succeeded first in isolating the fungus and then in causing orchid seeds to germinate by infecting them with it.

After Bernard's death in 1911 research on orchid symbiosis was taken up mainly at the University of Würzburg under Burgeff. He and his students found that many fungi are capable of promoting the germination of orchid seeds by penetrating the embryo and influencing its metabolic activity. The work of Bernard and Burgeff made possible the germination of orchid seeds in the laboratory. The method used by both men was to put seeds and fungus simultaneously in culture tubes. Most of the seeds died, but a few germinated and grew to maturity. By this time it was commonly believed that an orchid could neither germinate nor grow without its fungus. The British mycologist J. Ramsbottom went so far as to state that an orchid seedling without its fungus is "like *Hamlet* without the Prince of Denmark."

One investigator who was doubtful about the universal validity of this dictum was Knudson. He speculated that the fungus may contribute no more to the orchid than some enzymes that can break down polysaccharides—sugar polymers such as starch or cellulose—and other compounds, thereby making possible their utilization by the orchid as food. To test this hypothesis Knudson placed orchid seeds on a mixture of sugar and mineral nutrients. The seeds germinated and the seedlings grew.

Knudson's achievement did not convince all those who believed that orchids could not grow normally without fungus infection. Several critics argued that Knudson's seedlings were abnormal and would not produce flowering orchids. Knudson responded by growing an orchid plant from seed to flower on his culture medium with no mycorrhizal fungus present in the roots.

Knudson's experiments demonstrated that an orchid can exist without its fungus, but his findings did not elucidate the role of the fungus. That remains uncertain. It is possible, as Knudson speculated, that the fungus merely contributes its enzymes. If that is so, all orchid seeds should germinate on mix-

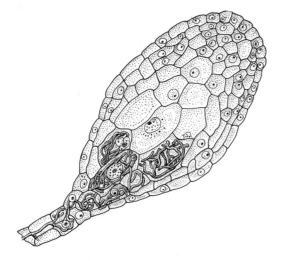

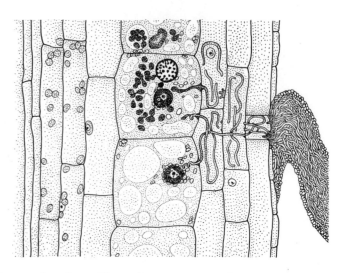

FUNGUS INFECTION that normally must occur before an orchid seed will germinate fully is shown in two stages. At left a fungus has penetrated a seed. Later the fungus takes up a permanent association with the root, as indicated at right in a depiction of a small section of root. The symbiotic association of fungus and orchid is called mycorrhiza from the Greek words for "fungus" and "root." The fungus apparently contributes certain enzymes and perhaps some vitamins and hormones that the orchid needs for development.

tures of sugar and minerals. The fact is that some orchid seeds do not germinate on Knudson's medium or similar ones, or on media containing highly purified sugars. Seeds planted in such media have responded, however, to the addition of fungus extracts, various other plant extracts and certain vitamins.

It may be, then, that the fungus is contributing more than its enzymes. Perhaps it supplies the seeds and seedlings with certain hormones, vitamins or other growth factors. Many investigators have studied the effect of vitamins on germinating orchid embryos. In most cases their investigations were designed to answer questions other than what role the fungus plays—questions relating to such matters as the embryology of flowering plants in general or to purely horticultural matters such as how to germinate more orchid seeds and achieve better growth of seedlings. In most of these studies it has been shown that the B vitamin niacin (nicotinic acid) promotes the germination of seeds and the growth of seedlings.

I have thought it worthwhile to explore this matter further, particularly with a view to explaining more fully the function of the fungus in the growth of orchids. The pathways by which most living things manufacture niacin have been thoroughly studied; they are well understood in mammals and in a few birds, some fungi and certain bacteria. The mode of synthesis of niacin in green plants, however, is obscure. Most of the evidence brought forward so far is contradictory, probably

in part because the plants studied have not been appropriate for the experiments. It seemed to me that orchid seeds, being deficient in storage tissues and reserves of growth-promoting factors, were particularly well suited to such an investigation.

One approach commonly used to study what ingredients go into the synthesis of a vitamin and what pathways are taken in the process is to provide the organism with radioactively labeled ingredients that might be used in the synthesis and to follow the labeled intermediates through whatever synthetic pathways they take. It is also possible to provide an organism with unlabeled intermediates and look for evidence that they have indeed been used as precursors of the end product. This evidence can appear either in the form of improved growth rates or as increased amounts of the end product (or some of its precursors and metabolic products) in the experimental organism.

Because none of the labeled intermediates of the kind needed to experiment with niacin metabolism in orchids as I wanted to approach the problem were available commercially at the time, and because it was impractical for me to make them, I adopted the second approach. I placed orchid seeds on media containing the suspected precursors of niacin and also on some media that contained niacin and some that did not. Comparing the growth and differentiation of the seedlings on all media, I found that the experiments indicated that the synthesis of niacin in orchids may, at least in part, proceed along a

pathway similar to that found in mammals and in the bread mold Neurospora crassa. The findings suggest that the fungus does indeed have a role in supplying vitamins to the orchid seedling.

I mentioned briefly that orchid seeds have been used by many investigators in experiments designed to yield new information on the embryology of flowering plants. The seeds are useful for this purpose because of their special structure, unique mode of development and peculiar requirements for germination. The use of culture media with varied components showed some time ago that young orchid seedlings prefer ammonium to nitrate as a source of nitrogen. Recently John G. Torrey of Harvard University, working with V. Raghavan, conducted experiments indicating that Cattleya seedlings cannot utilize nitrate until they are 60 days old, simply because they lack the necessary enzyme: nitrate reductase. At an age of 60 days the seedlings start to produce the enzyme and become capable of utilizing nitrate.

This finding can be taken as evidence that a subtle biochemical differentiation can occur in the young seedlings. The implications go far beyond orchids. Such findings open up avenues of research on the mechanism of differentiation, the role of the genetic code in it and the relation between the differentiation and the code in terms of the selective activation or suppression of genes. These avenues of research may lead in turn to further understanding of the anatomical and chemical changes that occur in living things as they grow.

The Author

JOSEPH ARDITTI is instructor in botany and cell physiology at the University of Southern California. He was 12 years old when the Soviet army advanced into Bulgaria, where he was born; he and his parents left that country for Palestine. Arditti later served two and a half years in the Israeli army. On his discharge in 1954 he emigrated to the U.S., arriving with $50 as his total wealth. While working at a commercial orchid farm in California, first as a laborer and then as chief grower, he attended the University of California at Los Angeles, receiving a degree in floriculture in 1959. Last year he obtained a Ph.D. in plant physiology at the University of Southern California.

Bibliography

ABC OF ORCHID GROWING. John V. Watkins. Prentice-Hall, Incorporated, 1956.

GENERIC NAMES OF ORCHIDS: THEIR ORIGIN AND MEANING. Richard Evans Schultes and Arthur Stanley Pease. Academic Press Inc., 1963.

THE ORCHID-GROWER'S MANUAL. B. S. Williams. Hafner Publishing Company, Inc., 1961.

ORCHIDS. Walter Kupper and Walter Linsenmaier. Thomas Nelson and Sons Ltd., 1961.

THE ORCHIDS: A SCIENTIFIC SURVEY. Edited by Carl L. Withner. The Ronald Press Company, 1959.

SCIENTIFIC
AMERICAN   January 1966, Vol. 214, No. 1, pp. 94-101

OFFPRINT 1032

ADAPTATIONS TO COLD

by Laurence Irving

One mechanism is increased generation of heat by a rise in the rate
of metabolism, but this process has its limits. The alternatives
are insulation and changes in the circulation of heat by the blood.

All living organisms abhor cold. For many susceptible forms of life a temperature difference of a few degrees means the difference between life and death. Everyone knows how critical temperature is for the growth of plants. Insects and fishes are similarly sensitive; a drop of two degrees in temperature when the sun goes behind a cloud, for instance, can convert a fly from a swift flier to a slow walker. In view of the general hostility of cold to life and activity, the ability of mammals and birds to survive and flourish in all climates is altogether remarkable.

It is not that these animals are basically more tolerant of cold. We know from our own reactions how sensitive the human body is to chilling. A naked, inactive human being soon becomes miserable in air colder than 28 degrees centigrade (about 82 degrees Fahrenheit), only 10 degrees C. below his body temperature. Even in the Tropics the coolness of night can make a person uncomfortable. The discomfort of cold is one of the most vivid of experiences; it stands out as a persistent memory in a soldier's recollections of the unpleasantness of his episodes in the field. The coming of winter in temperate climates has a profound effect on human well-being and activity. Cold weather, or cold living quarters, compounds the misery of illness or poverty. Over the entire planet a large proportion of man's efforts, culture and economy is devoted to the simple necessity of protection against cold.

Yet strangely enough neither man nor other mammals have consistently avoided cold climates. Indeed, the venturesome human species often goes out of its way to seek a cold environment, for sport or for the adventure of living in a challenging situation. One of the marvels of man's history is the endurance and stability of the human settlements that have been established in arctic latitudes.

The Norse colonists who settled in Greenland 1,000 years ago found Eskimos already living there. Archaeologists today are finding many sites and relics of earlier ancestors of the Eskimos who occupied arctic North America as long as 6,000 years ago. In the middens left by these ancient inhabitants are bones and hunting implements that indicate man was accompanied in the cold north by many other warm-blooded animals: caribou, moose, bison, bears, hares, seals, walruses and whales. All the species, including man, seem to have been well adapted to arctic life for thousands of years.

It is therefore a matter of more than idle interest to look closely into how mammals adapt to cold. In all climates and everywhere on the earth mammals maintain a body temperature of about 38 degrees C. It looks as if evolution has settled on this temperature as an optimum for the mammalian class. (In birds the standard body temperature is a few degrees higher.) To keep their internal temperature at a viable level the mammals must be capable of adjusting to a wide range of environmental temperatures. In tropical air at 30 degrees C. (86 degrees F.), for example, the environment is only eight degrees cooler than the body temperature; in arctic air at −50 degrees C. it is 88 degrees colder. A man or other mammal in the Arctic must adjust to both extremes as seasons change.

The mechanisms available for making the adjustments are (1) the generation of body heat by the metabolic burning of food as fuel and (2) the use of insulation and other devices to retain body heat. The requirements can be expressed quantitatively in a Newtonian formula concerning the cooling of warm bodies. A calculation based on the formula shows that to maintain the necessary warmth of its body a mammal must generate 10 times more heat in the Arctic than in the Tropics or clothe itself in 10 times more effective insulation or employ some intermediate combination of the two mechanisms.

We need not dwell on the metabolic requirement; it is rarely a major factor. An animal can increase its food intake and generation of heat to only a very modest degree. Moreover, even if metabolic capacity and the food supply were unlimited, no animal could spend all its time eating. Like man, nearly all other mammals spend a great deal of time in curious exploration of their surroundings, in play and in family and social activities. In the arctic winter a herd of caribou often rests and ruminates while the young engage in aimless play. I have seen caribou resting calmly with wolves lying asleep in the snow in plain view only a few hundred yards away. There is a common impression that life in the cold climates is more active than in the Tropics, but the fact is that for the natural populations of mammals, including man, life goes on at the same leisurely pace in the Arctic as it does in warmer regions; in all climates there is the same requirement of rest and social activities.

The decisive difference in resisting cold, then, lies in the mechanisms for conserving body heat. In the Institute of Arctic Biology at the University of Alaska we are continuing studies that have been in progress there and elsewhere for 18 years to compare the

ARCTIC ZONE (20 TO −60 DEGREES C.)

TEMPERATE ZONE (20 TO −20 DEGREES C.)

TROPICAL ZONE (35 TO 25 DEGREES C.)

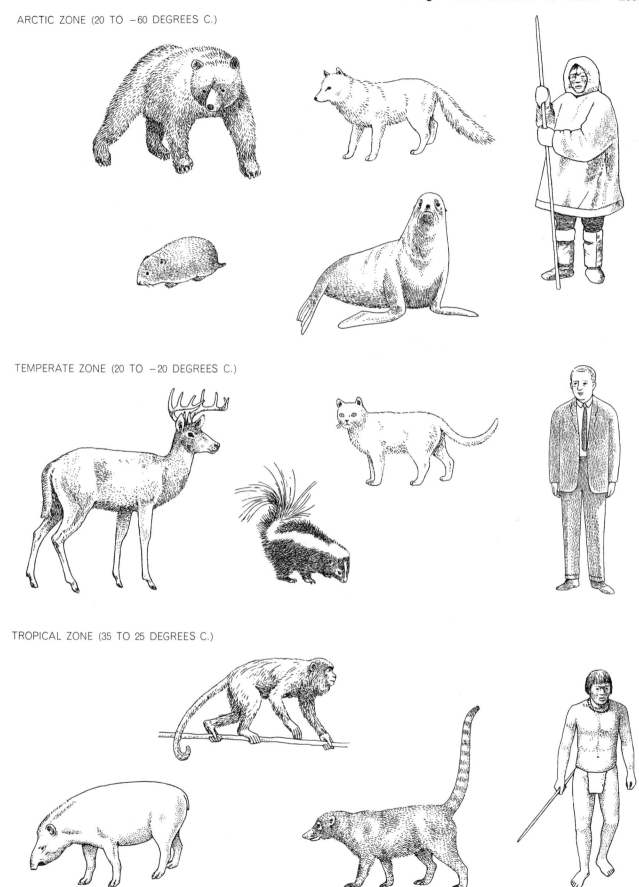

RANGE OF TEMPERATURES to which warm-blooded animals must adapt is indicated. All the animals shown have a body temperature close to 100 degrees Fahrenheit, yet they survive at outside temperatures that, for the arctic animals, can be more than 100 degrees cooler. Insulation by fur is a major means of adaptation to cold. Man is insulated by clothing; some other relatively hairless animals, by fat. Some animals have a mechanism for conserving heat internally so that it is not dissipated at the extremities.

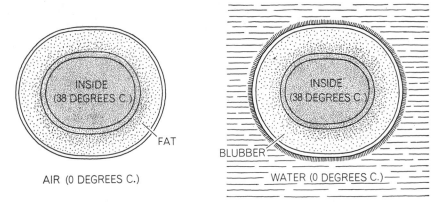

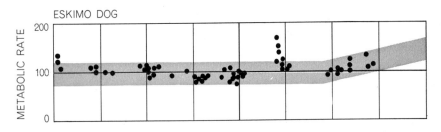

TEMPERATURE GRADIENTS in the outer parts of the body of a pig (*left*) and of a seal (*right*) result from two effects: the insulation provided by fat and the exchange of heat between arterial and venous blood, which produces lower temperatures near the surface.

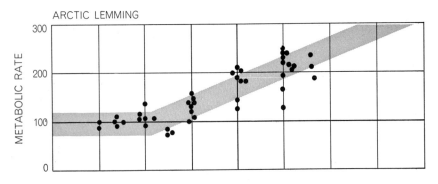

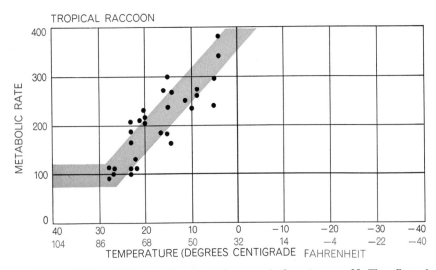

RATE OF METABOLISM provides a limited means of adaptation to cold. The effect of declining temperatures on the metabolic rate is shown for an Eskimo dog (*top*), an arctic lemming (*middle*) and a tropical raccoon (*bottom*). Animals in warmer climates tend to increase metabolism more rapidly than arctic animals do when the temperature declines.

mechanisms for conservation of heat in arctic and tropical animals. The investigations have covered a wide variety of mammals and birds and have yielded conclusions of general physiological interest.

The studies began with an examination of body insulation. The fur of arctic animals is considerably thicker, of course, than that of tropical animals. Actual measurements showed that its insulating power is many times greater. An arctic fox clothed in its winter fur can rest comfortably at a temperature of −50 degrees C. without increasing its resting rate of metabolism. On the other hand, a tropical animal of the same size (a coati, related to the raccoon) must increase its metabolic effort when the temperature drops to 20 degrees C. That is to say, the fox's insulation is so far superior that the animal can withstand air 88 degrees C. colder than its body at resting metabolism, whereas the coati can withstand a difference of only 18 degrees C. Naked man is less well protected by natural insulation than the coati; if unclothed, he begins shivering and raising his metabolic rate when the air temperature falls to 28 degrees C.

Obviously as animals decrease in size they become less able to carry a thick fur. The arctic hare is about the smallest mammal with enough fur to enable it to endure continual exposure to winter cold. The smaller animals take shelter under the snow in winter. Weasels, for example, venture out of their burrows only for short periods; mice spend the winter in nests and sheltered runways under the snow and rarely come to the surface.

No animal, large or small, can cover all of its body with insulating fur. Organs such as the feet, legs and nose must be left unencumbered if they are to be functional. Yet if these extremities allowed the escape of body heat, neither mammals nor birds could survive in cold climates. A gull or duck swimming in icy water would lose heat through its webbed feet faster than the bird could generate it. Warm feet standing on snow or ice would melt it and soon be frozen solidly to the place where they stood. For the unprotected extremities, therefore, nature has evolved a simple but effective mechanism to reduce the loss of heat: the warm outgoing blood in the arteries heats the cool blood returning in the veins from the extremities. This exchange occurs in the *rete mirabile* (wonderful net), a network of small arteries and veins near the junction between the trunk of the animal and the extremity [see "'The Wonderful Net,'" by P. F. Scholander; SCIENTIFIC AMERICAN, April, 1957]. Hence the extremities can become much colder than the body without either draining off body heat or losing their ability to function.

This mechanism serves a dual purpose. When necessary, the thickly furred animals can use their bare extremities to release excess heat from the body. A heavily insulated animal would soon be overheated by running or other active exercise were it not for these outlets. The generation of heat by exercise turns on the flow of blood to the extremities so that they radiate heat. The large, bare flippers of a resting fur seal are normally cold, but we have found that when these animals on the Pribilof Islands are driven overland at their laborious gait, the flippers become warm. In contrast to the warm flippers, the rest of the fur seal's body surface feels cold, because very little heat escapes through the animal's dense fur. Heat can also be dissipated by evaporation from the mouth and tongue. Thus a dog or a caribou begins to pant, as a means of evaporative cooling, as soon as it starts to run.

In the pig the adaptation to cold by means of a variable circulation of heat in the blood achieves a high degree of refinement. The pig, with its skin only thinly covered with bristles, is as naked as a man. Yet it does well in the Alaskan winter without clothing. We can read the animal's response to cold by its expressions of comfort or discomfort, and we have measured its physiological reactions. In cold air the circulation of heat in the blood of swine is shunted away from the entire body surface, so that the surface becomes an effective insulator against loss of body heat. The pig can withstand considerable cooling of its body surface. Although a man is highly uncomfortable when his skin is cooled to 7 degrees C. below the internal temperature, a pig can be comfortable with its skin 30 degrees C. colder than the interior, that is, at a temperature of 8 degrees C. (about 46 degrees F.). Not until the air temperature drops below the freezing point (0 degrees C.) does the pig increase its rate of metabolism; in contrast a man, as I have mentioned, must do so at an air temperature of 28 degrees C.

With thermocouples in the form of needle we have probed the tissues of pigs below the skin surface. (Some pigs, like some people, will accept a little

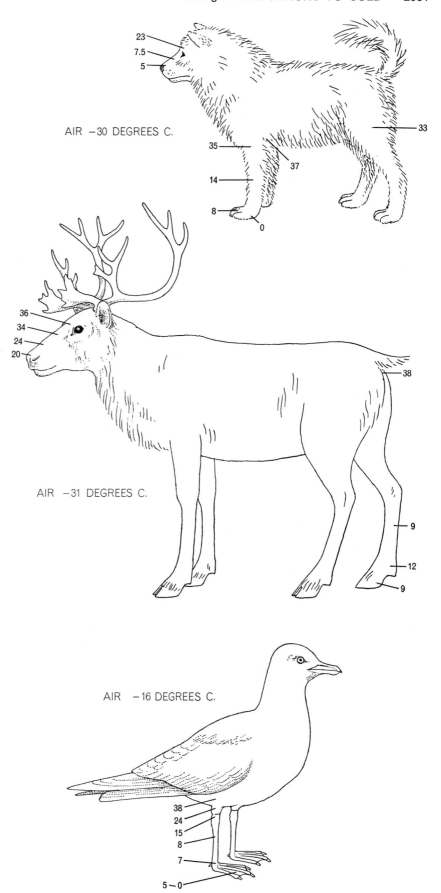

TEMPERATURES AT EXTREMITIES of arctic animals are far lower than the internal body temperature of about 38 degrees centigrade, as shown by measurements made on Eskimo dogs, caribou and sea gulls. Some extremities approach the outside temperature.

pain to win a reward.) We found that with the air temperature at −12 degrees C. the cooling of the pig's tissues extended as deep as 100 millimeters (about four inches) into its body. In warmer air the thermal gradient through the tissues was shorter and less steep. In short, the insulating mechanism of the hog involves a considerable depth of the animal's fatty mantle.

Even more striking examples of this kind of mechanism are to be found in whales, walruses and hair seals that dwell in the icy arctic seas. The whale and the walrus are completely bare; the hair seal is covered only with thin, short hair that provides almost no insulation when it is sleeked down in the water. Yet these animals remain comfortable in water around the freezing point although water, with a much greater heat capacity than air, can extract a great deal more heat from a warm body.

Examining hair seals from cold waters of the North Atlantic, we found that even in ice water these animals did not raise their rate of metabolism. Their skin was only one degree or so warmer than the water, and the cooling effect extended deep into the tissues—as much as a quarter of the distance through the thick part of the body. Hour after hour the animal's flippers all the way through would remain only a few degrees above freezing without the seals' showing any sign of discomfort. When the seals were moved into warmer water, their outer tissues rapidly warmed up. They would accept a transfer from warm water to ice water with equanimity and with no diminution of their characteristic liveliness.

How are the chilled tissues of all these animals able to function normally at temperatures close to freezing? There is first of all the puzzle of the response of fatty tissue. Animal fat usually becomes hard and brittle when it is cooled to low temperatures. This is true even of the land mammals of the Arctic, as far as their internal fats are concerned. If it were also true of extremities such as their feet, however, in cold weather their feet would become too inflexible to be useful. Actually it turns out that the fats in these organs behave differently from those in the warm internal tissues. Farmers have known for a long time that neat's-foot oil, extracted from the feet of cattle, can be used to keep leather boots and harness flexible in cold weather. By laboratory examination we have found that the fats in the bones of the lower leg and foot of the caribou remain soft even at 0 degrees C. The melting point of the fats in the leg steadily goes up in the higher portions of the leg. Eskimos have long been aware that fat from a caribou's foot will serve as a fluid lubricant in the cold, whereas the marrow fat from the upper leg is a solid food even at room temperature.

About the nonfatty substances in tissues we have little information; I have seen no reports by biochemists on the effects of temperature on their properties. It is known, however, that many of the organic substances of animal tissues are highly sensitive to temperature. We must therefore wonder how the tissues can maintain their serviceability over the very wide range of temperatures that the body surface experiences in the arctic climate.

We have approached this question by studies of the behavior of tissues at various temperatures. Nature offers many illustrations of the slowing of tissue functions by cold. Fishes, frogs and water insects are noticeably slowed down by cool water. Cooling by 10 degrees

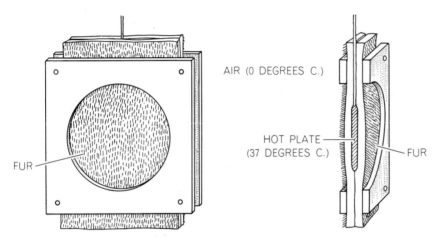

INSULATION BY FUR was tested in this apparatus, shown in a front view at left and a side view at right. The battery-operated heating unit provided the equivalent of body temperature on one side of the fur; outdoor temperatures were approximated on the other side.

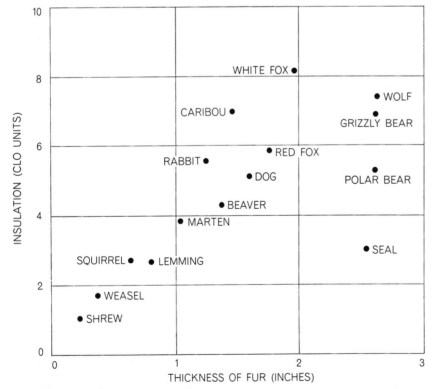

INSULATING CAPACITY of fur is compared for various animals. A "clo unit" equals the amount of insulation provided by the clothing a man usually wears at room temperature.

C. will immobilize most insects. A grasshopper in the warm noonday sun can be caught only by a swift bird, but in the chill of early morning it is so sluggish that anyone can seize it. I had a vivid demonstration of the temperature effect one summer day when I went hunting on the arctic tundra near Point Barrow for flies to use in experiments. When the sun was behind clouds, I had no trouble picking up the flies as they crawled about in the sparse vegetation, but as soon as the sun came out the flies took off and were uncatchable. Measuring the temperature of flies on the ground, I ascertained that the difference between the flying and the slow-crawling state was a matter of only 2 degrees C.

Sea gulls walking barefoot on the ice in the Arctic are just as nimble as gulls on the warm beaches of California. We know from our own sensations that our fingers and hands are numbed by cold. I have used a simple test to measure the amount of this desensitization. After cooling the skin on my fingertips to about 20 degrees C. (68 degrees F.) by keeping them on ice-filled bags, I tested their sensitivity by dropping a light ball (weighing about one milligram) on them from a measured height. The weight multiplied by the distance of fall gave me a measure of the impact on the skin. I found that the skin at a temperature of 20 degrees C. was only a sixth as sensitive as at 35 degrees C. (95 degrees F.); that is, the impact had to be six times greater to be felt.

We know that even the human body surface has some adaptability to cold. Men who make their living by fishing can handle their nets and fish with wet hands in cold that other people cannot endure. The hands of fishermen, Eskimos and Indians have been found to be capable of maintaining an exceptionally vigorous blood circulation in the cold. This is possible, however, only at the cost of a higher metabolic production of body heat, and the production in any case has a limit. What must arouse our wonder is the extraordinary adaptability of an animal such as the hair seal. It swims in icy waters with its flippers and the skin over its body at close to the freezing temperature, and yet under the ice in the dark arctic sea it remains sensitive enough to capture moving prey and find its way to breathing holes.

Here lies an inviting challenge for all biologists. By what devices is an animal able to preserve nervous sensitivity in tissues cooled to low temperatures? Beyond this is a more universal and more

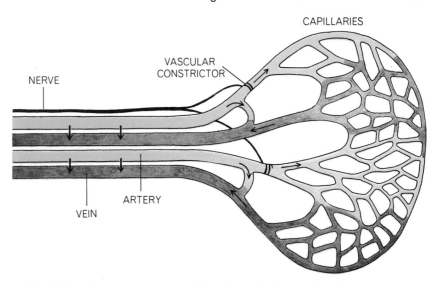

ROLE OF BLOOD in adaptation to cold is depicted schematically. One mechanism, indicated by the vertical arrows, is an exchange of heat between arterial and venous blood. The cold venous blood returning from an extremity acquires heat from an arterial network. The outgoing arterial blood is thus cooled. Hence the exchange helps to keep heat in the body and away from the extremities when the extremities are exposed to low temperatures. The effect is enhanced by the fact that blood vessels near the surface constrict in cold.

interesting question: How do the warm-blooded animals preserve their overall stability in the varying environments to which they are exposed? Adjustment to changes in temperature requires them to make a variety of adaptations in the various tissues of the body. Yet these changes must be harmonized to maintain the integration of the organism as a whole. I predict that further studies of the mechanisms involved in adaptation to cold will yield exciting new insights into the processes that sustain the integrity of warm-blooded animals.

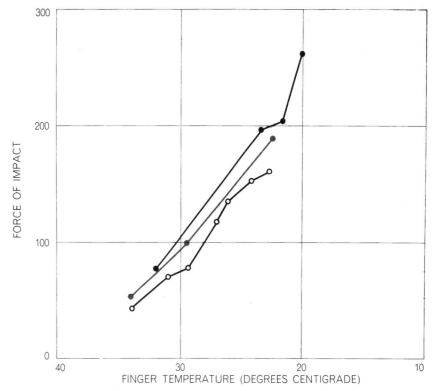

FINGER EXPERIMENT performed by the author showed that the more a finger was chilled, the farther a one-milligram ball had to be dropped for its impact to be felt on the finger. The vertical scale is arbitrary but reflects the relative increase in the force of impact.

The Author

LAURENCE IRVING is director of the Institute of Arctic Biology and professor of zoophysiology at the University of Alaska. A graduate of Bowdoin College, he received a master's degree at Harvard University in 1917 and a Ph.D. at Stanford University in 1924. He has worked in Alaska since 1947, going there after more than 20 years of teaching, mostly at Swarthmore College. "I have long been inclined to study the physiological adaptations that enable men and animals to succeed in extreme natural conditions," he writes. "It turned out that the natural physiological reactions of arctic animals to cold were of dimensions large enough to demonstrate general principles of adaptation to various temperatures that we had been unable to ascertain in mild climates and by the use of domesticated animals."

Bibliography

BODY INSULATION OF SOME ARCTIC AND TROPICAL MAMMALS AND BIRDS. P. F. Scholander, Vladimir Walters, Raymond Hock and Laurence Irving in *The Biological Bulletin,* Vol. 99, No. 2, pages 225–236; October, 1950.

BODY TEMPERATURES OF ARCTIC AND SUBARCTIC BIRDS AND MAMMALS. Laurence Irving and John Krog in *Journal of Applied Physiology,* Vol. 6, No. 11, pages 667–680; May, 1954.

EFFECT OF TEMPERATURE ON SENSITIVITY OF THE FINGER. Laurence Irving in *Journal of Applied Physiology,* Vol. 18, No. 6, pages 1201–1205; November, 1963.

METABOLISM AND INSULATION OF SWINE AS BARE-SKINNED MAMMALS. Laurence Irving, Leonard J. Peyton and Mildred Monson in *Journal of Applied Physiology,* Vol. 9, No. 3, pages 421–426; November, 1956.

PHYSIOLOGICAL INSULATION OF SWINE AS BARE-SKINNED MAMMALS. Laurence Irving in *Journal of Applied Physiology,* Vol. 9, No. 3, pages 414–420; November, 1956.

TERRESTRIAL ANIMALS IN COLD: INTRODUCTION. Laurence Irving in *Handbook of Physiology, Section 4: Adaptation to the Environment.* American Physiological Society, 1964.

SPECIAL NOTE TO TEACHERS: Each article in this volume, plus more than 660 others, is available as a separate, self-bound SCIENTIFIC AMERICAN Offprint. Offprints may be ordered in any combination and in any quantity. Teachers who want to adopt articles for their courses, therefore, can ensure that each student has his own set. Students' sets are collated by the publisher before shipment.

SCIENTIFIC
AMERICAN   February 1966, Vol. 214, No. 2, pp. 30-39   OFFPRINT 1033

THE NUCLEOTIDE SEQUENCE OF
A NUCLEIC ACID

by Robert W. Holley

For the first time the specific order of subunits in one
of the giant molecules that participate in the synthesis
of protein has been determined. The task took seven years.

Two major classes of chainlike molecules underlie the functioning of living organisms: the nucleic acids and the proteins. The former include deoxyribonucleic acid (DNA), which embodies the hereditary message of each organism, and ribonucleic acid (RNA), which helps to translate that message into the thousands of different proteins that activate the living cell. In the past dozen years biochemists have established the complete sequence of amino acid subunits in a number of different proteins. Much less is known about the nucleic acids.

Part of the reason for the slow progress with nucleic acids was the unavailability of pure material for analysis. Another factor was the large size of most nucleic acid molecules, which often contain thousands or even millions of nucleotide subunits. Several years ago, however, a family of small molecules was discovered among the ribonucleic

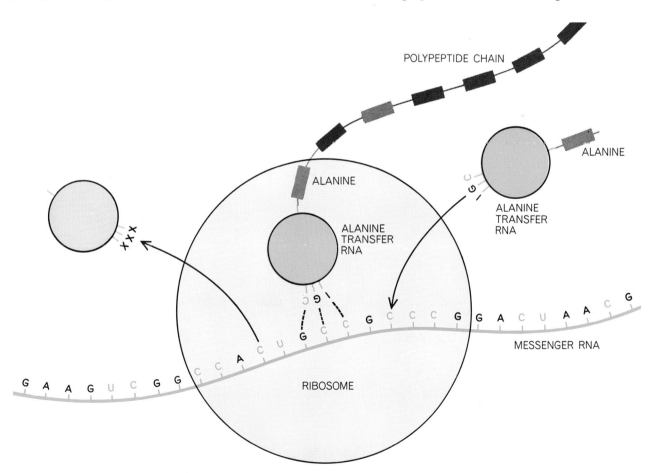

ROLE OF TRANSFER RNA is to deliver a specific amino acid to the site where "messenger" RNA and a ribosome (which also contains RNA) collaborate in the synthesis of a protein. As it is being synthesized a protein chain is usually described as a polypeptide. Each amino acid in the polypeptide chain is specified by a triplet code, or codon, in the molecular chain of messenger RNA.

The diagram shows how an "anticodon" (presumably I—G—C) in alanine transfer RNA may form a temporary bond with the codon for alanine (G—C—C) in the messenger RNA. While so bonded the transfer RNA also holds the polypeptide chain. Each transfer RNA is succeeded by another one, carrying its own amino acid, until the complete message in the messenger RNA has been "read."

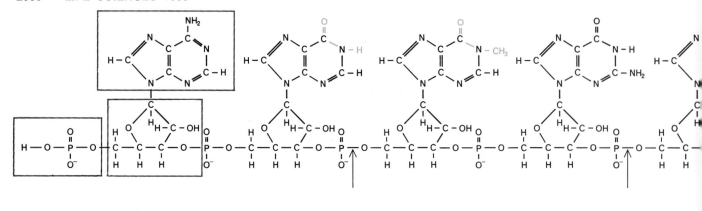

ADENYLIC ACID
p A

INOSINIC ACID
I

1-METHYLINOSINIC ACID
I^m

GUANYLIC ACID
G

1-METHYLGUAN
G^m

NUCLEOTIDE SUBUNITS found in alanine transfer RNA include the four commonly present in RNA (A, G, C, U), plus seven others that are variations of the standard structures. Ten of these 11 different nucleotide subunits are assembled above as if they were linked together in a single RNA chain. The chain begins at the left with a phosphate group (*outlined by a small rectangle*) and is followed by a ribose sugar group (*large rectangle*); the two groups alternate to form the backbone of the chain. The chain ends at the right with

acids. My associates and I at the U.S. Plant, Soil and Nutrition Laboratory and Cornell University set ourselves the task of establishing the nucleotide sequence of one of these smaller RNA molecules—a molecule containing fewer than 100 nucleotide subunits. This work culminated recently in the first determination of the complete nucleotide sequence of a nucleic acid.

The object of our study belongs to a family of 20-odd molecules known as transfer RNA's. Each is capable of recognizing one of the 20 different amino acids and of transferring it to the site where it can be incorporated into a growing polypeptide chain. When such a chain assumes its final configuration, sometimes joining with other chains, it is called a protein.

At each step in the process of protein

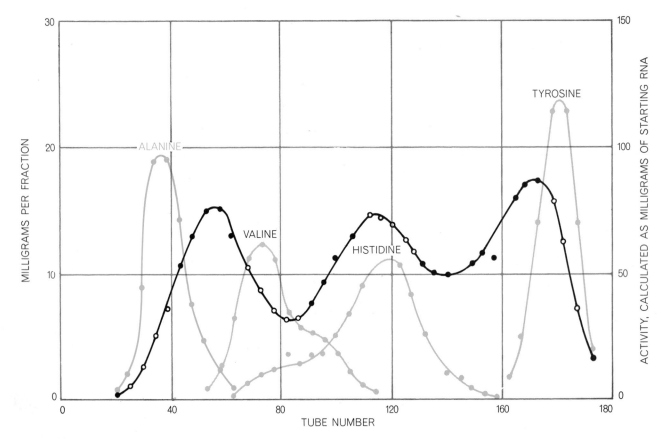

COUNTERCURRENT DISTRIBUTION PATTERN shows two steps in the separation of alanine transfer RNA, as carried out in the author's laboratory. After the first step the RNA content in various collection tubes, measured by ultraviolet absorption, follows the black curve. Biological activity, indicated by the amount of a given amino acid incorporated into polypeptide chains, follows the colored curves. Pure transfer RNA's of four types can be obtained by reprocessing the tubes designated by open circles.

▲RIBOTHYMIDYLIC ACID
T

DIHYDROURIDYLIC ACID
U^h

MIXTURE OF URIDYLIC AND
DIHYDROURIDYLIC ACIDS

N^2-DIMETHYLGUANYLIC ACID
G^m

CYTIDYLIC ACID
C

URIDYLIC ACID
U

U*

PSEUDOURIDYLIC ACID
ψ OH

a hydroxyl (OH) group. Each nucleotide subunit consists of a phosphate group, a ribose sugar group and a base. The base portion in the nucleotide at the far left, adenylic acid, is outlined by a large rectangle. In the succeeding bases the atomic variations are shown in color. The base structures without color are those commonly found in RNA. Black arrows show where RNA chains can be cleaved by the enzyme takadiastase ribonuclease T1. Colored arrows show where RNA chains can be cleaved by pancreatic ribonuclease.

synthesis a crucial role is played by the structure of the various RNA's. "Messenger" RNA transcribes the genetic message for each protein from its original storage site in DNA. Another kind of RNA—ribosomal RNA—forms part of the structure of the ribosome, which acts as a jig for holding the messenger RNA while the message is transcribed into a polypeptide chain [see illustration on page 2065]. In view of the various roles played by RNA in protein synthesis, the structure of RNA molecules is of considerable interest and significance.

The particular nucleic acid we chose for study is known as alanine transfer RNA—the RNA that transports the amino acid alanine. It was isolated from commercial baker's yeast by methods I shall describe later. Preliminary analyses indicated that the alanine transfer RNA molecule consisted of a single chain of approximately 80 nucleotide subunits. Each nucleotide, in turn, consists of a ribose sugar, a phosphate group and a distinctive appendage termed a nitrogen base. The ribose sugars and phosphate groups link together to form the backbone of the molecule, from which the various bases protrude [see illustration at top of these two pages].

The problem of structural analysis is fundamentally one of identifying each base and determining its place in the sequence. In practice each base is usually isolated in combination with a unit of ribose sugar and a unit of phosphate, which together form a nucleotide. Formally the problem is analogous to de-

termining the sequence of letters in a sentence.

It would be convenient if there were a way to snip off the nucleotides one by one, starting at a known end of the chain and identifying each nucleotide as it appeared. Unfortunately procedures of this kind have such a small yield at each step that their use is limited. The alternative is to break the chain at particular chemical sites with the help of enzymes. This gives rise to small fragments whose nucleotide composition is amenable to analysis. If the chain can be broken up in various ways with different enzymes, one can determine how the fragments overlap and ultimately piece together the entire sequence.

One can visualize how this might work by imagining that the preceding sentence has been written out several times, in a continuous line, on different strips of paper. Imagine that each strip has been cut in a different way. In one case, for example, the first three words "If the chain" and the next three words "can be broken" might appear on separate strips of paper. In another case one might find that "chain" and "can" were together on a single strip. One would immediately conclude that the group of three words ending with "chain" and the group beginning with "can" form a continuous sequence of six words. The concept is simple; putting it into execution takes a little time.

For cleaving the RNA chain we used two principal enzymes: pancreatic ribonuclease and an enzyme called takadiastase ribonuclease T1, which was discovered by the Japanese workers K. Sato-Asano and F. Egami. The first

enzyme cleaves the RNA chain immediately to the right of pyrimidine nucleotides, as the molecular structure is conventionally written. Pyrimidine nucleotides are those nucleotides whose bases contain the six-member pyrimidine ring, consisting of four atoms of carbon and two atoms of nitrogen. The two pyrimidines commonly found in RNA are cytosine and uracil. Pancreatic ribonuclease therefore produces fragments that terminate in pyrimidine nucleotides such as cytidylic acid (C) or uridylic acid (U).

The second enzyme, ribonuclease T1, was employed separately to cleave the RNA chain specifically to the right of nucleotides containing a structure of the purine type, such as guanylic acid (G). This provided a set of short fragments distinctively different from those produced by the pancreatic enzyme.

The individual short fragments were isolated by passing them through a thin glass column packed with diethylaminoethyl cellulose—an adaptation of a chromatographic method devised by R. V. Tomlinson and G. M. Tener of the University of British Columbia. In general the short fragments migrate through the column more rapidly than the long fragments, but there are exceptions [see illustration on next page]. The conditions most favorable for this separation were developed in our laboratories by Mark Marquisee and Jean Apgar.

The nucleotides in each fragment were released by hydrolyzing the fragment with an alkali. The individual nucleotides could then be identified by paper chromatography, paper electrophoresis and spectrophotometric analysis. This procedure was sufficient to establish the sequence of each of the dinucleotides, because the right-hand member of the pair was determined by the particular enzyme that had been used to produce the fragment. To establish the sequence of nucleotides in larger fragments, however, required special techniques.

Methods particularly helpful in the separation and identification of the fragments had been previously described by Vernon M. Ingram of the Massachusetts Institute of Technology, M. Las-kowski, Sr., of the Marquette University School of Medicine, K. K. Reddi of Rockefeller University, G. W. Rushizky and Herbert A. Sober of the National Institutes of Health, the Swiss worker M. Staehelin and Tener.

For certain of the largest fragments, methods described in the scientific literature were inadequate and we had to develop new stratagems. One of these involved the use of an enzyme (a phosphodiesterase) obtained from snake venom. This enzyme removes nucleotides one by one from a fragment, leaving a mixture of smaller fragments of all possible intermediate lengths. The mixture can then be separated into fractions of homogeneous length by passing it through a column of diethylaminoethyl cellulose [*see illustration on opposite page*]. A simple method is available for determining the terminal nucleotide at the right end of each fraction of homogeneous length. With this knowledge, and knowing the length of each fragment, one can establish the sequence of nucleotides in the original large fragment.

A summary of all the nucleotide sequences found in the fragments of transfer RNA produced by pancreatic ribonuclease is shown in Table 1 on page 2070. Determination of the structure of the fragments was the work of James T. Madison and Ada Zamir, who were postdoctoral fellows in my laboratory. George A. Everett of the Plant, Soil and Nutrition Laboratory helped us in the identification of the nucleotides.

Much effort was spent in determining the structure of the largest fragments and in identifying unusual nucleotides not heretofore observed in RNA molecules. Two of the most difficult to identify were 1-methylinosinic acid and 5,6-dihydrouridylic acid. (In the illustrations these are symbolized respectively by I^m and U^h.)

Because a free 5′-phosphate group (p) is found at one end of the RNA molecule (the left end as the structure is conventionally written) and a free 3′-hydroxyl group (oh) is found at the other end, it is easy to pick out from Table 1 and Table 2 the two sequences that form the left and right ends of the alanine transfer RNA molecule. The left end has the structure pG—G—G—C— and the right end the structure U—C—C—A—C—Coh. (It is known, however, that the active molecule ends in C—C—Aoh.)

The presence of unusual nucleotides

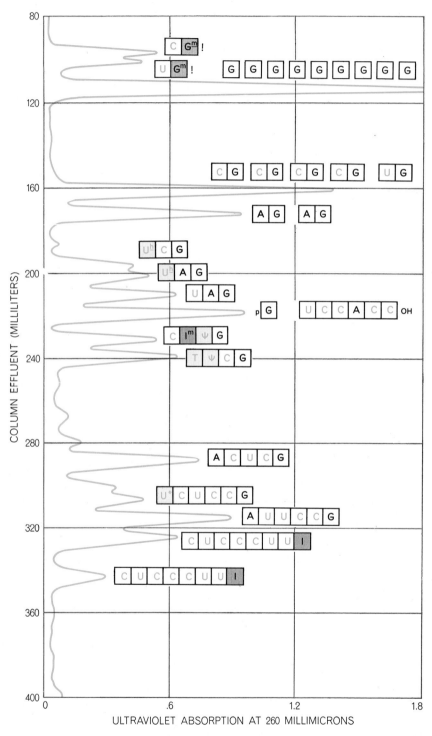

SEPARATION OF RNA FRAGMENTS is accomplished by chromatography carried out in a long glass column packed with diethylaminoethyl cellulose. The curve shows the separation achieved when the column input is a digest of alanine transfer RNA produced by takadiastase ribonuclease T1, an enzyme that cleaves the RNA into 29 fragments. The exclamation point indicates fragments whose terminal phosphate has a cyclical configuration. Such fragments travel faster than similar fragments that end in a noncyclical phosphate.

and unique short sequences made it clear that certain of the fragments found in Table 1 overlapped fragments found in Table 2. For example, there is only one inosinic acid nucleotide (I) in the molecule, and this appears in the sequence I–G–C– in Table 1 and in the sequence C–U–C–C–C–U–U–I– in Table 2. These two sequences must therefore overlap to produce the overall sequence C–U–C–C–C–U–U–I–G–C–. The information in Table 1 and Table 2 was combined in this way to draw up Table 3, which accounts for all 77 nucleotides in 16 sequences [*see illustration on page 2071*].

With the knowledge that two of the 16 sequences were at the two ends, the structural problem became one of determining the positions of the intermediate 14 sequences. This was accomplished by isolating still larger fragments of the RNA.

In a crucial experiment John Robert Penswick, a graduate student at Cornell, found that a very brief treatment of the RNA with ribonuclease T1 at 0 degrees centigrade in the presence of magnesium ions splits the molecule at one position. The two halves of the molecule could be separated by chromatography. Analyses of the halves established that the sequences listed in the first column of Table 3 are in the left half of the molecule and that those in the second column are in the right half.

Using a somewhat more vigorous but still limited treatment of the RNA with ribonuclease T1, we then obtained and analyzed a number of additional large fragments. This work was done in collaboration with Jean Apgar and Everett. To determine the structure of a large fragment, the fragment was degraded completely with ribonuclease T1, which yielded two or more of the fragments previously identified in Table 2. These known sequences could be put together, with the help of various clues, to obtain the complete sequence of the large fragment. The process is similar to putting together a jigsaw puzzle [*see illustrations on pages 2072 and 2073*].

As an example of the approach that was used, the logical argument is given in detail for Fragment A. When Fragment A was completely degraded by ribonuclease T1, we obtained seven small fragments: three G–'s, C–G–, U–G–, U–Gm– and pG–. (Gm is used in the illustrations to represent 1-methylguanylic acid, another of the unusual nucleotides in alanine transfer RNA.) The presence of pG– shows that Frag-

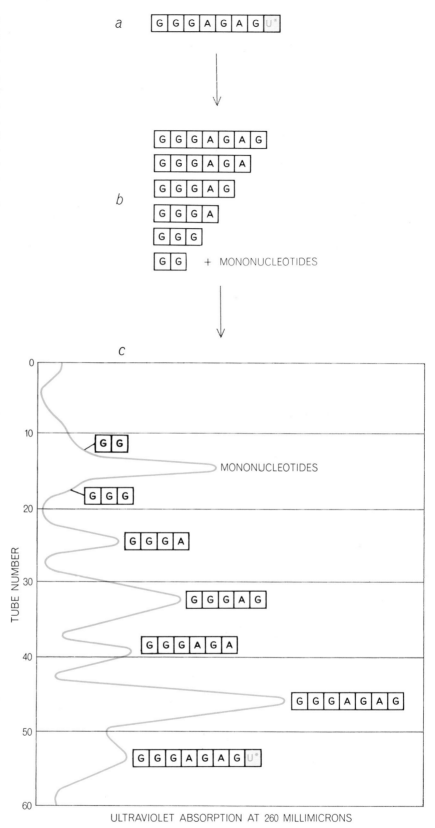

NEW DEGRADATION METHOD was developed in the author's laboratory to determine the sequence of nucleotides in fragments five to eight subunits in length. The example above begins with a fragment of eight subunits from which the terminal phosphate has been removed (*a*). When the fragment is treated with phosphodiesterase found in snake venom, the result is a mixture containing fragments from one to eight subunits in length (*b*). These are separated by chromatography (*c*). When the material from each peak is hydrolyzed, the last nucleoside (a nucleotide minus its phosphate) at the right end of the fragment is released and can be identified. Thus each nucleotide in the original fragment can be determined.

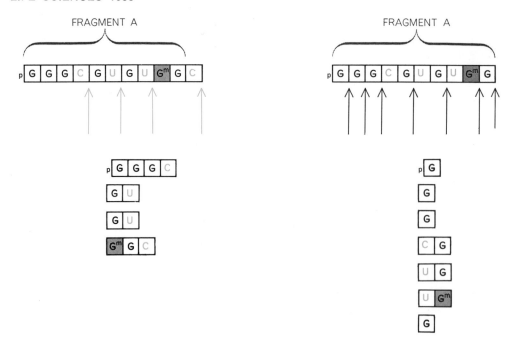

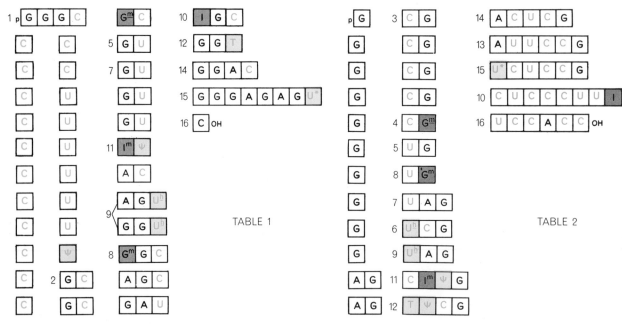

TABLE 1

TABLE 2

ACTION OF TWO DIFFERENT ENZYMES is reflected in these two tables. Table 1 shows the fragments produced when alanine transfer RNA is completely digested by pancreatic ribonuclease, which cleaves the molecule to the right of nucleotides containing bases with pyrimidine structures (C, U, U^h, ψ and T). The diagram at top left shows how pancreatic ribonuclease would cleave the first 11 nucleotides of alanine transfer RNA. The diagram at top right shows how the same region would be digested by takadiastase ribonuclease T1. Table 2 contains the fragments produced by this enzyme; they all end in nucleotides whose bases contain purine structures (G, G^m, $G^{\underline{m}}$ and I). The numbers indicate which ones appear in the consolidated list in Table 3 on the opposite page.

ment A is from the left end of the molecule. Since it is already known from Table 3 that the left terminal sequence is pG–G–G–C–, the positions of two of the three G–'s and C–G– are known; the terminal five nucleotides must be pG–G–G–C–G–.

The positions of the remaining G–, U–G– and U–G^m– are established by the following information. Table 3 shows that the U–G^m– is present in the sequence U–G^m–G–C–. Since there is only one C in Fragment A, and its position is already known, Fragment A must terminate before the C of the U–G^m–G–C– sequence. Therefore the U–G– must be to the left of the U–G^m–, and the structure of Fragment A can be represented as pG–G–G–C–G–...U–G–...U–G^m–, with one G– remaining to be placed. If the G– is placed to the left or the right of the U–G– in this structure, it would create a G–G–U– sequence. If such a sequence existed in the molecule, it would have appeared as a fragment when the molecule was treated with pancreatic ribonuclease; Table 1 shows that it did not do so. Therefore the remaining G– must be to the right of the G^m–, and the sequence of Fragment A is pG–G–G–C–G–U–G–U–G^m–G–.

Using the same procedure, the entire structure of alanine transfer RNA was worked out. The complete nucleotide sequence of alanine transfer RNA is shown at the top of the next two pages.

The work on the structure of this molecule took us seven years from start to finish. Most of the time was consumed in developing procedures for the isolation of a single species of transfer RNA from the 20 or so different transfer RNA's present in the living cell. We finally selected a fractionation technique known as countercurrent distribution, developed in the 1940's by Lyman C. Craig of the Rockefeller Institute.

This method exploits the fact that similar molecules of different structure will exhibit slightly different solubilities if they are allowed to partition, or distribute themselves, between two nonmiscible liquids. The countercurrent technique can be mechanized so that the mixture of molecules is partitioned hundreds or thousands of times, while the nonmiscible solvents flow past each other in a countercurrent pattern. The solvent system we adopted was composed of formamide, isopropyl alcohol and a phosphate buffer, a modification of a system first described by Robert C. Warner and Paya Vaimberg of New York University. To make the method applicable for fractionating transfer RNA's required four years of work in collaboration with Jean Apgar, B. P. Doctor and Susan H. Merrill of the Plant, Soil and Nutrition Laboratory. Repeated countercurrent extractions of the transfer RNA mixture gave three of the RNA's in a reasonably homogeneous state: the RNA's that transfer the amino acids alanine, tyrosine and valine [see bottom illustration on page 2066].

The starting material for the countercurrent distributions was crude transfer RNA extracted from yeast cells using phenol as a solvent. In the course of the structural work we used about 200 grams (slightly less than half a pound) of mixed transfer RNA's isolated from 300 pounds of yeast. The total amount of purified alanine transfer RNA we had to work with over a three-year period was one gram. This represented a practical compromise between the difficulty of scaling up the fractionation procedures and scaling down the techniques for structural analysis.

Once we knew the complete sequence, we could turn to general questions about the structure of transfer RNA's. Each transfer RNA presumably embodies a sequence of three subunits (an "anticodon") that forms a temporary bond with a complementary sequence of three subunits (the "codon") in messenger RNA. Each codon triplet identifies a specific amino acid [see "The Genetic Code: II," by Marshall W. Nirenberg; SCIENTIFIC AMERICAN Offprint 153].

An important question, therefore, is which of the triplets in alanine transfer RNA might serve as the anticodon for the alanine codon in messenger RNA. There is reason to believe the anticodon is the sequence I–G–C, which is found in the middle of the RNA molecule. The codon corresponding to I–G–C could be the triplet G–C–C or perhaps G–C–U, both of which act as code words for alanine in messenger RNA. As shown in the illustration on page 2065, the I–G–C in the alanine transfer RNA is upside down when it makes contact with the corresponding codon in messenger RNA. Therefore when alanine transfer RNA is delivering its amino acid cargo and is temporarily held by hydrogen bonds to messenger RNA, the I would pair with C (or U) in the messenger, G would pair with C, and C would pair with G.

We do not know the three-dimensional structure of the RNA. Presumably there is a specific form that interacts with the messenger RNA and ribosomes. The diagram on page 2074 shows three hypothetical structures for alanine transfer RNA that take account of the propensity of certain bases to pair with other bases. Thus adenine pairs with uracil and cytosine with guanine. In the three hypothetical structures the I–G–C sequence is at an exposed position and could pair with messenger RNA.

The small diagram on page 2074 indicates a possible three-dimensional folding of the RNA. Studies with atomic models suggest that single-strand regions of the structure are highly flexible. Thus in the "three-leaf-clover" configuration it is possible to fold one side leaf on top of the other, or any of the leaves back over the stem of the molecule.

One would also like to know whether or not the unusual nucleotides are concentrated in some particular region of the molecule. A glance at the sequence shows that they are scattered throughout the structure; in the three-leaf-clo-

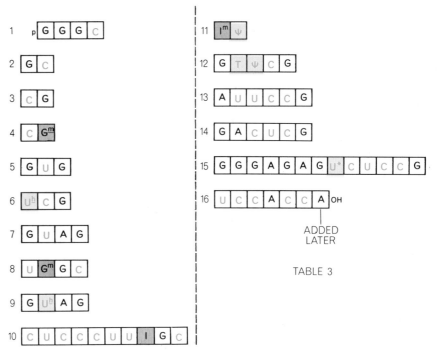

CONSOLIDATED LIST OF SEQUENCES accounts for all 77 nucleotides in alanine transfer RNA. The consolidated list is formed by selecting the largest fragments in Table 1 and Table 2 (opposite page) and by piecing together fragments that obviously overlap. Thus Fragment 15 has been formed by joining two smaller fragments, keyed by the number 15, in Table 1 and Table 2 on the opposite page. Since the entire molecule contains only one U*, the two fragments must overlap at that point. The origin of the other fragments in Table 3 can be traced in similar fashion. A separate experiment in which the molecule was cut into two parts helped to establish that the 10 fragments listed in the first column are in the left half of the molecule and that the six fragments in the second column are in the right half.

FRAGMENT A
FRAGMENT B
FRAGMENT E

COMPLETE MOLECULE of alanine transfer RNA contains 77 nucleotides in the order shown. The final sequence required a careful piecing together of many bits of information (*see illustration at bottom of these two pages*). The task was facilitated by degrada-

ver model, however, the unusual nucleotides are seen to be concentrated around the loops and bends.

Another question concerns the presence in the transfer RNA's of binding sites, that is, sites that may interact specifically with ribosomes and with

the enzymes involved in protein synthesis. We now know from the work of Zamir and Marquisee that a particular sequence containing pseudouridylic acid (Ψ), the sequence G–T–Ψ–C–G, is found not only in the alanine transfer RNA but also in the transfer RNA's for

tyrosine and valine. Other studies suggest that it may be present in all the transfer RNA's. One would expect such common sites to serve a common function; binding the transfer RNA's to the ribosome might be one of them.

Work that is being done in many

FRAGMENT A

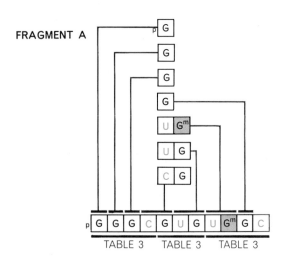

TABLE 3   TABLE 3   TABLE 3

FRAGMENT B

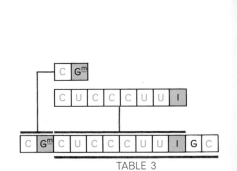

TABLE 3

FRAGMENT E

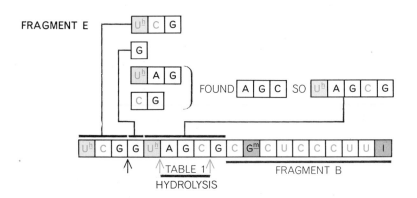

FOUND AGC SO U^h A G C G

TABLE 1
HYDROLYSIS

FRAGMENT B

REMAINDER OF LEFT HALF OF MOLECULE

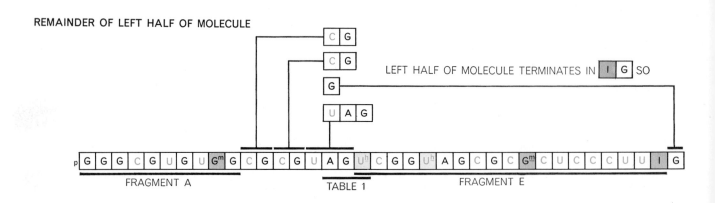

LEFT HALF OF MOLECULE TERMINATES IN I G SO

FRAGMENT A   TABLE 1   FRAGMENT E

FRAGMENT C / FRAGMENT D

FRAGMENT F / FRAGMENT G

tion experiments that cleaved this molecule into several large fragments (*A, B, C, D, E, F, G*), and by the crucial discovery that the molecule could be divided almost precisely into two halves. The division point is marked by the "gutter" between these two pages.

laboratories around the world indicates that alanine transfer RNA is only the first of many nucleic acids for which the nucleotide sequences will be known. In the near future it should be possible to identify those structural features that are common to various transfer RNA's, and this should help greatly in defining the interactions of transfer RNA's with messenger RNA, ribosomes and enzymes involved in protein synthesis. Further in the future will be the description of the nucleotide sequences of the nucleic acids—both DNA and RNA— that embody the genetic messages of the viruses that infect bacteria, plants and animals. Much further in the future lies the decoding of the genetic messages of higher organisms, including man. The work described in this article is a step toward that distant goal.

FRAGMENT C

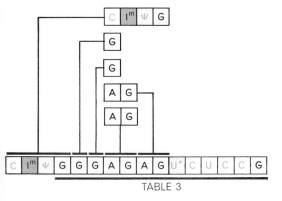

TABLE 3

FRAGMENT D

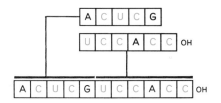

FRAGMENT F

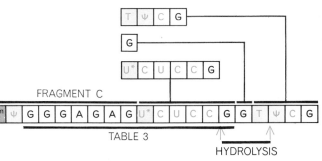

FRAGMENT C

TABLE 3

HYDROLYSIS

FRAGMENT G

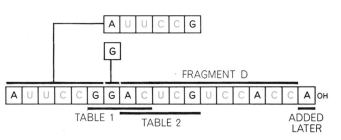

FRAGMENT D

TABLE 1   TABLE 2   ADDED LATER

ASSEMBLY OF FRAGMENTS resembled the solving of a jigsaw puzzle. The arguments that established the sequence of nucleotides in Fragment *A* are described in the text. Fragment *B* contains two subfragments. The larger is evidently Fragment 10 in Table 3, which ends in G—C—. This means that the C—Gᵐ— fragment must go to the left. Fragment *E* contains Fragment *B* plus four smaller fragments. It can be shown that *E* ends with I—, therefore the four small pieces are again to the left. A pancreatic digest yielded A—G—C—, thus serving to connect Uʰ—A—G— and C—G—. A partial digestion with ribonuclease T1 removed Uʰ—C—G—, showing it to be at the far left. The remaining G— must follow immediately or a pancreatic digest would have yielded a G—G—C— sequence, which it did not. Analyses of Fragments *A* and *E* accounted for everything in the left half of the molecule except for four small pieces. The left half of the molecule was shown to terminate in I—G—, thus the remaining three pieces are between *A* and *E*. Table 1 shows that one Uʰ is preceded by A—G—, therefore U—

A—G— must be next to *E*. The two remaining C—G—'s must then fall to the left of U—A—G—. Fragment *C* contains five pieces. Table 3 (Fragment 15) shows that the two A—G—'s are next to U* and that the two G—'s are to the left of them. It is also clear that C—Iᵐ—Ψ—G— cannot follow U*, therefore it must be to the left. Fragment *D* contains two pieces; the oh group on one of them shows it to be to the right. Fragment *F* contains Fragment *C* plus three extra pieces. These must all lie to the right since hydrolysis with pancreatic ribonuclease gave G—G—T— and not G—T—, thus establishing that the single G— falls as shown. Fragment *G* gave *D* plus two pieces, which must both lie to the left (because of the terminal Coh). Table 1 shows a G—G—A—C— sequence, which must overlap the A—C— in A—C—U—C—G— and the G— at the right end of the A—U—U—C—C—G—. Fragments *F* and *G* can join in only one way to form the right half of the molecule. The molecule is completed by the addition of a final Aoh, which is missing as the alanine transfer RNA is separated from baker's yeast.

HYPOTHETICAL MODELS of alanine transfer ribonucleic acid (RNA) show three of the many ways in which the molecule's linear chain might be folded. The various letters represent nucleotide subunits; their chemical structure is given at the top of pages 2066 and 2067. In these models it is assumed that certain nucleotides, such as C—G and A—U, will pair off and tend to form short double-strand regions. Such "base-pairing" is a characteristic feature of nucleic acids. The arrangement at the lower left shows how two of the large "leaves" of the "clover leaf" model may be folded together. The triplet I—G—C is the presumed anticodon shown in the illustration on the opposite page. The region containing the sequence G—T—Ψ—C—G may be common to all transfer RNA's.

The Author

ROBERT W. HOLLEY is professor of biochemistry and chairman of the section of biochemistry and molecular biology of the division of biological sciences at Cornell University. He was graduated from the University of Illinois in 1942 and obtained a Ph.D. at Cornell in 1947. He joined the Cornell faculty in 1948, and during his years there he has also worked with the U.S. Plant, Soil and Nutrition Laboratory at the university. Holley and his colleagues spent four years isolating one gram of pure transfer ribonucleic acid and three more years ascertaining its chemical structure. Holley received the 1965 Albert D. Lasker award for basic medical research for the work described in his article.

Bibliography

ISOLATION OF LARGE OLIGONUCLEOTIDE FRAGMENTS FROM THE ALANINE RNA. Jean Apgar, George A. Everett and Robert W. Holley in *Proceedings of the National Academy of Sciences,* Vol. 53, No. 3, pages 546–548; March, 1965.

LABORATORY EXTRACTION AND COUNTERCURRENT DISTRIBUTION. Lyman C. Craig and David Craig in *Technique of Organic Chemistry, Volume III, Part I: Separation and Purification,* edited by Arnold Weissberger. Interscience Publishers, Inc., 1956. See pages 149–332.

SPECIFIC CLEAVAGE OF THE YEAST ALANINE RNA INTO TWO LARGE FRAGMENTS. John Robert Penswick and Robert W. Holley in *Proceedings of the National Academy of Sciences,* Vol. 53, No. 3, pages 543–546; March, 1965.

STRUCTURE OF A RIBONUCLEIC ACID. Robert W. Holley, Jean Apgar, George A. Everett, James T. Madison, Mark Marquisee, Susan H. Merrill, John Robert Penswick and Ada Zamir in *Science,* Vol. 147, No. 3664, pages 1462–1465; March 19, 1965.

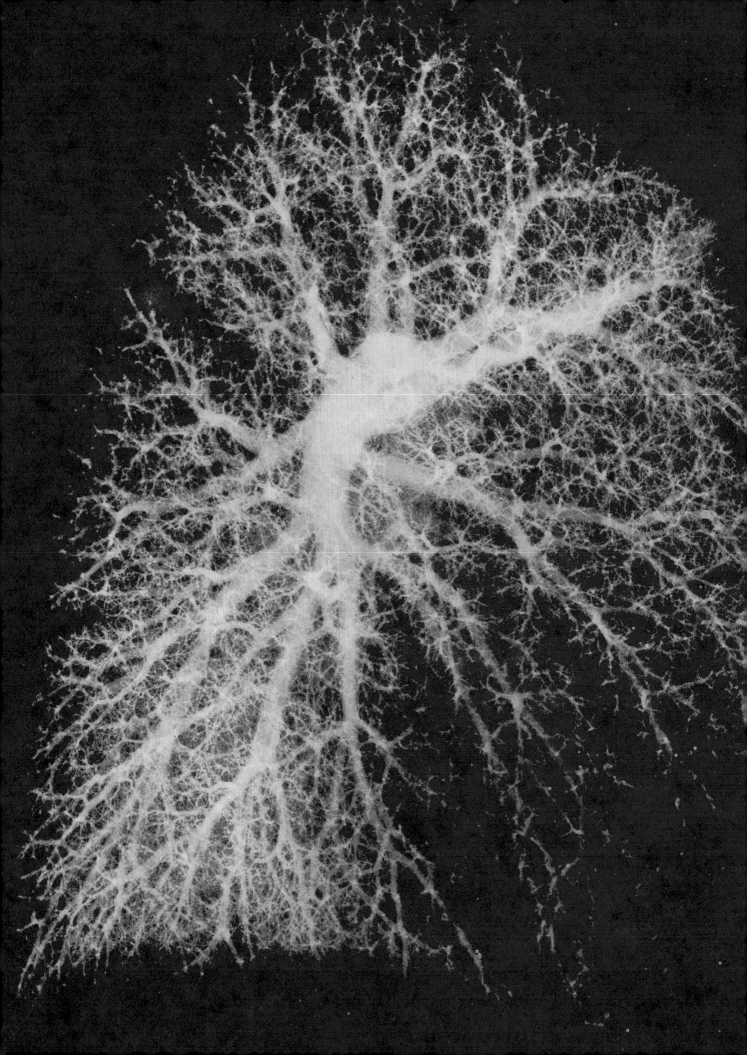

SCIENTIFIC
AMERICAN February 1966, Vol. 214, No. 2, pp. 56-68   OFFPRINT 1034

THE LUNG

by Julius H. Comroe, Jr.

This elaborately involuted tissue of air sacs and blood vessels serves
to exchange gases between the air and the blood. In man the total
area of the membrane between the two systems is 70 square meters.

Each year an adult human inhales and exhales between two million and five million liters of air. Each breath consists of about half a liter of air, 20 percent of which is molecular oxygen (O_2); the air swirls briefly through a maze of branching ducts leading to tiny sacs that comprises a gas-exchange apparatus in which some of the oxygen is added to the blood. The apparatus I am describing is of course the lung: the central organ in the system the larger land animals have evolved as a means of supplying each of their cells with oxygen.

Oxygen is essential to most forms of life. A one-celled organism floating in water requires no complex apparatus to extract oxygen from its surroundings; its needs are satisfied by the process of diffusion—the random movement of molecules that results in a net flow of oxygen from regions of abundance to regions of scarcity. Over very short distances, such as the radius of a cell, the diffusion of oxygen is rapid. Over larger distances diffusion is a much slower process; it cannot meet the needs of any many-celled organism in which the distance between the source of oxygen and the most remote cell is greater than half a millimeter.

The evolution of large animals has therefore required the development of various special systems that deliver oxygen from the surrounding medium to

each of the animal's cells. In higher vertebrates such as man this system consists of a gas pump (the thorax) and two fluid pumps (the right and left ventricles of the heart). The fluid pumps are linked to networks of capillaries, through the walls of which the actual exchange of gas molecules takes place. The capillary network that receives its blood from the left ventricle distributes oxygen throughout the body. The network that receives its blood from the right ventricle serves a different purpose. In it the actions of the fluid pump and the gas pump are combined to obtain the oxygen needed by the body from the surrounding atmosphere.

This integrated system works in the following manner. The expansion of the thorax allows air to flow into ducts that divide into finer tubes that terminate in the sacs called alveoli. The rhythmic contraction of the right ventricle of the heart drives blood from the veins through a series of vessels that spread through the lung and branch into capillaries [see illustration on opposite page]. These blood-filled pulmonary capillaries surround the gas-filled alveoli; in most places the membrane separating the gas from the blood is only a thousandth of a millimeter thick. Over such a short distance the molecules of oxygen, which are more abundant in the inhaled air than in the venous blood, diffuse readily into the blood. Conversely the molecules of the body's waste product carbon dioxide, which is more abundant in the venous blood than in the inhaled air, diffuse in the opposite direction. In the human lung the surface area available for this gas exchange is huge: 70 square meters—some 40 times the surface area of the entire body. Accordingly gas can be transferred to and from the blood quickly and in large amounts.

The gas exchange that occurs in the lungs is only the first in a series of events that meet the oxygen needs of the human body's billions of cells. The second of the two liquid pumps—the left ventricle of the heart—now distributes the oxygenated blood throughout the body by means of arteries and arterioles that lead to a second gas-exchange system. This second system is in reality composed of billions of individual gas-exchangers, because each capillary is a gas-exchanger for the cells it supplies. As the arterial blood flowing through the capillary gives up its oxygen molecules to the adjacent cells and absorbs the cells' waste products, it becomes venous blood and passes into the collecting system that brings it back to the right ventricle of the heart [see illustration on next page].

The customary use of the term "pulmonary circulation" for that part of the circulatory system which involves the right ventricle and the lungs, and of the term "systemic circulation" for the left ventricle and the balance of the circulatory system, seems to imply that the body has two distinct blood circuits. In actuality there is only one circuit; the systemic apparatus is one arc of it and the pulmonary apparatus is the other. The systemic part of the circuit supplies arterial blood, rich in oxygen and poor in carbon dioxide, to all the capillary gas-exchangers in the body; it also collects the venous blood, poor in oxygen and rich in carbon dioxide, from these exchangers and returns it to the right ventricle. The pulmonary part of the circuit delivers the venous blood to the pulmonary gas-exchanger and then sends it on to the systemic part of the circuit.

This combination of two functions not only provides an adequate exchange of oxygen and carbon dioxide but also

ARTERIAL SYSTEM of the human lung (*opposite page*) is revealed by X-ray photography following the injection of a radio-opaque fluid. The finest visible branches actually subdivide further into capillaries from five to 10 microns in diameter that surround the lung's 300 million air sacs.

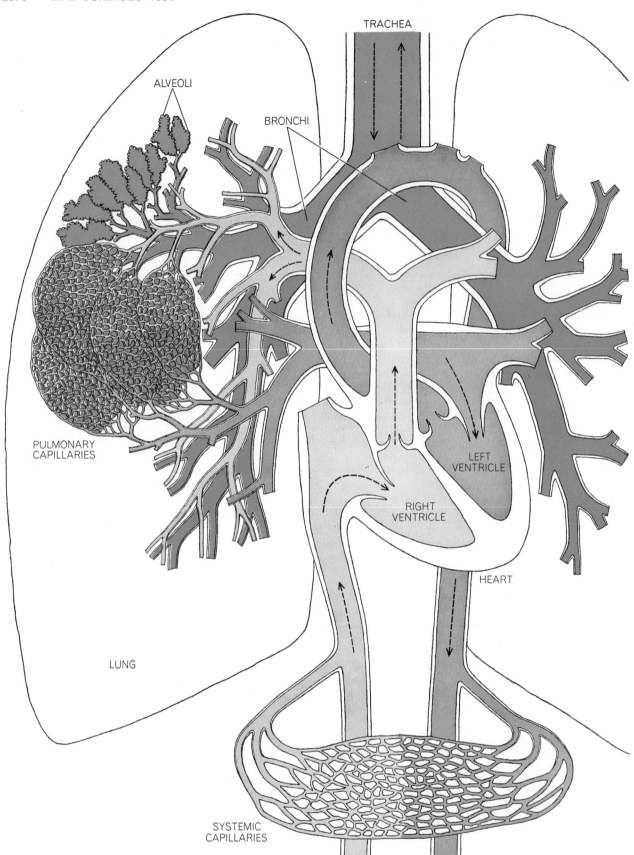

THREE PUMPS operate the lungs' gas-exchange system. One gas pump, the thorax (*see illustration on opposite page*), moves from five to seven liters of air (*color*) in and out of the lungs' air sacs every minute. At top left these alveoli are shown without their covering of pulmonary capillaries, which are shown at center left. One fluid pump, the heart's right ventricle, forces from 70 to 100 cubic centimeters of blood into the pulmonary capillaries at each contraction. This blood (*light gray*) is low in oxygen and high in carbon dioxide; oxygen, abundant in the air, is diffused into the blood while carbon dioxide is diffused from the blood into the air. Oxygenated and low in carbon dioxide, the blood (*dark gray*) then reaches the third pump, the left ventricle, which sends it on to the systemic capillaries (*example at bottom of illustration*) that deliver oxygen to and collect carbon dioxide from all the body's cells.

supplies a variety of nutrients to the tissues and removes the products of tissue metabolism, including heat. Complex regulatory mechanisms ensure enough air flow and blood flow to meet both the body's overall needs and the special needs of any particular part of the body according to its activity.

The Respiratory System

To the physiologist respiration usually means the movement of the thorax and the flow of air in and out of the lungs; to the biochemist respiration is the process within the cells that utilizes oxygen and produces carbon dioxide. Some call the first process external respiration and the second internal respiration or tissue respiration. Here I shall mainly discuss those processes that occur in the lung and that involve exchanges either between the outside air and the gas in the alveoli or between the alveolar gas and the blood in the pulmonary capillaries.

The structure of the respiratory system is sometimes shown in an oversimplified way that emphasizes only the conducting air path and the alveoli. The system is far more complex. It originates with the two tubes of the nose (the mouth can be regarded as a third tube), which join to become one: the trachea. The trachea then subdivides into two main branches, the right bronchus and the left. Each of the bronchi divides into two, each of them into two more and so on; there are from 20 to 22 bronchial subdivisions. These subdivisions give rise to more than a million tubes that end in numerous alveoli, where the gas exchange occurs. There are some 300 million alveoli in a pair of human lungs; they vary in diameter from 75 to 300 microns (thousandths of a millimeter). Before birth they are filled with fluid but thereafter the alveoli of normal lungs always contain gas. Even at the end of a complete exhalation the lungs of a healthy adult contain somewhat more than a liter of gas; this quantity is known as the residual volume. At the end of a normal exhalation the lungs contain more than two liters; this is called the functional residual capacity. When the lungs are expanded to the maximum, a state that is termed the total capacity, they contain from six to seven liters.

More important than total capacity, functional residual capacity or residual volume is the amount of air that reaches the alveoli. An adult human at rest inhales and exhales about half a liter of gas with each breath. Ideally each

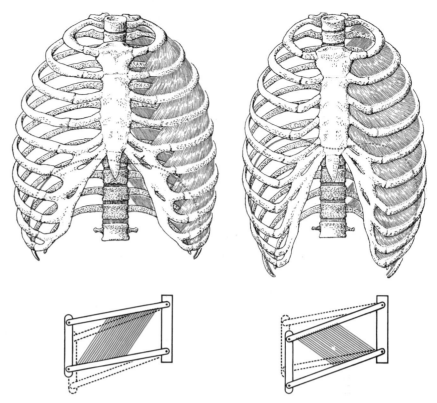

INHALATION takes place when the thorax expands, thus forcing the lungs to enlarge and bringing the pressure of the gas within them below atmospheric pressure. The expansion (*top left*) is principally the work of the diaphragm but also involves the muscles of the rib cage (*detail at bottom left*). Exhalation occurs when passive relaxation reduces the size of the thorax (*top right*), thereby raising the gas in the lungs to greater than atmospheric pressure. Only under conditions of stress do muscles (*detail at bottom right*) aid exhalation.

breath supplies his two-liter reservoir of gas—the functional residual capacity—with a volume of oxygen equal to the volume absorbed from the reservoir by the blood flowing through the pulmonary capillaries. At the same time each breath removes from the reservoir a volume of carbon dioxide equal to the volume produced by the body's cells and yielded to the lungs by the venous blood. The resting adult breathes from 10 to 14 times a minute, with the result that his ventilation—the volume of air entering and leaving the lungs—is from five to seven liters per minute. The maximum human capacity for breathing is about 30 times the resting ventilation rate, a flow of from 150 to 200 liters per minute. Even during the most intense muscular exercise, however, ventilation averages only between 80 and 120 liters per minute; man obviously has a great reserve of ventilation.

The volume of ventilation that is important in terms of gas exchange is less than the total amount of fresh air that enters the nose and mouth. Only the fresh air that reaches the alveoli and mixes with the gas already there is useful. Unlike the blood in the circulatory system, the air does not travel only in

one direction. There are no valves in the bronchi or their subdivisions; incoming and outgoing air moves back and forth through the same system of tubes. Little or no gas is exchanged in these tubes. They represent dead space, and the air that is in them at the end of an inhalation is wasted because it is washed out again during an exhalation. Thus the useful ventilation obtained from any one breath consists of the total inhalation—half a liter, or 500 cubic centimeters—minus that part of the inhalation which is wasted in the dead space. In an adult male the wasted volume is about 150 cubic centimeters.

From an engineering standpoint this dead space in the air pump represents a disadvantage: more ventilation, which necessitates more work by the pump, is required to overcome the 30 percent inefficiency. The dead space may nonetheless represent a net advantage. The use of a single system of ducts for incoming and outgoing air eliminates the need for a separate set of ducts to carry each flow. Such a dual system would certainly encroach on the lung area available for gas exchange and might well result in more than a 30 percent inefficiency.

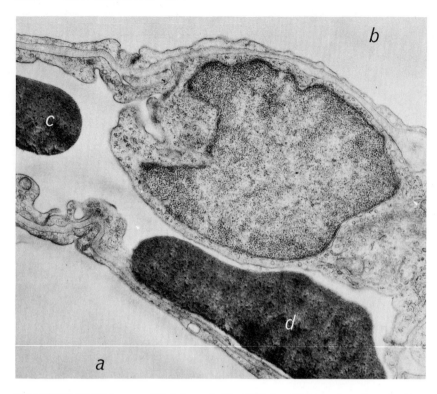

DIFFUSION PATH from gas-filled air sac to blood-filled capillary can be extremely short. In this electron micrograph of mouse lung tissue, *a* and *b* are air spaces; between these lies a capillary in which there are two red blood cells, *c* and *d*. The large light gray mass is the nucleus of an endothelial cell. The distances from air space *a* to red cell *d* and from air space *b* to red cell *c* are less than half a micron; the diffusion of gases across these gaps is swift.

Ventilation of the alveoli is not enough to ensure an adequate supply of oxygen. The incoming air must also be distributed uniformly so that each alveolus receives its share. Some alveoli are very close to the main branchings of the bronchi; others at the top and bottom of the lung are 20 or 30 centimeters away from such a branch. It is a remarkable feat of engineering to distribute the proper amount of fresh air almost simultaneously to 300 million alveoli of varying sizes through a network of a million tubes of varying lengths and diameters.

By the same token, ideal gas exchange requires that the blood be evenly distributed to all the pulmonary capillaries—that none of it should escape oxygenation by flowing through shunts in the capillary bed. Under abnormal circumstances, however, some alveoli are poorly ventilated, and venous blood flowing through the adjacent capillaries is not properly oxygenated. Conversely, there are situations when the flow of blood through certain capillaries is inadequate or nonexistent; in these cases good ventilation of the neighboring alveoli is wasted.

In spite of such deficiencies, the gas exchange can remain effective if the defects are matched (if the same regions that have poor ventilation, for example, also have poor blood flow), so that regions with increased ventilation also have increased blood flow. Two mechanisms help to achieve this kind of matching. First, a decrease in the ventilation of a group of alveoli results in a constriction of the blood vessels and a decrease in the blood flow of the affected region. This decrease is not the result of a nerve stimulus or a reflex but is a local mechanism, probably initiated by oxygen deficiency. Second, a local deficiency in blood flow results in a constriction of the pathways that conduct air to the affected alveoli. The resulting increase in airway resistance serves to direct more of the air to alveoli with a normal, or better than normal, blood supply.

The Pulmonary Circulation

The system that distributes blood to the lungs is just as remarkable as the system that distributes air. As I have noted, the right ventricle of the heart receives all the venous blood from every part of the body; the contraction of the heart propels the blood into one large tube, the pulmonary trunk. Like the trachea, this tube divides and subdivides, ultimately forming hundreds of millions of short, narrow, thin-walled capillaries. Each capillary has a diameter of from five to 10 microns, which is just wide enough to enable red blood cells to pass one at a time. The wall of the capillary is less than .1 micron thick; the capillary's length ranges from .1 to .5 millimeter.

If the pulmonary capillaries were laid end to end, their total length would be hundreds of miles, but the overall capillary network offers surprisingly little resistance to the flow of blood. In order to pump from five to 10 liters of blood per minute through the pulmonary system the right ventricle needs to provide a driving pressure of less than 10 millimeters of mercury—a tenth of the pressure required of the left ventricle for systemic circulation. With only a small increase in driving pressure the pulmonary blood flow can be increased to 30 liters per minute.

Although the total surface area provided by the pulmonary capillaries is enormous, at any instant the capillary vessels contain only from 70 to 100 cubic centimeters of blood. This volume is almost identical with the volume of blood the right ventricle ejects with each contraction. Thus with each heartbeat the reoxygenated blood in the pulmonary capillaries is pushed on toward the left ventricle and venous blood refills the capillaries. In the human body at rest each red blood cell remains in a pulmonary capillary for about three-quarters of a second; during vigorous exercise the length of its stay is reduced to about a third of a second. Even this brief interval is sufficient, under normal conditions, for gas exchange.

Electron microscopy reveals that the membrane in the lung that separates the gas-filled alveolus from the blood-filled capillary consists of three distinct layers. One is the alveolar epithelium, the second is the basement membrane and the third is the capillary endothelium. The cellular structure of these layers renders between a quarter and a third of the membrane's 70 square meters of surface too thick to be ideal for rapid gas exchange; over the rest of the area, however, the barrier through which the gas molecules must diffuse is very thin—as thin as .2 micron. Comparison of the gas-transfer rate in the body at rest with the rate during vigorous exercise provides a measure of the gas-exchange system's capacity. In the body at rest only 200 to 250 cubic centimeters of oxygen diffuse per minute; in the exercising body the system can deliver as much as 5,500 cubic centimeters per minute.

The combination of a large diffusion area and a short diffusion path is responsible for much of the lung's efficiency in gas exchange, but an even more critical factor is the remarkable ability of the red blood pigment hemoglobin to combine with oxygen. If plasma that contained no red cells or hemoglobin were substituted for normal blood, the adult human heart would have to pump 83 liters per minute through the pulmonary capillaries to meet the oxygen needs of a man at rest. (Even this assumes that 100 percent of the oxygen in the plasma is delivered to the tissues, which is never the case.) In contrast, blood with a normal amount of hemoglobin in the red cells picks up 65 times more oxygen than plasma alone does; the heart of a man at rest need pump only about five and a half liters of blood per minute, even though the tissues normally extract only from 20 to 25 percent of the oxygen carried to the cells by the red blood corpuscles.

The Mechanics of Breathing

Just as water inevitably runs downhill, so gases flow from regions of higher pressure to those of lower pressure. In the case of the lung, when the total gas pressure in the alveoli is equal to the pressure of the surrounding atmosphere, no movement of gas is possible. For inhalation to occur, the alveolar gas pressure must be less than the atmospheric pressure; for exhalation, the opposite must be the case. There are two ways in which the pressure difference required for the movement of air into the lungs can be created: either the pressure in the alveoli can be lowered below atmospheric pressure or the pressure at the nose and mouth can be raised above atmospheric pressure. In normal breathing man follows the former course; enlarging the thorax (and thus enlarging the lungs as well) enables the alveolar gas to expand until its pressure drops below that of the surrounding atmosphere. Inhalation follows automatically.

The principal muscle for enlarging the thorax is the diaphragm, the large dome-shaped sheet of tissue that is anchored around the circumference of the lower thorax and separates the thoracic cavity from the abdominal cavity. When the muscle of the diaphragm contracts, the mobile central portion of the sheet moves downward, much as a piston moves in a cylinder. In addition, skeletal muscles enlarge the bony thoracic cage by increasing its circumference [see illustration on page 2079]. Lungs, of course, lie entirely within the thorax. They have no skeletal muscles and cannot increase their volume by their own efforts, but their covering (the visceral pleura) is closely linked to the entire inner lining of the thorax (the parietal pleura). Only a thin layer of fluid separates the two pleural surfaces; when the thorax expands, the lungs must follow suit. As the pressure of the alveolar gas drops below that of the atmosphere, the outside air flows in through the nose, mouth and tracheobronchial air paths until the pressure is equalized.

This kind of pulmonary ventilation requires work; the active contraction of the thoracic muscles provides the force necessary to overcome a series of opposing loads. These loads include the recoil of the elastic tissues of the thorax, the recoil of the elastic tissue of the lungs, the frictional resistance to the flow of air through the hundreds of thousands of ducts of the tracheobronchial tree, and the surface forces created at the fluid-gas interfaces in the alveoli [see "Surface Tension in the Lungs," by John A. Clements; SCIENTIFIC AMERICAN Offprint 142].

In contrast to inhalation, exhalation is usually a passive process. During the active contraction of muscles that causes the enlargement of the thorax, the tissues of thorax and lungs are stretched and potential energy is stored in them. The recoil of the stretched tissue and the release of the stored energy produce the exhalation. Only at very high rates of ventilation or when there is an obstruction of the tracheobronchial tree is there active contraction of muscles to assist exhalation.

Artificial ventilation can be produced either by raising external gas pressure or by lowering internal pressure. Body respirators of the "iron lung" type lower the pressure of the air surrounding the thorax in part of their cycle of operation. As a consequence the volume of the thorax increases, the alveolar pressure falls and, since the patient's nose and mouth are outside the apparatus, air at atmospheric pressure flows into his lungs. Later in the cycle the pressure within the respirator rises; the volume of the thorax decreases and the patient exhales.

Other types of artificial ventilation depend on raising the external pressure at the nose and mouth above the atmospheric level. Some mechanical respirators operate by supplying high-pressure

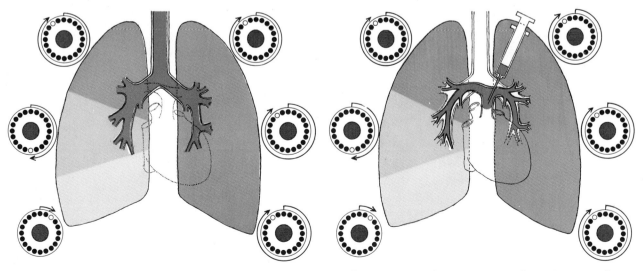

RADIOACTIVE TRACERS such as xenon 133 can assess the performance of the two components in the lungs' gas-exchange system. Inhaled as a gas (*left*), the xenon will be unevenly distributed if the air ducts are blocked; zones that are poorly ventilated will produce lower scintillation-counter readings than normal ones will. Injected in a solution into the bloodstream (*right*), the xenon will diffuse unevenly into the air sacs if the blood vessels are blocked. Such faulty blood circulation also causes low readings.

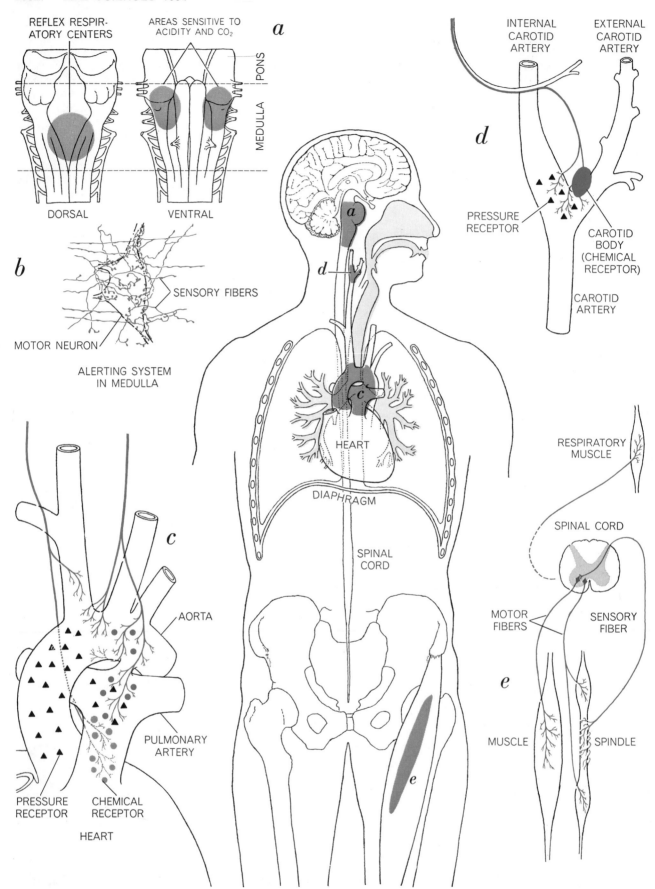

REFLEX RESPIR-
ATORY CENTERS

AREAS SENSITIVE TO
ACIDITY AND CO$_2$

a

PONS

MEDULLA

DORSAL   VENTRAL

b

SENSORY FIBERS

MOTOR NEURON

ALERTING SYSTEM
IN MEDULLA

INTERNAL
CAROTID
ARTERY

EXTERNAL
CAROTID
ARTERY

d

PRESSURE
RECEPTOR

CAROTID
BODY
(CHEMICAL
RECEPTOR)

CAROTID
ARTERY

HEART

DIAPHRAGM

SPINAL
CORD

c

AORTA

PULMONARY
ARTERY

PRESSURE
RECEPTOR

CHEMICAL
RECEPTOR

HEART

RESPIRATORY
MUSCLE

SPINAL CORD

MOTOR
FIBERS

SENSORY
FIBER

e

MUSCLE   SPINDLE

REGULATION OF BREATHING is controlled not only by the lower brain but also by a variety of other receptor and reflex centers. Portions of the pons and medulla of the lower brain (*a*) react to increases in acidity and carbon dioxide pressure. Other sensitive cells are attached to the aorta and pulmonary artery (*c*) and the carotid artery (*d*). The spindle receptors of skeletal muscles (*e*) also affect breathing, as do such external factors as temperature and vibration and such psychological ones as anxiety and wakefulness.

air at rhythmic intervals to the nose or mouth or more directly to the trachea. In mouth-to-mouth resuscitation the person who administers the air conveys it to the person who receives it by contracting his thorax and pushing air into the other person's lungs. Frogs can push air into their lungs by first filling their cheeks and then contracting their cheek muscles; some people whose respiratory muscles are paralyzed but whose head and neck muscles are not can learn to do this "frog breathing."

Still another way to increase the amount of oxygen available to human tissues is to place a hospital patient in an oxygen tent, in which the concentration of oxygen is increased, or to supply oxygen to him in a hyperbaric chamber, in which the total gas pressure is increased to two or three atmospheres. The extra oxygen that is taken up by the blood under these circumstances may be of help if the patient's clinical problem requires for its correction only more oxygen in the blood and tissues; such is the case, for example, when a patient has an infection caused by anaerobic bacteria. But supplying oxygen in greater than normal amounts does not increase ventilation and therefore cannot eliminate more carbon dioxide, nor does it increase the amount of blood being circulated. In the first instance, help in eliminating carbon dioxide is of prime importance in cases of pulmonary or respiratory disease; in the second, the tissues of patients with circulatory problems need not only more oxygen but also the added glucose, amino acids, lipids, white blood cells, blood platelets, proteins and hormones that can only be obtained from adequate blood flow.

The Measurement of Lung Function

Before the 1950's only a few tests of specific lung function had been devised. These included measurements of the amount of air in the lungs at the end of a full inhalation, the amount in the lungs at the end of a full exhalation, and the maximum amount exhaled after a full inhalation; these three volumes were known respectively as the total lung capacity, the residual volume and the vital capacity. In addition, some measurements had been made of the way in which gas was distributed throughout the tracheobronchial tree during inhalation by means of observing the dilution of a tracer gas such as helium or the exhalation of nitrogen following the inhalation of pure oxygen. Since the 1950's, however, pulmonary physiologists have developed a number of

new instruments and test techniques with which to measure objectively, rapidly and accurately not only lung volume and the distribution and diffusion of gases but also the pulmonary circulation and the physical properties of the lung and its connecting air paths.

One such new instrument is the plethysmograph (also known as the body box), which can measure the volume of gas in the lungs and thorax, the resistance to air flow in the bronchial tree and even the blood flow in the pulmonary capillaries. For the first measurement the subject sits in the box (which is airtight and about the size of a telephone booth) and breathes the supply of air in the box through a mouthpiece fitted with a shutter and a pressure gauge. To measure the volume of gas in the subject's lungs at any moment an observer outside the box triggers a circuit that closes the shutter in the mouthpiece and then records the air pressure both in the subject's lungs and in the body box as the subject attempts to inhale; Boyle's law yields a precise measurement of the volume of gas in the subject's lungs.

In order to measure the blood flow in the pulmonary capillaries the subject in the body box is provided with a bag that contains a mixture of 80 percent nitrous oxide and 20 percent oxygen. At a signal the subject inhales a single breath of this mixture and holds the breath for a few seconds. Nitrous oxide dissolves readily in the blood; as its molecules diffuse from the alveoli to enter the blood flowing through the pulmonary capillaries, the total number of gas molecules in the alveoli obviously decreases. But the nitrous oxide that dissolves in the blood does not increase the volume of the blood; therefore the total gas pressure must decrease as the nitrous oxide molecules are subtracted. Knowing the total volume of gas in the lungs, the volume of nitrous oxide and the solubility of nitrous oxide in the blood, one can calculate the flow of blood through the pulmonary capillaries instant by instant. These calculations can be used both to measure the amount of blood pumped by the heart—and thus to arrive at an index of cardiac performance—and to detect unusual resistance to blood flow through the pulmonary capillaries.

To measure resistance to air flow in the bronchial tree the subject in the body box is instructed to breathe the air about him without any interruption while the observer continuously records changes in pressure in the box. One would expect that in a closed system

the mere movement of 500 cubic centimeters of gas from the supply in the box into the lungs of a subject also in the box would not bring about any overall change in pressure. In actuality the pressure in the box increases. The reason is that gas can flow only from a region of higher pressure to a region of lower pressure. The subject cannot inhale unless the pressure of the gas in his lungs is lower than the pressure of the gas in the box; therefore the molecules of gas in his lungs during inhalation must occupy a greater volume than they did in the box before inhalation. The expansion of the subject's thorax, in turn, compresses—and thus is the equivalent of adding to—the rest of the gas in the body box; the effect is reversed as the thorax contracts during exhalation. An appropriately calibrated record of these pressure changes makes it possible for the pressure of the gas in the subject's alveoli to be calculated at any moment in the respiratory cycle. This test can be used to detect the increased resistance to air flow that arises in patients with bronchial asthma, for example, and to evaluate the effectiveness of antiasthmatic drugs.

Another useful instrument for the study of lung function is the nitrogen meter, developed during World War II by John C. Lilly at the University of Pennsylvania in order to detect leaks in or around aviators' oxygen masks. The instrument operates as an emission spectroscope, continuously sampling, analyzing and recording the concentration of nitrogen in a mixture of gases; its lag is less than a tenth of a second. Pulmonary physiologists use the nitrogen meter to detect uneven distribution of air within the lung. Assume that when one breathes ordinary air, the lungs contain 2,000 cubic centimeters of gas, 80 percent of which is nitrogen. If one next inhales 2,000 cubic centimeters of pure oxygen, and if this oxygen is distributed uniformly to the millions of alveoli, each alveolus should now contain a gas that is only 40 percent nitrogen instead of the former 80 percent. If, however, the 2,000 cubic centimeters of oxygen are not evenly distributed, some alveoli will receive less than their share, others will receive more, and the composition of the alveolar gas at the end of the oxygen inhalation will be decidedly nonuniform. In the alveoli that receive the most oxygen the proportion of nitrogen may be reduced to 30 percent; in those that receive little oxygen the proportion of nitrogen may remain as high as 75 percent.

It is impossible to put sampling

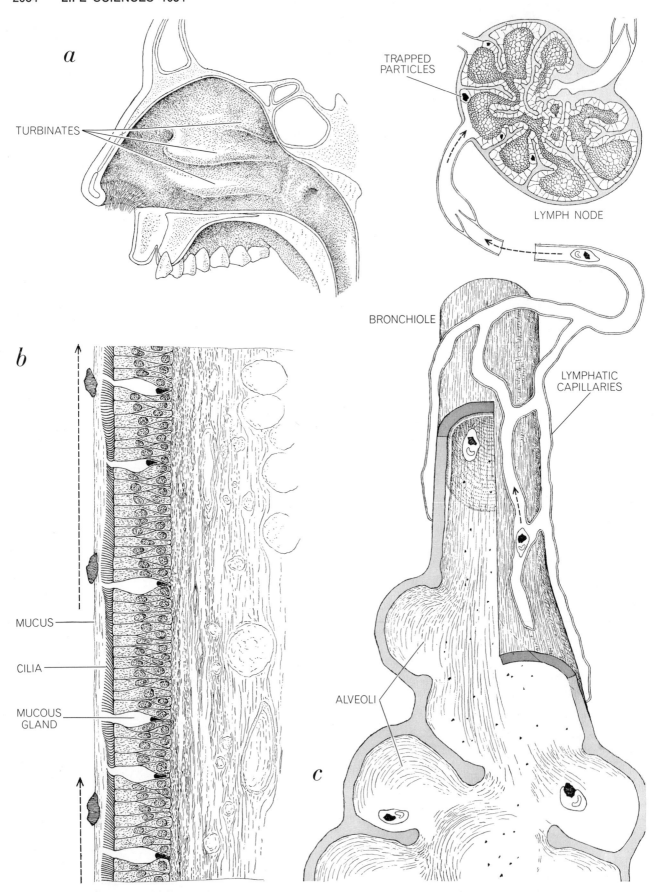

a

TURBINATES

TRAPPED
PARTICLES

LYMPH NODE

b

BRONCHIOLE

LYMPHATIC
CAPILLARIES

MUCUS

CILIA

MUCOUS
GLAND

ALVEOLI

c

BAFFLE SYSTEM protects the lung's interior from intrusion by particles of foreign matter. Hairs in the nose and the convolutions of the turbinate bones (*a*) entrap most particles larger than 10 microns in diameter. Particles of from two to 10 microns in diameter usually settle on the walls of the trachea, the bronchi or the bronchioles, where the escalator action of mucus-covered cilia (*b*) carries them up to the pharynx for expulsion. Particles smaller than two microns in diameter reach the lung's air sacs (*c*). Some are engulfed by scavenger cells; others are carried to the nearest lymph node. Any that remain may cause fibrous tissue to form.

needles into thousands of alveoli in order to determine what mixture of gas each of them contains, but the nitrogen meter easily samples and analyzes the gas leaving the alveoli as the subject exhales. The first part of the exhaled gas comes from the outermost part of the tracheobronchial tree; it contains pure oxygen that has not traveled far enough down the conducting air path to mix with any alveolar gas. The second part of the exhalation shows a rapidly rising concentration of nitrogen; it represents alveolar gas that has washed some pure oxygen out of the conducting air path during exhalation and has mixed with it in the process. Once the conducting air path has been washed clear of oxygen, the remainder of the exhalation will be entirely alveolar gas. Analysis of the amount of nitrogen in the third part of the exhalation quickly shows whether or not the oxygen is distributed uniformly. If the distribution is uniform, the nitrogen-meter record for this part of the exhalation will be a horizontal line: from beginning to end the alveolar gas will be 40 percent nitrogen. If, on the other hand, the distribution is uneven, the nitrogen-meter record for the third part of the exhalation will rise continuously because the first part of the alveolar gas will come from well-ventilated areas of the lung and the last from poorly ventilated ones. In less than a minute the nitrogen meter can separate individuals with uneven ventilation from individuals whose ventilation is normal.

Having discovered by means of the nitrogen meter that a subject suffers from uneven ventilation somewhere in his lungs, the pulmonary physiologist can now use radioactive gases to determine exactly here the unevenness lies. The subject inhales a small amount of a relatively insoluble radioactive gas such as xenon 133 and holds his breath. A battery of three radiation counters on each side of the thorax measures the amount of radioactivity in the alveolar gas contained in the upper, middle and lower portions of each lung. Well-ventilated lung areas show a high level of radioactivity; poorly ventilated areas, a low level.

Radiation-counter readings can also be used to measure the uniformity of blood flow through the pulmonary capillaries. In order to do this the radioactive xenon is dissolved in a saline solution and the solution is administered intravenously. As it flows through the pulmonary capillaries the xenon comes out of solution and enters the alveolar gas. A high local concentration of xenon is

an indication of a good flow of blood in that area; a low concentration indicates the contrary.

Another use of radioactive tracers to check on blood circulation involves the deliberate clogging of some fine pulmonary blood vessels. Radioactive albumin is treated so that it forms clumps that are about 30 microns in diameter—a size somewhat larger than the pulmonary capillaries or the vessels that lead into them. When the clumps are administered intravenously, they cannot enter blood vessels that are obstructed by disease; instead they collect in the parts of the lung with good circulation, where they block some of the fine vessels for a few hours. The whole thorax can now be scanned for radioactivity; in 10 or 20 minutes the activity of the albumin produces a clear image in which the regions of the lung with good pulmonary blood flow are clearly delineated.

Still another test, which measures the rate of gas exchange across the alveolar membrane, is made possible by the fact that hemoglobin has an extraordinary capacity for combining with carbon monoxide. The subject inhales a very low concentration of this potentially toxic gas. The carbon monoxide molecules diffuse across the capillary membranes and combine with the hemoglobin in the red blood cells. Assuming a normal amount of blood in the pulmonary capillaries, the rate at which the carbon monoxide disappears from the alveolar gas is directly proportional to its rate of diffusion. Unlike the somewhat similar test involving nitrous oxide, the carbon monoxide test measures only the rate of gas diffusion, not the rate of capillary blood flow. The affinity between the gas and the hemoglobin is so great that, even if the circulation of the blood were briefly halted, the stagnant red blood cells could still absorb carbon monoxide. A slow rate of carbon monoxide diffusion therefore indicates that the alveolar membranes have become thickened or that some abnormal fluid or tissue is separating many of the alveoli from the pulmonary capillaries.

The Regulation of Ventilation

The blood and air pumps that feed the lung's gas-exchange apparatus must be able to vary their performance to suit environments that range from sea level to high altitudes and activities that range from complete rest to violent exercise. Whatever the circumstances, exactly the right amount of oxygenated blood must be provided to meet the

body's needs; to achieve this result responsive decision centers in the body, controlling both respiration and circulation, must not only be supplied with the necessary information but also possess the capacity to enforce decisions.

The first of these respiratory control centers was discovered by César Legallois of France in 1811. He found that if the cerebrum, the cerebellum and part of the upper brainstem were removed from a rabbit, the animal's breathing remained rhythmic, but that if a small region of the lower medulla was damaged or removed, breathing ceased. In the century and a half since Legallois' time physiologists have continued to accord this region of the brain —a group of interconnected nerve cells in the lower medulla—the paramount role in the control of respiration. This is not, however, the only region of the brain concerned with the regulation of breathing; there are chemically sensitive regions near the lateral surfaces of the upper medulla that call for an increase in ventilation when their carbon dioxide pressure or their acidity increases. Some other parts of the medulla, the cerebral cortex and the part of the brain called the pons can also influence respiration.

In addition to these areas in the brain a variety of respiratory receptors, interconnecting links, pathways and reflexes are found elsewhere in the body. Chemically sensitive cells in the regions of the carotid artery and the aorta initiate reflexes that increase respiration when their oxygen supply is not sufficient to maintain their metabolic needs or when the local carbon dioxide pressure or acidity increases. Stretch-sensitive receptors in the major arteries act through reflexes to increase or decrease respiration in response to low or high arterial blood pressure. Other receptors in the circulatory system, sensitive both to chemical stimuli and to mechanical deformation, can set off reflexes that slow or stop breathing. Respiration can also be regulated by the degree of inflation or deflation of the lungs, by the individual's state of wakefulness or awareness, by the concentration of certain hormones in the blood and by the discharge of the special sensory receptors known as spindles in skeletal muscles (including the respiratory muscles themselves).

We still do not know how some or all of these central and peripheral components interact to achieve the most important (and the most frequent) change in ventilation: the change that takes place when the body's metabolic activity increases. We know that during exercise both the body's oxygen consumption and its carbon dioxide production increase, and that so does the rate of ventilation. It is therefore logical to assume that ventilation is regulated by receptors somewhere in the body that are sensitive to oxygen or to carbon dioxide or to both. A puzzling fact remains: mild and even moderate exercise simply does not decrease the amount of oxygen or increase the amount of carbon dioxide in the arterial blood, yet the respiration rate rises. What causes this increase, which is enough to satisfy both the ordinary needs of the body and the extraordinary needs of exercising muscles? No one knows.

The Upper Respiratory Tract

In the course of taking from four to 10 million breaths a year each individual draws into the alveoli of his lungs air that may be hot or cold, dry or moist, possibly clean but more probably dirty. Each liter of urban air, for example, contains several million particles of foreign matter; in a day a city-dwelling adult inhales perhaps 20 billion such particles. What protects the lungs and the air ducts leading to them from air with undesirable physical characteristics or chemical composition? Sensory receptors in the air ducts and the lungs can initiate protective reflexes when they are suitably stimulated; specialized cells can also engulf foreign particles that have penetrated far into the lung. The main task of protecting the lungs, however, is left to the upper respiratory tract.

The nose, the mouth, the oropharynx, the nasopharynx, the larynx, the trachea and those bronchi that are outside the lung itself together constitute the upper respiratory tract. Although the obvious function of this series of passages is to conduct air to and from the lung, the tract is also a sophisticated air conditioner and filter. It contains built-in warning devices to signal the presence of most pollutants and is carpeted with a remarkable escalator membrane that moves foreign bodies upward and out of the tract at the rate of nearly an inch a minute. Within quite broad limits the initial state of the air a man breathes is of little consequence; thanks to the mediation of the upper respiratory tract the air will be warm, moist and almost free of particles by the time it reaches the alveoli.

The first role in the conditioning process is played by the mucous membrane of the nose, the mouth and the pharynx; this large surface has a rich blood supply that warms cold air, cools hot air and otherwise protects the alveoli under a wide range of conditions. Experimental animals have been exposed to air heated to 500 degrees centigrade and air cooled to −100 degrees C.; in both instances the trip through the respiratory tract had cooled or warmed the air almost to body temperature by the time it had reached the lower trachea.

The upper respiratory tract also filters air. The hairs in the nose block the passage of large particles; beyond these hairs the involuted contours of the nasal turbinate bones force the air to move in numerous narrow streams, so that suspended particles tend to approach either the dividing septum of the nose or the moist mucous membranes of the turbinates. Here many particles either impinge directly on the mucous membranes or settle there in response to gravity.

The filter system of the nose almost completely removes from the air particles with a diameter larger than 10 microns. Particles ranging in diameter from two to 10 microns usually settle on the walls of the trachea, the bronchi and the bronchioles. Only particles between .3 micron and two microns in diameter are likely to reach the alveolar ducts and the alveoli. Particles smaller than .3 micron, if they are not taken up by the blood, are likely to remain in suspension as aerosols and so are washed out of the lungs along with the exhaled air.

Foreign bodies that settle on the walls of the nose, the pharynx, the trachea, the bronchi and the bronchioles may be expelled by the explosive blast of air that is generated by a sneeze or a cough, but more often they are removed by the action of the cilia. These are very primitive structures that are found in many forms of life, from one-celled organisms to man. Resembling hairs, they are powered by a contractile mechanism; in action each cilium makes a fast, forceful forward stroke that is followed by a slower, less forceful return stroke that brings the cilium into starting position again. The strokes of a row of cilia are precisely coordinated so that the hairs move together as a wave. The cilia of the human respiratory tract do not beat in the open air; they operate within a protective sheet of the mucus that is secreted by glands in the trachea and the bronchi. The effect of their wavelike motion is to move the entire mucus sheet—and anything trapped on it—up the respiratory tract to the pharynx, where it can be swallowed or spat out.

The ciliary escalator is in constant operation; it provides a quiet, unobtrusive, round-the-clock mechanism for the removal of foreign matter from the upper respiratory tract. The speed of this upward movement depends on the length of the cilia and the frequency of their motion. Calculations show that a cilium that is 10 microns long and that beats 20 times per second can move the mucus sheet 320 microns per second, or 19.2 millimeters per minute. Speeds of 16 millimeters per minute have actually been observed in experiments.

In spite of all such preventive measures some inhaled particles—particularly those suspended in fluid droplets—manage to pass through the alveolar ducts and reach the alveoli. How do these deeper surfaces, which have no cilia or mucous glands, cleanse themselves? The amoeba-like lymphocytes of the bloodstream and their larger relatives the macrophages engulf and digest some particles of foreign matter. They can also surround the particles in the air ducts and then ride the mucus escalator up to the nasopharynx. Other particles may pass into lymphatic vessels and come to rest in the nearest lymph nodes. Some remain permanently attached to the lung tissue, as the darkened lungs of coal miners demonstrate. Many such intrusions are essentially harmless, but some, for example particles of silica, can result in the formation of tough fibrous tissue that causes serious pulmonary disease.

The filtration mechanism of the upper respiratory tract can thus be credited with several important achievements. It is responsible for the interception and removal of foreign particles. It can remove bacteria suspended in the air and also dispose of bacteria, viruses and even irritant or carcinogenic gases when they are adsorbed onto larger particles. Unless the filter system is overloaded, it keeps the alveoli practically sterile. This, however, is not the only protection the lungs possess. Among the reflex responses to chemical or mechanical irritation of the nose are cessation of breathing, closure of the larynx, constriction of the bronchi and even slowing of the heart. These responses are aimed at preventing potentially harmful gases from reaching the alveoli and, through the alveoli, the pulmonary circulation.

In many animals, for instance, the act of swallowing results in reflex closure of the glottis and the inhibition of respiration. Because the pharynx is a passageway both for air and for food and water, this reflex prevents food or water from entering the respiratory passages during the journey from the mouth to the esophagus. Because the reflex does not operate during unconsciousness it is dangerous to try to arouse an unconscious person by pouring liquids such as alcohol into his mouth.

When specific chemical irritants penetrate beyond the larynx, the reflex response is usually a cough combined with bronchial constriction. Like the swallowing reflex, the cough reflex is depressed or absent during unconsciousness. It also is less active in older people; this is why they are more likely to draw foreign bodies into their lungs.

Bronchial constriction is a response to irritation of the air paths that is less obvious than a cough. When the concentration of dust, smoke or irritant gas is too low to elicit the cough reflex, this constrictive increase in air-path resistance is frequently evident. Smoking a cigarette, for example, induces an immediate twofold or threefold rise in air-path resistance that continues for 10 to 30 minutes. The inhalation of cigarette smoke produces the same effect in smokers and nonsmokers alike. It does not cause shortness of breath, as asthma does; the air-path resistance must increase fourfold or fivefold to produce that effect. Nor has the reflex anything to do with nicotine; no increase in air-path resistance is caused by the inhalation of nicotine aerosols, whereas exactly the same degree of resistance is induced by smoking cigarettes with a normal (2 percent) or a minimal (.5 percent) nicotine content. The reflex is evidently triggered by the settling of particles less than a micron in diameter on the sensory receptors in the air path.

Other air pollutants—irritant gases, vapors, fumes, smokes, aerosols or small particles—may give rise to a similar bronchial constriction. It is one of the ironies of man's urban way of life that exposure to the pollutants that produce severe and repeated bronchial constriction results in excessive secretion of mucus, a reduction in ciliary activity, obstruction of the fine air paths and finally cell damage. These circumstances enable bacteria to penetrate to the alveoli and remain there long enough to initiate infectious lung disease. They are also probably a factor in the development of such tracheobronchial diseases as chronic bronchitis and lung cancer. Thus man's advances in material culture increasingly threaten the air pump that helped to make his evolutionary success possible.

The Author

JULIUS H. COMROE, JR. is professor of physiology and director of the Cardiovascular Research Institute at the San Francisco Medical Center of the University of California. He went to the institute in 1957 after 21 years as a member of the faculty at the Graduate School of Medicine of the University of Pennsylvania. Earlier he had received undergraduate and medical degrees from that university. Comroe is involved as writer, editor or consultant in many activities related to his professional interests. He was president of the American Physiological Society in 1960–1961.

Bibliography

THE MECHANISM OF BREATHING. Wallace O. Fenn in *Scientific American*, Vol. 202, No. 1, pages 138–148; January, 1960.

THE PHYSIOLOGY OF EXERCISE. Carleton B. Chapman and Jere H. Mitchell in *Scientific American*, Vol. 212, No. 5, pages 88–96; May, 1965.

SURFACE TENSION IN THE LUNGS. John A. Clements in *Scientific American*, Vol. 207, No. 6, pages 121–130; December, 1962.

SPECIAL NOTE TO TEACHERS: Each article in this volume, plus more than 660 others, is available as a separate, self-bound SCIENTIFIC AMERICAN Offprint. Offprints may be ordered in any combination and in any quantity. Teachers who want to adopt articles for their courses, therefore, can ensure that each student has his own set. Students' sets are collated by the publisher before shipment.

SCIENTIFIC
AMERICAN February 1966, Vol. 214, No. 2, pp. 82-90

OFFPRINT 1035

THE HAGFISH

by David Jensen

This primitive animal has teeth on its tongue, secretes a viscid
slime and can tie itself in a knot. It also has four hearts, the
nature of which may clarify cardiac function in higher animals.

The reader may find it difficult to conceive of a fish that has four hearts, only one nostril and no jaws or stomach; that can live for months without feeding; that performs feats of dexterity by literally tying itself in knots. The organism nonetheless exists; it is called the hagfish. In appearance it is undistinguished: it is an animal Linnaeus classified as an intestinal worm and fishermen sometimes call the slime eel. Tasting strongly of fish oil and rubber-like in texture, it is not considered worth eating by man or any other animal predator. For a biologist, however, the hagfish holds much interest. Its anatomy and its habits are revealing. As the lowest form of true fish and vertebrate, the "hag" offers a matchless opportunity to investigate a stage in the evolution of vertebrates at a most primitive level.

The hagfishes are undoubtedly a very archaic form of life. They belong to a class of animals (the cyclostomes, or round-mouths) that includes the blood-sucking lampreys [see "The Sea Lamprey," by Vernon C. Applegate and James W. Moffett; SCIENTIFIC AMERICAN, April, 1955]. The hags burrow into their prey (usually dead or dying fish) and devour the flesh and viscera, leaving only a bag of skin and bones. Although the hagfishes and lampreys are obviously primitive and ancient forms, unfortunately their ancestry and early development cannot be traced back in the geological record; no fossils of these soft-bodied animals have been found. Some investigators believe they may have descended from the ostracoderms, a group of ancient extinct armored fishes, because fossils of those animals show some of the same anatomical peculiarities, including a single nostril in the middle of the head and the lack of a lower jaw or paired fins. The question of cyclostome ancestry is far from settled, however.

The hagfishes are particularly intriguing because they remain puzzling in many respects in spite of long study. Even their method of reproduction is still a mystery in its details. A century ago (in 1864) the Copenhagen Academy of Science offered a prize for a solution to the questions of how the hagfish reproduces; to date no one has been able to claim the award.

The hagfish is strictly an ocean dweller, living on the sea bottom, principally in the temperate latitudes. Its habitat is restricted by the requirement that the water must be cold and quite salty. There are about two dozen species of the fish; I shall devote my account mainly to the one I know best: a Pacific Ocean species, *Eptatretus stoutii*, which inhabits the western continental shelf of North America from Alaska to Baja California at depths ranging from as

HAGFISH RESTS at the bottom of an aquarium tank, its flattened oarlike tail curled into a circle. The light patches on either side of the head are the animal's two pigmented eyespots; these and a few other photosensitive skin areas allow the virtually blind hagfish to discriminate only between light and darkness. The animal depends on olfaction and touch rather than sight to find the dead or dying fishes that are its usual prey; visible at the front of its head are two of the three pairs of fleshy barbels that the hagfish uses to feel its way about.

little as 60 feet to as much as 1,800 feet.

From its habits one deduces at once that the hagfish is a remarkably sluggish animal. It spends much of its time lying quietly on the sea floor or in a burrow in the muddy bottom. (It appears to dislike sand and to avoid sandy areas.) When hungry, it is capable of swimming rapidly with a sinuous, snake-like motion, but normally it is quite torpid. Evidently it needs to feed only at infrequent intervals; it stores a high content of body fat and has a low rate of metabolism, abetted by its cold environment. Analysis by Winton Tong

and his co-workers at the University of California at Berkeley has revealed that the hagfish produces very little of the metabolism-activating thyroid hormone thyroxin. In my laboratory at the University of California at San Diego a female hagfish has gone as long as seven months without feeding and at the end of that time has even laid a full quota of eggs (although the eggs were infertile).

As can be expected of an animal that lives on the dark sea bottom, the hag is almost completely blind. It has only rudimentary eyes—two pigmented

cups in its head that serve as retinas—and a few sensitive skin areas on its head and around its cloaca that can discriminate light from darkness. In compensation for its lack of vision the animal has keenly developed senses of smell and touch. Serving the sense of touch are three pairs of barbels, or fleshy tentacles, around the mouth and nostril on the front end of the head. When the hagfish is hungry, it goes hunting for food by raising its head, extending its barbels and dilating its nostril. It swims along slowly, turning its head gently from side to side like a

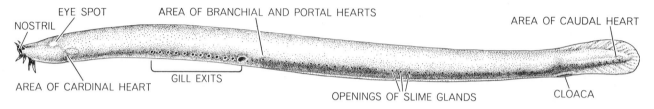

HAGFISH IN PROFILE shows an array of tiny pores along its side from head to tail; these are the openings that lead to the slime glands, from which a milky fluid exudes when the hagfish is disturbed. The larger opening, to the rear of the 11 visible gill exit ducts, is an outlet for any of the water, drawn in through the single nostril, that has not been discharged through a gill exit. Hidden in this pharyngeal duct is the 12th gill exit. The hagfish's four hearts are in the areas outlined in color (see illustration below).

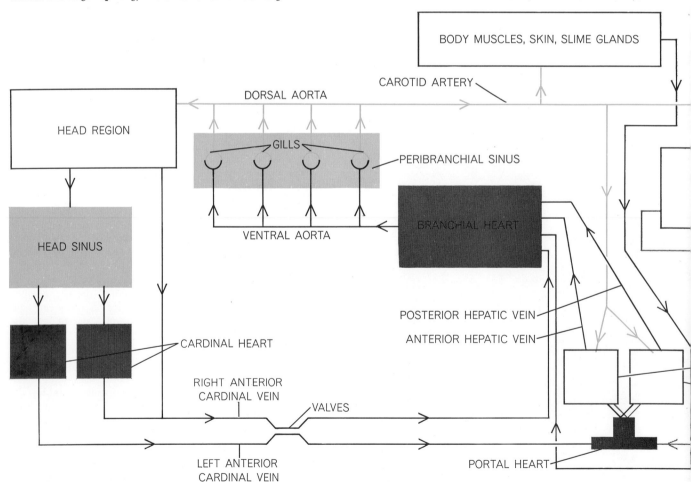

PRIMITIVE CIRCULATORY SYSTEM of the hagfish is shown as a block diagram. The system requires four hearts (gray areas) because in three major body regions (colored boxes) the blood perco- lates through large open spaces before reentering blood vessels; this free flow produces a sharp drop in blood pressure on the venous side of the circulatory system. The action of the cardinal

dog sniffing the air. The fish makes its way upcurrent toward a food odor it has detected; once it has located the food it darts in and feeds voraciously and quickly. Hagfishes are primarily scavengers on dead or dying fish, but they will also eat worms when the preferred fare is not available.

The hagfish makes its entry into the body of a fish by means of strong, horny rows of teeth on the sides of its tongue [*see illustration on next page*]. Thrusting the tongue outward, it rasps pieces of tissue from its quarry. When the hagfish needs extra leverage to tear flesh out of a larger fish, it loops its body into a knot and thereby augments the strength of its pull by pressing the knot against the side of the fish [*see "d" in illustration on page 2092*].

The knotting ability of the hagfish, altogether unique in the animal kingdom, serves more than one purpose. Among other things, it provides the hagfish with a cleaning mechanism. The animal's principal means of self-defense, which apparently helps to account for the fact that it has no known natural predators, is its ability to cover itself with a slippery slime. When it is disturbed or roughly handled, the hagfish will exude drops of a milky fluid through tiny pores situated in two rows along the lower sides of its body from the snout to the tip of the tail. On contact with the seawater, threadlike cells in this fluid break open and, with the water, form an extremely tenacious slime. In its cocoon of slime the hagfish is almost impossible to grasp. Afterward, however, the animal must free itself of the slimy coat lest it suffocate because of blockage of its gills and nostril. The supple hagfish accordingly loops its body into a half hitch, pulls itself through the loop and thus wipes off the slime. By the same maneuver the animal can generate enough pulling power to slide out of a man's grip. The hag is rather versatile as a contortionist: in addition to the half hitch it can also form a figure-eight loop.

Let us look closer into the anatomy of this remarkable animal. The hagfish is only a rudimentary vertebrate. Its "backbone" is a notochord, formed entirely of cartilage; hence its suppleness. The average adult Pacific hagfish is 10 to 15 inches long, with a cylindrical body flattened toward the rear end into an oarlike tail. On its head are two oval spots of light-colored skin that signify the location of the "eyes"; whether these are seeing organs in the early stages of evolution or degenerate remains of more complex eyes such as lampreys have is not known. Along the lower sides of the hagfish behind the eyespots are two rows of about a dozen whitish dots that are the gill openings. Spread more widely over the body are the much smaller slime pores, the openings of slime glands situated inside the body.

The hag's respiratory system has several unusual features. Its main oxygen supply comes from the water drawn in through the nostril. On entering the throat the water is pumped by a pair of muscular flaps (the velum) to the dozen or so pairs of gill pouches arrayed along the body [*see upper illustration, page 2094*]. There the water

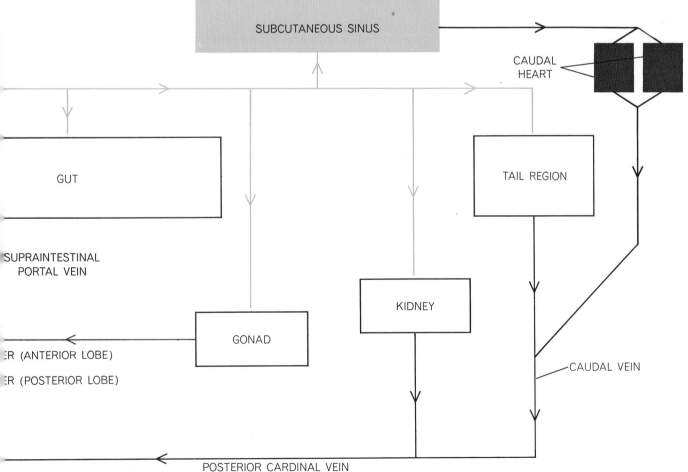

and portal hearts (*bottom left and center*) helps to restore some of the pressure lost in the peribranchial and head sinuses; the caudal heart (*top right*) does the same for the venous blood draining from the subcutaneous sinus. Where the arterial blood (*color*) enters a labeled box and venous blood (*black*) leaves it, the organs that are specified receive oxygen by means of a normal capillary bed.

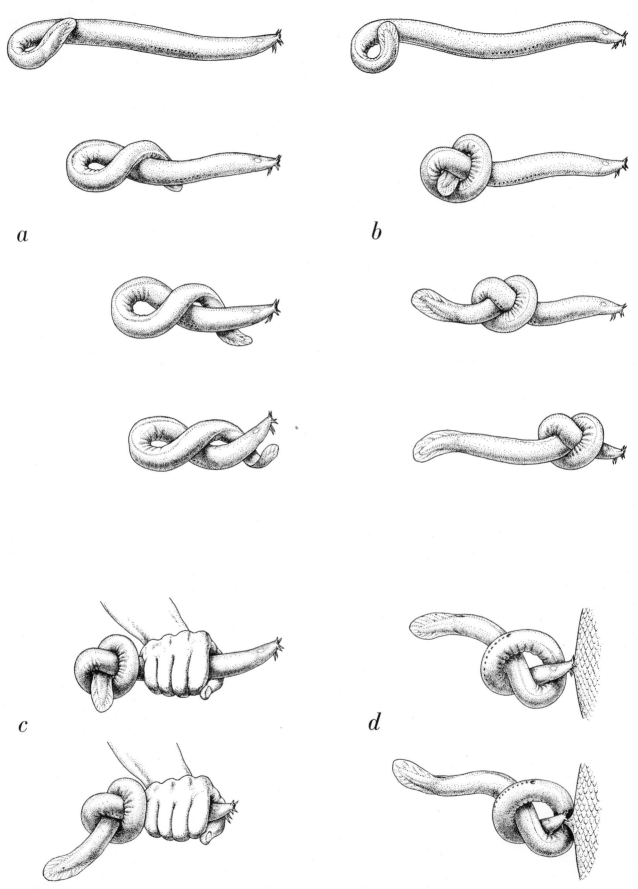

a

b

c

d

FLEXIBILITY of the hagfish is a result of its vertebrate "back-bone" being formed entirely of cartilage. This enables it not only to curl into such odd configurations as a figure eight (*a*) but also to knot itself in ways that serve useful purposes. When the hagfish has become coated with slime, for example, it can rub the slime off by rolling a knot progressively from its tail to its head (*b*). The same movement helps the animal to escape capture (*c*) and to apply leverage when tearing at the surface of a food object (*d*).

RASPING TONGUE, set with parallel rows of teeth, lets the hagfish burrow into its prey. The hagfish then devours both flesh and viscera until nothing remains but skin and bones.

flows out of the gill openings by way of ducts, while blood flowing in the opposite direction in vessels in the gills picks up oxygen from the water. This "countercurrent system," which facilitates the rapid exchange of gases, is common in fishes.

If foreign bodies or slime happen to clog the hag's nostril, it emits a powerful sneeze to clear the passage. Just how this is accomplished is not clear; the sneeze is not simply a reversal of the velum's inward pumping. It seems that the hagfish may be able to obtain some oxygen through its skin as well as through the nostril-and-gill apparatus, because the animal can survive for a considerable length of time even when its nostril is plugged.

The cardiovascular system of the hagfish is a curious and complex affair [see *illustration, bottom of pages 2090 and 2091*]. Its principal organ is the branchial heart, which pumps blood through the gills and thence by way of arteries to the rest of the body. Assisting this main pump are three accessory hearts, all on the venous side of the circulation. They are necessitated by the peculiar fact that part of the hagfish's venous circulation is not connected to the arterial side in the ordinary way. In most of its organs the animal does possess a typical vertebrate circulation—the blood passes from the arteries to the veins by way of a capillary bed in the nourished tissues; this is true of the gills, the gut and the body muscles. In certain areas

of the body, however, there is no capillary bed; instead the arterial blood is discharged into large open spaces, called sinuses, through which it percolates before entering the veins. (An "open" circulation of this kind is common among invertebrates but rare in a vertebrate.) The result is that the blood pressure on the venous side of the animal's circulation is very low. Consequently the three auxiliary hearts are required to pump the blood back to the branchial heart. Each returns blood from separate parts of the body.

In addition to the four pumps, certain muscles of the body take part in driving the blood forward. The gill pouches can assist the branchial heart by performing rhythmic contractions that milk the blood in the gills toward an aorta and the carotid arteries and thence into the rest of the body. On the venous side, when the animal is active, contractions of the body muscles against various blood vessels help to squeeze blood toward the branchial heart. Strategically placed throughout the body are valves that prevent any backflow.

Perhaps the most curious aspect of this complex circulatory system is that the several hearts are not coordinated with one another. Each beats at its own pace, quite independently of the others. Indeed, the hagfish has no sympathetic nervous system or any other mechanism that could serve as a general coordinator of these organs.

The branchial heart itself is a three-chambered organ consisting of a sinus venosus (a cavity to which the veins deliver their blood), an atrium (the heart antechamber) and a ventricle (the pump). Surprisingly, there are no coronary arteries to nourish the branchial heart tissues (or the other hearts, for that matter). They are nourished only by the venous blood that bathes them. The branchial heart lies close to the animal's two-lobed liver, and it pumps its output to the gills by way of a ventral aorta.

Ordinarily when the hagfish is at rest, this output is small, the blood pressure developed by the branchial heart amounting to only about one to five millimeters of mercury. When the animal's activity requires it, however, the heart can increase this pressure to about 25 millimeters of mercury. For more than half a century, ever since it was discovered that there are no nerves regulating the beat of the hagfish's heart, that fact has been one of the main reasons for research interest in the animal. How does the hagfish raise its cardiac output to meet increased demands? More fundamentally, what mechanism is responsible for the rhythmic contractions of the heart muscles that constitute its heartbeat? This question is particularly interesting because the heart of an adult hagfish resembles in several basic respects the heart in the early embryo of a mammal. Like the hagfish heart, the myocardium (muscular wall) of the mammalian embryo's heart contracts rhythmically without regulation by nerves. What makes it do so? Here we are close to the key to the origin of the heartbeat, and the hagfish heart, which is large enough for experimental studies, offers a convenient subject for fundamental investigation of the question.

Physiological studies show that the stimulus responsible for the increase of output by the hagfish's branchial heart is an increase in the inflow of venous blood into the heart. The distension of the heart by this augmented load produces two effects: it speeds up the heartbeat and it causes the heart muscles to contract with more force. Thus it obeys the well-known Frank-Starling law of the heart observed in the higher vertebrates: within limits, the more the heart muscle is stretched, the more strongly it contracts.

As for the pacemaking mechanism that maintains the rhythm of the hagfish heartbeat, a few clues have turned up. The ventricle has a comparatively thick, spongy wall. Its muscle tissue is striated, like the cardiac muscle tissue of other vertebrates, but the cells are smaller, spindle-shaped and woven together loosely in a framework of connective tissue. The hagfish heart is amazingly tenacious of life. Removed surgically from its owner and planted under the skin of another hagfish, where it floats in normal body fluids, the transplanted heart will beat strongly for three weeks or longer, as I have found in repeated experiments with the branchial heart and the portal heart, one of the auxiliary pumps in the hagfish. These hearts will beat for several days even in ordinary seawater or an artificial salt solution similar in composition to seawater. Furthermore, tiny fragments of the heart tissue can survive dissection: they will go on contracting rhythmically, each at the rate characteristic of the tissue from which it was excised.

From such experiments and exploration of the heart with microelectrodes we can draw the conclusion that the pacemaker cells responsible for exciting the muscular contractions are scattered randomly throughout the heart struc-

ture. Occasionally a microelectrode will puncture a cell that has electrical characteristics similar to those of cells in the specialized pacemaking nodes of the hearts of higher vertebrates. The coordinating mechanism that keeps the hagfish's branchial heart beating smoothly apparently lies in the sinus venosus; this area has a faster inherent rate of excitation than the other areas of the branchial heart and dominates them. Similarly, the coordinating mechanism

for the portal heart seems to be localized in the last few millimeters of the vein from the gut where it enters the heart.

The portal heart is a tubular affair roughly in the shape of a T, one arm of the T receiving venous blood from the gut and the gonad, the other from the head end of the animal. This heart pumps the blood through the two lobes of the liver. The liver is between the

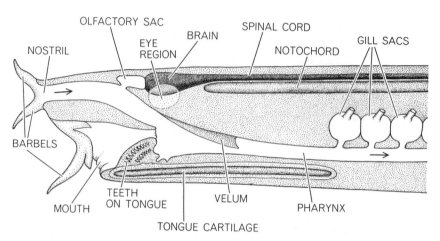

FLOW OF WATER from which the hagfish draws its oxygen enters the single nostril (*left*). When the water reaches the velum, a pair of muscle flaps (*center*), it is pumped both past and into a row of gill sacs, one of which is illustrated in section below. The hagfish has no jaws; the horny teeth with which it rasps its food grow in rows on its protrusible tongue.

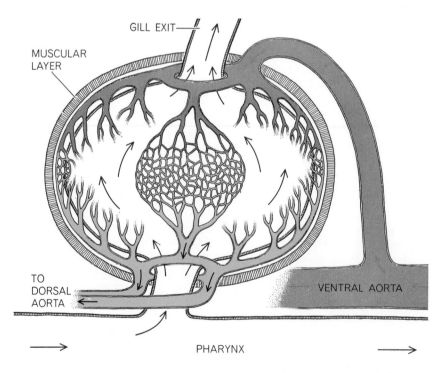

COUNTERCURRENT FLOW of water and blood in the hagfish gill sac (*arrows*) facilitates gas exchange that simultaneously adds oxygen to and removes carbon dioxide from the fish's blood. The light and dark colors distinguish oxygenated from nonoxygenated blood. Countercurrent flow is common in fishes, but only hagfishes have this gill sac arrangement.

branchial heart and the portal heart; the portal heart lies toward the lower right side of the hagfish. Anatomically and physiologically the portal heart shares many attributes of the branchial heart; it is smaller and simpler in structure, however, and usually beats at a faster rate.

The hagfish's other two hearts can be considered true hearts because they pump blood, but in structure and mechanism of action they differ basically from the branchial and portal hearts. One, called the "cardinal heart," pumps venous blood from the head region; the other, called the "caudal heart," is located in the tail. The cardinal heart consists of a pair of sacs in the head region of the animal. It has no muscles or machinery of its own for producing rhythmic impulses; its pumping action actually is operated by rhythmic contractions of skeletal muscles that lie outside the sacs in the head region. These contractions, activated by nerves, compress the sacs and thereby squeeze the blood in the cardinal veins toward the branchial or the portal heart.

The caudal heart, like the cardinal heart, consists of a pair of tiny sacs, guarded by valves at their inlets and outlets. Between these two small chambers is a rod of cartilage, to which are attached two muscles running the length of each sac on the outside [*see illustration at left below*]. The muscles contract alternately in an oscillating rhythm, bending the rod first in one direction and then in the other, so that the two sacs are compressed alternately, as the illustration shows. In effect the organ acts as a reciprocating pump, pumping blood from each chamber alternately while the other one fills. The strangest aspect of the caudal heart is its apparent unimportance. To begin with, it is so small—about the size of a pinhead—that its pumping capacity must be very small indeed. Moreover, its operation seems to be quite capricious. It will stop beating for a time for no obvious reason and then start again. In sharp contrast to the branchial and portal hearts, the caudal heart is activated by nerves, the stimulating impulses coming from a reflex center in the spinal cord. Stimulation of the hagfish's skin will inhibit the caudal heartbeat completely; so does extreme activity by the animal. All in all it appears that the caudal heart plays only a minor role and is not necessary for the animal's survival. Removal of the tail, including the caudal heart, apparently does not inconvenience the hagfish greatly, aside from handicapping its swimming.

Still another, and more important, surprise has turned up in the investigation of the hagfish's hearts. Examining the cells of the branchial and portal hearts in the Pacific hagfish with the electron microscope, I found some large, granule-containing cells that looked like cells of a gland rather than heart cells; independently, Gunnar Bloom and his collaborators in Sweden discovered the same cells in the branchial and portal hearts of the Atlantic hagfish (*Myxine glutinosa*). Experiments revealed that these cells, which lie below the lining of the heart (the endothelium), secrete the common adrenal hormones adrenalin and noradrenalin. I

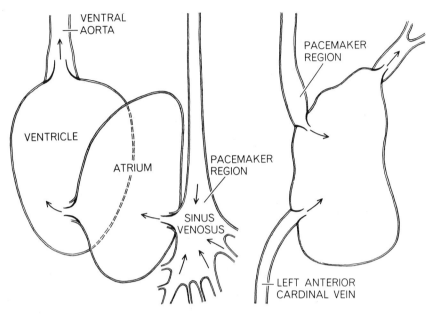

MAJOR PUMPS that power the hagfish's circulatory system are the branchial heart (*left*) and the portal heart (*right*). The sinus venosus of the branchial heart collects blood from all parts of the body; the blood enters the atrium and is then pushed on to the gill sacs by rhythmic contractions of the ventricle. The portal heart, in contrast, pumps only part of the blood supply (*see illustration at bottom of pages 2090 and 2091*). This blood enters the liver and passes on to the branchial heart. Both hearts are thus closely related, but they do not have a common rhythm. Instead each one beats at a rate determined by the volume of blood reaching its "pacemaker" region, an area with the fastest inherent excitation rate.

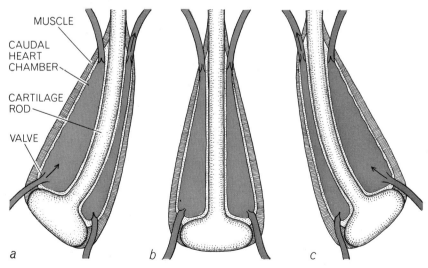

MINOR PUMP, the caudal heart, lies less than half an inch from the end of the hagfish's tail. A cartilage rod lies between two valved chambers; paired muscles, attached to the rod, pass along the outside of the chambers. Contraction of the left muscle (*a*) expels blood collected in the right chamber and allows the left chamber to fill; the opposite contraction (*c*) empties the left chamber and fills the right one. The caudal heart beats irregularly; unlike the two nerveless major hearts, it is controlled by nerve impulses from the spinal cord.

have isolated a third heart-stimulating substance, probably also a hormone, that may possibly be produced by the same cells. It seems, then, that the hagfish heart is not only a pump but also an endocrine gland! Considering that the hagfish has no adrenal medulla or sympathetic nervous system (the usual regulator of the adrenal gland), it is indeed strange to find adrenal hormones in its nerveless heart.

Like the cardiovascular system, the hag's digestive system also has its striking features. From the throat to the anus a long, rather unspecialized intestine runs straight through the animal. There is no stomach as such; the intestine is merely divided into a foregut and a hindgut by a circular band of muscle behind the throat that serves to prevent respiratory water from flowing back into the digestive region. When the animal feeds, this muscle relaxes, enabling food to pass into the hindgut. Interestingly enough, as it passes through the gut a mass of food becomes enveloped in a thin, highly permeable coating of cells (like a sausage in its skin), much as in insects. This "peritrophic membrane" surrounds the waste matter left within it when the waste is discharged.

The lining of the intestine is corrugated by long ridges that increase its surface area for the absorption of nutrients. It seems that in the hagfish the liver and the gallbladder, judging from their comparatively large size, probably play active roles, along with the intestine, in the digestion of food. The hagfish pancreas, unlike that of most vertebrates, is divided into two completely separate parts, one secreting digestive juices, the other insulin. The hormone insulin presumably regulates the blood-sugar level in the hagfish as it does in higher vertebrates. Surprisingly, however, it has been reported that surgical removal of the insulin-secreting portion of the hagfish pancreas, which in other vertebrates would quickly lead to a diabetic condition, does not result in any elevation of the sugar level in the blood, even as much as five days later. This peculiar circumstance remains unexplained. Another unusual finding is that the gut of the hagfish not only is a digestive organ but also produces the red blood cells.

One of the most striking demonstrations of the hagfish's primitive physiology is its salt and water balance. The salt concentration of its blood is essentially the same as that of the seawater

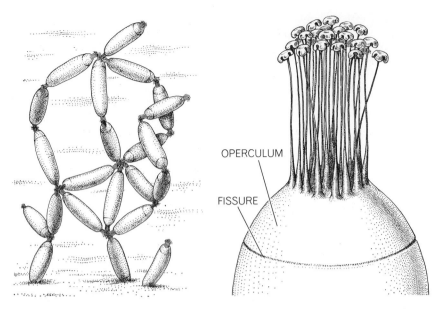

HAGFISH EGGS are much larger than the eggs of more advanced fishes and are produced in far smaller numbers. They are nearly an inch long, with tufts of filaments at each end that serve to attach them to one another (*left*) and to the ocean floor; the average number of eggs per spawning is 22. At maturity the egg breaks apart along the line of the opercular fissure (*right*) and the hagfish then emerges as a small adult rather than in a larval form.

in which it lives; in this the hagfish is unique among marine vertebrates. The reason is that it has only a very primitive kidney. The kidney consists of two parts: the pronephros, whose function is unclear, and the mesonephros, or kidney proper, which filters the blood. This organ, however, lacks the tubules that in other vertebrates enable the kidney to select substances in the blood for excretion or reabsorption into the body; the hagfish kidney consists only of Malpighian corpuscles containing the filtering glomeruli. As a result the animal has little ability to regulate the excretion of salt through its urine, and it cannot survive long in water that has either a very high or a very low concentration of salt; it is barred, for example, from living in an estuary where the salt concentration is diluted. A few experiments suggest that adrenocortical hormones are probably responsible for what little capacity the hagfish has for regulating the osmotic pressure of its blood.

Finally, the hagfish provokes much curiosity by certain enigmas that surround its method of breeding. Judging from the tremendous numbers of hagfishes found in certain localities, the organism's reproduction and survival are notably successful, yet details of the process are shrouded in uncertainty. No hagfish has yet been coaxed into producing fertile eggs in the laboratory.

The female hagfish is usually much larger than the male. This observation gave rise to the idea that the animal was a protandric hermaphrodite, that is, it starts as a male early in life and then develops into a female. Detailed investigation of its development showed, however, that when it is young the animal is in an "indifferent," or neutral, form combining the elements of both sexes and that it becomes either a male or a female as it matures.

The hagfish, along with the lamprey, is set apart from all other vertebrates by the fact that it possesses only a single gonad, or sex organ. The gonad is an elongated structure that extends the length of the animal from just behind the liver to the region of the cloaca at the rear; it hangs from a delicate membrane on the right side of the intestine in the abdominal cavity. In early life the forward part of the organ clearly has the nature of an ovary, whereas the hind third of its length is composed of immature testicular tissue. When the animal matures, the male or female portion of the gonad develops and the other part is repressed, presumably under the influence of hormones from the pituitary gland. Thus the mature hagfish becomes a distinctly differentiated individual: a large female with a fully developed ovary or a male with a developed testis.

Neither the male nor the female possesses any copulatory organ that would allow fertilization of the female's eggs internally. The eggs must therefore be fertilized after they have been deposited in the seawater. The female's eggs and the male's germ cells are discharged not through specific ducts but through openings in the cloaca.

The eggs are extremely large for a fish: about an inch long, elliptical in shape and covered with a horny shell. The egg is yellowish, because it consists mainly of yolk. At both ends of the egg are tufts of filaments, which serve to anchor the eggs to one another and to rocks on the sea bottom so that they are not washed away from the spawning area. We do not know how the fertilization of the eggs is accomplished; what is clear is that they are not fertile when they are freshly laid by the female. Accordingly true hermaphroditism is ruled out. When the eggs hatch, the young emerge not as larvae but as small hagfish; in this they differ from the lampreys, which pass through a long larval stage after hatching.

Not the least remarkable of the many peculiarities of the hagfish is the apparently high survival rate of its young. Compared with other fishes, the female hagfish is a very small producer. It takes many months to develop the eggs within its body, and the average number laid at one time is only about 22—very few indeed compared with the thousands of eggs laid by other fishes at a single spawning. Yet the ocean abounds in enormous numbers of hagfishes. I myself have collected about 29,000 of these animals off the Pacific Coast—approximately 15,000 of them from one comparatively small area near San Diego. The almost astronomical fecundity of other marine organisms is offset by an extremely high rate of attrition among the eggs and the young, so that relatively few individuals survive to maturity. Quite evidently the hagfish is a far hardier animal.

One reason may be its remarkable immunity to infectious disease. A wound in a hagfish will remain clean for weeks with no sign of infection (or of healing either). This is particularly surprising because no one has yet been able to discover the basis of the immunity. Robert A. Good and Ben Papermaster of the University of Minnesota School of Medicine have established that hagfishes do not manufacture antibodies; indeed, they apparently lack the thymus tissue that is usually involved in the synthesis of antibodies. I have searched for a possible antibiotic in the body of the hagfish but have failed to find any in its slime, skin, blood or body organs. Here is one more of the many provocative features that make the hagfish a most fascinating animal to study.

The Author

DAVID JENSEN works in the division of marine biology at the Scripps Institution of Oceanography of the University of California at San Diego, where he is an Established Investigator of the American Heart Association. Jensen received bachelor's, master's and doctor's degrees in physiology from the University of California at Berkeley. He has spent 10 years in cardiac research and nine years studying the hagfish, an animal to which he turned because he thought it might prove useful for basic research on cardiac physiology. "Subsequent events seem to have vindicated this opinion," he writes. He is working also "on the electrophysiology of cardiac automatism in several species of animal."

Bibliography

THE ANEURAL HEART OF THE HAGFISH. David Jensen in *Annals of the New York Academy of Sciences,* Vol. 127, Article 1, pages 443–458; September 8, 1965.

EPTATRETIN: A POTENT CARDIOACTIVE AGENT FROM THE BRANCHIAL HEART OF THE PACIFIC HAGFISH, EPTATRETUS STOUTII. David Jensen in *Comparative Biochemistry and Physiology,* Vol. 10, No. 2, pages 129–151; October, 1963.

ON CIRCULATORY CONTROL MECHANISMS IN THE PACIFIC HAGFISH. Carleton B. Chapman, David Jensen and Kern Wildenthal in *Circulation Research,* Vol. 12, No. 5, Part I, pages 427–440; May, 1963.

SCIENTIFIC
AMERICAN   March 1966, Vol. 214, No. 3, pp. 24-33   OFFPRINT 1036

LIVING UNDER THE SEA

by Joseph B. MacInnis

To learn more about the ocean and harvest its resources, men must be able to live and work as free divers on the continental shelf. Several research programs are currently developing this ability.

It is one thing to glimpse a new world and quite another to establish permanent outposts in it, to explore it and to work and live in it. In recent years parts of the ocean floor have been studied in considerable detail, but almost entirely by surface-bound investigators. They have sounded the oceans with electronic devices, dangled instruments thousands of feet below the surface and secured samples of the bottom, and a few have undertaken brief expeditions in submersible vehicles to the greatest depths. Now, however, men are beginning to try to live underwater—to remain on the bottom exposed to the ocean's pressure for long periods and to move about and work there as free divers.

The submerged domain potentially available to man for firsthand investigation and eventual exploitation can be regarded as a new continent with an area of about 11,500,000 square miles—the size of Africa. It comprises the gently sloping shoulders of the continents, the continental shelves that rim the ocean basins. The shelves range up to several hundred miles in width and are generally covered by 600 feet of water or less. That they are submerged at all is an accident of this epoch's sea level: the ocean basins are filled to overflowing and the sea has spilled over, making ocean floor of what is really a seaward extension of the coastal topography. Geologically the shelf belongs more to the continents than to the

oceans. Its basement rock is continental granite rather than oceanic basalt and is covered largely with continental sediments rather than abyssal ooze.

Not surprisingly, mineral deposits similar to those under dry land lie under the shelf. Oil and natural gas are the foremost examples. In 1964 alone the petroleum industry spent $5 billion to find and recover offshore oil; only recently the continental shelf in the North Sea has become the site of extensive exploration for oil and gas. Drilling and capping a well from the surface is not easy. The prospect of more efficient oil and gas operations in deeper water by men working on the floor of the shelf is one of the primary reasons for the surge of activity directed toward living under the sea. There are other reasons. One is the increasing interest in all aspects of oceanography, coupled with an awareness of the geological, biological and meteorological information to be gained in direct undersea investigations. Another is the advance in free-diving techniques that began with the invention of "self-contained underwater breathing apparatus" (SCUBA) in the 1940's. Finally, there is a need for improved methods of underwater salvage and submarine rescue.

The reasons for going underwater are balanced by an impressive list of potential hazards. Most of them stem from the effects of pressure, which increases at the rate of one atmosphere

(14.7 pounds per square inch, or 760 millimeters of mercury) with every 33 feet of depth in seawater.

The best-known hazard and one of the most dangerous is decompression sickness—"the bends." Under pressure the inert gas in a breathing mixture (nitrogen or helium) diffuses into the blood and other tissues. If the pressure is relieved too quickly, bubbles form in the tissues much as they do in a bottle of carbonated water when it is opened. Sudden decompression from a long, deep dive can be fatal; even a slight miscalculation of decompression requirements can cause serious injury to the joints or the central nervous system. A diver must therefore be decompressed slowly, according to a careful schedule, so that the inert gas can be washed out of the tissues by the blood and then exhaled by the lungs. Whereas the demands of decompression become more stringent with depth, with time they increase only up to a point. After about 24 hours at a given depth the tissues become essentially saturated with inert gas

UNDERWATER DWELLING called the SPID (for "submerged, portable, inflatable dwelling") was designed by Edwin A. Link as a base of operations for long dives to the continental shelf. In the photograph on the opposite page the SPID is undergoing a pressure test at 70 feet. In the summer of 1964 two divers occupied the SPID for two days at 432 feet below the surface.

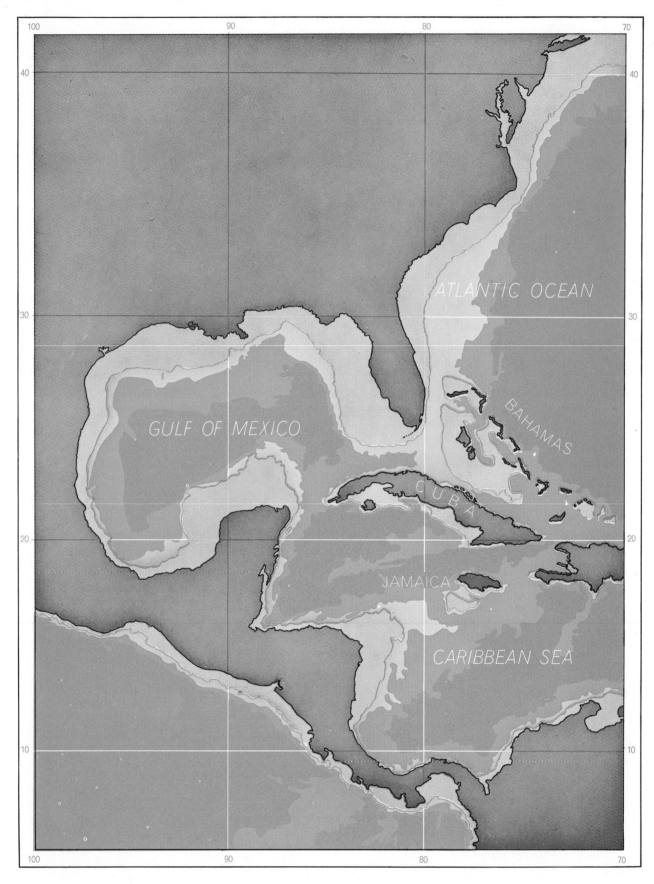

CONTINENTAL SHELF (*lightest areas*) off part of North America is shown. It is less a part of the ocean basin than it is an extension of the continental land mass. As in most parts of the world, the shelf slopes gently to about 600 feet below sea level; then the continental slope plunges toward the floor of the ocean basin. On this map, based on charts of the International Hydrographic Bureau, the contour intervals are in meters rather than feet. The lightest tone shows the bottom from sea level down to 200 meters (655 feet); successively darker blacks indicate bottom from 200 to 1,000, 1,000 to 3,000 and deeper than 3,000 meters.

at a pressure equivalent to the depth; they do not take up significantly more gas no matter how long the diver stays at that level. Therefore if a diver must descend to a certain depth to accomplish a time-consuming underwater task, it is far more efficient for him to stay there than to return to the surface repeatedly, spending hours in decompression each time. Although this "saturation diving" is efficient, it imposes an extra technical burden, because the schedules for the ultimate decompression must be calculated and controlled with particular care.

Pressure also has significant effects on a diver's breathing requirements. For one thing, hyperoxia (too much oxygen) becomes almost as dangerous as hypoxia (too little). Acute hyperoxia can affect the central nervous system, causing localized muscular twitching and convulsions; chronic hyperoxia impairs the process of gas exchange in the alveoli, or air sacs, of the lung. Optimum oxygen levels are still under investigation; they vary with the duration, depth and phase of the dive and the muscular effort required of the diver. It is clear, however, that the "partial pressure" of oxygen should be kept between about 150 and 400 millimeters of mercury during the at-depth phase of a long saturation dive. The partial pressure of oxygen in the air we breathe at sea level is 160 millimeters of mercury (21 percent of 760). If oxygen is kept at 21 percent of the mixture, however, its partial pressure increases with depth—rising to 1,127 millimeters 200 feet down, for example. As a result the proportion of oxygen in the air or other breathing mixture must be cut back sharply from 21 percent. The band of permissible percentages narrows rapidly with depth [see illustration on page 2104], calling for increasing accuracy in systems that analyze and control the gas mixture.

Nitrogen, which is physiologically inert at sea level, has an anesthetic effect under pressure. At depths greater than 100 feet it begins to produce "nitrogen narcosis," an impairment in judgment and motor ability that can render a diver completely unable to cope with emergencies. Helium has been found to be much less narcotic and is currently used instead of nitrogen in almost all deep-sea dives. Being less dense, it also offers less breathing resistance under pressure; this can be important to a working diver. Helium has two disadvantages, however. Because its thermal conductivity is almost six times as great as nitrogen's, it accelerates the loss of body heat and makes a

diver uncomfortably cold even at temperatures of 70 or 80 degrees. Helium also distorts the resonance of a diver's voice, making his speech almost unintelligible and thus giving rise to a serious communication problem.

In any confined environment the buildup of exhaled carbon dioxide must be monitored carefully. In our diving experiments for Ocean Systems, Inc., we try to keep the partial pressure of this gas below seven millimeters of mercury (compared with the sea-level pressure in fresh air of .3 millimeter), but at the U.S. Naval Medical Research Laboratory in New London, Conn., Karl E. Schaefer has found that at sea level slightly higher levels are tolerable for several weeks. In any case, carbon dioxide accumulates rapidly in a small space and soon reaches a toxic level, causing dizziness, headache and an increase in the rate of breathing. It must therefore be continuously "scrubbed" out of the diver's atmosphere, usually by being passed through some chemical with which it will react. Other gases, such as carbon monoxide and certain volatile hydrocarbons, can also reach toxic levels quickly if they are allowed to concentrate in the diver's breathing mixture.

There are sometimes other obstacles to casual access to the ocean floor: a demoralizing lack of visibility, strong currents, uncertain bottom profiles. There are also dangerous marine animals, ranging in size from a unicellular infective fungus to the widely feared great white shark. Finally, the water of the continental shelf is cold. Temperatures average between 40 and 60 degrees, and without protective clothing a diver soon becomes totally ineffective.

Faced with these difficulties commercial divers and undersea investigators found it impossible to spend time and do useful work on the continental shelf. Those who went down in pressurized suits and thick-hulled submersible vehicles were held prisoner by their protective armor. Free divers, on the other hand, could not go very deep or stay very long. In 1956 Edwin A. Link, the inventor of the Link Trainer for simulated flight training, was engaged in undersea archaeological investigations. He recognized that a diver could work more effectively at substantial depths if he could live there for prolonged periods instead of having to be decompressed to the surface after each day's work. Link set out to build a vehicle that could operate as an underwater elevator, a diving bell and a decompression cham-

ber. The "submersible decompression chamber" (SDC) he designed is an aluminum cylinder 11 feet long and three feet in diameter [see illustration, page 2103]. With its outer hatches closed it is a sealed capsule in which a diver can be lowered to the bottom. On the bottom, with the internal gas pressure equal to ambient water pressure and the hatches open, the SDC serves as a dry refuge from which the occupant can operate as a free diver. Then, with the hatches again closed, it becomes a sealed chamber in which the diver can be decompressed safely and efficiently on shipboard or during his ascent to the surface. An inner hatch provides an air lock through which someone else can enter the chamber (or pass food and other supplies into it) during the decompression phase.

Before open-sea experiments with the SDC were possible some preliminary research was necessary. How deep could a man go as a free diver? How long could he stay down? What would be the acute and the long-term medical effects of the pressure itself and of the synthetic atmosphere? What would be the response to the cold, the confinement and the psychological hazards of deep submergence? Some early and significant answers were provided by Captain George F. Bond, a U.S. Navy physician who in 1957 conceived and carried out a series of simulated dives in a compression chamber on land at the Naval Medical Research Laboratory. Bond's group first exposed small animals, including some primates, to a pressure equivalent to a depth of 200 feet. Volunteer Navy divers then lived in the chamber under precisely controlled conditions of pressure, temperature and humidity. These experiments showed, among other things, that men could breathe helium instead of nitrogen for long periods without ill effects and encouraged Link to move ahead.

Early in September, 1962, the SDC underwent its critical test in the Mediterranean Sea off Villefranche on the French Riviera. A young Belgian diver, Robert Sténuit, descended in it to 200 feet and lived there for 24 hours, swimming out into the water to work and returning to rest in the warm safety of the pressurized chamber. When the time came to return to the surface, Sténuit did not have to face hours of dangling on a lifeline or perching on a platform, decompressing slowly in the cold water. Instead he sealed himself into the chamber, was hoisted to the deck of Link's research vessel, the Sea Diver, and there was decompressed in

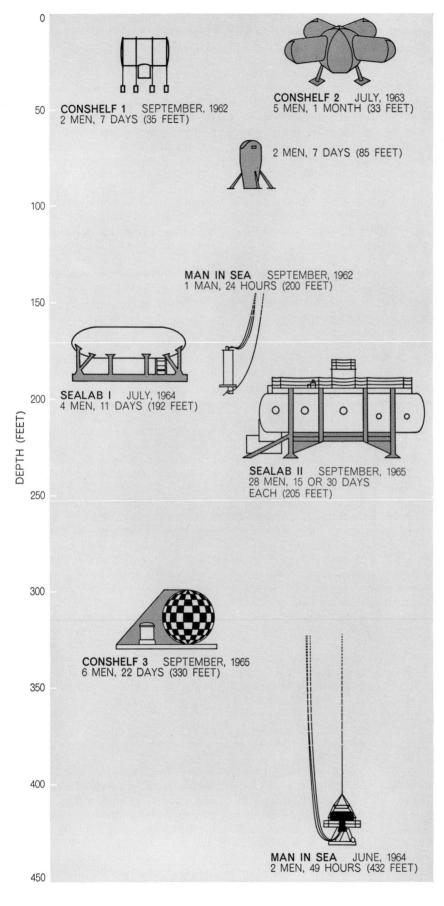

CONSHELF 1   SEPTEMBER, 1962
2 MEN, 7 DAYS (35 FEET)

CONSHELF 2   JULY, 1963
5 MEN, 1 MONTH (33 FEET)

2 MEN, 7 DAYS (85 FEET)

MAN IN SEA   SEPTEMBER, 1962
1 MAN, 24 HOURS (200 FEET)

SEALAB I   JULY, 1964
4 MEN, 11 DAYS (192 FEET)

SEALAB II   SEPTEMBER, 1965
28 MEN, 15 OR 30 DAYS
EACH (205 FEET)

CONSHELF 3   SEPTEMBER, 1965
6 MEN, 22 DAYS (330 FEET)

MAN IN SEA   JUNE, 1964
2 MEN, 49 HOURS (432 FEET)

DEPTH (FEET)

SATURATION DIVING, in which the divers stay down for prolonged periods, is made possible by underwater shelters. The chart gives data for seven such dives. "Man in Sea" is the Link project, "Conshelf" is Jacques-Yves Cousteau's and "Sealab" is the U.S. Navy's.

safety and relative (although somewhat cramped) comfort.

Meanwhile, moving ahead independently, the French undersea investigator and inventor of the aqualung, Jacques-Yves Cousteau, had undertaken experiments aimed at establishing manned undersea stations on the continental shelf. The first experiment in his "Conshelf" program was carried out near Marseilles in mid-September, 1962, when two men lived under 35 feet of water for a week. The divers worked in the sea several hours a day, returning to a cylindrical cabin to eat and sleep.

Cousteau's group went on, in the summer of 1963, to establish a complex underwater settlement at the remote Sha'ab Rumi Reef in the Red Sea. The hub of the settlement was "Starfish House," an assembly of cylindrical chambers in 33 feet of water. It housed five men and their eating, sleeping and laboratory facilities for a month. Nearby was a submarine "hangar" from which a two-man "diving saucer," with its pilot and passenger protected from the sea pressure, made a number of trips as deep as 1,000 feet to collect samples and make observations at the edge of the reef. Down the coral slope from Starfish House, at a depth of 85 feet, two men lived in the controlled oxygen-helium-nitrogen environment of a "deep cabin" for seven days, making short excursion dives as deep as 360 feet. One of the most interesting things about Conshelf II was its demonstration that—at least for relatively shallow depths—the participants did not have to be experienced divers or even young men in particularly good physical condition. Instead they were picked for their vocational ability as mechanics, scientific workers, cooks and so on. The experiment showed that biological investigations and submarine operations could be carried out from submerged stations.

In the U.S. meanwhile Link and Bond were designing pressure experiments and engineering diving systems that would enable free divers to reach greater depths safely. From late 1963 until March, 1964, a series of simulated saturation dives—the first such dives deeper than 200 feet—were carried out under the technical direction of Captain R. D. Workman at the Navy's Experimental. Diving Unit in Washington. The tests showed that divers suffered no harmful effects when exposed to depths of 300 and 400 feet for 24 hours and that they could be decompressed successfully on a linear decompression schedule.

Link had decided that the second

phase of his "Man in Sea" project would attempt to demonstrate that men could work effectively at 400 feet for several days. He established a "life-support" team under the direction of Christian J. Lambertsen of the University of Pennsylvania School of Medicine to undertake preliminary research and supervise the medical aspects of the dive. Under Lambertsen's direction James G. Dickson and I first evaluated the accuracy and reliability of gas analyzers that would monitor the divers' breathing atmosphere. In addition to proving out the system, our experiments showed that mice could tolerate saturation at (and decompression from) pressures equivalent to 4,000 feet of seawater.

The 400-foot dive required the design of a larger and more comfortable "dwelling" on the ocean floor. Such a dwelling presents unusual engineering problems. It must provide shelter and warmth and be easy to enter and leave underwater, simple to operate and resistant to the corrosive effects of seawater. The dwelling must be heavy enough to settle on the bottom but not so heavy that it is hard to handle from the deck of a support ship. Link's unique solution was

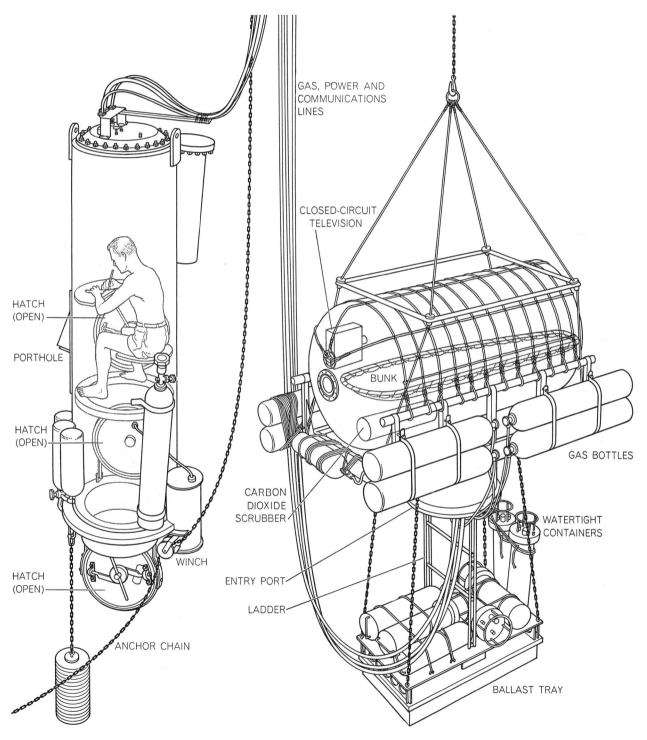

GAS, POWER AND COMMUNICATIONS LINES

CLOSED-CIRCUIT TELEVISION

HATCH (OPEN)

PORTHOLE

HATCH (OPEN)

HATCH (OPEN)

WINCH

CARBON DIOXIDE SCRUBBER

ENTRY PORT

LADDER

ANCHOR CHAIN

BUNK

GAS BOTTLES

WATERTIGHT CONTAINERS

BALLAST TRAY

TWO CHAMBERS used in the Man in Sea 432-foot, two-day dive are diagrammed. The "submersible decompression chamber," or SDC (*left*), is an aluminum cylinder 11 feet long and three feet in diameter. With the hatches open and the inside gas pressure equal to the external water pressure, the SDC serves as a diving bell. The SPID (*right and photograph on page 2099*) is an eight-by-four-foot inflatable rubber dwelling with a steel frame and ballast tray. Access to it is through an entry port at the bottom.

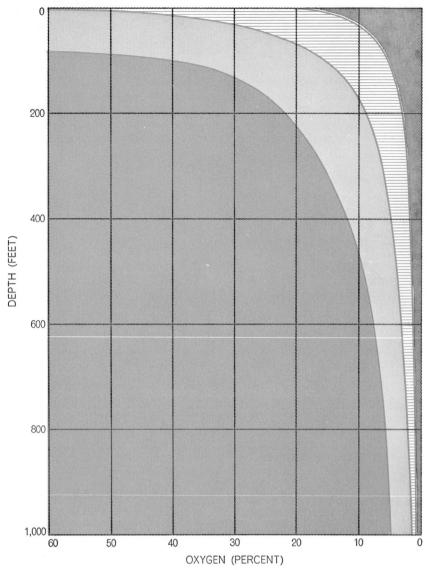

PERMISSIBLE RANGE (*barred white band*) of oxygen content in the breathing gas supplied to a diver narrows sharply with depth, requiring close control in order to avoid zones in which there is a danger of hypoxia (*gray*) or hyperoxia damaging to the lungs (*light color*) and the central nervous system (*dark color*). For several days' exposure at sea level a safe range is from 20 to 60 percent. With depth the "partial pressure" of oxygen increases, however; at 300 feet, or 10 atmospheres, 2 percent of the breathing mixture represents as much oxygen as 20 percent would represent under sea-level conditions.

in effect an underwater tent: a fat rubber sausage eight feet long and four feet in diameter, mounted on a rigid steel frame [*see illustration on preceding page*]. Deflated at the surface, the "submerged, portable, inflatable dwelling" (SPID) is remarkably easy to handle—an important advantage when undersea habitations are established in remote locations. As it is submerged, the tent is inflated so that its internal gas pressure is equal to the ambient water pressure. There are no hatches; an open, cufflike entry port in the floor of the SPID allows easy access and provides the necessary vertical latitude for variations in the pressure differential. Inside the SPID and in watertight containers on the

frame and on the ballast tray below it are stored supplies and equipment: gas cylinders and the gas-circulating system, a closed-circuit television camera, communications equipment, food, water, tools and underwater breathing gear.

In the 400-foot dive the SPID was to be one of three major pressure chambers. The second was the proved SDC and the third was a new deck decompression chamber. This time the SDC was to serve as an elevator and also as a backup refuge on the bottom but not as the main decompression chamber. After a long, deep dive decompression takes several days, and it is important that the divers be as comfortable as possible. An eight-by-five-foot decompres-

sion chamber with a four-foot air lock was therefore secured to the deck of the *Sea Diver*. The SDC could be mated to it so that the divers could be transferred to it under deep-sea pressure. Decompression could then proceed under the direct supervision of life-support personnel.

Early in June, 1964, Link and his research group sailed to the Bahamas to test the three-chamber diving concept. We checked the chambers with dives to 40 and 70 feet, spending several weeks refining techniques for handling the SDC and the SPID and coping with potential emergencies. The exact site for the dive, chosen with the cooperation of Navy personnel using sonar and underwater television, was a gentle coral sand slope 432 feet deep, about three miles northwest of Great Stirrup Cay.

On June 28 the underwater dwelling, with its vital gear carefully stowed aboard, was lowered slowly to the ocean floor. When it had settled on the shelf, the oxygen level inside was adjusted to 3.8 percent, the equivalent of a sea-level partial pressure of 400 millimeters of mercury. The inert gas was helium with a trace of nitrogen (because there had been air in the tent to start with). Then the SPID was left, a habitable outpost autonomous except for communications, power and gas lines, ready for its occupants.

The next step was to transport Sténuit and Jon Lindbergh, another experienced diver, to the shelf. As usual, the SDC was placed in the water at the surface so that the divers could enter it from below. At 10:15 A.M. on June 30 Sténuit and Lindbergh went over the side and swam up into the chamber, closed the outer hatches and checked their instruments. At 10:45, still at the surface, the SDC was pressurized to the equivalent of 150 feet with oxygen and helium to check for leaks; one minor leak was discovered and repaired. At noon the chamber started down, slipping through the clear purple water toward the deep shelf. When it reached 300 feet, Lindbergh reported the bottom in sight. At 1:00 P.M. the anchor weights touched bottom and the chamber came to a stop five feet above the sand. It was just 15 feet from the waiting SPID. During the descent the SDC's internal pressure had been brought to 200 feet; now pressurization was completed. At 1:15 the bottom hatches were opened and Sténuit swam over and entered the dwelling. Lindbergh joined him and they began to arrange the SPID for their stay.

At that point Lindbergh reported that the carbon dioxide scrubber had been flooded and was not functioning. The divers found the backup scrubber in its watertight container and prepared to set it up as the carbon dioxide level rose to almost 20 millimeters of mercury. Then they found they could not get at the reserve scrubber: the pressure-equalizing valve that would make it possible to open the container was missing. With the carbon dioxide level rising rapidly as a result of their muscular exertion, they had to leave the dwelling and return to the SDC. We had hoped to maintain the diving team on the shelf with a minimum of support from the surface, but it now became necessary to send a spare scrubber down on a line from the *Sea Diver*. The divers installed it in the SPID and the dwelling was soon habitable.

Later that evening the divers took over control of the dwelling's atmosphere, monitoring it with their own high-pressure gas analyzer and adding makeup oxygen as required. We kept watch from the surface by closed-circuit television as Sténuit and Lindbergh settled down for the night. While one slept the other kept watch, checking instruments and communications (a procedure that, as confidence in the system increases, should not be necessary in the future). The water temperature that night was 72 degrees and the dwelling was at 76 degrees, yet both divers later reported that the helium atmosphere was too cold for comfortable sleeping.

In the morning the divers swam over to check the SDC, making sure that it was available as a refuge in case of trouble in the SPID. For the rest of the day both men worked out of the dwelling, observing, photographing and collecting samples of the local marine life. While they were in the water the divers breathed from a "closed" rebreathing system connected to the SPID rather than from an "open" SCUBA system. An open apparatus spills exhaled gas into the sea. At 432 feet, under 14 atmospheres of pressure, each exhalation expends gas equal to a sea-level volume of some seven liters, which would be prohibitively wasteful. Link had designed a system that pumped the dwelling atmosphere through a long hose to a breathing bag worn by the diver. Exhaled gases were drawn back to the dwelling through a second hose to be purified and recirculated. The apparatus worked well except that the breathing mixture was so dense under 14 atmospheres that the pumps could

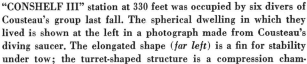

"CONSHELF III" station at 330 feet was occupied by six divers of Cousteau's group last fall. The spherical dwelling in which they lived is shown at the left in a photograph made from Cousteau's diving saucer. The elongated shape (*far left*) is a fin for stability under tow; the turret-shaped structure is a compression chamber for emergency escape to the surface. The major task accomplished by the divers was the installation and repair of an oil-well head (*right*). They were able to manipulate repair tools to handle emergency breakdown situations met in actual production. In the photograph a diver is guiding a tool pipe into the wellhead.

DEFLATED SPID is hoisted over the side of Link's vessel *Sea Diver*. One end of the SDC is visible in the left foreground, with part of the deck decompression chamber beyond it.

not move quite enough of it to meet the divers' maximum respiratory demand.

During the second evening we carried out and recorded voice-communication tests with the divers breathing either pure air or a mixture of 75 percent air and 25 percent helium. Voice quality was considerably better than in a helium atmosphere, but even 30 seconds of breathing air caused a noticeable degree of nitrogen narcosis. At 11:00 P.M. the two men bedded down for the second night. They were disturbed from time to time by heavy thumps against the outside of the dwelling. It developed that large groupers, attracted by the small fishes that swarmed into the shaft of light spilling from the open port of the SPID, were charging the swarm and hitting the dark bulk of the dwelling.

The next day the divers measured the visibility in the remarkably clear water; they could see almost 150 feet in the horizontal plane and 200 feet vertically. Then they took more photographs and collected animal and plant specimens. At 1:30 P.M. on July 2 both men were back in the SDC with the hatches secured. At 2:20, after 49 hours on the deep shelf, the SDC began its ascent. The internal pressure was maintained at 432 feet; although the divers were being lifted toward the surface, they were not yet being decompressed. At 3:15 the dripping SDC was hoisted onto its

cradle aboard the *Sea Diver*. Now the internal pressure was decreased to 400 feet to establish a one-atmosphere differential between the divers' tissues and the chamber environment and make it possible for helium to begin escaping effectively from their tissues. Then, at 4:00, the SDC was mated to the deck decompression chamber, which was also at a pressure of 400 feet. Sténuit and Lindbergh, transferred to the deck chamber, and we began to advance them to surface pressure at the rate of five feet, or about .15 atmosphere, per hour. With the divers safe in their chamber another advantage of deck decompression became evident: mobility. While decompression proceeded the *Sea Diver* weighed anchor and steamed for Florida. By the time it moored in Miami on the afternoon of July 5 the pressure had been reduced to 35 feet.

During the shallow stages of decompression, breathing pure oxygen establishes a larger outward pressure gradient in the lung for the inert gas one is anxious to flush out of the diver's tissues and thus helps to prevent the bends. Since breathing pure oxygen under pressure for a sustained period can cause lung damage, Lambertsen had in the past suggested alternating between pure oxygen and compressed air. We instituted this interrupted oxygen-breathing schedule when the divers

reached 30 feet. Still, we had one period of concern about decompression sickness. At about 20 feet Sténuit reported a vague "sawdust feeling" in his fingers that seemed to progress to the wrists. I examined him under pressure in the chamber. There were no abnormal neurological findings, but decompression sickness is so diverse in its manifestations that almost any symptom has to be taken seriously. Dickson and I therefore recompressed the chamber one atmosphere and then resumed decompression at the slower rate of four feet per hour. Finally, at noon on July 6, Sténuit and Lindbergh emerged from the chamber in excellent condition after 92 hours of decompression. The important point about saturation diving is that their decompression time would have been the same if they had stayed down 49 days instead of 49 hours.

Their dive had shown that men could live and work effectively more than 400 feet below the surface for a substantial period, protected by an almost autonomous undersea dwelling, and be successfully recovered from such depths and decompressed on the surface at sea. More specifically, it demonstrated the flexibility and mobility of the three-chamber concept. It also emphasized some problems, including the voice distortion caused by helium and the need for a larger breathing-gas supply to support muscular exertion. It showed that the control of humidity in an atmosphere in direct contact with the sea is extraordinarily difficult. The relative humidity in the chamber was close to 100 percent and both divers complained of softened skin and rashes. Temperature was a problem too. Both men preferred having the chamber temperature between 82 and 85 degrees. In the water, we realized, heated suits are required to keep divers comfortable even in the Caribbean Sea.

There have been a number of other recent saturation diving experiments, two of them conducted by Bond's Navy group. The first, "Sealab I," took place off Bermuda later in July, 1964. Four men lived for 10 days in a large cylindrical chamber 192 feet below the surface. Last summer the Navy conducted "Sealab II," a massive 45-day effort involving three teams of 10 men, each of which spent 15 days underwater. (One man went down for two nonconsecutive 15-day periods and one, the astronaut Scott Carpenter, stayed for 30 consecutive days.) The base of operations was a cabin 57 by 12 feet in size submerged in 205 feet of water near the Scripps Institution of Oceanography at La Jolla, Calif. The Sealab "aquanauts" salvaged an airplane hulk, did biological and oceanographic research and conducted psychological and physiological tests. Electrically heated suits made it possible for them to work comfortably in the 55-degree water.

In the Mediterranean off Cap Ferrat, Cousteau's group last fall made another significant advance in underwater living. Six men lived in a spherical dwelling 330 feet below the surface for almost 22 days, linked to the surface only by an electrical and communications cable. Cousteau's "oceanauts" concentrated on difficult underwater work, including the successful emplacement and operation at 370 feet of a five-ton oil-well head in which oil under pressure was simulated by compressed air.

As men go deeper and stay longer the hazards increase and safety margins narrow. New questions arise. At what depth will even helium become too narcotic or too dense to breathe? Can hydrogen serve as an acceptable substitute? At what depth will pressure effects cause unacceptable changes in tissue structure? What will be the decompression obligation after saturation at 1,000 feet or more? And what are the residual effects of repeated exposure to great depths?

Again, the answers are beginning to come from dry-land experimentation. Last fall two Ocean Systems divers simulated a dive to 650 feet in our test chamber. They stayed at that pressure for 48 hours, becoming completely saturated with 20 atmospheres of helium. Our results indicated that helium is safe—at least at the depth and for the length of time involved in the test—and suggested that it may be possible to continue with helium as the inert gas even beyond 1,000 feet. We found that breathing an oxygen-neon mixture for 30 minutes at 650 feet caused no measurable narcotic or other detrimental effects and that it markedly improved voice quality. Heart and lung function, exercise tolerance, psychomotor performance and blood and urine characteristics were all within normal limits. I think the most significant result of this longest deep-pressure experiment to date was our impression that divers will be able to perform physical and mental work almost as effectively at 650 feet as at the surface.

There do not, then, seem to be any physiological or psychological barriers that will prevent the occupation of any part of the continental shelf. Nonetheless, it is important to recognize that so far all efforts to live under the sea have been investigations or demonstrations of man's ability to do so. In the last analysis men will live underwater only when specific tasks, with economic or other motivations, present themselves. At this point, however, the gates of the deep shelf have been opened.

"SEALAB II" CHAMBER housed 10 Navy divers at a time during a 45-day test at 205 feet last summer. The chamber is a 57-by-12-foot cylinder with several interior compartments. Entry is through the port at the lower left, which is protected by a wire shark barrier.

The Author

JOSEPH B. MacINNIS is director of diving research for Ocean Systems, Inc. He is a Canadian who obtained a medical degree at the University of Toronto in 1962, turned to the subject on which he writes after having studied high-pressure physiology at the University of Pennsylvania School of Medicine. His chief interests are the psychological and physiological responses of humans to diving, living and working in the deep sea and the development of life-support systems that facilitate human activity under the sea. MacInnis, who held three Canadian swimming records in 1956 and 1957, has himself taken part in dives as deep as 600 feet, made several underwater films, conducted research on diving problems and written extensively about the pleasures and problems of undersea activity by humans.

Bibliography

THE DEEPEST DAYS. Robert Sténuit in *National Geographic,* Vol. 127, No. 4, pages 534–547; April, 1965.

OUTPOST UNDER THE OCEAN. Edwin A. Link in *National Geographic,* Vol. 127, No. 4, pages 530–533; April, 1965.

PROCEEDINGS OF THE SECOND SYMPOSIUM ON UNDERWATER PHYSIOLOGY. Edited by Christian J. Lambertsen and Leon J. Greenbaum, Jr. National Academy of Sciences—National Research Council Publication 1181, 1963.

UNDERWATER MEDICINE. Stanley Miles. J. B. Lippincott Company, 1966.

WORLD WITHOUT SUN. Jacques-Yves Cousteau. Edited by James Dugan. Harper & Row, Publishers, 1965.

SPECIAL NOTE TO TEACHERS: Each article in this volume, plus more than 660 others, is available as a separate, self-bound SCIENTIFIC AMERICAN Offprint. Offprints may be ordered in any combination and in any quantity. Teachers who want to adopt articles for their courses, therefore, can ensure that each student has his own set. Students' sets are collated by the publisher before shipment

SCIENTIFIC
AMERICAN   March 1966, Vol. 214, No. 3, pp. 34-41

OFFPRINT 1037

THE FOOTPRINTS OF TUMOR VIRUSES

by Fred Rapp and Joseph L. Melnick

Some viruses that cause tumors in animals are not found in the tumors
but their antigens are. This suggests that the absence of a virus in
a human cancer does not necessarily mean that a virus did not cause it.

The viruses that cause cancers, like viruses in general, can be divided into two broad classes: those that contain ribonucleic acid (RNA) as their genetic material and those that contain deoxyribonucleic acid (DNA). The two classes exhibit a curious difference in behavior. The RNA-containing viruses can readily be found in the tumors to which they give rise; in tumors induced by DNA-containing viruses, on the other hand, the virus itself disappears. Because the DNA viruses cannot be recovered from tumors for study, most of the investigations of virus-induced cancer in animals have concentrated on RNA viruses, specifically those that cause leukemia. A recent discovery, however, has opened a way to investigation of tumor-causing viruses of the DNA class. It was ascertained that, although the viruses themselves cannot be found in the tumors, they leave footprints, in the form of antigens, that identify them. This finding has made possible a broad study of the transformation of normal cells into tumorous ones by DNA-containing viruses.

In our laboratory at the Baylor University College of Medicine we have been studying two types of DNA-containing virus: the adenoviruses (responsible for colds and other respiratory diseases) and the papovavirus of monkeys known as SV 40 (simian virus 40). The two types of virus differ from each other in many respects, but they are alike in two significant properties: they often generate latent infections that produce no sign of illness, and they can produce cancer when inoculated into newborn hamsters (and in the case of some of the adenoviruses, in newborn mice as well).

Adenoviruses were first recognized and isolated in 1953 in cell cultures derived from the adenoids of infected children. Since then more than 30 anti-

genic types of this virus have been found in man and other types in monkeys, cattle, dogs, mice and chickens. At least five types are now known to be capable of producing tumors in newborn hamsters. The simian virus was discovered in cultures of monkey kidney cells that were used to prepare vaccines against poliomyelitis and other virus diseases, including those caused by adenoviruses. There is no evidence that SV 40 produces any disease in man; nevertheless, after its discovery all virus vaccines were carefully tested to make sure that this contaminant was excluded, and experimental studies were undertaken to examine the virus's fundamental properties and effects on various cells. These studies quickly showed that in cell cultures SV 40 was capable of transforming normal cells into abnormal forms; it could produce these inheritable changes not only in hamster cells but also in human cells. The transformed hamster cells proved to be capable of producing tumors when they were implanted in young adult hamsters.

Grown in a glass dish, the cells transformed by the simian virus multiply into colonies that look like molds to the unaided eye. Under the microscope they show various abnormalities, such as aberrations in the chromosomes (breaks, translocations and deletions) and a three-dimensional piling up of the cells [see top illustration, page 2116]. This last marks them as abnormal because normal cells grown in a dish are inhibited from climbing over one another and hence form only a single sheet of cells.

No virus could be found in the tumors arising from cells transformed by either the adenoviruses or SV 40. In the adenotumors particles with some resemblances to the virus were found, but the particles were plainly not complete viruses. The SV 40 tumors yielded no

such particles at all. What, then, could account for the permanently changed behavior of the transformed cells, persisting in generation after generation of these cells? Did the virus endow the cells with a portion of its set of genes—a portion that, although not sufficient for reproduction of the virus itself, imposed a control over certain properties of the cell? If so, could evidence of the presence of these genes—footprints of the virus, so to speak—be found among the chemical products of the transformed cell? Did the transformed cell, for instance, produce a substance that was not produced by normal cells and that could be linked to the virus?

The first indication that such footprints might indeed be found was reported by Robert J. Huebner and his colleagues at the National Institutes of Health. They applied the well-known complement-fixation test for detecting antigen-antibody reactions to the serum of hamsters bearing tumors that had been initiated by an adenovirus, and they observed that the animals produced specific antibodies that reacted with antigens obtained from the tumor. Huebner, and Albert B. Sabin of the University of Cincinnati College of Medicine as well, went on to apply the same test to hamsters with tumors induced by SV 40, with the same result: these animals synthesized antibodies capable of reacting with a specific antigen derived from the tumor extracts containing the simian virus but not with the virus itself. The antigen was therefore called a "tumor" antigen.

Other evidence for the existence of virus-induced cellular antigens emerged from studies in our laboratory. If hamsters were first inoculated with the SV 40 virus, they later rejected implants of SV 40 tumor cells. Evidently infection with

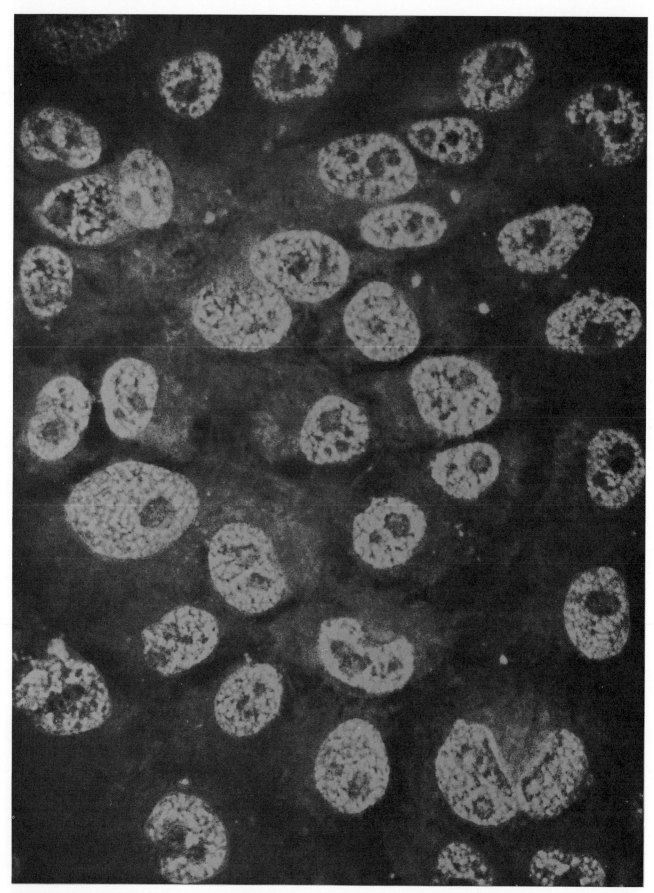

TUMOR-VIRUS ANTIGEN appears as the luminous granular green areas in this photomicrograph of hamster cells made by the technique of immunofluorescence. The cells had originally been infected with the tumor virus SV 40 (simian virus 40), which then disappeared. Later the cells were treated with antibody to the SV 40 virus; this antibody had been labeled with the fluorescent dye fluorescein isothiocyanate. When the cells were illuminated with ultraviolet radiation, the dye fluoresced, revealing the presence of the antibody. This indicated that, even though the virus itself was absent, it had left behind antigen that could react with antibody.

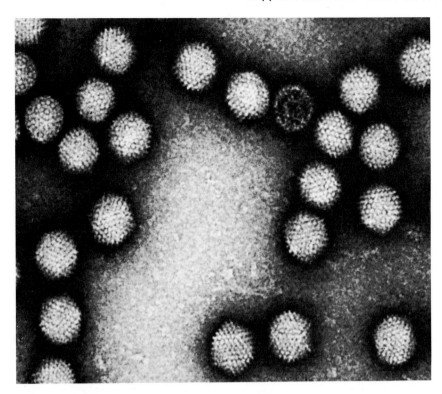

ADENOVIRUSES appear in this electron micrograph. Each has an actual diameter of about 70 millimicrons and a capsid, or outer protein coat, with 252 subunits. These viruses and those in the electron micrograph at the bottom of this page contain DNA as their genetic material. Such viruses disappear from the tumors they cause, unlike tumor-causing RNA viruses, and so have been difficult to investigate as tumor-causing agents. The discovery that some DNA viruses leave "footprints" in the form of antigen facilitates the study of them.

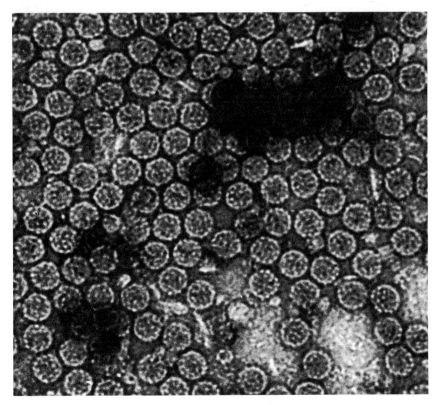

SV 40 VIRUSES, which are a type of papovavirus, also contain DNA. Each virus is about 45 millimicrons in diameter and has a capsid with either 42 or 72 subunits. These and various adenoviruses figured in the investigation by the authors of tumor-causing DNA viruses.

the virus caused the animals to synthesize an antigen eliciting the synthesis of antibodies that in turn attacked any graft of cells containing the same antigen; in short, the viral-induced antigen, which we call transplantation antigen, acted as a vaccine, making the animal immune to inoculation with the tumor cells. Recent studies suggest that the transplantation antigen is synthesized on the surface of the transformed cells. The surface of such cells will react with serum from a hamster that is immune to inoculation with an SV 40 tumor but not with the serum of a hamster hospitable to the tumor. The surface antigen seems to be the transplantation antigen, which stimulates the production of antibodies directed against the tumor cell. Because of these antibodies such an animal will resist the transplantation of tumor cells [see illustration on following page]. Such antibodies are not present in susceptible animals in which the tumor is able to grow. Antibodies in the tumor-bearing animals are able to react with the complement-fixing tumor antigen but not with the surface antigen.

There was every evidence that the tumor antigen was a new creation—a substance not present in the virus itself or in the original cell but one that the virus caused the transformed cells to manufacture. What could be learned about this antigen? Using serum from hamsters with SV 40 tumors and applying the immunofluorescence technique to observe reactions between the serum and the cells, Janet S. Butel of our laboratory found that every hamster cell transformed by SV 40 (either in vivo or in vitro) synthesized the tumor antigen, or T antigen, as it came to be called. The same antigen was also found in cells of other animals (including man) that were transformed by SV 40, but not in cells transformed by other viruses. The antigen was located in small particles within the nucleus of the cell. What was more, it showed up in the nuclei that had been newly formed as the cell divided. Obviously, therefore, the parent cell passed on information for the synthesis of this antigen to its daughter cells.

The fact that transformed cells of various species of animals synthesized the same antigen clearly indicated that this synthesis must be controlled by genes from the virus, incorporated in the transformed cells. This conclusion was strengthened by a discovery that directly linked the virus itself to the synthesis of the antigen. It was found, by investigators in Huebner's and Sabin's laboratories and in ours, that cells infected with SV 40 (but not transformed) synthesized the same antigen that transformed cells did. They produced the antigen during the early phases of the reproduction of the virus in the cell. This antigen production, not previously observed, was now found to occur in cells of monkeys, hamsters, rabbits and man when the cells were inoculated with SV 40 and then tested with serum from hamsters containing the specific antibody.

When the SV 40 virus invades a monkey kidney cell, it takes about 30 to 36 hours to produce a new crop of virus progeny. The protein coats of the new viruses are not synthesized until near the end of that period. Long before that happens—as early as 18 hours after the infection—the cell begins to produce the tumor antigen. We soon learned that poisons that inhibit the synthesis of the virus's DNA do not inhibit the production of the tumor antigen. This indicated that replication of the viral DNA is not necessary for the synthesis of the antigen. We found, however, that the synthesis does depend on messenger RNA in the cell, because production of the antigen could be suppressed by the administration of the antibiotic actinomycin D, which blocks the formation of messenger RNA [see illustration on next page].

Experiments with adenoviruses, carried out in a number of laboratories, have yielded results similar to those with SV 40. We can conclude in general that cells transformed to malignancy by DNA-containing viruses have as one of their distinctive properties the production of a specific antigen in the nucleus. The nature of this antigen is not yet known. There are indications that it may be an enzyme; similarities have been found between the induction of the tumor antigen and a step-up in the production of thymidine kinase, one of the enzymes involved in the synthesis of DNA, during the early stages of the replication of SV 40 in monkey cells. It seems from the work of Saul Kit at the Baylor College of Medicine that the thymidine kinase produced by infected cells is somewhat different from that in normal cells. No precise information has been obtained so far, however, on what relation, if any, exists between the tumor antigen and thymidine kinase.

The tumor antigen, then, furnished a clear and definite link connecting the viruses in question with cancers. As events turned out, the antigen also became something more than that: it proved to be a marker capable of providing information about the genetic transformation of cells. Within a few months after the discovery of the SV 40 tumor antigen a genetic relation between SV 40 and certain adenoviruses was discovered, both in our laboratory and at the National Institutes of Health. It developed that these adenoviruses could cause cells to produce precisely the same antigen the SV 40 virus did!

The first adenovirus involved was one called Type 7, which was used as the seed for the preparation of an adenovirus vaccine. It had been found that during the culture of this virus, involving many passages in monkey kidney cells, the strain became contaminated with SV 40. The cultures in which it was growing were therefore treated with a specific antiserum to eliminate SV 40. The treatment succeeded in yielding a culture that was free of any SV 40 capable of producing infection;

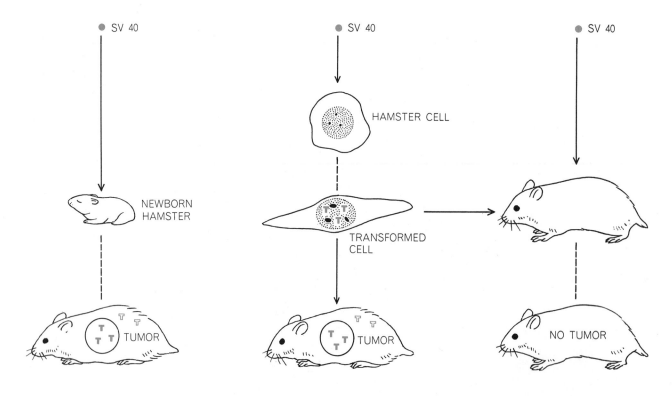

T TUMOR ANTIGEN   T ANTIBODY SPECIFIC TO TUMOR ANTIGEN

SECOND ANTIGEN became evident in a series of experiments. Newborn hamsters inoculated with SV 40 (left) often developed tumors and a tumor antigen. Similarly, hamster cells grown in culture and transformed by SV 40 (given permanent inheritable changes) often induced tumors when transplanted to young adult hamsters (center). However, hamsters to which transformed cells were transplanted after inoculation of the animals with SV 40 resisted the tumor-causing effect of the transformed cells (right). The virus acts as a vaccine: it induces an antigen, evidently the same as the "transplantation antigen" carried by the transformed cells.

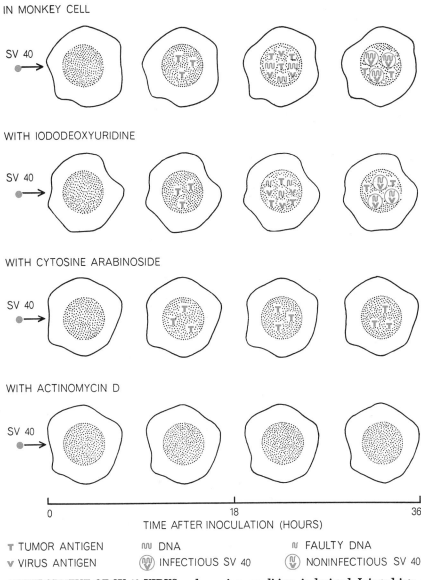

IN MONKEY CELL

SV 40

WITH IODODEOXYURIDINE

SV 40

WITH CYTOSINE ARABINOSIDE

SV 40

WITH ACTINOMYCIN D

SV 40

0   18   36
TIME AFTER INOCULATION (HOURS)

T TUMOR ANTIGEN   ᴍ DNA   ᴎ FAULTY DNA
ᴠ VIRUS ANTIGEN   ⓦ INFECTIOUS SV 40   ⓤ NONINFECTIOUS SV 40

DEVELOPMENT OF SV 40 VIRUS under various conditions is depicted. Injected into a monkey cell, it replicates in about 36 hours. Tumor antigen and viral DNA appear earlier. The use of inhibitors shows the sequence of events. For example, the synthesis of tumor antigen does not require new viral DNA, whose formation is blocked by cytosine arabinoside.

yet, when the decontaminated Type 7 adenovirus culture was tested by inoculation into newborn hamsters, it induced tumors. When added to cells in culture, the virus caused them to produce the SV 40 tumor antigen. Apparently the adenovirus was now carrying some genetic determinants that had belonged to SV 40. Had the two viruses combined their genetic material and formed a hybrid virus?

Further experiments showed that a serum against SV 40 or against its tumor antigen did not prevent induction of the antigen by the "hybrid" virus, but a serum against the adenovirus did block synthesis of the antigen [see illustration on following page]. The results strongly suggested that SV 40 genetic material responsible for the antigen synthesis was encased in a protein coat of Type 7

adenovirus; the serum against Type 7 adenovirus would prevent the virus from entering the cells, since the protein coat is the agency by which a virus attaches to and invades cells. On the other hand, we were able to show that when the "hybrid" virus was allowed to gain entry into cells, the production of the antigen (and of thymidine kinase) followed the pattern exhibited by cells inoculated with SV 40.

The picture became complicated, however, when the effect on human cells was examined. We purified the "hybrid" virus both in monkey kidney cells and in human kidney cells (from embryos) by growing clones, or colonies, from single cells containing the virus. It turned out that in the monkey cells the virus progeny induced synthesis of the SV 40 tumor antigen; in the human cells

they did not. Was the viral particle that carried the antigen determinant unable to reproduce itself in human cells? Was the "hybrid" population of viruses perhaps made up of two separate particles, one capable of replicating itself in human cells and the other (carrying the antigen determinant) reproducing only in monkey cells? Or might some combination of these ideas explain the results? These hypotheses were tested experimentally in our laboratory.

The reproduction of viruses in a cell culture can be measured by counting the number of "plaques," or areas of cell destruction, each representing a focus of infection, that are produced in the culture by inoculation with a given dose of the virus. If only one virus particle is required to generate reproduction of the virus (and hence formation of a plaque), then dilution of the inoculated dose should result in a directly proportional reduction in the number of plaques. For example, if the inoculation is diluted tenfold, only a tenth as many plaques should be produced. If two virus particles are required to infect a cell and initiate a plaque, the reduction in plaques should be proportional to the square of the dilution: a tenfold dilution of the dose should result in reducing the number of plaques to a hundredth, instead of a tenth, of the former number.

When this test was applied to the "hybrid" combination of Type 7 adenovirus and SV 40, the results indicated that in human cells the required ratio was one virus particle for one plaque; in monkey cells, however, two particles seemed to be necessary to initiate a plaque. What was missing in the latter case? If single virus particles were sufficient for infection and replication in the human cells, why not in the monkey cells? It was clear that the population of virus progeny generated in the human cells was not the same as that produced in the monkey cells; the purified virus from the human cells no longer contained SV 40 determinants, and when it was inoculated alone into monkey cells, it produced no plaques. In all likelihood, however, this form of the virus (let us for the moment call it Virus A, for adenovirus) was one of the two virus particles required for infection and virus replication in the monkey cells. Perhaps the other particle carrying the SV 40 genes was not produced in human cells. If that was the case, we should find that the production of plaques in cultures of monkey cells could be greatly increased by adding purified Virus A to the inoculation of "hybrid" virus into the monkey cells.

We performed that test. Monkey cells were first saturated with a concentration of Virus A (obtained from human-cell cultures) that was sufficient to infect every cell in the culture; then the cells were inoculated with the "hybrid" virus in various dilutions. The results bore out the hypothesis. In these cultures the number of plaques produced was more than 100 times greater than that in comparable cultures without the Virus A booster.

Taking all the findings together, we were able to conclude that the hybrid population of virus produced in monkey cells does indeed consist of two distinct viruses. One (the particle that replicates by itself in human cells) is an adenovirus. The other (carrying the SV 40 genetic material that induces the tumor antigen) we have named PARA, for "particle aiding replication of adenovirus." In monkey cells the two viruses are mutually dependent. Only by combined action can they produce the plaques that signal reproduction of these viruses. We confirmed by further experiments that the PARA virus cannot replicate itself without the help of the adenovirus, and that the adenovirus requires the aid of either PARA or SV 40 to multiply in monkey cells.

A series of highly interesting observations followed from this germinal finding. It developed that at least five other types of adenovirus in addition to Type 7 could act as helpers for the replication of PARA. In each case the progeny carried the specific protein coat of the adenovirus that had taken part in the reproduction of the PARA virus. The change in the coat of PARA from one type of adenovirus to another is now called transcapsidation, and it is of major significance for the oncogenic, or tumor-causing, potential of viruses. By means of the transcapsidation reaction a nononcogenic population of viruses can be converted into an oncogenic one. For example, an oncogenic PARA virus with a Type 7 coat can be made to undergo a transcapsidation reaction with a nononcogenic Type 2 adenovirus to yield a PARA virus with a Type 2 coat, and this virus is now oncogenic [*see top illustration on next page*]. The oncogenicity of the original PARA virus could be blocked only by Type 7 adeno-antiserum; that of the new PARA virus can be blocked only by Type 2 adeno-antiserum.

All the experimental evidence now points clearly to the conclusion that we are dealing with a partnership in which PARA supplies information that enables

the adenovirus to reproduce and the adenovirus supplies information for the synthesis of the protein coat that endows PARA with the power of infection. Since PARA evidently plays a key role in the transformation of cells to malignancy, investigators are naturally eager to learn more about the nucleic acid—the genetic constitution—of this virus. Efforts to isolate PARA (that is, separate it from the adenovirus in the hybrid population) have been unsuccessful so far, but some pieces of genetic

information have emerged from recent experiments in our laboratory. It appears that the PARA virus contains determinants not only for the tumor antigen but also for other antigens (mentioned earlier) that are found on the surface of transformed cells. Presumably for this reason hamsters that have been inoculated with the "hybrid" virus show an immune reaction to attempted implants of the cells that have been transformed by SV 40 virus.

The findings reviewed in this article

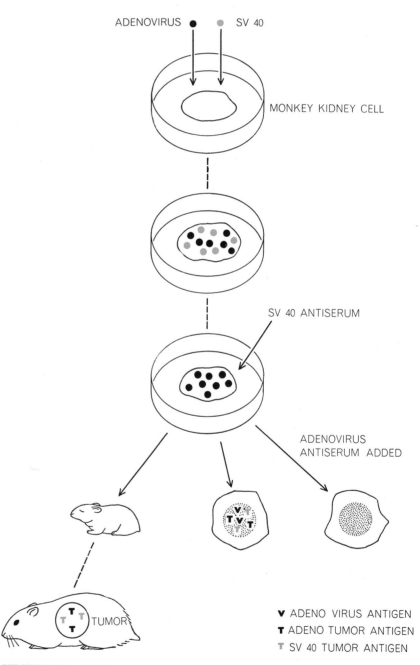

GENETIC RELATION between an adenovirus and SV 40 appeared when a strain of adenovirus being cultured by repeated passages through monkey kidney cells became contaminated with SV 40. Addition of an antiserum designed to eliminate SV 40 yielded a culture that had no SV 40 able to cause infection; yet on injection into newborn hamsters the purified adenovirus caused tumors; added to hamster cells in culture, it induced SV 40 tumor antigen. Evidently the adenovirus had acquired some of SV 40's genetic determinants.

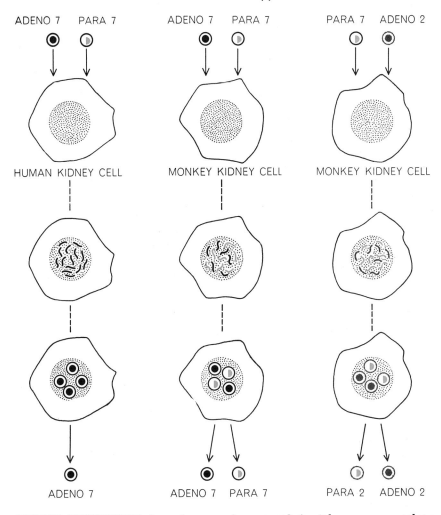

ADENO 7   PARA 7   ADENO 7   PARA 7   PARA 7   ADENO 2

HUMAN KIDNEY CELL   MONKEY KIDNEY CELL   MONKEY KIDNEY CELL

ADENO 7   ADENO 7   PARA 7   PARA 2   ADENO 2

MUTUAL DEPENDENCE of two viruses was demonstrated after it became apparent that a purified adenovirus carried SV 40 genetic determinants. In human kidney cells (*left*) this presumed "hybrid" did not reproduce itself; only adenovirus was reproduced. In monkey kidney cells (*center*) the adenovirus reproduced with SV 40 DNA (*color*). Evidently this requires two viruses: an adenovirus and PARA ("particle aiding replication of adenovirus"). The phenomenon occurs with other adenoviruses (*right*). The process involved is transcapsidation: the change in PARA's protein coat from one type of adenovirus to another.

	ADENOVIRUS	PARA	PARA-ADENO	SV 40 VIRUS
INDUCTION OF SV 40 TUMOR ANTIGEN			YES	YES
INDUCTION OF SV 40 VIRUS ANTIGEN				YES
INDUCTION OF ADENO 7 TUMOR ANTIGEN	YES		YES	
INDUCTION OF ADENO 7 VIRUS ANTIGEN	YES		YES	
REPLICATION IN MONKEY KIDNEY CELLS			YES	YES
REPLICATION IN HUMAN KIDNEY CELLS	YES		YES	SLIGHTLY

CHARACTERISTICS OF VIRUSES involved in such phenomena as transcapsidation and production of tumor antigen are summarized. A blank space means the event does not occur.

have raised many new questions and seem certain to change many ideas about the relation of viruses to cancer. For one thing, they suggest that the failure to find viruses in human cancers does not necessarily argue against the possibility of viruses being the cause of these cancers. It is apparent that DNA viruses, in the process of transforming cells, may surrender the power to reproduce themselves but leave in the cells a portion of their set of genes that will induce malignant growth or remain associated with such growth. Now that techniques have been developed for recognizing the footprints of such viruses (of the adenovirus and papovavirus SV 40 breeds) in the tumors of experimental animals such as the hamster, techniques may be found for detecting viral footprints in human tumors as well.

The adenovirus-PARA partnership is another surprising discovery. Other cases of mutual relations between viruses have been reported [see "A Defective Cancer Virus," by Harry Rubin; SCIENTIFIC AMERICAN Offprint 185], but they involve viruses that are mutants of each other or otherwise closely related. The adenovirus-PARA collaboration is the first that has been found between viruses of completely different genetic lineage.

It is startling to find that one virus can usurp the protein coat of another and thereby endow a previously nononcogenic adenovirus with new powers —which can include the power to produce cancer. PARA is the result of such a transfer of viral constituents and is like a wolf in sheep's clothing. Particles like it may be much more widespread than we now suppose. PARA itself was discovered because it contains an identifying marker (induction of the tumor antigen); perhaps the footprints of other viruses of this kind will be discovered. It is conceivable that all cancer-causing virus populations of the class containing DNA include such particles.

If, as we have seen, viruses can carry pieces of genetic information donated by other viruses, perhaps they can also carry pieces of DNA picked up from the cells in which they are synthesized. The finding that animal viruses are not restricted to carrying genes for their own replication but can act as carriers of foreign genetic information—particularly determinants that transform cells to malignant growth—is an intriguing development that opens new perspectives in virology and cell pathology.

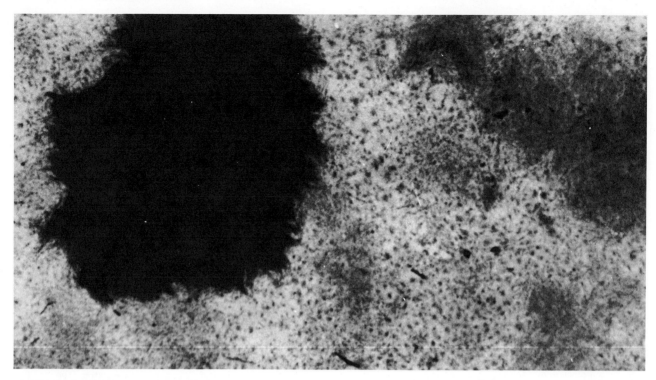

TRANSFORMATION OF CELLS by SV 40 is evident in the dark area of this photograph. It is a colony of hamster cells that are growing in a three-dimensional heap in a glass plate. In contrast, the surrounding normal cells grow in a two-dimensional sheet.

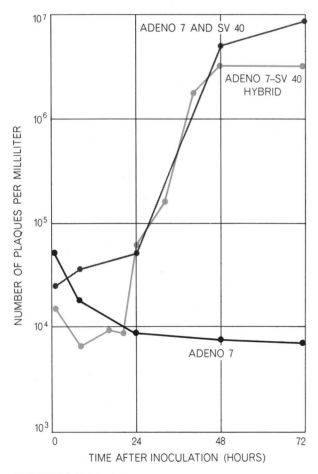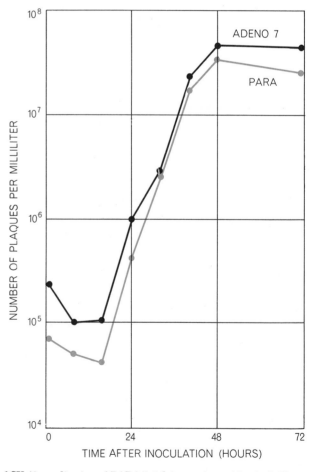

GROWTH RATES of the adenovirus and the PARA virus in the hybrid population are measured separately by means of plaque formation. A plaque is an area of cell destruction representing a focus of infection. The replication of adenovirus in the hybrid population (left) resembled that of adenovirus grown in the presence of SV 40; replication of PARA (right) was almost identical. These curves contributed to the evidence that the adenovirus did not reproduce in the absence of either PARA or added SV 40, and that PARA could not multiply without the helper adenovirus. Hence the curves showed the mutual dependence of adenovirus and PARA.

The Authors

FRED RAPP and JOSEPH L. MEL-NICK work at the Baylor University College of Medicine, where Rapp is associate professor of virology and Melnick is professor of virology and epidemiology and chairman of his department. Rapp, a graduate of Brooklyn College, received a Ph.D. at the University of Southern California at Berkeley in 1958. He taught there for a year and at the Cornell University Medical College for three years before going to Baylor in 1962. Melnick, who was graduated from Wesleyan University, obtained a Ph.D. at Yale University in 1939 and remained there for 18 years as a member of the faculty of the School of Medicine. He was chief of the virus laboratories in the division of biologics standards at the National Institutes of Health for a year before going to Baylor in 1958. Rapp and Melnick, who have begun investigating cancer after years of research in virology, have learned how to confer a tumor-causing potential on viruses that do not normally have that property; they write that they "are interested in learning how to make the converse operational."

Bibliography

DIFFERENTIAL EFFECTS OF INHIBITORS ON THE STEPS LEADING TO THE FORMATION OF SV 40 TUMOR AND VIRUS ANTIGENS. F. Rapp, J. S. Butel, L. A. Feldman, T. Kitahara and J. L. Melnick in *The Journal of Experimental Medicine*, Vol. 121, No. 6, pages 935–944; June 1, 1965.

MOLECULAR BIOLOGY OF THE GENE. J. D. Watson. W. A. Benjamin, Inc., 1965.

SV40-ADENOVIRUS "HYBRID" POPULATIONS: TRANSFER OF SV40 DETERMINANTS FROM ONE TYPE OF ADENOVIRUS TO ANOTHER. Fred Rapp, Janet S. Butel and Joseph L. Melnick in *Proceedings of the National Academy of Sciences*, Vol. 54, No. 3, pages 717–724; September, 1965.

SV40-ADENOVIRUS "HYBRIDS": PRESENCE OF TWO GENOTYPES AND THE REQUIREMENT OF THEIR COMPLEMENTATION FOR VIRAL REPLICATION. Albert Boeyé, Joseph L. Melnick and Fred Rapp in *Virology*, Vol. 28, No. 1, pages 56–70; January, 1966.

VIRUSES AND CANCER. Technical Report Series No. 295. World Health Organization, 1965.

SCIENTIFIC
AMERICAN   March 1966, Vol. 214, No. 3, pp. 74-82

OFFPRINT 1038

THE NERVE AXON

by Peter F. Baker

The fiber that conducts the nerve impulse is a tubelike structure.
Its operation can be studied by squeezing the contents out of the
giant axon of the squid and replacing them with various solutions.

Axons are the communication lines of the nervous system, and along them message-bearing electrical impulses travel from one part of the body to another. They are sometimes compared to electric cables, but they do not carry an electric current the way a wire does. Whereas in a copper wire electricity travels at a speed approaching the velocity of light, in an axon an impulse moves at only about 100 meters per second at best. The interior of an axon is about 100 million times more resistant to the flow of electricity than a copper wire is. Moreover, the membrane sheathing the axon is about a million times leakier to electric current than the sheath of a good cable. If the propagation of electricity in an axon depended on conduction alone, a current fed into it would die out within a few millimeters. The fact is that the axon propagates a current not by simple conduction but by means of a built-in amplifying and relay system.

How does the system work? This is a central question in the investigation of the nervous system, and it has long intrigued physiologists. This article is primarily an account of one of the new techniques developed for investigating the process of nerve-impulse conduction. The technique can be described briefly as experimenting with perfused axons.

The electrical activity of an axon is based on the interaction of three elements: (1) the fluid contents of the axon, called the axoplasm, (2) the membrane that encloses these contents and (3) the outside fluid that bathes the axon. The key to the axon's propagation of an impulse lies in the membrane. Essentially our technique consists in emptying the axon of its contents and perfusing the emptied tube with various experimental solutions, the ob-

ject being to determine just what factors are required to make an electric current travel along the axon.

These studies, like many others that have been done on the transmission of nerve impulses, are made possible by that remarkably convenient gift of nature: the giant axon of the squid. This axon measures up to a millimeter in diameter. The axons of human nerve cells, in contrast, are only about a hundredth of a millimeter in diameter. For the squid the giant axon represents an adaptation to a vital need in its particular way of life. For the physiologist this axon provides an ideal experimental preparation. All the available evidence suggests that experimental results obtained with squid axons are applicable to all other nerve fibers.

Why some animals and not others have evolved giant axons is not fully understood, but such axons appear to be involved in escape responses. The giant axon of the squid is part of the mechanism by which the animal flees its enemies in the water. In order to dart away rapidly the squid uses a jet-propulsion system, squirting water out of a tube at one end of its body. This calls for the synchronous contraction of muscles located throughout its body mantle, and therefore all those muscles must receive the message from the brain simultaneously. The device that takes care of this timing is a variation in the size of the axons radiating from the brain to the various muscles. The farther the muscle is from the brain, the thicker is the axon leading to it, and experiments have shown that the thicker the axon, the faster it conducts impulses. Hence the diameter of the axon is adjusted to the length of the route to be covered, and this ensures that the

signal will reach all the muscles at the same time.

The giant axon is easily dissected out of the squid. It is by probing the isolated axon with microelectrodes and by other means that Kenneth S. Cole in the U.S., A. L. Hodgkin, A. F. Huxley and Bernhard Katz in Britain and other investigators have since 1939 developed an outline of the main events that take place when an electrical impulse passes along a nerve fiber. Much of this story has already been related in *Scientific American*. I shall only briefly review the principal features of the picture.

Between the axoplasm inside the axon and the fluid bathing the axon on the outside there are distinct chemical and electrical differences. Chemically the axoplasm is distinguished by the presence of various organic molecules and a comparatively high content of potassium. The outside fluid, on the other hand, is quite similar to seawater: it principally contains sodium ions and chloride ions. The concentration of potassium is about 30 times higher inside the axon than outside; the concentration of sodium is about 10 times higher outside than inside. Because of these differences potassium ions tend to leak out of the axon (by diffusion) and sodium ions to leak in, to the extent that the membrane will allow the ions to pass. (We can disregard the axoplasm's organic molecules and the outside fluid's chloride in this connection, because the membrane is highly impermeable to them.)

The electric-charge situation complicates the picture. Inside the axon we have a high concentration of positively charged potassium ions; outside, a high concentration of positively charged so-

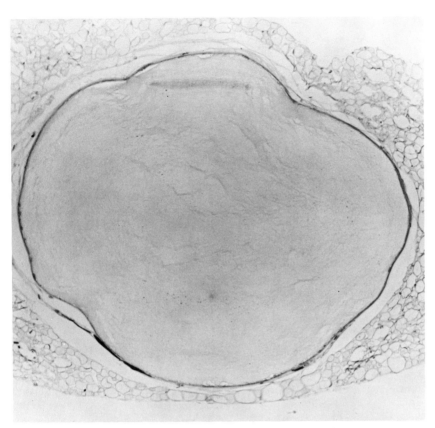

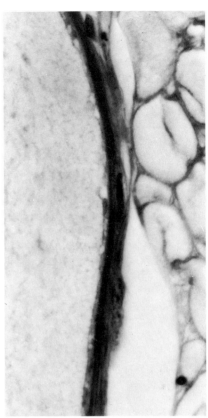

INTACT SQUID AXON is seen in transverse section in these photomicrographs made by J. S. Alexandrowicz of the Plymouth Marine Laboratory. The section is enlarged 140 diameters (*left*). A segment of the axon's perimeter is enlarged 1,150 diameters (*right*). The gray material inside the axon is the axoplasm. The dark boundary of the axon is composed primarily of a layer of Schwann cells.

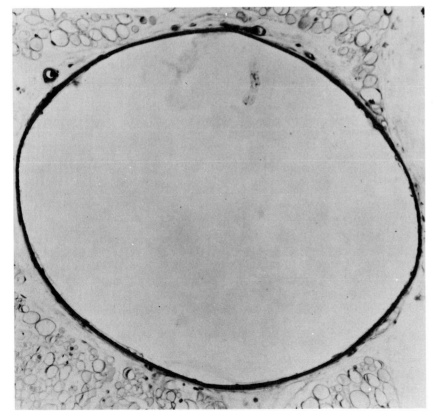

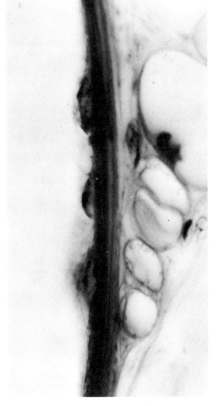

PERFUSED AXON (*left*) and part of its perimeter (*right*) are enlarged as in the top micrographs. The axoplasm has been replaced with a potassium sulfate solution. The small amount of grayish residual axoplasm is thickest near a nucleus of a Schwann cell (*right*).

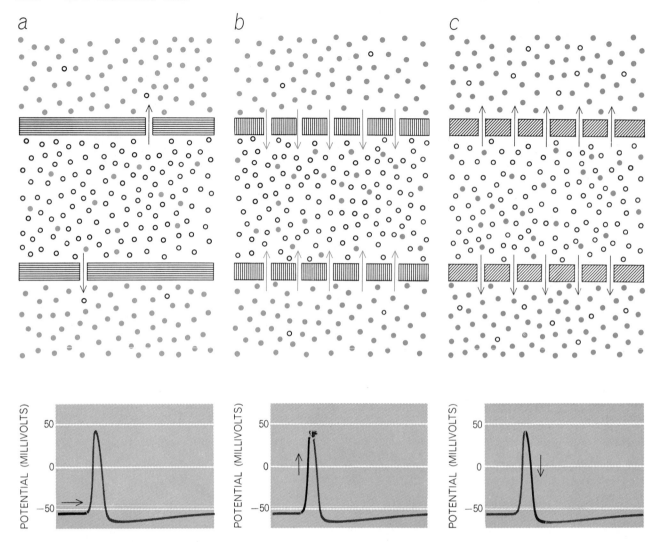

INTERNAL POTENTIAL of an axon is established by the concentration gradients of potassium and sodium ions and by the axon membrane's changing permeability to these two positive ions. Because it is more concentrated inside the axon than outside, potassium (*open circles*) tends to diffuse out; sodium (*colored dots*), more concentrated outside than inside, diffuses in. A normal resting axon membrane is more permeable to potassium than to sodium. The resulting net outward diffusion of potassium establishes the inside-negative resting potential (*a*). An action potential occurs when the nerve is depolarized (by a nerve impulse or artificial stimulation). The action potential has two phases. First the membrane becomes very permeable to sodium, which enters the axon and makes the inside positive (*b*). Then the sodium "gates" close; the membrane thereupon becomes very permeable to potassium, which moves out, making the interior negative again (*c*). A reduction in potassium permeability reestablishes the resting condition.

dium ions. When the membrane is in its unstimulated resting condition, it is highly permeable to potassium but only slightly permeable to sodium. Because of potassium's relative freedom to pass through the membrane and its steep concentration gradient, it tends to leak out of the axon at a high rate. The result is that the inside of the axon becomes electrically negative with respect to the outside. There is a limit to this process; an equilibrium is reached when the tendency for potassium to diffuse out is balanced by the electric field that has been set up. At this point the interior of the axon is about 60 millivolts (thousandths of a volt) negative in relation to the external fluid. That difference—a negative potential of 60 milli-

volts—is called the resting potential of the nerve cell. It is created, in effect, by a potassium battery.

It is relevant to inquire what would happen to the potential if the membrane were highly permeable not to potassium but to one of the other ions. The concentration gradient of the positively charged sodium ions is from outside to inside, acting to make the inside of the axon positive. The gradient of the negatively charged organic molecules is from inside to outside and will also act to make the inside positive. The negatively charged chloride ions are more concentrated outside the axon than inside and will act to make the inside negative. Altering the permeability of the membrane to these ions can estab-

lish a wide range of potentials, the inside being negative (because of potassium or chloride) or positive (because of sodium or organic ions) or anything in between (because of a mixture). The possibilities this variability offers for the control of membrane potential have been thoroughly exploited by the cells of the central nervous system.

Obviously any change in the membrane's permeability to one of the ions can change the potential. This is precisely what happens when an electrical impulse passes along the axon. The current reduces the potential at the point of its arrival, and the resting potential there drops toward zero; the membrane is said to be depolarized. In response to the drop in potential the membrane's permeability to sodium suddenly increases; this further reduces the potential, which in turn makes the membrane still more permeable to sodium. As if a door were suddenly opened wide, sodium ions from the surrounding fluid rush into the axon. The result is that within a small fraction of a second the interior of the axon switches from a *negative* potential of about 60 millivolts to a *positive* potential of about 50 millivolts. The new condition is the first phase of what is called an action potential.

The local region within the axon is now positive, whereas the next adjacent section, which still has a normal resting potential, is negative. Consequently a current flows from the positive to the negative region, completing the circuit by returning to the positive region through the conducting solution outside the axon. The current arriving in the region of normal resting potential opens the membrane door to sodium and thus triggers the generation of an action potential like that in the region it has just left. In this manner the impulse is regenerated from point to point along the axon and flows from one end of it to the other. In each region, shortly after an action potential has been generated, the membrane's permeability to sodium is switched off and its permeability to potassium increases, and as a result that section of the axon returns to the resting potential. The entire local action potential lasts only about a millisecond.

For many years physiologists have been looking into this process experimentally. What would happen if the concentration of ions on one side of the membrane or the other was changed artificially? Isolated axons remain functional for many hours when they are immersed in a simple salt solution containing the major ions present in seawater. It is an easy matter to vary the concentration of these ions in order to study their influence on the process of impulse conduction. Experimenters found that when they added potassium to the medium, thereby reducing the potassium gradient between the inside of the axon and the outside, the resting potential dropped. When they removed sodium from the medium (replacing it with an osmotically equivalent amount of sugar or the positive organic molecule choline), the axon became incapable of propagating an electrical impulse. These results supported the general view of the critical roles normally played by the sodium and potassium

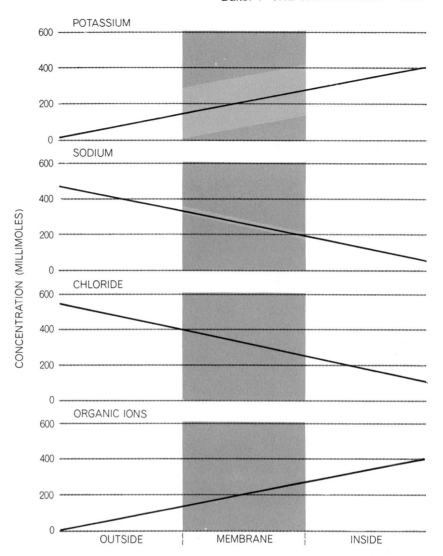

CONCENTRATION GRADIENTS for the major nerve-axon ions are shown. The concentration of each ion on the outside (*left*) and inside (*right*) of the membrane (*color*) is given; the slope shows the direction of the concentration gradient, down which the ions have a tendency to diffuse. This diffusion is blocked by the membrane, which resists mixing of internal and external ions except as it is permeable to one or another of them. The permeability of the membrane during the normal resting phase is suggested here: it is 10 times as permeable to sodium as to organic ions or chloride, 10 times as permeable to potassium as to sodium. Sodium and potassium ions are positive, chloride and organic ions negative.

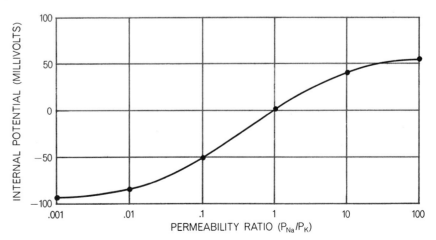

MEMBRANE PERMEABILITY to potassium and sodium ions can be varied. The curve shows, for the concentrations given in the chart at the top of the page, the effect on the internal potential of changes in the membrane's relative permeability to sodium and potassium.

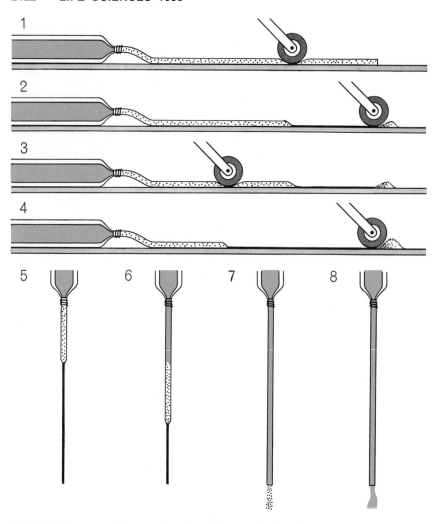

AXOPLASM is removed from a piece of squid axon and replaced with an experimental solution. A piece of axon with a cannula fixed to its smaller end is placed on a rubber pad and axoplasm is squeezed out of it by successive passes with a rubber roller (1–4). Then the nearly empty sheath is suspended vertically in seawater (5) and the perfusion fluid is forced through it, removing the remaining plug of axoplasm and refilling the axon (6–8).

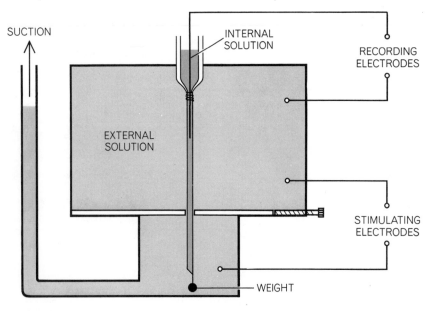

PERFUSED AXON is mounted so as to allow solutions to be changed with an internal electrode in position. To fill it with a new solution, suction is applied to the external fluid.

gradients in the generation of the action potential and the resting potential.

Experiments were also performed in changing the composition of the axoplasm within the axon. To inject extra sodium or potassium into the intact fiber a special microsyringe was used by Harry Grundfest, C. Y. Kao and M. Altamirano at the Columbia University College of Physicians and Surgeons, and also by Hodgkin and Richard D. Keynes at the University of Cambridge. It is not possible to change the inside-outside gradients of ions by any great amount in this way, but when extra sodium was injected into the axon, raising its concentration closer to the level of the sodium outside, the action potential produced by an electrical impulse was smaller than normal, presumably because the usual inrush of sodium ions was checked.

Could one find a way to remove the core of the axon and substitute a strictly experimental solution inside the fiber? Recently two different techniques for doing this were developed almost simultaneously, one by Ichiji Tasaki and his co-workers at the Marine Biological Laboratory in Woods Hole, Mass., and the other by T. I. Shaw and the author at the Plymouth Marine Laboratory in Britain. In Tasaki's method a fine capillary tube is used to ream out some of the axoplasm, and then a fluid is run through the tube to wash out as much of the remaining material as possible. It is an extremely tricky operation, particularly on the comparatively small "giant" axons of the squid found in North American waters, and a considerable amount of axoplasm is left in the fiber.

Our technique is crude by comparison, but we have found that it effectively removes most of the axoplasm. It is based on an old stratagem: in 1937 Richard S. Bear, Francis O. Schmitt and J. Z. Young, working at the Marine Biological Laboratory in Woods Hole, discovered that if an end of an axon was cut, they could squeeze the axoplasm out of it much as one squeezes toothpaste out of a tube. We were led to wonder about the casing left by this operation. Did the squeezing spoil the membrane's properties or could it still conduct an electrical impulse? We undertook an experiment to answer the question. We laid a section of axon about eight centimeters long (a little more than three inches) on a rubber pad and squeezed axoplasm out of the wider end by a series of fairly firm strokes with a rubber-covered roller. When the axoplasm had been extruded from half of the axon's length, leaving that part a flattened sheath, we rolled the other half to push some of its axoplasm into the emptied section. To our surprise we found that the roughly handled membrane could still conduct and boost electrical impulses. This experiment showed that the excitable properties of the membrane are not destroyed by extrusion and encouraged us to try to replace the axoplasm with artificial solutions.

Our procedure was to insert a small glass cannula into the narrower end of the axon and squeeze out as much of the axoplasm as possible; then, attaching the cannula to a motor-driven syringe, we suspended the nerve in seawater and forced "artificial axoplasm" through the flattened sheath. When the nerve was refilled, its excitability was tested, and in about 75 percent of the experiments the preparation was found to function like a normal nerve. With this method about 95 percent of the axoplasm is extruded and a long length of axon can be perfused. Once perfused, the axon can be tied off at both ends and handled like a normal axon. It is more convenient, however, to mount it in such a way that a microelectrode can be inserted into the axon and, with the electrode in place, the perfusion fluid can be changed repeatedly [see illustrations on opposite page]. It is also possible to change the external solution.

We now undertook a series of perfusion experiments in collaboration with Hodgkin. The first question we asked was: What substances must the axoplasm contain in order to generate a resting potential and an action potential? The requirements turned out to be simple indeed. The only essentials are that the solution be rich in potassium ions and poor in sodium ions, and that it have about the same osmotic pressure and concentration of hydrogen ions as normal axoplasm. As for the negatively charged ions (which normally are ionized organic molecules), their nature is not critical; we have used a wide variety of negative ions successfully. A particularly convenient solution is buffered potassium sulfate. When axons are perfused with this solution, they produce resting and action potentials that are almost identical with those generated by intact fibers [see top illustration at right].

It appears, then, that the bulk of the natural axoplasm is not necessary for the propagation of impulses. Are crucial remnants of the original material left in our axons—substances that could not be dispensed with and that make conduction possible? It is not easy to answer categorically; all that can be said is that the axons are still fully functional and can conduct up to half a million impulses, even after they have been washed by a flow of artificial solution amounting to 100 times the volume of the original fluid. If essential molecules were diffusing from the remaining axoplasm to the membrane, they should have been completely washed out by such a massive flow. There remains the possibility that something essential for impulse conduction is supplied by a layer of cells that surrounds the giant axon. The function of these cells, called Schwann cells, is obscure. Various kinds of evidence suggest, however, that they are not directly involved in electrical conduction. For instance, when the Venezuelan workers R. Villegas, Maximo Gimenez and L. Villegas inserted two microelectrodes into a squid nerve—one into a Schwann cell and the other into the axon—they were unable to detect any electrical change in the Schwann cell when an action potential passed along the axon.

Perhaps the most remarkable finding is the fact that apparently no source of energy other than the difference in ion concentrations on the two sides of the membrane is needed to amplify an electical impulse and propagate it along the axon. Our artificial axoplasm contained no sugar, adenosine triphosphate (ATP) or other chemical source of energy, and it is unlikely that any ATP was produced by the traces of original axoplasm left in the sheath. Yet the axon could generate both resting and action potentials whenever the inside and outside solutions had the right concentrations of potassium ions and sodium ions.

To produce the resting potential we need only make sure that the fluid perfusing the experimental axon is primed with a sufficiently high concentration of potassium. If we substitute sodium for potassium in the potassium sulfate perfusion fluid, the resting potential drops, and the amount of this drop depends on the extent of the substitution; when the concentration of potassium inside the axon is reduced to the same level as that outside, the potential drops to zero. If we make the potassium concentration outside much higher than that inside, the inside of the axon becomes positive,

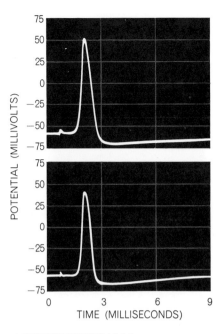

ACTION POTENTIALS from an axon perfused with potassium sulfate (top) and from an intact axon (bottom) are quite similar.

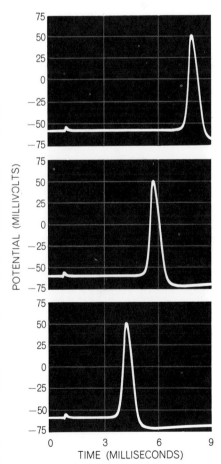

DEGREE OF INFLATION with perfusion fluid does not change the action potential but does increase the conduction velocity. These potentials were recorded from an empty axon (top), a partly inflated one (middle) and a fully inflated one (bottom).

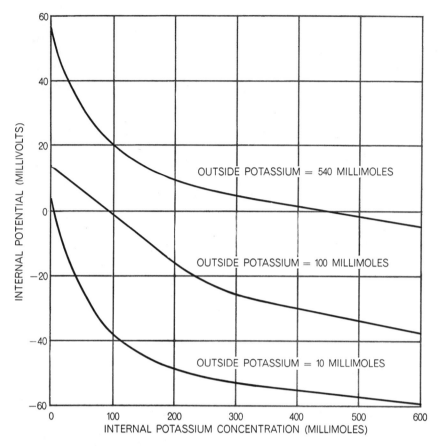

RESTING POTENTIALS of perfused axons depend on the potassium concentration gradient. The internal potassium content was changed by substituting sodium chloride for potassium chloride inside the axons. The lower the potassium gradient, the less negative the internal potential became. With the gradient reversed the internal potential became positive.

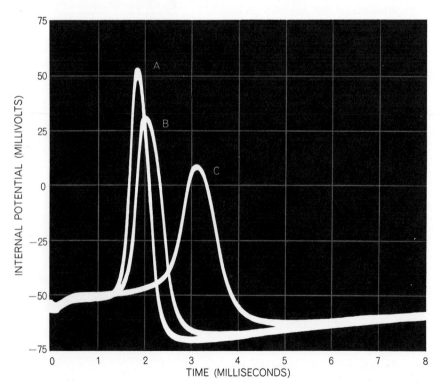

"OVERSHOOT," the amount by which the action potential rises above zero, decreases as the sodium gradient is reduced. These potentials are from a normally perfused axon (*A*) and axons in which a quarter (*B*) and half (*C*) of the potassium was replaced with sodium.

that is, the sign of the resting potential is plus instead of minus. These observations are what would be expected if the resting nerve membrane is freely permeable to potassium ions but not to other ions. The magnitude and the sign of the potential generated are dependent on the steepness and the direction of the potassium concentration gradient.

These experiments also show that the inward diffusion of the negatively charged chloride ions contributes very little to the resting potential. When there is no potassium concentration gradient, there is still a steep gradient for chloride, and yet the measured resting potential is close to zero. This type of experiment suggests that the resting membrane is highly impermeable to negative ions but freely permeable to potassium. A similar argument applied to sodium indicates that the resting membrane is also impermeable to this ion.

During the action potential, on the other hand, the permeability to sodium ions is markedly increased, but the amount by which the action potential overshoots zero and becomes positive is dependent on the sodium concentration gradient. The progressive replacement of potassium inside the axon by sodium reduces the overshoot and finally abolishes the axon's ability to conduct impulses; the ability is restored as the sodium is washed out and replaced with potassium. A rather interesting corollary is the change in action potential that occurs when most of the potassium sulfate in the perfusion fluid is replaced by an osmotically equivalent amount of sugar. Under these conditions the overshoot of the action potential is increased, only to fall again when the axon is refilled with potassium sulfate. This suggests that when potassium is present within the axon, it acts to some extent as a barrier to the inflow of sodium. That is to say, the potassium ions serve in some degree as if they were sodium ions, and when they are absent, the sodium gradient from outside to inside is steepened.

In performing these experiments we noticed that, although the substitution of sugar for potassium sulfate enhanced the action potential, it slowed the axon's conduction of impulses. Presumably this could be attributed to the low electrical conductivity of sugar, which would shorten the range of each stage of propagation (that is, each local circuit) and thereby slow the overall rate of travel. Indeed, we found by experiment that the higher the electrical conductivity of the material we used for perfusing the axon, the faster the speed of impulse propagation.

Recent experiments on perfused axons have been directed toward a detailed analysis of the properties of the action-potential mechanism. These investigations have depended to a large extent on the device known as the voltage clamp. This technique was devised almost 20 years ago by Cole and his co-workers and by Hodgkin, Huxley and Katz, and in their hands it provided almost all the detailed evidence for the sequence of changes in membrane permeability that occurs during the action potential.

The technique is simple in principle but often very difficult in practice. The idea is to produce a sudden displacement of the membrane potential from its resting value and to hold the potential at this new fixed level by means of a feedback amplifier. The current that flows through a definite area of membrane under the influence of the impressed voltage is measured with a separate amplifier [see illustration at right].

When the membrane of an intact axon is depolarized and the potential is held at some value close to zero, the current that flows is at first directed inward, but it rapidly reverses its direction and continues to flow outward as long as the membrane is kept depolarized. There is every indication that the initial inward current is carried by a rapid inflow of sodium ions resulting from a transient increase in the membrane's permeability to sodium, and that the delayed outward current results from a prolonged increase in its permeability to potassium. For one thing, experiments with the same technique show that if sodium is absent from the outside medium, so that the downward gradient of sodium concentration is from inside to outside instead of the other way around, there is a small initial outward flow of current instead of an inward one. Sodium ions now move from inside to outside through the door of increased permeability opened by depolarization of the membrane. The same result can be obtained, even when the axon is bathed on the outside by seawater, by reversing the resting potential, that is, by making the inside of the axon positive instead of negative and holding the potential at the positive value. The potential difference then drives sodium ions out of the axon against the chemi-

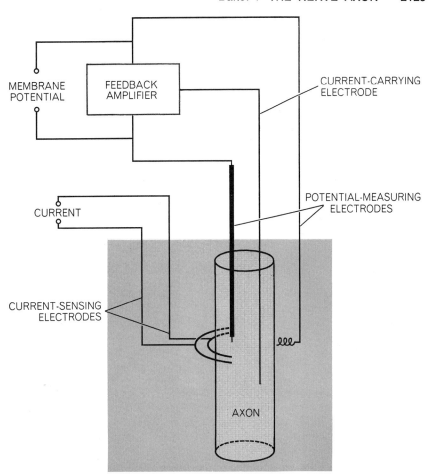

"VOLTAGE CLAMP" is set up as shown in this schematic diagram. A change in membrane potential is produced by the current-carrying electrode. Sensed by two other electrodes, the potential is thereafter maintained by a small current regulated by feedback. The current that flows through a known area of membrane at this fixed potential is then measured.

cal gradient, and a current flows outward. At some intermediate value the applied potential just balances the tendency of sodium ions to enter the axon and there is no detectable early current. This potential is called the sodium equilibrium potential.

The technique of perfusing axons allows the voltage clamp to be applied to situations in which the interior of the axon, as well as the external environment, can be varied. What will happen if sodium is completely absent both outside and inside the axon? In such a case we might expect that, if the axon contains only potassium, depolarization of the membrane should simply bring about a lasting outward current, carried by potassium ions diffusing out of the axon. When Knox Chandler and Hans Meves of our laboratory applied the voltage clamp, they found that depolarization always resulted promptly in a small outward current that was identical in its prop-

erties with the one normally carried by sodium ions. Were potassium ions in the axon acting like sodium ions in this case, passing out through the same membrane channel that opened up for sodium ions during depolarization?

Chandler and Meves tested this surmise by adding sodium to the formerly sodium-free outside medium. If the potassium ions within the axon did not behave like sodium, the downward gradient of sodium concentration from outside to inside would be very steep; hence a large inside-positive potential should be required to prevent a flow of current across the membrane. Actually the experiments showed that the equilibrium potential (the potential required to abolish the early inward current) had the value that would be expected if the potassium inside the axon acted like a small amount of sodium. These results indicate that the channel by which sodium ions enter the axon during an action potential is not completely specific for sodium ions. Chandler and

Meves were able to calculate from their measurements that the "sodium channel" enables sodium ions to pass about 12 times more easily than potassium ions.

This conclusion has recently been strengthened by a different approach. The fish known as the puffer manufactures a potent nerve poison called tetrodotoxin; analysis by means of the voltage clamp of how this poison acts has shown that it very specifically blocks the increase in permeability to sodium that occurs immediately following depolarization. It has no effect on the delayed increase in permeability to potassium. When tetrodotoxin was applied to perfused axons, Chandler and Meves found that it also blocks the early current carried by potassium ions, thus confirming the view that the potassium is passing through the "sodium channel."

The axon membrane loses its capacity for increasing its permeability to sodium when its resting potential is kept at progressively less negative levels. Hence as the resting potential is reduced toward zero (for instance by the replacement of potassium ions inside the axon with sodium or choline) the mechanism for admitting sodium is progressively inactivated, and therefore the axon's capacity for producing an action potential becomes progressively smaller. If, however, the potassium in the perfusion fluid is replaced by sugar instead of another ion, this loss is not so sharp; the membrane maintains its activity, or ability to increase its permeability to sodium, at much lower levels of resting potential. Chandler, Hodgkin and Meves have proposed a possible explanation for this puzzling result. They suggest that the reduction or elimination of ions in the perfusion fluid uncovers negatively charged groups of atoms on the inner face of the membrane. This process would increase the electric field within the membrane without altering the total potential difference between the internal and external solutions. Accordingly a charged molecule within the membrane will experience an imposed electric field identical with that which it experiences in an intact axon at the resting potential.

Experiments with perfused axons have yielded results that would have been impossible to obtain with intact axons and thus represent a considerable advance, but in general they have not produced any revolutionary changes in ideas about the mechanism of propagation of the nerve impulse. They have, however, served to define more sharply the questions to be answered about the basic chemistry of the process. How do ions pass through the membrane? What makes the resting membrane so much more permeable to potassium than to sodium? What specific change in the membrane (brought about by a drop in potential) causes it suddenly to open its doors to sodium?

There are many hypotheses on these questions but so far no convincing items of evidence. The difficulties facing those who are trying to solve such problems in chemical terms are immense. Many of the unique properties of living membranes are dependent on the potential that normally exists across them. The application of the routine biochemical technique of homogenizing cells in order to isolate the cell membrane would break up the membrane and destroy the potential across it; this might so alter the architecture of the molecular groups involved in nerve activity that they would be unrecognizable. Moreover, the relevant groups are probably quite thinly scattered through the membrane material and hence much diluted by less interesting molecules. Perhaps artificial membranes, synthesized from substances extracted from natural ones, will yield some clues, but a complete explanation of the behavior of the nerve membrane in molecular terms is probably still a long way off.

Further experiments with perfused axons may tell us something about the process of recovery from nerve activity. During the passage of an impulse in an intact nerve there is a small net gain of sodium and a small net loss of potassium. If this were to continue unchecked, the nerve would lose potassium and gain sodium, and the concentration gradients on which nerve activity depends would be destroyed. The tendency is counteracted by the mechanism known as the "sodium pump," which uses metabolic energy in the form of ATP to extrude sodium ions from the axon in exchange for potassium ions. Although an intact nerve can function for some time without an operating sodium pump, the pump is essential for the long-term maintenance of nerve activity. In perfused axons this is not the case, since fresh fluid can be constantly passed through the axon. There is evidence, however, that the pump mechanism survives perfusion and that it can be activated by adding ATP and small amounts of magnesium and sodium to the perfusion fluid.

The Author

PETER F. BAKER is a university demonstrator in physiology at the University of Cambridge and also a fellow of the university's Emmanuel College. He did his undergraduate work at the university and stayed on to obtain a Ph.D., which involved him in work on the phosphorus metabolism of nerve. During that work he became interested in axons. In 1964 he visited the U.S. as a guest investigator at Rockefeller University.

Bibliography

THE CONDUCTION OF THE NERVOUS IMPULSE. A. L. Hodgkin. Liverpool University Press, 1964.

SCIENTIFIC
AMERICAN   March 1966, Vol. 214, No. 3, pp. 95-100

OFFPRINT 1039

FALSE SCORPIONS

by Theodore H. Savory

These small, harmless relatives of the true scorpions are
surprisingly abundant in woodland regions. Their retiring
way of life conceals some fascinating patterns of behavior.

If a group of animals delights a naturalist—and the animals happen to
be numerous, easy to observe and yet
unfamiliar to most people—he feels com-
pelled to share his pleasure with others.
Such is my feeling about the false scorpions, harmless relatives of the ven-

omous true scorpions that are well
known and feared in hot countries. The
false scorpions look like tiny tailless
scorpions less than a quarter of an inch
long. There are nearly 2,000 species
of them, constituting an order in the
class Arachnida (which includes the

spiders, the harvestmen, or "daddy
longlegs," and the mites). False scorpions can be found in wooded regions
throughout the world. The fact that
many people never see one is due to
the animals' retiring way of life, not to
their scarcity. In the woods or a subur-

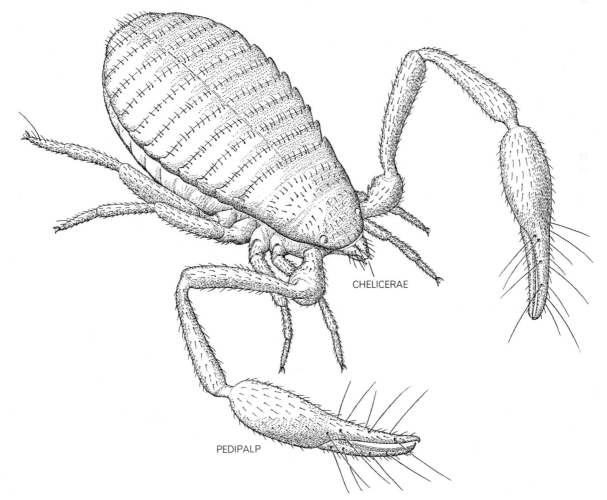

CHELICERAE

PEDIPALP

FALSE SCORPION of the species *Chelifer cancroides* is enlarged
some 30 diameters in this drawing. The nearly 2,000 species of
false scorpion make up an order in the class Arachnida. The large
pedipalpi that resemble a crab's claws are used mainly as weapons

in predation. The small organs between the pedipalpi, the chelicerae, contain extensions of the mouth that flood the prey with
digestive juices and later imbibe it in dissolved form. The chelicerae also contain glands that secrete a silk similar to that of spiders.

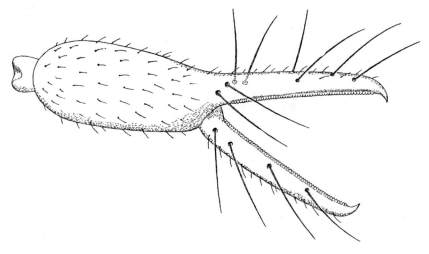

PEDIPALP is used by the false scorpion as a pincer for attack and defense. The animal's two pincers are huge in proportion to its body; when extended, they about double its length The long hairs on the pincers (and chelicerae) are thought to be sensitive organs of touch.

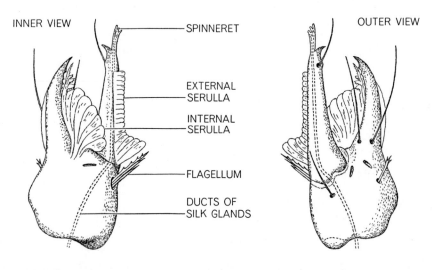

INNER VIEW

OUTER VIEW

SPINNERET

EXTERNAL SERULLA

INTERNAL SERULLA

FLAGELLUM

DUCTS OF SILK GLANDS

CHELICERA, one of two manipulative organs near the mouth, consists of a fixed finger (smaller extension) and a movable one. Ducts of the silk glands open onto the spinneret at tip of movable finger; other ducts open onto the serrulae. Role of the flagellum is unknown.

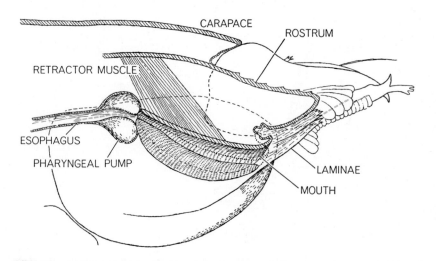

CARAPACE

ROSTRUM

RETRACTOR MUSCLE

ESOPHAGUS

PHARYNGEAL PUMP

LAMINAE

MOUTH

MOUTH PARTS of the chelicerae include a set of grooves and channels through which digestive juices flow outward and food is imbibed. Arrows show route of intake. Retractor muscle and pharyngeal pump are part of sucking apparatus. Laminae are extensions of mouth.

ban backyard 100 or more specimens can be taken from an area of 10 square yards in a month if one knows their likely whereabouts.

The best way to get to know false scorpions for oneself is to go into a wooded area with a wide-mesh strainer and sift handfuls of fallen leaves in it so that any small animals in the leaves will shower down on a sheet of newspaper. If one is reasonably lucky, there will be one or two false scorpions among them. An aid to identification is provided by Robert Hooke's description of three centuries ago: a "crab-like insect" with 10 legs, two of which resemble crab's claws, and "other hands, very near placed to its mouth." At first, after falling onto the paper, the animals will have drawn in their legs and will be still, but after perhaps half a minute they will begin to move. They stretch out their legs, spread their large pedipalpi (the crablike claws, or pincers) in front of them like the antennae of an insect and begin to walk slowly across the paper with an oddly dignified air that distinguishes them at once from any other living creature. As soon as one sees them thus one cannot help being struck by their character: here are small animals displaying in their general bearing the equivalent of human personality.

Perhaps as the false scorpion proceeds across the paper it meets some other animal and touches it lightly with one of the long, hairlike bristles that cover its limbs. The reaction is immediate. The pincers are withdrawn and the scorpion darts backward with a speed that is astonishing compared with its earlier majestic progress. This rapid retreat is characteristic of false scorpions. Not many animals can go backward as easily as forward and very few can go backward much more rapidly.

After such an intriguing introduction false scorpions invite closer acquaintance. To bring them home alive and install them in suitable cages does not require elaborate arrangements. Laboratory zoologists often follow the soulless procedure of putting the false scorpion in a plain glass tube with a loose cotton plug and a slip of paper on which the animal can rest. I have had good results using a glass dish, such as a Petri dish, with moist filter paper on the bottom. If one plans to keep the animals for long periods, it is well to cover the bottom of the dish with small stones and on top of this to sprinkle a layer of white sand. The gravel can be kept moist (an essential condition) and the sand makes a light background against which the inhabitants can be seen clearly. A few small stones will provide them with the shelter they seem to enjoy. The dish must be covered because the animals are able to climb the vertical sides.

In captivity false scorpions will live for weeks or months in apparent comfort. They must, of course, be fed. False scorpions, like true scorpions and like spiders and daddy longlegs, are predators that normally catch and kill their prey. Unlike daddy longlegs, however, they refuse to eat anything that is not alive, and so living things must be supplied to them. An obvious source of food for a false scorpion would be the small animals that fell through the strainer in its company. Among these may be daddy longlegs, tiny spiders, mites, flies, the wingless insects known as springtails and other false scorpions. I have seen false scorpions respond to each of these potential meals. The ones I have kept would neglect the mites, flies and daddy longlegs, and would back away from spiders. Once I swung a small spider on its thread into the jaws of a false scorpion. The spider was killed instantly, but no attempt was made to eat it. The springtails were seized with avidity; a dozen or more would vanish in an hour, leaving no trace. Occasionally false scorpions (as well as true ones) will make a meal of a wounded or ailing member of their own species, but this is rare if other food is available.

The way in which a false scorpion feeds is unusual, with the process of digestion beginning before the animal has taken its prey into its body. The victim is grasped by the pincers; then the chelicerae—the small organs Hooke described as hands located near the mouth —tear it open and are thrust into it. Glands in the chelicerae flood the prey with a saliva containing digestive ferments. These convert the victim into a nutrient solution that the false scorpion imbibes.

One of the surprising aspects of a false scorpion's feeding is the complete consumption of its food. Whereas spiders and daddy longlegs leave a debris of emptied legs and dried carapaces, false scorpions leave hardly any trace of their meal. In another respect, however, the feeding pattern of false scorpions is like that of other arachnids: they do not require frequent, regular meals and

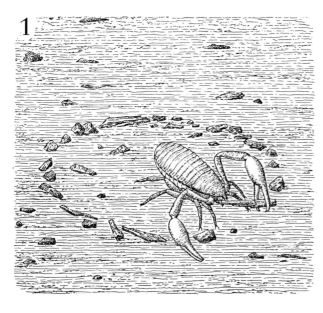

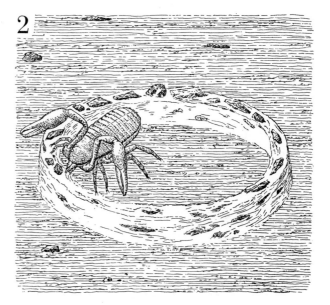

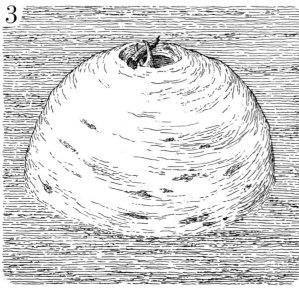

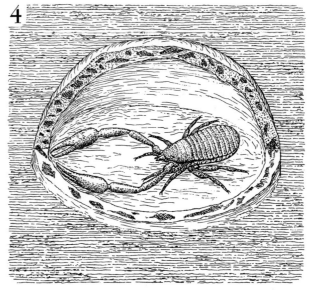

BUILDING OF A COCOON in the open is depicted in four stages. The false scorpion surrounds itself with "bricks" of wood and stone (1). Brushing the bricks with its chelicerae to supply a silken mortar, it assembles them into a dome (2 and 3). Finishing the cocoon, which may be used for molting, hibernating or laying eggs, the animal rests (4). A cocoon in a crevice would be cylindrical.

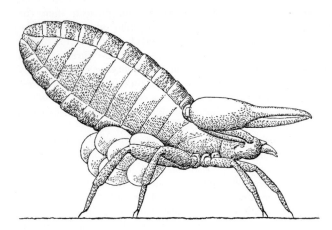 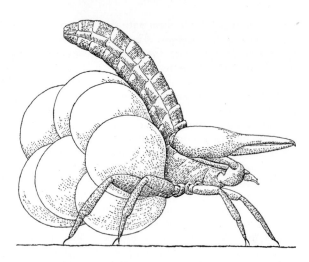

INCUBATION CHAMBER of the mother false scorpion is secreted by glands in the walls of her oviduct and remains attached to her body (*left*). The eggs are fertilized as they descend into the chamber. The larvae come out of the individual egg membranes still attached by short beaks to the mother. After several days she forces yolk into their bodies, which become greatly inflated. The incubation chamber swells, flattening the mother's abdomen (*right*). For about two weeks the larvae absorb this meal; they then reach the first nymphal, or preadult, stage. At this point they break out of the chamber and leave the cocoon in which the process takes place.

seem indifferent to semistarvation. Zoologists who keep spiders know that they do not have to feed the animals often and that many a spider is overfed if given one fly a day. False scorpions may be fed daily, but Herbert W. Levi, who studied them at the University of Wisconsin, found that adults fed once a week seemed better off than those leading their natural lives in the woods.

At the start of a meal—often, in fact, when prey has only been sighted—a false scorpion begins to rub its chelicerae with its pincers. This procedure is not analogous to a man's washing his hands, although it looks as if the animal were scraping or sucking dirt from its limbs. Actually the pincers are cleaning the mouth parts of the chelicerae, a complex arrangement of grooves and channels through which digestive juices flow outward and digested solutions are sucked inward. It is essential that the chelicerae be kept clear for this dual purpose. The pincers are fundamentally weapons of attack and defense and can remain soiled.

The chelicerae have yet another important function. They contain silk glands that secrete a viscous fluid that hardens into fine thread. The silk is probably similar to that of spiders (no biochemist has chosen to analyze it), but for false scorpions its use is limited. Spiders have so exploited the silk they produce that their lifelong behavior is dominated by it. False scorpions use their silk only on the occasions when they construct a cocoon-like shelter in which to pass the winter, lay their eggs and shed their skins.

False scorpions grow discontinuously by molting the hard outer skeleton that covers their body. They undertake this major operation in the safety of a cocoon built in one of two forms, depending on the physical surroundings. If a cocoon is to occupy a crevice, it will consist of a circular base or mat of silk with sides rising to the roof of the crevice and making a roughly cylindrical chamber. If the chamber is built in the open, it will resemble an igloo with a dome-shaped top [*see illustration on preceding page*].

Before construction begins the false scorpion can be seen wandering about as if it were searching for a suitable spot. Once this is found the animal starts to collect material such as small pieces of wood or bark, bits of stone and so on, which it arranges in a circle around itself. Joining the pieces with strands of silk, the animal lays foundations on which it places more wood and stone, brushing each addition to the rising wall with its chelicerae to provide a silken fixative. Soon it becomes necessary to go outside and collect more material. The false scorpion steps over the wall, picks up a splinter or two in its pincers, transfers the material to its chelicerae and carries it back. One is reminded of a bird flying back to its nest with straws in its beak.

As the wall rises and arches inward, the unfilled hole in the center gets smaller, yet the scorpion seems to have little difficulty forcing its way in and out. Finally the last brick is laid and the builder is imprisoned in the structure. This incarceration does not stop its activities; the animal continues to add silk to the wall of the cocoon, sweeping its chelicerae over the surface like a paintbrush. Silk threads emerge and coalesce, eventually to cover the entire inside with a continuous sheet of what may well be described as silk wallpaper. Several days may have passed before this last phase is complete.

Secure now from outside interference, the false scorpion will shed its skin. First it rests for a day or so with closed pincers and legs rigid and straight. Its abdomen, normally flattened, swells by becoming narrower and deeper. Suddenly the carapace breaks loose from the front part of the body, rising upward with an almost explosive force. Then the old skin begins to slide backward to the accompaniment of some twitching of the abdomen. The legs remain still. The whole affair, which is much more passive than the strenuous molting of a spider, may occupy the better part of a day. When it is over, the false scorpion moves its legs into their usual position and is able to walk about. It proceeds slowly for the first day or two; if it falls over, it will have some difficulty righting itself. In the course of their lives false scorpions, at least those that have been thoroughly observed, shed their skin four times.

Clearly the chelicerae of a false scorpion are organs of great value and versatility, although to the casual observer they are overshadowed by the enormous pincers. Each chelicera consists of two parts [*see middle illustration on page 2128*]. There is a broad, flat "hand," elongated at one point to form a fixed "finger." Close to the fixed finger there is a movable finger that forms a grasping organ. At the base of the fixed finger a group of spines forms a flagellum of uncertain function; on its inner edge is a comblike organ called the interior serrula. The fixed finger ends in a sharp point; at the tip of the movable one is a rounded spinneret onto which the ducts of the silk glands open; this spinneret takes a wide variety of forms in the different genera of false scorpions. A second comb, the exterior serrula, is found on the inner edge of the fixed finger. In addition to the silk and digestive glands there are two other glands in each chelicera; one of them secretes through a single duct near the tip of each finger, the other through many ducts onto the combs.

Normally the chelicerae are held horizontally and pointing forward, but they can be moved and in fact are very active. They serve as jaws in feeding, cutting open the prey. They also pick up, hold, carry and distribute silk. The combs are used in cleaning the rostrum (a beaklike part of the mouth) and other mouth parts. They are lined with hairlike spines that probably serve as highly sensitive organs of touch. It is interesting to note that these spines are not scattered haphazardly over the surface; they occupy specific positions, and students can identify each one.

As I have indicated, false scorpions build cocoons for reasons other than molting. In the winter they build hibernation chambers (false scorpions may live for two or three years), which are shared by two or three individuals. Females build a variation of the cocoon, in the shelter of which they lay their eggs and bring up their young. The females also produce, as an extension of their bodies, an incubation chamber in which the eggs are actually laid. This chamber is made of a secretion from glands in the wall of the oviduct; when the secretion is extruded, it takes the form of an inverted mushroom with the stem attached to the oviduct opening [*see illustration on opposite page*]. The eggs are fertilized during their downward passage and about 20 fall one by one into the chamber. The chamber is not detached, as are most egg cocoons, but remains in position under the abdomen of the female. The eggs develop within it.

When the larvae break out of the egg membrane, they are still attached by short beaks to the body of the mother, absorbing a nourishment produced by the degeneration of her ovaries. A few days later a remarkable event takes place: the mother, by muscular contraction, forces yolk into the

bodies of the young larvae. They become inflated to about three times their previous size; the incubation chamber is enlarged and pushes the shriveled abdomen of the female into an almost vertical position. For about two weeks thereafter the inflated larvae absorb their enormous meal and develop into the first nymphal, or preadult, stage. This development involves the first molting of the false scorpion's life. In the first nymphal stage the larvae break out of the cocoon and begin to lead independent lives. They feed themselves and molt three more times before becoming adults about a year later.

Adulthood is defined by mating, a step preceded by a complicated courtship that marks the end of the false scorpion's retiring style of life. The courtship begins with a form of dance in which the male takes the initiative. He stops close to a female, shaking his abdomen and waving his pincers. The female is quiet with a significant still-

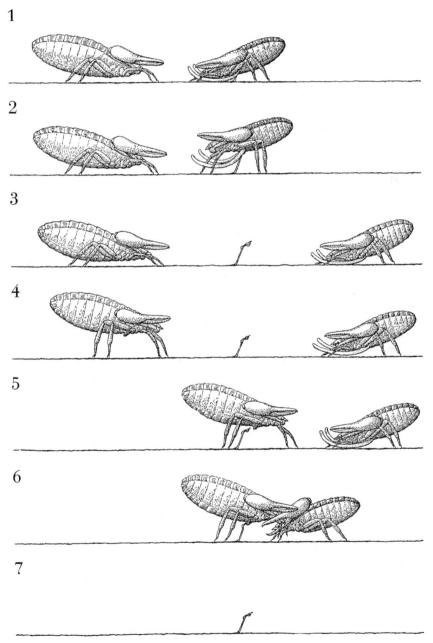

COURTSHIP of false scorpions takes the form of a mating dance begun by the male. He approaches the female (*from the right in this drawing*), shaking his abdomen and pincers (*1*). If she moves, he halts the procedure; if not, he drops a vertical thread from his genital opening (*2*). This hardens into a pillar on which he leaves seminal fluid before backing away (*3*). The female advances (*4*) and straddles the pillar (*5*). The male then returns and shakes her by the legs (*6*) to ensure that the fluid is detached within her body. The drawing is based on studies by Max Vachon of the National Museum of Natural History in Paris.

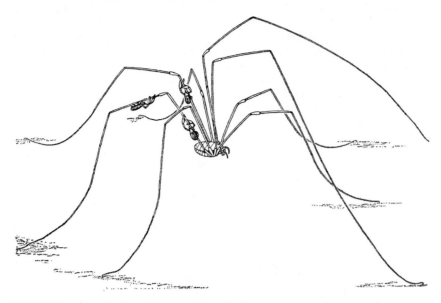

PHORESY, a method of travel used occasionally by false scorpions, involves grasping the legs of an animal such as a "daddy longlegs" so that the scorpions can move long distances without expending energy. Phoresy seems advantageous when food in an area is scarce.

ness: if she moves, the male stops his maneuvers; if not, he draws closer until his forelegs almost touch her. At this point he suddenly lowers his body and on rising is seen to have left a viscous vertical thread, drawn from his genital opening. In a few seconds the thread has hardened into a tiny pillar known as a spermatophore. The male backs away, leaving a drop of seminal fluid on the pillar that stands between the two dancers. Signaled by a particular movement of the male's pincers, the female moves forward in such a way that the spermatophore enters her body. The male then grasps her by the legs and shakes her vigorously so that the drop of fluid is detached and remains within her to fertilize the eggs when they are laid. The two false scorpions then part. If they meet again, they show no particular interest in each other.

Courtship of this kind, which is widespread among arachnids and other invertebrates, is easier to describe than to explain. It may have two functions: first, the mutual stimulation of the two participants, and second, the exact placing of the female so that the spermatophore will be oriented properly. Other interpretations have been suggested; it cannot be said that zoologists agree on the best explanation.

The false scorpions that live among the fallen leaves in woods are the easiest to find, but many others live in quite different kinds of surrounding. Some are almost always to be found under the loose bark of dead or dying trees, and others abound among stones and slates. A few species remain close to the sea; some live among rocks that are regularly covered by the tide. Others come into human habitations and may be found among books in the library or clothes in the closet. (A common name for the animal is "book scorpion.") Some species live in ants' nests, but this comes as no surprise; these habitats are popular with animals of almost every class and order. It is surprising, however, to find false scorpions in beehives. There is even some evidence that they eat the pollen from the bees' legs.

Having a wide choice of possible habitats is a sign that an animal is a success in the evolutionary struggle. Insects and birds are obvious examples of successful types of animal life; so too are spiders and roundworms. The success of false scorpions involves their ability to adapt their bodies to various degrees of moisture in the surrounding air. Almost all invertebrates that live on land need some protection against the excessive loss of water. Indeed, the retention of water often determines their behavior and distribution. Some invertebrates, for example, may be active only after sunset; they lie in shelter during the day. It is therefore of considerable interest to learn that false scorpions can survive in wholly dry air for times varying from a few hours (for the species that frequent fallen leaves) to many days (for those that live in dry places such as houses).

As a conclusion to this brief account of the order of false scorpions, one of its unsolved mysteries should be mentioned. It has long been known that false scorpions will at times cling to the legs of flies, daddy longlegs and other creatures so that they can be transported for relatively long distances with no expenditure of energy. False scorpions are not parasites, and there is no question of their having got into such a situation by accident. This mode of travel, known as phoresy, seems to be a response to specific conditions of the environment. Only a few species of false scorpion have been observed to use it, and they do so only at certain times of the year. In the periods when phoresy is employed, however, it seems to be the preferred means of transportation. In 1945 Max Vachon of the National Museum of Natural History in Paris recorded 78 false scorpions on the legs of 57 daddy longlegs in one week in August. The largest load carried by any one daddy longlegs was eight individuals. All were of the same species and all but one were mature females.

The fact that the females were mature indicated that phoresy is not reserved for the dispersal of the young. Vachon found that all his specimens had either recently mated or had just produced a brood of young. Since all were in need of food, he concluded that hunger had induced them to seize the legs of flies or daddy longlegs and thus travel to a neighborhood where prey might be more plentiful.

The study of false scorpions is enriched by the beauty and precision revealed when their bodies are examined in the microscope. The intricate design in the construction of their tiny frames is breathtaking. For example, the number and position of the spinelike hairs near the animal's mouth change in a characteristic way during the various stages of its growth. The devout assure us with confidence that the number of hairs on our heads is ordained; in the same spirit the zoologist can state that the very hairs on a false scorpion's jaws are arranged systematically.

Is it useful to know and record such facts? A professor of biology has recently written, "No merit attaches to the pursuit of useless knowledge," adding that the amount of useless information awaiting pursuit is greater than the united ability of men to follow it. If it can be said that any knowledge is useless, his dictum might cause some reflection among those who follow false scorpions. Useful or not, however, the pursuit of some types of knowledge brings an enjoyment unique in itself and a satisfaction one does not want to forgo.

The Author

THEODORE H. SAVORY is vice-principal of Stafford House, a tutorial college in Kensington, England. Although he describes himself as having spent most of his adult years leading "the typical life of a British public school master," he is in fact one of the world's foremost authorities on arachnids, the group of animals that includes spiders, daddy longlegs and scorpions. His interest was kindled when he was 16 and "contemplating the idea of specializing in some sort of animal." One day he was reading outdoors when a spider dropped from an oak tree onto his book. Savory "said to companion, casually, 'What about spiders?' 'Why not?' replied he, and so it was." After graduating from the University of Cambridge in 1918, Savory spent 31 years teaching science at Malvern College and seven years as senior biology master at the Haberdashers' School in Hampstead. He took his present position in 1958. The article on false scorpions is his third in SCIENTIFIC AMERICAN; the others were "Spider Webs" in April, 1960, and "Daddy Longlegs" in October, 1962.

Bibliography

ARACHNIDA. Theodore H. Savory. Academic Press Inc., 1964.

THE PSEUDOSCORPIONS OF ILLINOIS. G. Clayton Hoff in *Bulletin of the Illinois Natural History Survey*, Vol. 24, Article 4, pages 413–498; June, 1949.

THE SPIDER BOOK. John Henry Comstock. Comstock Publishing Co., 1948.

SCIENTIFIC
AMERICAN   April 1966, Vol. 214, No. 4, pp. 40-46

OFFPRINT 1040

CHROMOSOME ANALYSIS BY COMPUTER

by Robert S. Ledley and Frank H. Ruddle

Now that certain human disorders have been linked with chromosome abnormalities, it is desirable to examine large numbers of cells for such abnormalities. A computer regime has been devised for the purpose.

In recent years a number of human disorders have been found to be related to abnormalities in the chromosomes, the bodies in the living cell that contain the genetic material. Accordingly many medical institutions have undertaken programs of examining in the microscope the chromosomes of samples of tissue taken from numerous patients. Such programs have been limited by the fact that the examination of chromosomes takes time and calls for individuals who have been trained in recognizing chromosomal abnormalities. An obvious way to circumvent this limitation is to devise some kind of machine that can examine the chromosomes automatically, although of course it is less obvious how the machine would work. Such a machine, the central component of which is an electronic computer, has now been assembled and successfully operated.

Human somatic cells (as distinguished from sperm or egg cells) normally contain 46 chromosomes. The chromosomes can most conveniently be examined in the white cells of the blood, which are readily available in a blood sample. (Mature red blood cells contain no chromosomes.) After the white cells have been segregated, however, they must be kept alive in tissue culture and induced to undergo mitosis, or to divide; it is only during mitosis that chromosomes and their abnormalities are clearly visible. Treating the cells with the drug colchicine halts mitosis exactly at metaphase—the stage of somatic-cell division in which each chromosome has divided into two mirror-image halves lying side by side and connected at one point called the centromere. The cell preparation is now treated with a dilute salt solution, which causes the cells to swell and the chromosomes to move apart.

Finally the cells are fixed and stained, so that the chromosomes can be observed and photographed through the microscope [see upper illustration on page 2136].

For purposes of analysis a photomicrograph must be made and enlarged; then the chromosome images are cut out and arranged on a white card in what is called an idiogram. The chromosomes are matched into 22 pairs of homologous, or related, chromosomes, plus the two sex chromosomes. (One member of each pair and one sex chromosome is descended from each parent at the fertilization of the egg.) The pairs are arranged in a standardized order based on size, shape and the ratio of the length of the "arms" on each side of the centromere [see lower illustration on page 2136]. Only when cells are thus arranged can abnormalities be readily identified. Even when the abnormality is as gross as the presence of extra chromosomes the idiogram is needed to detect with which normal pair the extra chromosome is associated. Some of the disorders that have been linked with chromosomal abnormalities are Down's syndrome (mongolism), chronic myeloid leukemia, Klinefelter's syndrome (a congenital disorder of males involving infertility) and Turner's syndrome (a congenital disorder of females involving infertility). Also detectable by such analysis is chromosome damage caused by certain substances or by ionizing radiation; accordingly chromosome analysis can play an important role in the screening of foods and drugs and in the evaluation of radiation hazards.

The construction and examination of the idiogram—both of which are time-consuming and somewhat subjective procedures—are eliminated by the automatic regime we shall describe. This means of analysis still requires the collection of blood samples, of course, and the preparation of cells for photomicrography, but the photomicrographs need not be enlarged and the manual analysis need not be made. Instead a series of photomicrographs on a roll of film are "read" directly into the memory unit of a computer by a scanning device called FIDAC (Film Input to Digital Automatic Computer). The computer is programmed to recognize and classify the objects under consideration by doing the same things an investigator would: counting the total number of chromosomes and measuring their lengths, areas and other morphological features. The FIDAC procedure reduces the time required to study the human complement of 46 chromosomes to about 20 seconds; this is some 500 times faster than analysis by visual means.

When a roll of photographic film is ready for examination, it is placed in the film-transport unit of the FIDAC instrument and the "Start" button of the computer is pushed. The computer system—FIDACSYS, a combination of several basic programs for recognizing and analyzing patterns—signals FIDAC to consider the first frame. The instrument scans the photomicrograph and within .3 second

IMAGES OF CHROMOSOMES appear as grid of numerals in computer print-out that provides a rudimentary picture of a photomicrograph. Details of the micrograph were conveyed to memory unit of the computer by a scanning device called FIDAC. Numerals from 0 to 6 on a gray scale describe the darkness of corresponding points on micrograph, made during phase of cell division at which a chromosome consists of two strands (chromatids) connected in one area (the centromere). Dots correspond to the background.

transmits a digital image of it into the magnetic-core memory unit of the computer. In this digitalized image the photomicrograph is represented by a rectangular grid of numbers that correspond to the densities of points in a similar grid on the photomicrograph. The numbers on this "gray scale" run from 0 to 6; the number 7 is reserved

to denote boundaries during processing. If at this stage the contents of the memory are printed out, they form a rudimentary image of the objects in the photomicrograph [see *illustration on preceding page*].

No significant information is lost in translating the pictorial data into numerical data. The resolution of a good

optical microscope at a magnification of 1,000 is .2 micron, that is, .2 micron is the narrowest spacing that can be distinguished between two lines. The FIDAC instrument can sample three picture points within a span of .2 micron on the specimen; in other words, its resolution is comparable to that of the microscope. The instrument has another feature worth mentioning: because it transmits directly ("on line") into the computer's memory, information that would ordinarily be rerecorded onto intermediate magnetic storage tapes can remain instead on the original roll of photomicrographic film for reprocessing whenever it is desired. A 100-foot roll of this 16-millimeter film, containing 4,000 photomicrographs, can fit into a can smaller than four inches in diameter. Recording that much information on magnetic tapes would require more than 50 reels, making a stack more than four feet high.

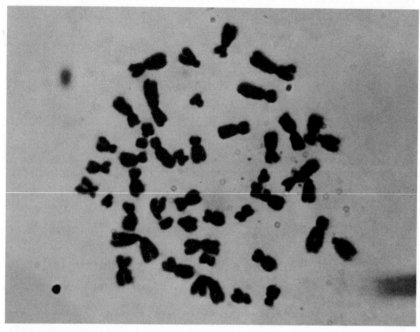

PHOTOMICROGRAPH OF CHROMOSOMES from the white blood cell of a man reveals an abnormal total of 47 (one too many). It is impossible to determine which one is in excess until the chromosomes are reassembled into a standard classification called an idiogram.

When the processing of a frame has been completed, the computer program signals FIDAC to advance the film and consider the next frame. If any frame is blank—that is, either 98 percent black or 98 percent white—the program signals FIDAC to move to the next frame. In this way blank frames or leader can be skipped automatically. If the frame is not blank, the computer program establishes a value on the gray scale as a cutoff level between those values that represent points inside the chromosomes and those that represent the background. The task of recognizing patterns in the frames as chromosomes is accomplished by first sweeping a programmable "bug," or detecting pointer, in a horizontal raster pattern to find points with a gray value greater than the cutoff level. The bug then traces around the boundary of each object, and every number in the original digital representation of the boundary that has a value just above the cutoff level is replaced by 7. The silhouette that is formed is now automatically examined to determine if it has the most obvious feature of a chromosome: arms originating at a centromere. If the silhouette does not meet this criterion, it is eliminated from further analysis.

When all the chromosomes in a frame have been silhouetted, the bug will have reached the lower right-hand corner of the frame. At this point the machine evaluates the contents of the frame. The chromosomes are counted and their total length is computed, so that the length of individual chromosomes can be considered as a fraction of the total

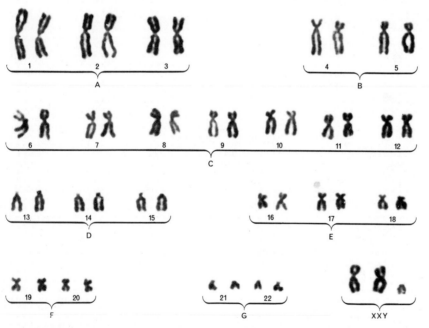

IDIOGRAM of a complement of human chromosomes reveals an abnormality. Chromosomes matched according to size, area and ratio of the lengths of the "arms" on each side of the centromere were put into sequence by Herbert A. Lubs, Jr., of Yale University. The three sex chromosomes at right of bottom row (normal men have one X and one Y sex chromosome) provide evidence of Klinefelter's syndrome, a disorder of males involving infertility.

length of the chromosomes in the frame. Homologous chromosomes are matched according to area, length and arm-length ratio, and the pairs are classified according to the standardized sequence of the idiogram. When the analysis of a frame is finished, the FIDAC instrument is instructed to move to the next frame and the process is repeated. After a predetermined number of frames have been processed the statistics of all the photomicrographs on the roll of film are automatically collated and analyzed.

Let us consider more closely the essential step in this procedure: the recognition and analysis of individual chromosomes. The location of anything encountered by the bug—the boundary of an object, for example—can be given in a Cartesian-coordinate system mapping the entire frame. Thus when the bug first meets an object, its point of contact can be located on a grid in terms of horizontal and vertical positions denoted by X and Y coordinates. The bug now proceeds along the boundary of the object in a clockwise direction, and points on the boundary are delineated in the same notation. When a certain number of boundary points have been traversed, they are said to constitute a segment. The bug continues to mark boundary points and segments until it returns to the original point of contact; it is now ready to search for a "next object."

The computer program characterizes the individual segments in terms of their direction and curvature. This involves several measurements. First the center point of a segment is ascertained. The arc of the segment reached by moving clockwise from the center point is called the leading half; the arc reached by moving counterclockwise, the trailing half. A vector arrow is drawn in each half; the length of the segment is chosen as a distance short enough so that the angle between the leading and the trailing vector will be an approximation of the segment's curvature. The arrow that is the vector sum of the leading and trailing vectors is approximately the tangent to the segment at its center point and so provides a measure of the direction of the segment.

In determining the curvature of the segments the FIDAC system uses a small vocabulary of 13 terms to describe degrees of curvature. For purposes of explanation let us consider a vocabulary of four terms: a fairly straight segment is called Type O; a clockwise curve, Type E; a slight counterclockwise curve, Type

COMPUTER AND SCANNING DEVICE used by the authors are located at the Goddard Space Flight Center outside Washington, D.C. The IBM 7094 computer (*foreground*) receives descriptions of photomicrographs of chromosomes from the FIDAC scanner (*background*), on the basis of which it counts, analyzes and collates data on the chromosomes.

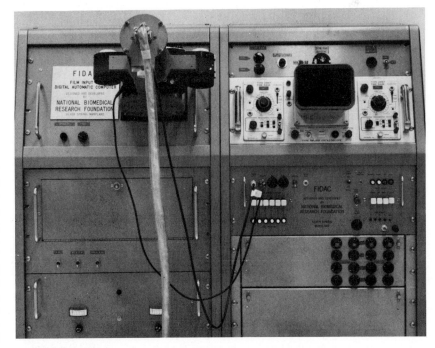

FIDAC INSTRUMENT is named for its function: "Film Input to Digital Automatic Computer." A roll of film containing a great many photomicrographs of chromosomes is put into the film transport unit at top left (*behind the cylindrical photomultiplier*). A detailed description of each micrograph is transmitted by FIDAC to the memory unit of the computer. A video amplifier displays the micrograph being scanned on the small screen at top right.

V, and a pronounced counterclockwise curve, Type Y. By combining such terms the complete outline of a chromosome can be described.

The program by which the computer "builds up" the shape of a chromosome from combinations of curve types is rel-

atively simple in conception. One arm of a chromosome, for example, might have Type O curves on its sides and a Type E curve at its end; between this arm and another on the same chromosome there would be a Type Y curve. The programmer's role is to set forth,

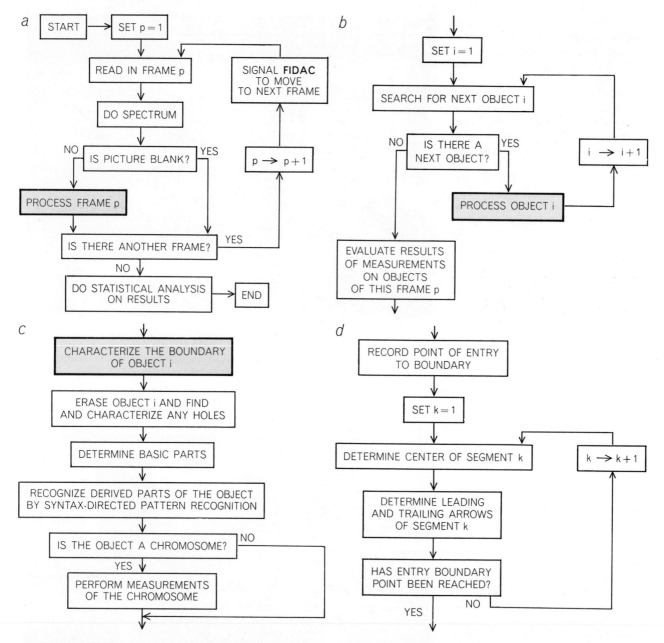

STEPS PERFORMED BY COMPUTER in examining photomicrographs of chromosomes are presented on four levels of detail. The overall procedure (*a*) entails advancing the roll of photomicrographic film, instructing FIDAC to "read" the image of a frame into the computer's memory unit, computing the spectrum of the image, processing the frame if it is not blank, again advancing the film and finally, when the roll is finished, collating data pertaining to all the photomicrographs that have been inspected. The key step

in the sequence is the processing of a frame (*b*), which involves a search for individual objects. The boundary of each object is considered (*c*) in terms of the segments that comprise it. The curvature and directionality of each segment are analyzed (*d*) and the segments are defined as "curve types." Certain sequences of curve types are recognized by the program as arms or other parts of chromosomes. (This is called "syntax-directed pattern recognition.") An object composed of such parts is thus identified as a chromosome.

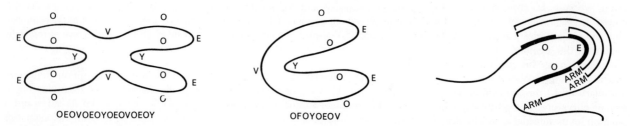

SEGMENTS on boundary of a chromosome are defined as types of curve. *O* is a fairly straight segment; *E*, a clockwise curve; *V*, a slight counterclockwise curve; *Y*, a sharp counterclockwise curve. Different sequences of curve types represent a four-armed submedian chromosome (*left*) and a teleocentric chromosome (*right*) in the computer program.

ARM IS IDENTIFIED in stages by program. Type *E* curve is tentatively called an arm (*notation outside brackets*). Scanning it between *O* types confirms this fact.

in the notation of symbolic logic, a recursive definition (one that can be used repetitively in the program) by which a "derived part" such as an arm can be recognized from its component curves [see bottom illustrations on opposite page]. The process is then taken up by an element of FIDACSYS called the mobilizer, which is analogous to the translator program for a computer language. The mobilizer operates on a list of terms describing the parts of a particular object; by using a general syntactical description of various kinds of chromosome it determines whether or not an object is a chromosome and, if so, what type of chromosome it is. This technique, called syntax-directed pattern recognition, was developed by one of the authors (Ledley) at the National Biomedical Research Foundation in Silver Spring, Md.

The results of each step in the analytic process can be printed out by the computer. First come data describing the coordinates of the chromosome's center of gravity, its area and its perimeter. The lengths of the arms are given and the arm-length ratio is computed by comparing the average length of the two long arms to the overall length of the chromosome [see illustration at right]. Next come the coordinates locating the centers of the boundary segments and designations describing the curvature of these "basic parts." FIDACSYS then prints out the derived parts, giving coordinates for the positions of the arms and the centromere. In the print-outs the code letter E is placed at points representing the ends of the arms, and the letter C at the points marking the centromere. On the basis of all these data an automatic plotting device makes a tracing of all the chromosomes in the original photomicrograph. The plotter also numbers the chromosomes and draws a line to indicate their centromeres [see illustration on next page].

There is still another way in which a computer programmed by FIDACSYS translates numerical data back into graphic form: the final print-out consists of a schematic idiogram of the complement of chromosomes under inspection. To evaluate the accuracy of chromosome analysis by computer we must ask: How does the automatic idiogram compare with one based on visual observation and measurement? Assessments made by the authors indicate that the figures for areas and arm lengths worked out by computer are sufficiently precise. There is reason to

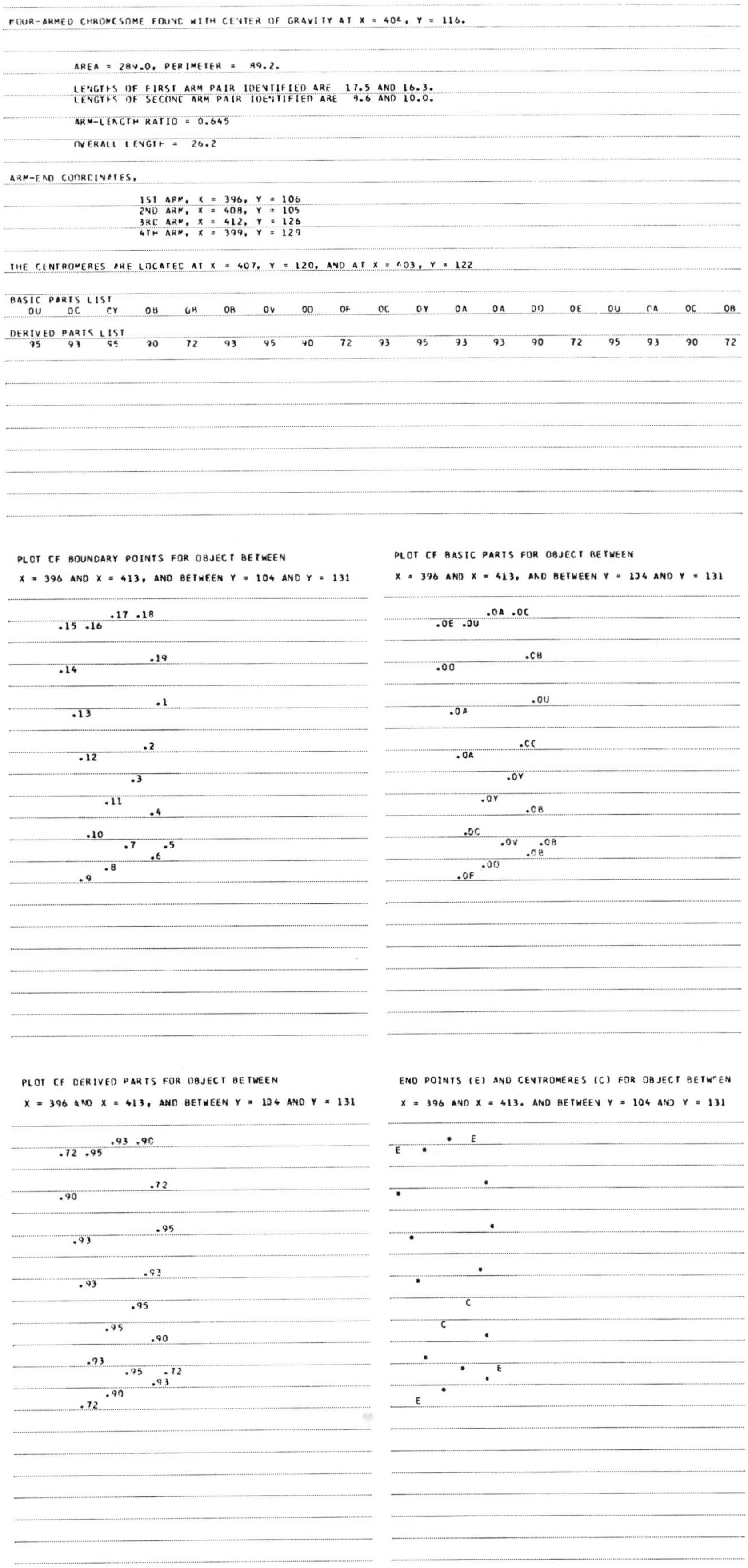

```
FOUR-ARMED CHROMOSOME FOUND WITH CENTER OF GRAVITY AT X = 404, Y = 116.

    AREA = 289.0, PERIMETER = 89.2.

    LENGTHS OF FIRST ARM PAIR IDENTIFIED ARE  17.5 AND 16.3.
    LENGTHS OF SECOND ARM PAIR IDENTIFIED ARE  9.6 AND 10.0.

    ARM-LENGTH RATIO = 0.645

    OVERALL LENGTH = 26.2

ARM-END COORDINATES.

        1ST ARM, X = 396, Y = 106
        2ND ARM, X = 408, Y = 105
        3RD ARM, X = 412, Y = 126
        4TH ARM, X = 399, Y = 129

THE CENTROMERES ARE LOCATED AT X = 407, Y = 120, AND AT X = 403, Y = 122

BASIC PARTS LIST
    OU   OC   CY   OB   OB   OB   OV   OO   OF   OC   OY   OA   OA   OU   OE   OU   CA   OC   OB

DERIVED PARTS LIST
    95   93   95   90   72   93   95   90   72   93   95   93   93   90   72   95   93   90   72
```

PLOT OF BOUNDARY POINTS FOR OBJECT BETWEEN
X = 396 AND X = 413, AND BETWEEN Y = 104 AND Y = 131

PLOT OF BASIC PARTS FOR OBJECT BETWEEN
X = 396 AND X = 413, AND BETWEEN Y = 104 AND Y = 131

PLOT OF DERIVED PARTS FOR OBJECT BETWEEN
X = 396 AND X = 413, AND BETWEEN Y = 104 AND Y = 131

END POINTS (E) AND CENTROMERES (C) FOR OBJECT BETWEEN
X = 396 AND X = 413, AND BETWEEN Y = 104 AND Y = 131

INTERMEDIATE PRINT-OUTS from computer examining chromosomes by syntax-directed pattern recognition are assembled. At top are data giving location and size of chromosome and its arm-length ratio; in middle, plots of boundary points and segments ("Basic parts"); at bottom, plots with labels for ends of arms and centromere ("Derived parts").

CHROMOSOME ANALYSIS SUMMARY

FR NO	CH NO	T	CENTER GRAVITY	PERI METER	OVRALL LENGTH	2 LONG LENGTHS	2 SHORT LENGTHS	LENGTH RATIO	AREA	LONG AREA	SHORT AREA	AREA RATIO
1	1	C	328,37	100.3	34.7	26.2,26.5	7.9,8.6	.761	499.	390.	105.	.788
1	2	A	321,70	183.6	73.3	38.5,37.9	34.9,35.2	.522	1013.	512.	489.	.512
1	3	C	245,69	89.5	28.8	19.2,19.5	8.6,10.3	.673	434.	303.	128.	.703
1	4	D	416,87	59.7	18.9	8.4,10.9	8.1,10.3	.511	219.	110.	110.	.501
1	5	C	259,90	81.2	29.0	24.9,24.7	3.8,4.5	.856	378.	357.	35.	.910
1	6	C	288,113	68.5	24.4	19.5,19.0	5.3,5.0	.788	295.	235.	56.	.808
1	7	D	338,134	53.5	16.1	8.6,8.6	7.3,7.8	.533	171.	93.	76.	.549
1	8	B	220,156	112.3	40.5	24.7,23.8	16.4,16.1	.598	572.	324.	242.	.572
1	9	D	248,146	64.5	20.1	12.0,10.8	8.9,8.5	.568	240.	143.	100.	.589
1	10	C	441,151	80.7	28.2	21.0,19.4	8.2,7.8	.750	397.	293.	97.	.750
1	11	A	427,183	199.7	78.7	42.3,40.9	37.5,36.7	.529	1114.	591.	499.	.542
1	12	D	208,184	49.5	15.6	8.7,7.5	7.6,7.4	.520	153.	79.	72.	.521
1	13	B	304,190	117.6	41.0	25.2,21.5	20.0,15.3	.570	531.	295.	237.	.555
1	14	B	356,208	99.2	32.1	18.5,18.7	12.7,14.2	.580	451.	246.	205.	.545
1	15	D	326,215	63.6	19.8	11.9,11.0	9.1,7.5	.580	219.	128.	87.	.596
1	16	C	265,264	51.7	16.5	8.7,9.2	7.9,7.1	.544	154.	81.	69.	.540
1	17	B	214,275	90.9	30.5	19.1,18.7	12.0,11.2	.619	382.	253.	125.	.669
1	18	C	442,274	76.5	24.7	21.0,18.5	5.3,4.6	.799	351.	277.	64.	.813
1	19	A	250,307	161.0	59.7	32.4,32.0	28.0,26.9	.540	895.	450.	426.	.514
1	20	C	285,305	71.6	23.9	23.2,21.6	1.5,1.5	.937	301.	297.	7.	.977
1	21	C	366,318	90.9	30.2	22.0,22.4	8.9,7.1	.735	382.	310.	69.	.818
1	22	A	303,356	203.2	83.0	45.4,46.0	36.5,38.2	.550	1139.	592.	550.	.518
1	23	B	356,394	120.5	39.3	23.5,19.9	20.5,14.7	.552	596.	318.	262.	.548

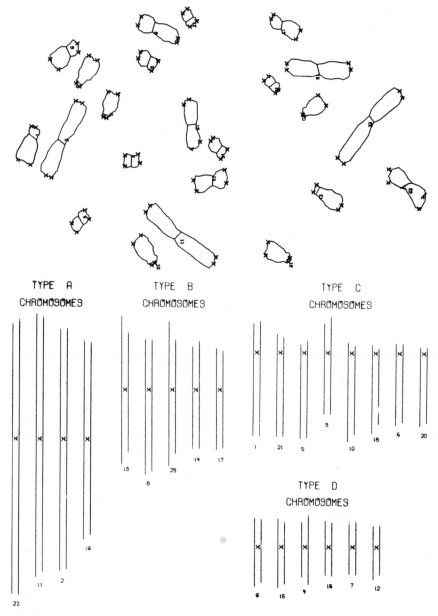

TYPE A CHROMOSOMES

TYPE B CHROMOSOMES

TYPE C CHROMOSOMES

TYPE D CHROMOSOMES

THREE DESCRIPTIONS of the complement of chromosomes of a Chinese hamster were printed by machine. At top are data describing the morphology of each of the animal's 23 chromosomes. In middle is a tracing of the chromosomes, made by an automatic plotting device in which chromosomes are numbered, ends of arms marked and centromeres represented by a line. At bottom is an idiogram of the chromosomes arranged by computer.

hope that analysis by computer will eventually uncover small but important chromosomal abnormalities that have not been discerned by eye. It is known, for example, that one of the chromosomes in the cells of individuals with chronic myeloid leukemia lacks only a small portion of one arm; it is quite likely that other small deletions or additions have been overlooked by investigators and will be revealed by means of the computer.

It can be said with some assurance that the procedure we have described will soon be sufficiently refined and tested for clinical use by physicians who want to examine the chromosomes of a significant number of people. The method will also be available for screening new drugs and biologicals (such as vaccines) for possible chromosomal effects. Moreover, it will now be possible to conduct large-scale studies in such matters as the effects of radiation and aging on chromosomes. The main limitations of the procedure—limits on the speed of the scan and on the number of points that are sampled per picture—are imposed not by the FIDAC device or the basic technique of syntax-directed pattern recognition but by the cycle time and capacity of the memory of the International Business Machines 7094 computer we have been using in our investigations. Newer machines, such as the IBM 360-series computers, will have a larger memory and greater speed, allowing an even faster and more accurate procedure.

It is also safe to predict that methods of automatic analysis closely akin to those described in this article will be employed by biologists and research physicians for tasks other than the study of human chromosomes. There are many branches of biology in which pictorial data have been collected in quantities so large that systematic analysis has heretofore seemed impractical. Examples of such material are sequences of pictures made through the microscope that show the myriad dendritic extensions of nerve cells; electron micrographs of muscle fibers or virus particles; autoradiographs showing the uptake of a tracer element, and X-ray pictures of bone revealing the distribution of calcium. Pictures from these and other categories of material, which describe the structural characteristics of cells in terms of lengths, areas, volumes and densities, can be translated into numerical information. Like photomicrographs of chromosomes, they readily lend themselves to study by computer.

The Authors

ROBERT S. LEDLEY and FRANK H. RUDDLE are respectively president of the National Biomedical Research Foundation and assistant professor of biology at Yale University. Ledley arrived at his position by an unusual route. At Columbia University he specialized in physics and mathematics, but since "in those days a mathematician or a physicist could not make too much of a living, my parents decided to make a dentist of me." As a dentist Ledley was sent by the Army to do dental research at the National Bureau of Standards. There he had occasion to use a computer, and since he was "not happy using an instrument without knowing how it worked," he became a digital-computer engineer and served for a time as associate professor of electrical engineering at George Washington University. In 1960 he organized the National Biomedical Research Foundation to "apply computers in biomedical research on a full-time basis." Ruddle, who met Ledley during a seminar at Yale, received bachelor's and master's degrees at Wayne State University and a Ph.D. at the University of California at Berkeley.

Bibliography

THE IDENTIFICATION OF INDIVIDUAL CHROMOSOMES, ESPECIALLY IN MAN. Klaus Patau in *The American Journal of Human Genetics*, Vol. 12, No. 3, pages 250–276; September, 1960.

USE OF COMPUTERS IN BIOLOGY AND MEDICINE. Robert Steven Ledley. McGraw-Hill Book Company, 1965.

SCIENTIFIC
AMERICAN   April 1966, Vol. 214, No. 4, pp. 102-109   OFFPRINT 1041

ANTIBIOTICS AND THE GENETIC CODE

by Luigi Gorini

The meaning of the code that directs the synthesis of proteins
can be changed by the action of streptomycin and related drugs.
They cause "misreading" by altering the structure of ribosomes.

A cell is characterized by the metabolic activities that occur within its boundaries. These activities proceed along chemical pathways involving numerous steps, each catalyzed by a different enzyme. The cell's characteristics are therefore maintained by its enzymes, and the conservation of these characteristics in a hereditary line of cells depends on their ability to synthesize the same set of enzymes in successive generations. Enzymes are proteins; their catalytic specificity is determined by their structure and that structure is encoded in the genetic material of the cell. It has become common knowledge that the transmission of genetic information from one generation to another is subject to mutations, or occasional errors, and that these mutations are the basis of biological evolution. Until recently, however, the possibility that errors might occur in the transfer of information within the cell, from the genetic material to the protein, was overlooked.

As molecular biologists and geneticists have learned more about the mechanism of this transfer they have wondered if it too might not be subject to error. It is. Not only can mutations affect the transfer mechanism, as one might have expected; in our laboratory at the Harvard Medical School we have discovered that the genetic information encoded within a cell is sometimes ambiguous and can be misunderstood. The ambiguity results from unexpected complex variations in the structure of the cell components known as ribosomes. And the misunderstanding can be prompted by antibiotics such as streptomycin in a manner that explains at least in part how such antibiotics kill cells.

Our work can best be understood in the context of much that has gone before, and so I must briefly review some of that history. In science a line of investigation may often be based on a postulate that in time proves not to have been correct but that nevertheless has great suggestive value. That is, the postulate serves as a starting point for valuable discoveries, with the result that a solid structure of knowledge may be erected in spite of an original oversimplification. So it has been with the celebrated "one gene, one enzyme" postulate put forward in 1941 by George W. Beadle and Edward L. Tatum at Stanford University. Their assumption that each gene defines the structure of one and only one protein ignored the possibility that a gene might make slightly different proteins at different times, but it nevertheless opened the door to biochemical genetics. It did so by providing experimenters with a set of principles: A mutant deficient in a specific enzyme must have a defect in the gene controlling the synthesis of that enzyme; if several metabolic products are lacking as the result of a single mutation, a single enzyme must be responsible and so the products must have a single precursor; a substance that allows the growth of a mutant with a defective enzyme must be the product of a step subsequent to that enzyme's action or of a reaction bypassing the missing enzyme.

By isolating and studying defective mutants and applying these few principles, investigators learned a great deal about the enzyme-catalyzed reactions that build up and break down small molecules in the cell. The principles were close enough to being correct to work well at that level. Their limited validity became apparent, however, as new information made it possible to look behind conventional enzymatic reactions and study the synthesis of the enzymes themselves. The synthesis of enzymes utilizes novel reactions that are directed by the template molecules deoxyribonucleic acid (DNA) and ribonucleic acid (RNA) and that involve the translation of a code.

Proteins are made up of one or more peptide chains, which are in turn linear arrays of linked subunits: the 20 amino acids. It is the sequence in which these amino acids are linked into structures several hundred units long that determines the coiling and folding, and hence the specific characteristics, of each protein. The synthesis of a protein involves the selection, from the pool of amino acids in the cell, of the proper amino acids and their linkage in the proper sequence. This is accomplished in several steps [see *illustrations on opposite page*].

The first step involves the transcription of the inherited instructions in a structural gene—a segment of DNA—into a template molecule of RNA. This "messenger RNA" is the basic link between a gene and its enzyme. Like other kinds of RNA, it is a polynucleotide chain: a strand made up of the nucleotide bases adenine, cytosine, guanine and uracil. The sequence of these bases follows that of the corresponding DNA bases and constitutes the code that establishes the order in which amino acids are assembled to form the protein. The codon, or code word, for each amino acid is a group of three "letters": a nucleotide triplet [see "The Genetic Code: II," by Marshall W. Nirenberg; SCIENTIFIC AMERICAN Offprint 153].

The second, or translation, step is to "plug in" the right amino acid at each codon of the messenger RNA

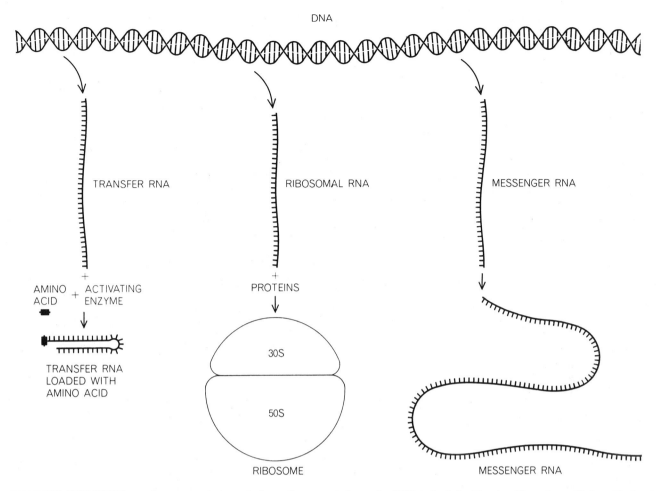

PROTEIN SYNTHESIS involves transcription of deoxyribonucleic acid (*DNA*) into several kinds of ribonucleic acid (*RNA*). Messenger RNA is a sequence of three-base codons, or code words, indicating the amino acid sequence of a protein. Each molecule of transfer RNA is loaded with a specific amino acid through the action of an activating enzyme. Ribosomal RNA and ribosomal proteins combine to constitute ribosomes, the components that are the sites of protein synthesis. The ribosomes have two subunits.

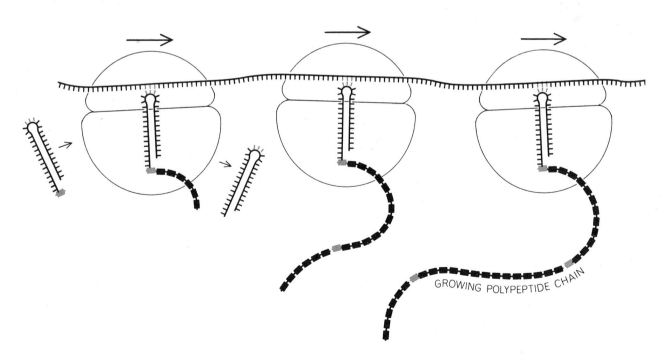

TRANSLATION of genetic instructions from RNA into protein involves the assembly of amino acids into a peptide chain in the sequence coded for by the codons of the messenger RNA. Transfer RNA loaded with an amino acid is thought to "recognize" the codon for that amino acid, perhaps through the binding to the codon of an anticodon of three complementary bases on transfer RNA.

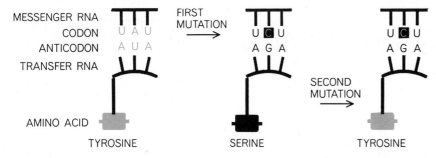

SUPPRESSION of a mutation can occur through the agency of a second mutation affecting transfer RNA or an activating enzyme. The triplet UAU normally codes for tyrosine, for example, perhaps by binding the anticodon AUA on tyrosine transfer RNA according to base-pairing rules (*left*). Mutated to UCU, it would encode serine (*middle*). Another mutation might insert correct amino acid again, perhaps by loading it on serine transfer RNA (*right*).

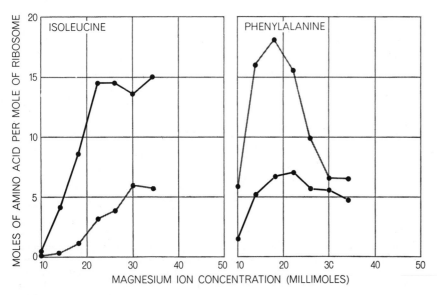

MISREADING is induced in a preparation containing ribosomes from streptomycin-sensitive cells and polyuridylic acid (UUU). The amino acid incorporated in the absence of streptomycin (*gray curves*) is primarily phenylalanine. When streptomycin is added (*black*), incorporation of phenylalanine is inhibited and incorporation of isoleucine is stimulated.

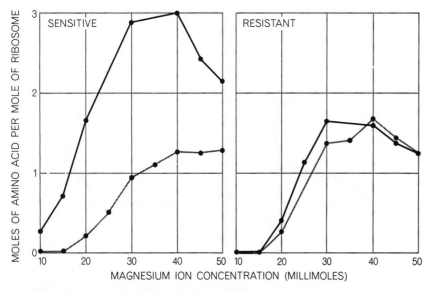

MORE ISOLEUCINE is incorporated in the presence of streptomycin (*black curves*) than in its absence (*gray*) in this system only if the ribosomes in the system are from streptomycin-sensitive cells (*left*). The incorporation varies with magnesium-ion concentration.

template. This is accomplished by a set of enzymes and specialized molecules of "transfer RNA." Each enzyme is able to "recognize," or interact with, one of the amino acids. Each transfer RNA molecule has two specificities: it can interact with one of the enzymes and so become "loaded" with the corresponding amino acid, and it can interact with the codon in the messenger RNA that designates that amino acid. In doing so it inserts the amino acid in the proper position in the developing peptide chain. The site on the transfer RNA that accomplishes this recognition is thought to be an "anticodon" of three bases that fit the three bases of the codon according to the rules of base-pairing: adenine pairs with uracil and guanine with cytosine. That is to say, an adenine-guanine-cytosine (AGC) codon would pair with a uracil-cytosine-guanine (UCG) anticodon. Now, in a code utilizing four letters, 64 triplets are possible, but there are only 20 amino acids to be coded for. The fact is that the code is "degenerate": most amino acids are indicated by several synonymous codons. In each case one of these synonyms seems to appear more frequently than the others—to be the "preferred" codon, in effect.

The translation step takes place in the ribosomes: ultramicroscopic particles made up of nucleic acid and protein. Each ribosome has a large and a small subunit designated (on the basis of their rates of sedimentation in a centrifuge) 50S and 30S. During protein synthesis the messenger RNA is apparently attached to the 30S subunit, the growing protein to the 50S subunit and the transfer RNA to both. The protein-synthesizing system seems to consist of groups of several ribosomes, or polyribosomes, traveling along a messenger RNA strand, each carrying an elongating peptide chain [see "Polyribosomes," by Alexander Rich; SCIENTIFIC AMERICAN Offprint 171]. The assumption has been that the ribosomes serve as inert jigs to hold the various reactants of the translation process in position with respect to one another.

Among the mutational events that might account for a defective mutant the most obvious (and the only one predicted by the one-gene, one-enzyme postulate) is one that occurs in the gene controlling the structure of a messenger RNA. Clearly a mutation that changes even one codon could either alter the message or deprive it of any sense at all and thus result in an altered or missing protein. As for the converse event, the "reversion" of a defective mutant to its parental characteristics, that would presumably be due to an analogous situation: the occurrence of a second mutation, with a "backward" effect, in the defective gene for the same messenger RNA.

Quite frequently, however, one finds a revertant in which the second mutation can be shown to occur in a gene different from that of the defective messenger RNA. Somehow this second mutation suppresses the effect of the original one; it enables the mutant cell to produce an active enzyme even though the gene for that enzyme is producing a defective messenger RNA. Such "suppressor" mutations have been known for more than 40 years. Barring a few cases for which conventional explanations could be found, however, they remained puzzling anomalies, quite in conflict with the one-gene, one-enzyme postulate.

In 1960, on the basis of the new knowledge of the steps in protein synthesis, Charles A. Yanofsky of Stanford University suggested that suppressor genes might be genes that control the structure of activating enzymes or of transfer RNA. A mutation altering the specificity of one of these tools of translation could result in the plugging in of an amino acid other than the one designated by the messenger RNA, and this substitution could reinstate the original structure of the affected enzyme. Such suppressor mutations have since been found. In them an incorrect messenger RNA is "read" by a transfer RNA carrying an amino acid other than the one coded for, and the net result of the double error is the synthesis of a correct protein. Since any given mutation in the tools of translation will suppress any messenger RNA mutations that stand to benefit by the given amino acid substitution, the one-gene, one-enzyme rule is violated: a single mutation can simultaneously produce changes in several proteins quite unrelated in their metabolic function.

In 1961, before much was known about translation errors, we isolated a peculiar mutant in our laboratory. We were working with a strain of the intestinal bacterium Escherichia coli that was unable to manufacture a necessary growth factor, the amino acid arginine. In the course of an experiment we "plated" some streptomycin-resistant mutants of these defective cells (which ordinarily could not grow unless arginine was supplied in their medium) on a medium containing streptomycin but no argi-

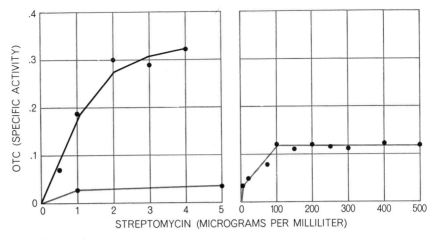

STREPTOMYCIN SUPPRESSION of a mutation affecting the synthesis of an enzyme (OTC) occurs at much lower concentrations in streptomycin-sensitive cells (black curve) than in resistant cells (gray curves). The concentration must be kept sublethal with sensitive cells. The curve for resistant cells has been shown on an expanded scale at the right.

nine. We expected no growth, but to our surprise we found that some of the resistant mutants no longer required arginine; streptomycin fulfilled their requirement. The requirement was due to a defective enzyme, ornithine transcarbamylase (OTC), and the peculiar thing was that OTC activity, which was lacking in cells grown in arginine, was present in cells grown in streptomycin. This meant that the antibiotic was not simply providing a chemical bypass that made arginine synthesis possible without OTC. Various experiments elimi-

nated several other conventional explanations involving the control of enzyme synthesis. We were left with the possibility that streptomycin was acting at the level of protein synthesis, somehow counteracting the effect of a mutation in a structural gene. The idea seemed too radical to pursue. We reported the finding, consigned the mutant to the category of the "funny mutants" one occasionally encounters and cannot explain, and paid no more attention to it.

It was only two years later, after the annual symposium on genetics held in

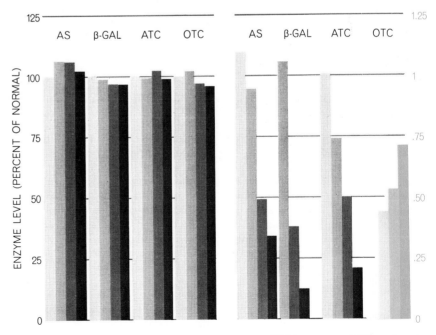

ERRORS are imposed in good enzymes as the error in OTC is suppressed. When the misreading level is too high, "oversuppression" may occur. In a streptomycin-resistant parent strain (left) synthesis of four enzymes is unaffected as the streptomycin concentration increases (successively darker bars) from zero to five, eight and 12 micrograms per milliliter. In an "oversuppressible" derivative of the conditionally streptomycin-dependent mutant (right) the drug increases the OTC level but decreases the level of the other three enzymes.

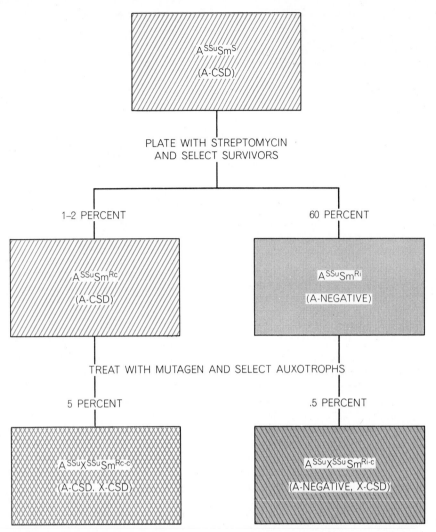

PLATE WITH STREPTOMYCIN
AND SELECT SURVIVORS

1–2 PERCENT

$A^{SSu}Sm^{Rc}$

(A-CSD)

60 PERCENT

$A^{SSu}Sm^{Ri}$

(A-NEGATIVE)

TREAT WITH MUTAGEN AND SELECT AUXOTROPHS

5 PERCENT

$A^{SSu}X^{SSu}Sm^{Rc-c}$

(A-CSD. X-CSD)

.5 PERCENT

$A^{SSu}X^{SSu}Sm^{Ri-c}$

(A-NEGATIVE, X-CSD)

GENETIC EXPERIMENT begins with a strain that has an arginine defect suppressible by streptomycin (A^{SSu}) and is sensitive to streptomycin (Sm^S). Its behavior is conditionally streptomycin-dependent as to arginine (*A-CSD*). Plated on streptomycin medium, it yields three mutants (*middle row*): 1 or 2 percent drug-resistant and "competent" for suppression of the defect (Sm^{Rc}), about 60 percent resistant and "incompetent" (Sm^{Ri}) and about 40 percent dependent on the drug (*not shown*). A second crop of mutants (*bottom row*) includes some with a new drug-suppressible defect (X^{SSu}). A few of the cells that were incompetent for the suppression of the first defect are competent for the suppression of the new one.

Cold Spring Harbor, N.Y., at which there was much discussion of mutations in the genetic-code-reading mechanism, that I became aware of the parallel between streptomycin's effect in our funny mutant and the mechanism being proposed for suppressor mutations. I wondered if streptomycin could interfere with the accuracy of the reading machinery in such a way that the incorrect reading of an incorrect messenger RNA could result in the production of a correct protein.

To support such a hypothesis it was absolutely necessary to show that streptomycin was not merely counteracting the effect of an enzyme specifically involved in arginine synthesis—that the correction induced by streptomycin was associated not with particular metabolic pathways but with particular kinds of mutation, regardless of the structural gene in which they might occur. The crucial experiment was performed by Eva Kataja, a graduate student. She treated a streptomycin-resistant strain of *E. coli* with a mutagen, isolated all the auxotrophs, or cells ordinarily requiring a growth factor, and screened them for the ability to multiply without the growth factor in the presence of streptomycin. She found that from 2 to 5 percent of the auxotrophs requiring different amino acids that were unrelated as to their synthesis were actually "conditional" auxotrophs: their need for the growth factor was conditional on the absence of streptomycin. We designated this new class of mutants "conditionally streptomycin-dependent."

The name has proved not broad enough, because this kind of suppression has now been reported by a number of laboratories to be prompted by other antibiotics and to involve various kinds of mutation other than auxotrophy, including the inability of certain mutant bacterial viruses to grow in a given strain of bacteria. We also find mutants that are in effect "conditionally streptomycin-resistant" in that streptomycin makes them dependent on, rather than independent of, some growth requirement; in this case streptomycin is apparently "impressing" an error rather than suppressing one. All these examples illustrate the same basic finding: Whatever its genetic inheritance (genotype), a cell's characteristics (phenotype) may vary under the influence of certain comparatively small molecules that change the meaning of the genetic code. The idea that the information encoded in DNA may not be inviolate had already been accepted, but it was assumed that the code could be interfered with only by a mutation in the tools of translation. Here we have examples of phenotypic interference with translation, brought about by small molecules present in the cell or in its surroundings.

At the time of our original experiment the relative infrequency of the conditionally streptomycin-dependent mutants among auxotrophs obtained from a single parent indicated that the reading inaccuracy induced by the antibiotic was profitable only to a restricted class of defects in the structural genes. It appeared, moreover, that the mutation to streptomycin resistance did not always result in cells that were "competent" for streptomycin-induced suppression of auxotrophy. That indicated a linkage between the suppressibility phenomenon and the particular mutation to streptomycin resistance. We suggested, therefore, that suppressibility might be dependent on the structure of the ribosome, because it was already known that the mutation from "wild type" streptomycin-sensitive cells to streptomycin-resistant cells involves a change in the structure of the ribosome. Charles R. Spotts and Roger Y. Stanier of the University of California at Berkeley had predicted as much in 1961, and Julian E. Davies of the Harvard Medical School and Joel G. Flaks of the University of Pennsylvania School of Medicine had each proved it in 1963.

They had done so by experimenting with the cell-free amino-acid-incorporating system perfected by Marshall W.

Nirenberg and J. Heinrich Matthaei of the National Institutes of Health in 1961 and since utilized for most of the research on the genetic code. In a system containing purified ribosomes, transfer RNA and enzymes from *E. coli* together with amino acids and a synthetic polynucleotide as an artificial messenger RNA, only the amino acids encoded by the polynucleotide are incorporated in peptide chains. A "homopolymer" such as polyuridylic acid (UUU) codes for phenylalanine, for example. Confirming and broadening previous reports, Davies and Flaks found that if streptomycin was added to a cell-free system containing polyuridylic acid and phenylalanine, it prevented the incorporation of the amino acid unless the ribosomes—and specifically the 30S subunit—had been extracted from streptomycin-resistant cells. Apparently streptomycin acted by somehow "poisoning" the 30S ribosomal subunit.

The behavior of the conditionally streptomycin-dependent mutants suggested, however, that streptomycin was altering code translation rather than simply inhibiting it. Davies, Walter Gilbert and I confirmed this prediction with an experiment in which we put all the amino acids, rather than just the one that should properly be incorporated, into a synthetic-nucleotide preparation with ribosomes, transfer RNA and enzymes from streptomycin-sensitive cells. We found that streptomycin not only inhibited incorporation of the correct polypeptide but also caused incorporation of incorrect ones. With polyuridylic acid as the messenger, for example, streptomycin decreased the incorporation of phenylalanine and also caused the misincorporation of substantial amounts of isoleucine, serine, tyrosine and leucine—amino acids for which UUU is not the correct codon. This misreading did not occur when the cell components came from streptomycin-resistant cells. By interchanging the components we established that the streptomycin misreading depended on the source of the 30S subunit of the ribosome only; the origin of the 50S subunit, the transfer RNA and the activating enzymes did not matter, so apparently these components were unaffected by the antibiotic.

It became evident that streptomycin, by altering the configuration of the 30S subunit (the subunit that attaches to the messenger RNA), disturbs the reading of the RNA code, and therefore that the ribosome controls the accuracy of codon-anticodon binding and that misreading is the result of misrecog-

nition between codon and anticodon. Nirenberg and his colleagues S. Pestka and R. Marshall tested the effect of streptomycin on the binding of amino-acid-loaded transfer RNA to ribosomes and got essentially the same results as we did studying incorporation. By examining this intermediate step in the translation process they confirmed that it is at the recognition stage and through ribosomal intervention that streptomycin-induced misreadings occur. Finally David Old and I analyzed the amino acid composition of the growing polypeptide attached to the ribosome. With polyuridylic acid as the messenger RNA and with no streptomycin, the peptide is a chain of phenylalanine. With streptomycin added, the polypeptide contains about 40 percent isoleucine.

To be sure, various ways of producing misreading in cell-free preparations are known. Misreading can be induced

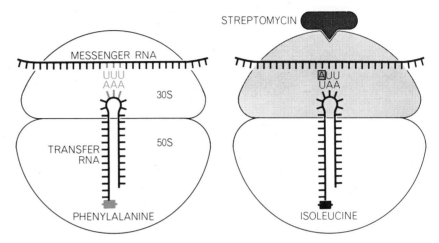

ACTION OF STREPTOMYCIN can be conceived of as an alteration, perhaps some kind of distortion, of the 30S subunit of the ribosome such that the codon is "read" incorrectly, binds the wrong transfer RNA and thus incorporates into the peptide chain an amino acid other than the one it coded for. This highly schematic diagram shows how a UUU codon should incorporate phenylalanine (*left*). Altered by a streptomycin molecule (*right*), the ribosome causes the UUU to be read as if it were AUU, and thus to incorporate isoleucine.

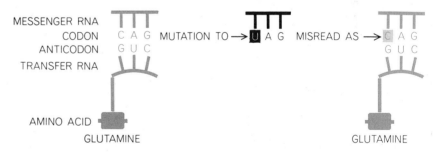

"NONSENSE" mutant is one in which the correct codon (*left*) is mutated to one that encodes no amino acid (*middle*), so no protein can be formed. Streptomycin might suppress the error by causing the nonsense codon to be misread as if it were the correct one (*right*).

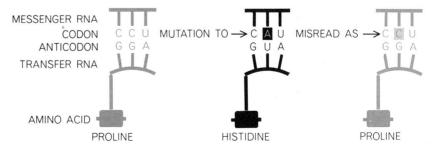

"MISSENSE" MUTANT is one in which the codon (*left*) is mutated to one incorporating a different amino acid (*middle*), making an inactive or perhaps unstable enzyme. Streptomycin-induced misreading might cause incorporation of the correct amino acid (*right*).

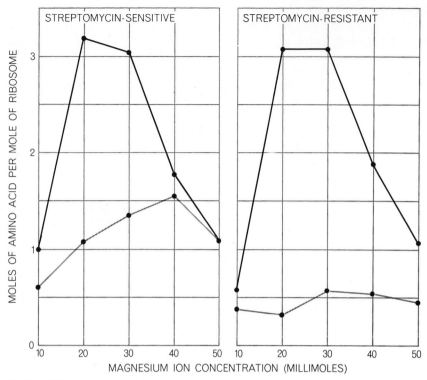

NEOMYCIN, a related antibiotic, stimulates the misincorporation of serine in a poly-uridylic acid preparation whether the ribosomes are from streptomycin-sensitive or resistant cells (*black curves*). In contrast, streptomycin (*gray curves*) has no effect on ribosomes from resistant cells (*right*); incorporation is the same as it is in the absence of the drug.

by changing the concentration of positive ions, the acidity or the temperature, or by adding certain organic solvents. The effects of these changes may be laboratory artifacts, however, quite without biological significance. In the case of the streptomycin effect it has been possible to throw a bridge between misreading in cell-free preparations on one hand and suppression in living mutant cells on the other.

At first there was some conflict between the two. Whereas the conditionally streptomycin-dependent cells had been streptomycin-resistant, ribosomes from resistant cells were not subject to misreading in our cell-free preparations. In those preparations it was ribosomes from drug-sensitive cells that seemed subject to misreading, but we had not tested the sensitive cells in vivo because we assumed that the streptomycin would kill them. We subsequently found that it is indeed possible to isolate conditionally streptomycin-dependent mutants among auxotrophs obtained from wild-type, sensitive strains, provided that streptomycin is added to the medium at a very low concentration. Sensitive cells respond readily to these small amounts of streptomycin. Resistant cells, however, respond sluggishly and require much more of the streptomycin in order to synthesize the

enzyme in which they are defective [*see top illustration on page 2145*]. This weak response in resistant conditionally streptomycin-dependent cells suggested that our failure to find even a little misreading with resistant ribosomes in the cell-free preparations was due to the low efficiency of our biochemical system. Sure enough, when we developed a highly purified system, we found that even some streptomycin-resistant ribosomes were subject to misreading.

All these experiments pointed to a picture of the ribosome as a cell component with a very complex function. The structure and function of ribosomes can be investigated by isolating and examining ribosomal mutants in much the same way that other mutants have been followed in genetic experiments to unravel the structure of enzymes. In this task one can select for altered ribosomes by taking advantage of the fact that streptomycin and other "aminoglycoside" antibiotics related to it cause changes in ribosome structure. So far it is clear that two classes of streptomycin-resistant cell can be isolated from a strain bearing a defect that can be suppressed by streptomycin. One is "competent" for the suppression and the other "incompetent." A graduate student in our laboratory, Lee Brecken-

ridge, succeeded in isolating a second crop of conditionally streptomycin-dependent mutants from competent and incompetent parents and found that a mutant that is incompetent for one defect may be competent for another. This confirms our impression that there is a relation between a specific change in ribosome structure and the defect that can be corrected. This is equivalent to saying that as a result of mutation or of the presence of streptomycin or related drugs a ribosome can assume different conformations that are specific for different types of misreading.

Other findings support this conclusion. For one thing, the pattern of misreading induced in a cell-free system by streptomycin and related drugs such as kanamycin and neomycin varies with the drug. Moreover, in experiments with living cells certain auxotrophs are suppressed by one drug and not by another. Even in the absence of inducing drugs, variations in ribosome structure play a role in the accuracy of translation. There seems to be a steady low level of misreading, and that level varies with specific ribosomal mutations. It has also been noted that a single mutation from drug-sensitive to resistant—which means a change in ribosome structure—is often accompanied by the appearance of other defects, such as auxotrophy, that suggest errors in translation.

All of this means that ambiguity of translation is inherent in the process of protein synthesis; the genetic script transcribed into messenger RNA is not read in only one way. A cell is capable of a certain frequency of misreading, and drugs or other agents in the environment can increase this frequency by acting on the ribosomes.

The misreading caused by streptomycin is not random; it makes poly-uridylic acid, for example, code for only a few incorrect amino acids. The results of experiments conducted in Nirenberg's laboratory and by Davies in our laboratory make it possible tentatively to define a simple pattern for these misreadings and to obtain some insight into the way in which antibiotics cause them and thus into the mechanism of translation. According to the available data and the code "dictionary" compiled to date, it is possible to suggest that streptomycin distorts the configuration of the ribosome in a way that affects the reading of only one base of a triplet at a time. It follows that the codon is read as if it were one of the triplets "connected" to it, that is, differing from it by only one base substitution. The ambiguity, as is evident in cell-free preparations, is still more selective in that the misreadings we find do not include all the possible connected codons but only some of them. This selectivity largely accounts for the relative infrequency of conditionally streptomycin-dependent mutants among all the auxotrophs derived from a given parent.

Another reason for this infrequency could be that a streptomycin-induced misreading can often lead to the incorporation of the same amino acid encoded by the messenger RNA, because connected codons are often synonymous. This might explain why a large fraction of the conditionally streptomycin-dependent auxotrophs we find are really "leaky," or incomplete, auxotrophs stimulated by streptomycin rather than strictly dependent on it: they produce too small a quantity of some growth factor rather than none at all, and streptomycin makes them produce more. A reasonable hypothesis is that their mutation was to a rarely used codon and that streptomycin suppresses that codon, reading instead a more frequently utilized synonym—that they too are corrected by streptomycin through misreading, but the correction is "silent" in the sense that one cannot demonstrate actual amino acid substitution.

This is only a hypothesis, however; the leaky auxotrophs might suggest, on the contrary, that streptomycin always acts in living cells by somehow stimulating enzyme production—a process for which several explanations other than codon misreading can be imagined. To convince ourselves that the misreading obtained in cell-free preparations does indeed account for the suppression observed in living cells, we need unequivocal demonstrations of the occurrence of misreading in such cells. The most direct approach would be to isolate, purify and analyze an enzyme and demonstrate that in the presence of streptomycin one actually gets a mixture of molecules with slightly different amino acid compositions. Unfortunately, this seems to be a very laborious and difficult task. Streptomycin correction is of the order of less than 1 percent, and the few corrected molecules may be impossible to distinguish from impurities.

Fortunately there is another way in which misreading can be demonstrated unequivocally. That is to inquire directly whether the two well-known types of mutation are susceptible to streptomycin correction. One is the "nonsense" mutation, in which the affected triplet codes for no amino acid at all, and the

protein corresponding to the mutated messenger is therefore missing. The mechanism of suppression of these mutations is well established and consists in making sense of the nonsense triplet, causing the protein to be formed [see "The Genetics of a Bacterial Virus," by R. S. Edgar and R. H. Epstein; SCIENTIFIC AMERICAN Offprint 1004]. Since it has been demonstrated, particularly in bacterial viruses, that streptomycin corrects mutants harboring a well-known and easily detected nonsense mutation, it is clear that streptomycin corrects by misreading a nonsense triplet into a "sense" amino acid codon. In a "missense" mutation, on the other hand, the wrong amino acid is encoded, resulting in an altered or inactive enzyme. Here streptomycin suppression through misreading could insert either the correct amino acid or another one that permits some enzyme activity. A mutant both conditionally streptomycin-dependent and temperature-sensitive—one that ordinarily produces an altered enzyme that is stable at one temperature but not stable at a higher temperature, but that in the presence of streptomycin produces at least some stable enzyme—offers unequivocal evidence of amino acid substitution. We have isolated such mutants and we are studying them.

Streptomycin-induced translation errors can of course hurt the cell as well as help it, since they affect certain codons in certain ways whether or not those codons are mutated. We studied the effect of misreading on the synthesis of four enzymes in a conditionally streptomycin-dependent mutant in which the effect of the drug was enhanced by a

second mutation. Increasing concentrations of streptomycin raised the level of the defective enzyme (OTC), but it also markedly reduced the level of the other three enzymes. We call this effect "oversuppression." It tends to flood a cell with faulty proteins.

Intuitively, misreading would seem to be the reason why streptomycin acts as an antibiotic, and there is very suggestive evidence that it is indeed the basis for an explanation of the aminoglycoside drugs' bactericidal effect. Bacteria resistant to the antibiotic effect of streptomycin are also resistant to its close relatives dihydrostreptomycin and bluensomycin, but they are killed by neomycin and kanamycin. The parallel to this is that in cell-free preparations in which streptomycin-resistant ribosomes are resistant to misreading induced by streptomycin and its close relatives they are nevertheless susceptible to misreading induced by neomycin and kanamycin, and neomycin-resistant mutants are susceptible to misreading induced by streptomycin. Although a flood of bad protein might well stop cell growth, however, its effect should be reversible. Special types of misreading or other effects would seem necessary to account fully for the killing of cells.

Apart from its pharmacological implications, our work with streptomycin adds a new dimension—the ribosomal dimension—to investigations into the mechanism of protein synthesis and provides the genetic tools with which to investigate it. Our findings also raise the broad question of the meaning of ambiguity in the genetic code. That ambiguity and the flexibility to which it gives rise may play an important role in the life of cells and in their evolution.

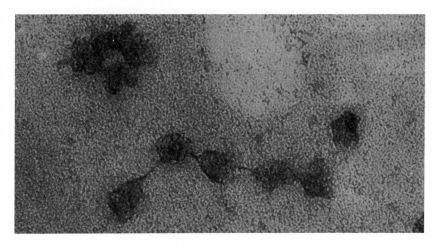

POLYRIBOSOMES from rabbit reticulocytes, the cells that make hemoglobin, are enlarged 370,000 diameters in this electron micrograph made by Henry S. Slayter of the Children's Cancer Research Foundation. They appear to be groups of ribosomes connected by strands of RNA, presumably the messenger RNA encoding the amino acid sequence of a protein.

The Author

LUIGI GORINI is American Cancer Society Professor of Bacteriology and Immunology at the Harvard Medical School. He is a native of Milan who was graduated from the University of Pavia in 1925 and began a career in scientific research at the University of Milan in 1928. Fascism caused a 20-year interruption of that career. As Gorini puts it: "For political reasons I was unable to hold an academic position in fascist Italy and resumed my scientific research after the war." In 1947 he accepted a research fellowship at the University of Paris (the Sorbonne). He came to the U.S. in 1955 as a visiting investigator at New York University, and in 1957 he joined the Harvard medical faculty. For his work on streptomycin he received last year the Ledlie Prize, which is awarded by Harvard University every two years for "the most valuable contribution to science or in any way for the benefit of mankind."

Bibliography

MECHANISM OF STREPTOMYCIN ACTION ON BACTERIA: A UNITARY HYPOTHESIS. Charles R. Spotts and R. Y. Stanier in *Nature*, Vol. 192, No. 4803, pages 633–637; November 18, 1961.

PHENOTYPIC REPAIR BY STREPTOMYCIN OF DEFECTIVE GENOTYPES IN E. COLI. Luigi Gorini and Eva Kataja in *Proceedings of the National Academy of Sciences*, Vol. 51, No. 3, pages 487–493; March, 1964.

ROLE OF RIBOSOMES IN STREPTOMYCIN-ACTIVATED SUPPRESSION. W. French Anderson, Luigi Gorini and Lee Breckenridge in *Proceedings of the National Academy of Sciences*, Vol. 54, No. 4, pages 1076–1083; October, 1965.

SPECIAL NOTE TO TEACHERS: Each article in this volume, plus more than 660 others, is available as a separate, self-bound SCIENTIFIC AMERICAN Offprint. Offprints may be ordered in any combination and in any quantity. Teachers who want to adopt articles for their courses, therefore, can ensure that each student has his own set. Students' sets are collated by the publisher before shipment.

SCIENTIFIC
AMERICAN   May 1966, Vol. 214, No. 5, pp. 76-88   OFFPRINT **1042**

HOW A TADPOLE BECOMES A FROG

by William Etkin

The dramatic changes of the process are stimulated by thyroid hormone. The level of hormone is regulated by a feedback system involving the hypothalamus of the brain and the pituitary gland.

Of all the mysteries of life one of the most intriguing is animal metamorphosis. The transformation of a caterpillar into a butterfly or of a tadpole into a frog has long fascinated naturalists, and it is currently yielding important information on various phenomena from evolutionary adaptation to the differentiation and specialization of cells. A recent article in *Scientific American* discussed chemical aspects of the transformation process [see "The Chemistry of Amphibian Metamorphosis," by Earl Frieden; Offprint 170]. The present article is an account of what has been learned about the hormonal mechanism that activates the chemical changes that transform a tadpole into a frog.

The frog starts life as a small swimming organism capable only of a fish-like mode of life in the water. It breathes by means of gills, feeds on water plants and pond debris and is equipped with swimming apparatus in the form of a long tail. The duration of the tadpole stage varies greatly: in some of the smaller species it lasts only two or three weeks and the tadpole grows to no more than an inch in length; in the case of the bullfrog the animal remains a tadpole for three years and reaches a length of up to nine inches.

The first sign of change comes when buds near the rear end of the animal's trunk begin to develop into limbs: the jumping legs of the frog. The development of these legs, accompanied by other, less conspicuous changes, takes two to six weeks, depending on the size of the tadpole. In this phase, called prometamorphosis, the animal remains a water-dweller. When the hind legs have grown to about the size of the animal's torso, the tadpole abruptly enters the stage of rapid changes called

the metamorphic climax. Forelegs suddenly erupt through small openings in the covering of the gills; the mouth widens and develops powerful jaws and a large tongue; the lungs and skin complete their transformation; nostrils and a mechanism for pumping air develop, and the gills and tail are resorbed by a process of self-digestion and thus disappear. Before the week of climax is over the animal emerges to a new life on land.

The process takes place in an orderly fashion and with exquisite timing, each new development fitting into a complex and perfectly coordinated pattern. The resorption of the swimming tail does not begin until the jumping legs have nearly completed their growth; the nostrils and air-pumping mechanism develop before the gills are resorbed. Clearly the metamorphic process as a whole must be organized by some master mechanism within the animal's regulatory system. The search for the nature of this mechanism has been pursued for more than half a century.

Our story begins with a discovery in 1912 by the German biologist Friedrich Gudernatsch. He fed extracts from various body organs to tadpoles and found that an extract from the thyroid gland had a striking effect. Within a week the treated tadpoles showed some of the typical signs of metamorphosis: rapid growth of legs, widening of the mouth, resorption of the tail. Biochemists eventually identified the thyroid substances that produced these changes as the hormone thyroxine and its three-iodine variant triiodothyronine.

The discovery that thyroid hormones played a critical part in producing metamorphosis raised more questions than it answered. How could this single stimu-

lus generate the entire orderly sequence of metamorphic change, affecting so many body tissues in so many different ways? This question particularly intrigued me when I first became interested in the investigation of metamorphosis more than 30 years ago.

One point seemed obvious: In all likelihood the progress of metamorphosis was connected with increasing activity of the thyroid. Microscopic examination of the gland supported this idea. In tadpoles that had not yet begun to metamorphose, the thyroid was small and its cells appeared inactive. During prometamorphosis, however, the gland grew rapidly, and by the time the animal reached metamorphic climax the thyroid was large and apparently extremely active. Further confirmation of a connection between the level of thyroid hormone and the metamorphic process was provided by experiments in which tadpoles were deprived of their thyroids by surgery and were then given various doses of thyroxine.

Exposing the animals to a low dose of the hormone produced the characteristic development of the prometamorphic stage, marked by rapid growth of the hind legs. If the hormone concentration was maintained at this low level, the later stages of metamorphosis developed only with extreme slowness. High levels of hormone, on the other hand, produced a normal rate of change for such climax events as tail resorption but did not allow enough time for other changes, such as hind-leg growth. The resulting animal was not viable; it could live neither in water nor on land. I found that to induce the normal speed and timing of metamorphosis the hormone concentration had to be started at a low level and then be increased at least twentyfold as the metamorphic process advanced to the final stage [*see illustrations on next page*].

In our laboratory at the Albert Einstein College of Medicine in New York we have developed a standard procedure for transforming immature tadpoles into frogs. We provide the hormone through the water medium in which the animals swim. We start with a concentration of one to three parts of thyroxine to a billion parts of water. When the growth of the tadpoles' hind legs, signaling prometamorphosis, has reached about a third of the normal length, we raise the thyroxine concentration to about 10 parts per billion. Finally, when the forelegs emerge, marking the start of metamorphic climax, we increase the thyroxine concentration to between 200 and 1,000 parts per billion. At this concentration of

hormone the final events of metamorphosis proceed at their normal pace.

The regulating agent for metamorphosis was thus shown to be the activity of the thyroid gland. But plainly this was not the ultimate control. What regulated the changing rate of activity of the thyroid? Earlier research had already suggested an answer. This regulation must lie in the pituitary gland, which holds the key to stimulation of the thyroid.

Bennet M. Allen, then working at the University of Kansas, and Philip E. Smith, then at the University of California at Berkeley, had found that tadpoles whose pituitary glands had been removed failed to metamorphose into frogs. (Smith's experiments on tadpoles were the beginning of his classic investigations of the pituitary, which helped

to establish the modern science of endocrinology by showing that the pituitary is the master gland regulating many other endocrine organs.) By the time I began my work on metamorphosis it was known that the thyroid's activity is controlled by a pituitary hormone called thyrotropin or thyroid-stimulating hormone (TSH).

What, in turn, regulates the output of TSH by the pituitary? It began to appear that tracking down the control of metamorphosis to its ultimate source might be an arduous task.

I considered three possible agencies that might stimulate the pituitary's secretion of TSH. The stimulus might come from another endocrine gland, from the brain (to which the pituitary is attached) or from some mechanism

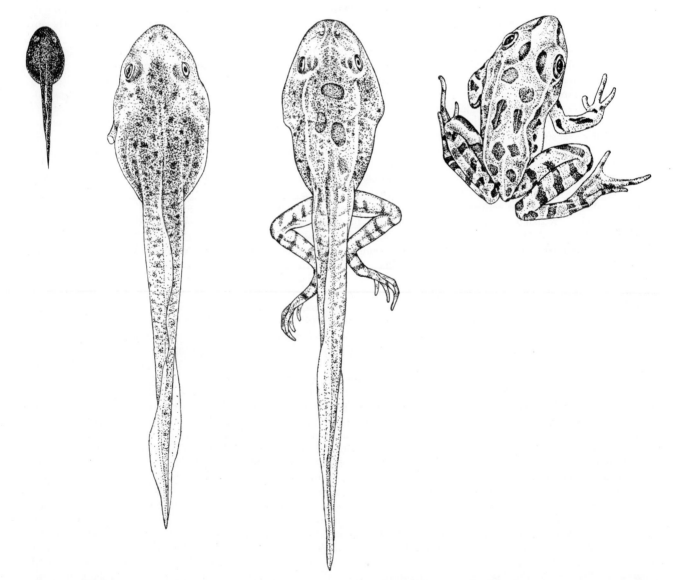

GRASS FROG (*Rana pipiens*) changes from an aquatic larval form into a terrestrial animal during metamorphosis. The tadpole is shown soon after hatching (*left*) and when it is full-grown, just before metamorphosis (*second from left*). Some 20 days later, late in prometamorphosis, the hind legs are largely developed (*third from left*). The completely transformed frog is shown at the right.

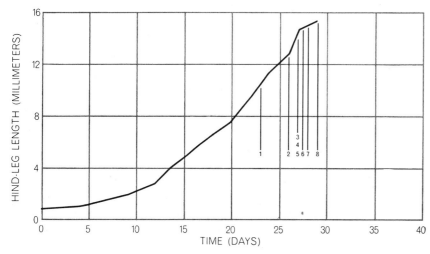

SEQUENCE OF EVENTS in the normal metamorphosis of the Western wood frog (*Rana cantabrigensis*) is plotted with hind-leg length. The events are the reduction (*1*) and complete resorption (*2*) of the anal canal piece, the appearance of a "skin window" for a foreleg (*3*), the emergence of a foreleg (*4*), marked reduction of lips and loss of horny teeth (*5*), loss of horny beaks (*6*) and the beginning (*7*) and completion (*8*) of tail-fin resorption.

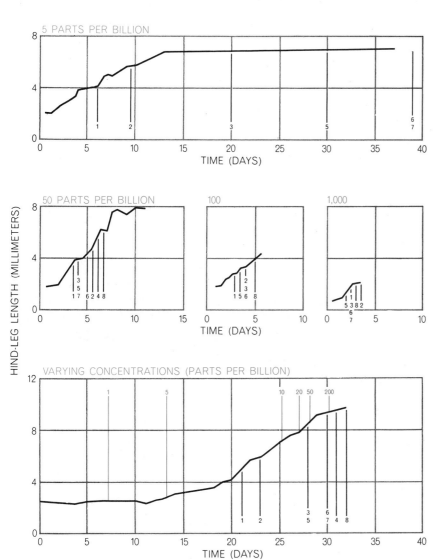

HORMONE CONCENTRATION governs the rate and sequence of changes in induced metamorphosis. At five parts per billion parts of water (*top*) the changes occur slowly. At high concentrations (*middle*) the changes occur out of sequence and before the legs grow. A normal pattern is approximated (*bottom*) when the hormone concentration is varied.

within the pituitary itself that began to operate when it reached a certain stage of development. To test these hypotheses I removed the tadpole's pituitary from its attachment to the brain and transplanted it to various other sites in the body, performing the operation during the gland's early development in the embryo. The results of the transplantation experiments were tantalizingly ambiguous. Most of the tadpoles eventually showed some leg growth, but their progress toward metamorphosis was long delayed and far slower than normal. Some of the animals simply went on growing as tadpoles without showing any sign of metamorphosis.

The failure of metamorphosis to develop normally indicated that the pituitary's function of promoting metamorphosis was not regulated by hormones from another gland, because such hormones should reach the pituitary by way of the bloodstream regardless of where the pituitary might be located in the body. On the other hand, the fact that many of the tadpoles showed signs of the beginning of metamorphosis, even though the pituitary was transplanted from its normal site on the underside of the brain, suggested that the metamorphic process did not depend on messages from the brain. (Actually, for reasons that will become clear, this interpretation was not valid.)

It seemed, then, that metamorphosis must be controlled by a developmental clock within the pituitary that timed the pattern of the gland's activity. The abnormally slow development of metamorphic changes when the pituitary was transplanted might therefore be due to some transplantation setback that slowed the clock.

Our studies of metamorphosis were interrupted (like a great deal of other work in biology) by World War II. By the time we resumed the investigation in the 1950's various new discoveries in endocrinology and studies of the functioning of the nervous system cast a totally new light on the questions we had been asking. A number of items of information were suddenly found to fit together, like the pieces of a jigsaw puzzle, to form a more meaningful picture of the mechanism of control of metamorphosis.

Tomomasa Uyematsu of the University of Kyoto had performed an experiment somewhat similar to ours. Instead of transplanting the pituitary from its attachment to the brain, he removed the part of the hypothalamus in the brain to which the pituitary is attached. He found that after this operation the metamorphosis of a toad tadpole could proceed through the early stages, but that the process stopped abruptly when it arrived at the climax stage. We repeated his experiments on frog tadpoles and also explored again the effects of transplantation of the pituitary; in both cases we found that the process of metamorphosis did indeed come to a halt at the beginning of climax.

Uyematsu had supposed that the metamorphic failure was due to degeneration of the pituitary, caused by its disconnection from the brain. In our experiments, however, we found that the pituitary was not impaired and was functional with respect to other hormones it produces. We therefore concluded that the failure of metamorphosis to proceed through climax was simply due to the lack of connection between the pituitary and the brain. This idea was confirmed in experiments on the common spotted salamander: when a barrier was interposed between the brain and the pituitary, the larva of that animal did not metamorphose.

It was now apparent that the brain does, after all, play a controlling role in metamorphosis. From the results of our earlier experiments we had judged that the brain was not involved, because disconnection of the pituitary from the brain did not prevent the development of prometamorphic changes. In retrospect we could see that we had sacrificed those animals (for morphological examination) too soon; if we had kept them for a longer period, we would have observed that the animals could not complete the climax phase of their transformation. Evidently prometamorphosis, requiring only a low level of stimulation by thyroid hormone, could proceed without direct stimulation from the brain, but to induce the metamorphic climax the brain had to stimulate the pituitary to increase its secretion of TSH to a high level and thus step up the thyroid's activity.

How did the brain transmit the stimulus to the pituitary? The answer to this question was surprising indeed. It emerged from two entirely separate discoveries that had intrigued and mystified anatomists for many years.

The first of these discoveries, developed by Ernst A. Scharrer and his wife Berta, was that certain nerve cells manufacture hormone-like substances ("neurosecretions") that travel along the nerve-cell fibers and are released at their terminals. The concept that nerve

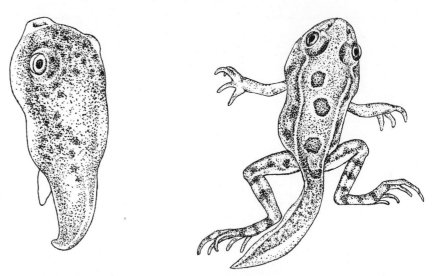

HIGH CONCENTRATION of thyroxine causes the tail to be resorbed before the legs have grown and the mouth parts to change in uncoordinated fashion (*left*). Varying the thyroxine concentration from a low to a high level produces more normal metamorphosis (*right*).

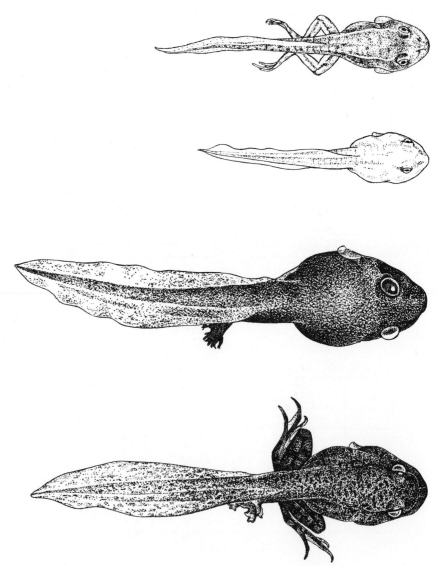

EFFECT OF PITUITARY on metamorphosis was studied by removing the gland and by transplanting it. A normally metamorphosing tadpole is shown at the top. An animal without a pituitary fails to metamorphose (*second from top*). If the pituitary is transplanted to the tail (*third and fourth from top*), metamorphosis is delayed and varies in different animals.

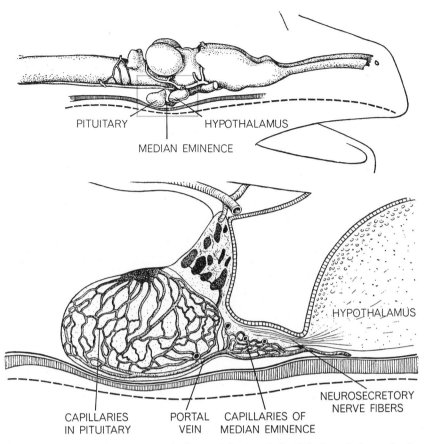

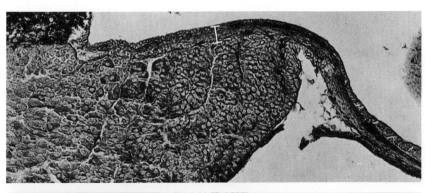

PITUITARY GLAND is just under the brain of the frog, behind the hypothalamus (*top*). As shown in the bottom drawing, blood from the capillary net in the median eminence flows out of the hypothalamus through "portal" veins directly into the anterior pituitary.

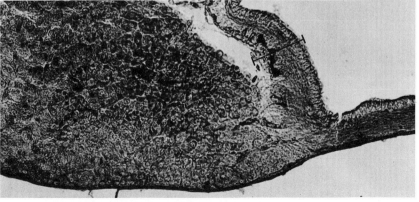

DEVELOPMENT OF MEDIAN EMINENCE is traced in photomicrographs, made by the author, of sections of the bullfrog tadpole pituitary region. Before metamorphosis (*top*) the nervous tissue connecting the hypothalamus and the pituitary (*left*) is thin and undeveloped (*bracket*). By climax (*bottom*) it has thickened and developed into a median eminence.

fibers might convey messages not only by electrical impulses but also by means of hormones seemed at first utterly bizarre, but it was abundantly confirmed by various kinds of evidence found by other investigators.

The other significant discovery was that the hypothalamus is connected to the anterior lobe of the pituitary by a special set of "portal" veins. In the hypothalamus these vessels receive blood from a net of capillaries within a structure known as the median eminence. Nerve fibers carrying neurosecretions were found to terminate in the median eminence. The blood from the median eminence goes through the portal veins directly to the anterior pituitary, not to the heart. Clearly the nerve fibers, the median eminence and the portal veins provided a channel whereby hormones secreted by the neurosecretory cells in the hypothalamus could be transported to the anterior pituitary without being diluted in the total blood volume. In short, the brain could directly send chemical stimuli to the pituitary.

The Scharrers, putting all the evidence together, developed a general concept that has proved to be one of the most fruitful generalizations of modern biology. (Indeed, I should like to dedicate this article to Ernst Scharrer, who at the time of his death last year was professor of anatomy at the Albert Einstein College of Medicine.) The concept pictures the neurosecretory apparatus as a connecting link between the two major control systems of the body: the nervous system and the anterior pituitary, the master gland of the endocrine system. On the nervous side the key centers are the areas of the brain known as the thalamus and the hypothalamus. The thalamus has aptly been called the Rome of the nervous system, because all roads from the sense organs lead to it. As the headquarters of the sense organs the thalamus receives the information coming in from the environment outside the body. The hypothalamus, just below the thalamus, is the highest receiving center for information from the organs within the body itself. Together the thalamus and the hypothalamus coordinate all the information from outside and inside; on the basis of this integration of information the nervous system forms a strategy of response. It then issues a command that is translated from a nerve impulse into a chemical message by the neurosecretory cells, acting as transducers. The command goes to the anterior pituitary, which transmits the chemical message to the appropriate destinations by way of the endocrine system.

All of this puts the question of the mechanism controlling metamorphosis in a new light. It suggests the view that the brain regulates metamorphosis not through nerves but by means of chemical messages passing by way of the portal veins to the pituitary. Much experimental evidence supports this concept. For example, in our experiments with the salamander larva, which showed that the interposition of a barrier between the brain and the pituitary could block metamorphosis, we found that metamorphosis was able to proceed normally when the animal regenerated blood vessels that bypassed the barrier. Many laboratories have established that in mammals the hypo-

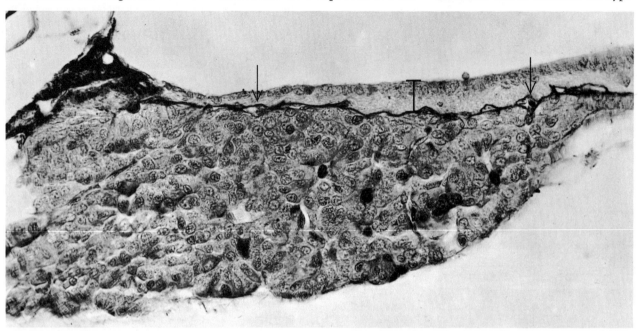

REMOVAL OF THYROID not only prevents metamorphosis but also prevents the development of the median eminence. This photomicrograph made by the author shows the pituitary region in a thyroidectomized grass frog tadpole. A thin layer of nervous tissue (*bracket*) extends over the anterior pituitary from the hypothalamus, with a thin network of capillaries (*arrows*) between them.

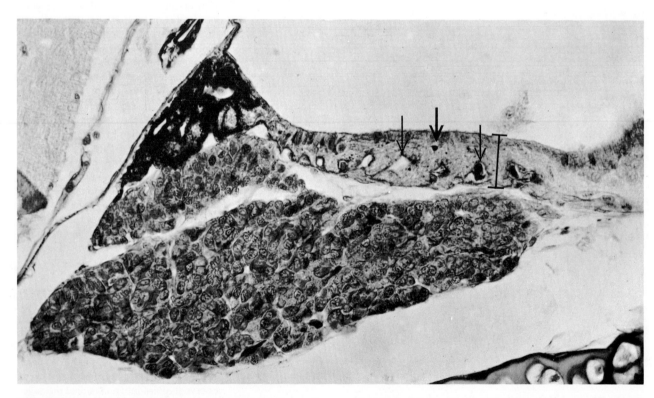

THYROXINE TREATMENT of a thyroidectomized tadpole caused metamorphosis and also, as demonstrated by this photomicrograph, development of a median eminence. The thin layer of nervous tissue has thickened (*bracket*) and is drained by a network of capillaries (*light arrows*) that can carry neurosecretory material (*heavy arrow*) to the portal veins for delivery to the pituitary gland.

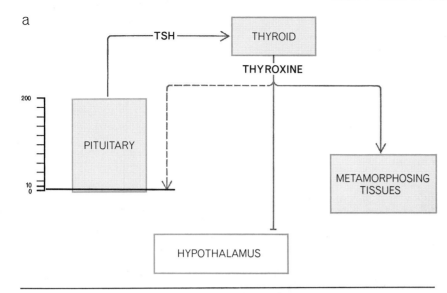

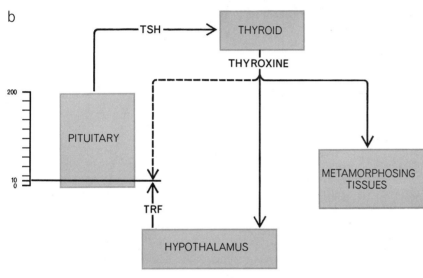

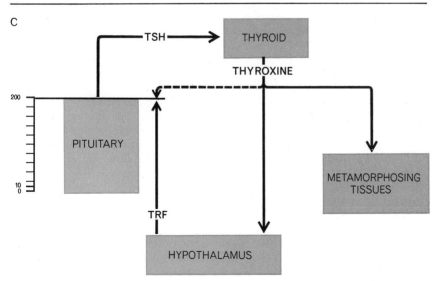

FEEDBACK MECHANISM that regulates metamorphosis is pictured at three stages. Before metamorphosis (a) the hypothalamus is insensitive to thyroxine stimulation. Pituitary TSH activity is inhibited by thyroxine; the "thyrostat" (left) is low. In prometamorphosis (b) the sensitized hypothalamus produces TRF under thyroxine stimulation; the TRF counteracts thyroxine inhibition of the pituitary and the thyrostat rises. The positive feedback loop builds up to an explosive production of thyroxine during the climax phase (c).

thalamus produces a chemical messenger, thyrotropin-releasing factor (TRF), that regulates production of TSH by the pituitary.

We have not yet, however, reached the end of the story. It seems that we have definitely traced command of the metamorphosis of the tadpole into a frog back to the hypothalamus. The transformation is directed by the thyroid, which in turn is controlled by the pituitary, which in turn is controlled by the hypothalamus. But what gives the order to the hypothalamus? Do we still have to search back further through some seemingly endless chain of command?

Examination of the anatomy of the tadpole gave a new direction to our thoughts on this question. We noted that young tadpoles lack a fully developed median eminence between the brain and the pituitary such as is found in the adult frog. This part of the neurosecretory apparatus does not develop until the prometamorphic stage that launches the tadpole's transformation. Since the median eminence seems an essential part of the transformation apparatus, we naturally asked: What stimulates the development of the median eminence?

We found that removal of a tadpole's thyroid, which was already known to prevent metamorphosis, also prevented development of the median eminence. On the other hand, when we administered thyroxine to a full-grown tadpole that had been thyroidectomized, the median eminence did develop. These results indicated that a positive feedback mechanism operates in the tadpole: the thyroid hormone causes the median eminence to develop and that structure in turn stimulates the pituitary to activate the thyroid to produce more hormone.

A positive feedback system of this kind will lead to an intense buildup of activity. This is precisely what we observe during the process of metamorphosis. From a level of activity that is extremely low before metamorphosis, the thyroid builds up through intermediate levels during prometamorphosis to an explosive release of hormone at climax.

Was the thyroid hormone really the stimulus that primed the cycle of metamorphic activity? As an experiment to test this hypothesis we tried administering thyroxine to young tadpoles to see if this would initiate a precocious development of the mechanism that caused them to metamorphose. The stratagem

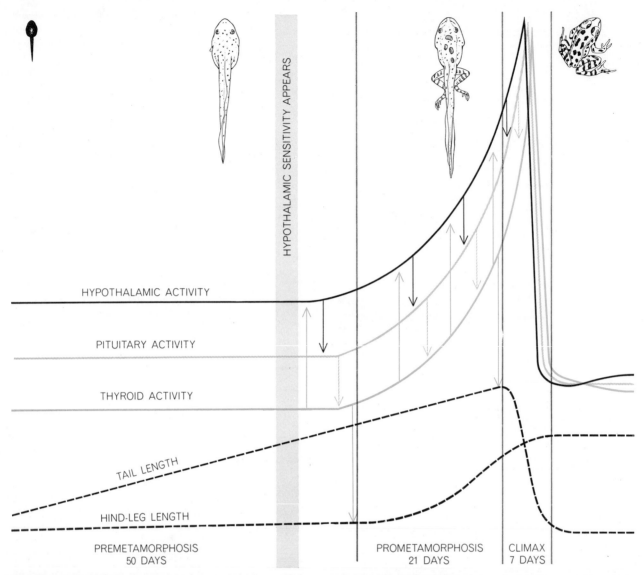

INTERACTIONS of the hypothalamus, pituitary and thyroid and the effect of thyroid hormone on metamorphosing tissues are illustrated schematically. Hormone cycling begins when the hypothalamus becomes sensitive to thyroxine. Soon enough thyroxine is being secreted to cause hind-leg growth and then resorption of the tail. The buildup of thyroid activity continues until the metamorphic system, like the other tissues, has completely matured, when its sensitivity to thyroxine ceases and hormone levels drop rapidly.

failed to induce such development. The failure led to the suggestion that perhaps the hormone could trigger the mechanism only after the tadpole had reached a certain stage of maturity. We therefore tested the effect of the hormone on development of the median eminence in tadpoles of various sizes and ages, and in this way we found that the animals showed a change in sensitivity to the hormone during growth. The median eminence of the tadpole of the grass frog, for instance, did not respond to thyroxine when the animal was smaller than 40 millimeters in length; it responded slightly at a size of 45 millimeters; at a size of 50 millimeters (five millimeters, or one week in time, before it would normally enter prometamorphosis) the tadpole responded to the extra dose of thyroxine with full development of the median eminence.

We have arrived, then, at a reasonably clear outline of the metamorphic mechanism. At a critical point in the tadpole's development some factor, presumably controlled by a genetic mechanism, renders the hypothalamus sensitive to the low level of thyroid hormone circulating in the animal's body. The neurosecretory apparatus of the hypothalamus responds by releasing a TRF substance that stimulates the anterior pituitary to secrete TSH, which turns on the orderly increase of thyroid secretion. That increase trips the orderly sequence of tissue changes that transforms the tadpole into a frog.

In actuality the feedback relations between hypothalamus, pituitary and thyroid may be still more complex. There is much evidence to indicate that thyroid hormone acts directly on the pituitary to inhibit its production of TSH. This negative feedback system keeps the level of thyroid hormone and TSH in balance with each other at a level that is determined by the sensitivity of the pituitary to thyroid inhibition. In analogy to the operation of a thermostat this system has been called a "thyrostat." It is evident that the TRF substance of the hypothalamus could be the agent that regulates the thyrostat level, and thus the rate of metamorphosis, by changing the sensitivity of the pituitary [see illustration on page 2157].

Of course there are many questions still to be answered. How is the sensitivity of the hypothalamus to the thyroid hormone turned on? Just how does the hormone bring about the metamorphic changes in tissues? What accounts for the diverse ways in which different tissues respond to the stimulus? What, for example, explains the fact that the hormone causes the tadpole's jaws to grow rapidly while at the same time it causes the lips, gills and tail to be resorbed? The investigation of metamorphosis brings us face to face with some of the most fundamental questions in biology.

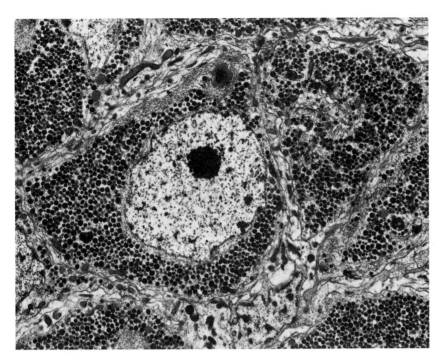

NEUROSECRETORY CELLS in the brain of an earthworm are enlarged 7,000 diameters in this electron micrograph made by the late Ernst A. Scharrer and Stanley Brown of the Albert Einstein College of Medicine. Neurosecretory granules fill the cytoplasm of each cell.

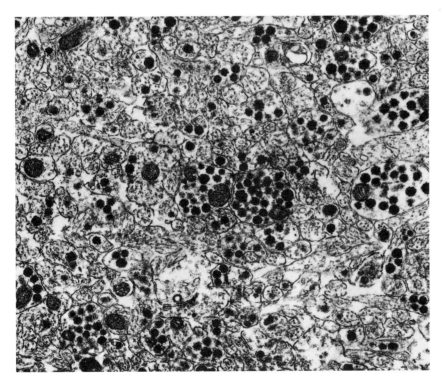

GRANULES can be seen inside the axons, or nerve fibers, of the hypothalamus of a toad tadpole in this electron micrograph made by Jack Rosenbluth. The axons, enlarged 22,500 diameters, are seen in cross section. The dense, dark gray structures are mitochondria.

The Author

WILLIAM ETKIN is professor of biology at the City College of the City University of New York and visiting research professor of anatomy at the Albert Einstein College of Medicine at Yeshiva University. Although his association has been mainly with City College, from which he was graduated in 1928, he has also done graduate work at Cornell University and at the University of Chicago (where he obtained a Ph.D. in 1934) and has done research in endocrinology at the American Museum of Natural History. Among his recent publications are a textbook, *Social Organization among Vertebrates,* and three theoretical papers on human evolution and the origin of culture. He is developing an introductory course in biology at Yeshiva College; he writes that its aim "is to bring out the significance modern biology has for an understanding of the entire phenomenon of man."

Bibliography

METAMORPHOSIS. William Etkin in *Physiology of the Amphibia,* edited by John A. Moore. Academic Press Inc., 1964.

NEUROENDOCRINOLOGY. Ernst Scharrer and Berta Scharrer. Columbia University Press, 1963.

SCIENTIFIC
AMERICAN   June 1966, Vol. 214, No. 6, pp. 42-52   OFFPRINT **1043**

MOLECULAR MODEL-BUILDING
BY COMPUTER

by Cyrus Levinthal

In which biochemists observe models of giant molecules
as they are displayed on a screen by a computer and try
to fold them into the shapes that they assume in nature.

Many problems of modern biology are concerned with the detailed relation between biological function and molecular structure. Some of the questions currently being asked will be completely answered only when one has an understanding of the structure of all the molecular components of a biological system and a knowledge of how they interact. There are, of course,

a large number of problems in biology into which biologists have some insight but concerning which they cannot yet ask suitable questions in terms of molecular structure. As they see such problems more clearly, however, they invariably find an increasing need for structural information. In our laboratory at the Massachusetts Institute of Technology we have recently started using a

computer to help gain such information about the structure of large biological molecules.

For the first half of this century the metabolic and structural relations among the small molecules of the living cell were the principal concern of biochemists. The chemical reactions these molecules undergo have been studied intensively. Such reactions are specifically catalyzed by the large protein molecules called enzymes, many of which have now been purified and also studied. It is only within the past few years, however, that X-ray-diffraction techniques have made it possible to determine the molecular structure of such protein molecules. These giant molecules, which contain from a thousand to tens of thousands of atoms, constitute more than half of the dry weight of cells. Protein molecules not only act as enzymes but also provide many of the cell's structural components. Another class of giant molecules, the nucleic acids, determine what kind of protein the cell can produce, but most of the physiological behavior of a cell is determined by the properties of its proteins.

The X-ray-diffraction methods for investigating the three-dimensional structure of protein molecules are difficult and time-consuming. So far the structures of only three proteins have been worked out: myoglobin, hemoglobin and lysozyme [see "The Three-dimensional Structure of a Protein Molecule," by John C. Kendrew, SCIENTIFIC AMERICAN Offprint 121, and "The Hemoglobin Molecule," by M. F. Perutz Offprint 196]. In their studies of the hemoglobin molecule M. F. Perutz and his associates at the Laboratory of Molecular Biology in Cambridge, England, have observed that the structure of the molecule changes slightly when

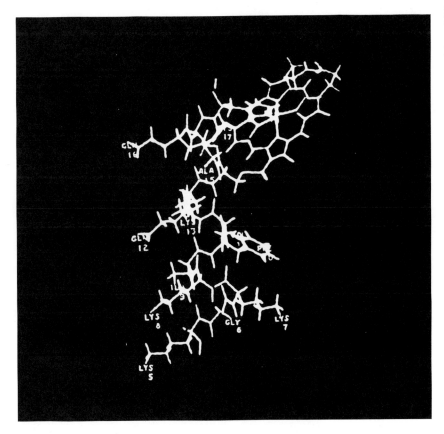

MOLECULAR MODEL of a segment of cytochrome *c*, a protein that plays an important role in cell respiration, is shown as it is displayed on an oscilloscope screen. The protein has 104 amino acid subunits; this segment consists of units 5 through 18 (designated here by their abbreviated names). The heme group, which acts as a carrier of electrons, is known to be attached to amino acids 14 and 17. In the hypothetical structure shown here this stretch of the molecule is assumed to be in the characteristic "alpha helix" configuration.

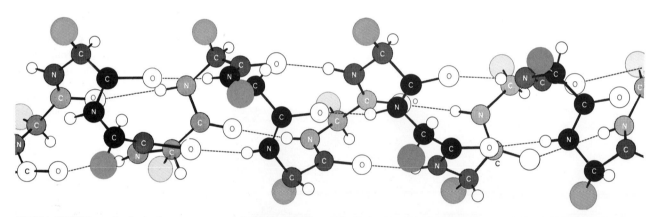

GLYCINE LEUCINE LEUCINE SERINE PHENYLALANINE

HISTIDINE LYSINE THREONINE ISOLEUCINE LEUCINE LYSINE

PROTEIN BACKBONE is a chain of peptide groups (six atoms: carbon, carbon, oxygen, nitrogen, hydrogen, carbon). Each amino acid in a chain contributes a group to the backbone and also has a distinguishing side group (*color tint*). The amino acid sequence of a number of proteins is known. What is shown here is a short segment of the protein myoglobin, which stores oxygen in muscle.

ALPHA HELIX results from the arrangement of planar peptide groups (CCONHC) pivoted about the carbons to which side groups (*color*) are attached. Shade of atoms indicates nearness to viewer. The entire helix is held rigid by hydrogen bonds (*broken lines*).

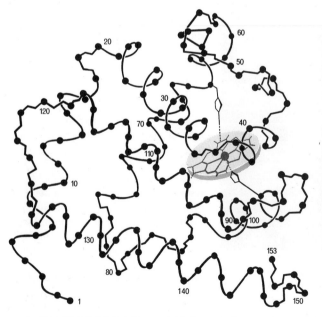

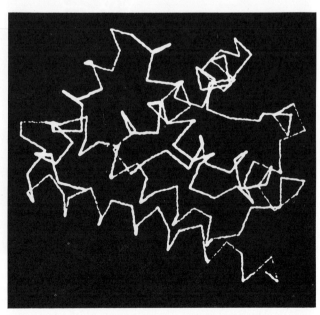

MYOGLOBIN MOLECULE is a folded, partly helical chain, as shown in drawing (*left*) of its form as determined through X-ray analysis by John C. Kendrew of the Laboratory of Molecular Biology in Cambridge, England. The chain enfolds an oxygen-carrying heme group (*colored disk*). Every 10th amino acid is numbered. The computer model of myoglobin is shown at right.

oxygen is attached to it or removed from it. The hemoglobin molecule is the only one for which this kind of study has as yet been carried out. It is known, however, that many proteins change their shape as they perform their functions and that their shape is further modified by the action of the small molecules that activate or inhibit them. The large number of enzyme systems involved in regulating the complex metabolic pathways of the living cell have been studied so far only at the level of the overall shape of the enzyme molecule; practically nothing is known of the specific structural changes that may be important for enzyme function and control.

Another problem currently being investigated by many workers concerns the way in which proteins achieve their final three-dimensional configuration when they are synthesized. During the past few years many of the processes involved in protein synthesis have become rather well understood. As a result one knows, at least in general terms, how the cell determines the sequence of amino acids from which protein molecules are assembled and how this sequence establishes the way in which the atoms of a protein are connected [see top illustration on opposite page]. It is not, however, the chemical sequence, or connectedness, that establishes the functional properties of a protein. These properties are a consequence of the exact three-dimensional arrangement of the molecule's atoms in space.

As a result of work in the past 15 years, there is now a considerable body of evidence showing that the three-dimensional configuration of a protein molecule is determined uniquely by its amino acid sequence. The number of possible sequences is immense because the cell has at its disposal 20 kinds of amino acid building block. The configuration assumed by any particular sequence reflects the fact that the molecule arranges itself so as to minimize its total free energy. In other words, each protein has the shape it has because outside energy would be needed to give it any other shape. The experimental evidence for this conclusion comes from results obtained with many different proteins.

The first really critical experiments in this regard were carried out by Christian B. Anfinsen and his collaborators at the National Institutes of Health with the enzyme ribonuclease, a protein consisting of 153 amino acids

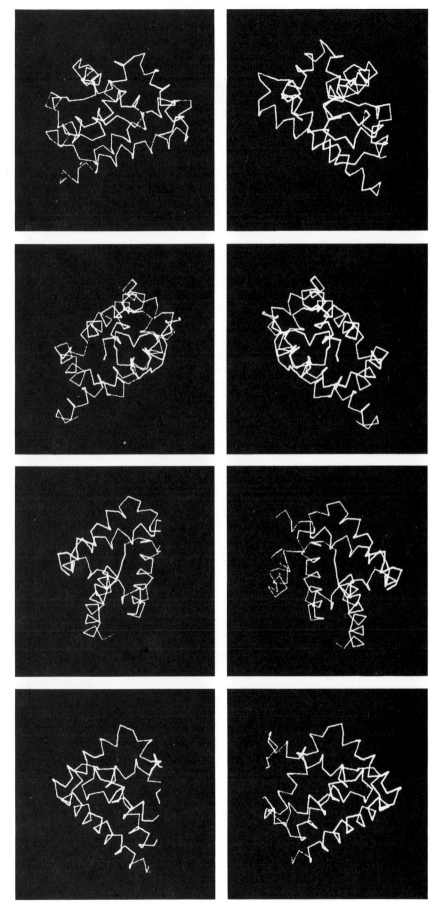

COMPUTER MODEL of myoglobin, which was based on coordinates supplied by Kendrew, is rotated on the screen in this sequence (*top to bottom, left to right*). This display omits the heme group. The pictures are selected frames from a 16-millimeter motion-picture film.

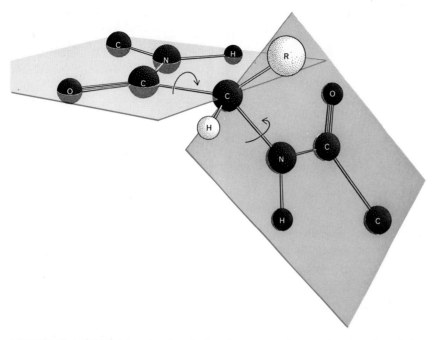

ROTATION ANGLES determine the relation of two successive peptide groups in a chain. Two such groups are shown here. The six atoms (CCONHC) of each group lie in a plane. Two adjacent planes have one atom—the carbon to which a hydrogen and a side group (R) are bonded—in common. Two rotation angles (*arrows*) give the relation of the two planes.

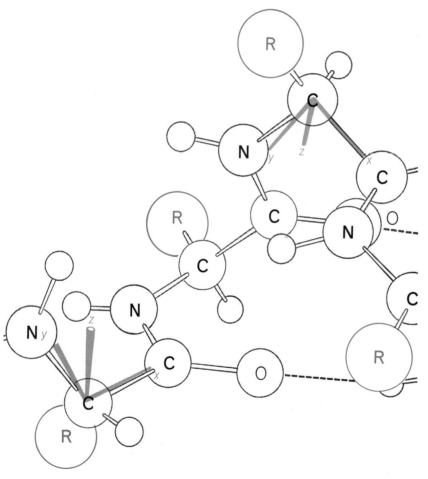

RECTANGULAR COORDINATE SYSTEMS establish the location of atoms in the model. One (*left*), at the amino end of the peptide chain, is the frame of reference for the entire chain. Others (*right*) are local systems defining positions of atoms in side groups. The computer calculates the transformation that refers local systems back to the original system.

in a single chain. In our laboratory we have studied the enzyme alkaline phosphatase, which consists of about 800 amino acids arranged in two chains. Both proteins can be treated so that they lose their well-defined three-dimensional configuration without breaking any of the chemical bonds that establish the connectedness of the molecule. In this "denatured" state the proteins are no longer enzymatically active. But if the denaturing agent is removed and the proteins are put in a solution containing certain salts and the correct acidity, the activity can be reestablished.

The alkaline phosphatase molecule has two identical subunits that are inactive by themselves. They can be separated from each other by increasing the acidity of the solution, and they reassemble to form the active "doublet" when the solution is made neutral once again. In addition the subunits themselves can be denatured, with the result that they become random, or structureless, coils. Under the proper conditions it takes only a few minutes to reestablish the enzymatic activity from this disrupted state, along with what appears to be the original three-dimensional configuration of the doublet molecule. An enzymatically active hybrid molecule can even be formed out of subunits from two different organisms. The individual subunits from the two organisms have different amino acid sequences, but they fold into a shape such that the subunits are still able to recognize each other and form an active molecule. These renaturation processes can take place in a solution containing no protein other than the denatured one, and without the intervention of other cellular components.

Apart from the renaturation experiments, the mechanism of synthesis has suggested an additional factor that may be relevant in establishing the correct three-dimensional form of the protein. It is known that the synthetic process always begins at a particular end of the protein molecule—the end carrying an amino group (NH_2)—and proceeds to the end carrying a carboxyl group (COOH). It is plausible to imagine that proteins fold as they are formed in such a way that the configuration of the amino end is sufficiently stable to prevent its alteration while the rest of the molecule is being synthesized. Although this hypothetical mechanism seems to be contradicted by the renaturation experiments just described, it may represent the way some proteins are folded. Because the mechanism would place certain constraints on the folding of a protein molecule, it implies that the active protein is not in a state in which free energy is at a minimum but rather is in a metastable, or temporarily stable, state of somewhat higher energy.

A molecular biologist's understanding of a molecular structure is usually reflected in his ability to construct a three-dimensional model of it. If the molecule is large, however, model-building can be frustrating for purely mechanical reasons; for example, the model collapses. In any event, the building of models is too time-consuming if one wishes to examine many different configurations, which is the case when one is attempting to predict an unknown structure. When one is dealing with the largest molecules, even a model is not much help in the task of enumerating and evaluating all the small interactions that contribute to the molecule's stability. For this task the help of a computer is indispensable.

Any molecular model is based on the nature of the bonds that hold particular kinds of atoms together. From the viewpoint of the model-builder the important fact is that these bonds are the same no matter where in a large molecule the atom is found. For instance, if a carbon atom has four other atoms bonded to it, they will be arranged as if they were located at the corners of a tetrahedron, so that any two bonds form an angle of approximately 109.5 degrees. The lengths of bonds are even more constant than their angles; bonds that are only one to two angstrom units long are frequently known to be constant in length with an accuracy of a few percent. In general the details of atomic spacing are known from the X-ray analysis of small molecules; this knowledge simplifies the task of building models of large molecules.

An example of the value of such knowledge was the discovery by Linus Pauling and Robert B. Corey at the California Institute of Technology that the fundamental repeating bond in protein structures—the peptide bond that joins the CO of one amino acid to the NH of the next—forms an arrangement of six atoms that lie in a plane. This knowledge enabled them to predict that the amino acid units in a protein chain would tend to become arranged in a particular helical form: the alpha helix. It was subsequently found that such helixes provide a significant portion of the structure of many protein molecules. Thus in advance of any crystallographic information about the structure of a particular protein molecule, one knows

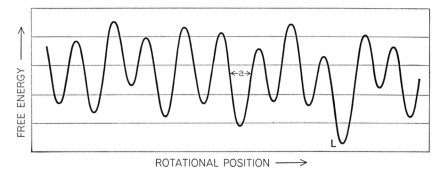

TOTAL ENERGY of a configuration varies with distance between atoms, which depends on all the rotation angles. It is easy to distinguish lowest-energy point L from local valleys, or metastable states, by visual inspection, but a computer must calculate each point in the curve, repeating the operation often enough not to miss a valley. It must calculate the energy at angles separated by no more than a small fraction of the interval indicated as a.

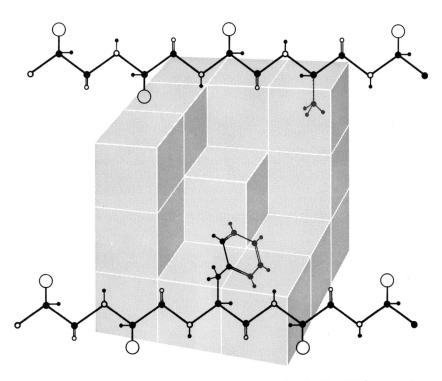

CUBING PROCEDURE eliminates unnecessary computation by identifying atoms that are sufficiently near each other to affect the molecule's energy. The computer searches the area around an atom residing in the center cube and reports if there are any atoms in the 26 adjacent cubes. This also helps to reveal a molecule's edges and holes inside it.

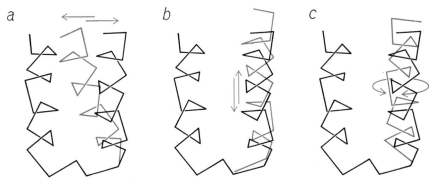

MANIPULATION of the computer-built model is accomplished by three different routines. The routine called "close" in effect puts a spring between any pair of points indicated by the investigator (a). The routine "glide" causes a single helical region to be pulled along its own axis (b). "Revolve" imposes a torque that rotates a region about its axis (c).

the spatial arrangement of atoms within the peptide bonds, as well as the detailed geometry of its alpha-helical regions.

The planar configuration of the peptide bond allows an enormous reduction in the number of variables necessary for a complete description of a protein molecule. Instead of three-dimensional coordinates for each atom, all one needs in order to establish the path of the central chain of the molecule are the two rotation angles where two peptide bonds come together [see top illustration on page 2164]. The complete description requires, in addition to this information, the specification of the rotation angles of the side chains in those amino acids whose side chains are not completely fixed.

A further reduction in the number of variables would be possible if one could predict from the amino acid sequence which parts of the molecule are in the form of alpha helixes. The few proteins whose structures have been completely determined provide some indication of which amino acids are likely to be found in helical regions, but not enough is yet known to make such predictions with any assurance.

Because protein chains are formed by linking molecules that belong to a single class (the amino acids), the linkage process can be expressed mathematically in a form that is particularly suited for a high-speed digital computer. We have written computer programs that calculate the coordinates of each atom of the protein, using as input variables only those angles in which rotational changes can occur; all other angles and bond lengths are entered as rigid constraints in the program. The method of calculation involves the use of a local coordinate system for the atoms in each amino acid unit and a fixed overall coordinate system into which all local coordinates are transformed.

The transformation that relates the local coordinate systems to the fixed coordinate system is recalculated by the computer program each time a new atom is added to the linear peptide backbone. Each chemical bond is treated as a translation and a rotation of this transformation. The process requires a substantial amount of calculation, but each time the backbone reaches the central atom of a new amino acid the relative positions of the side-group atoms can be taken from the computer memory where this information is stored for each of the 20 varieties of amino acid. It is then a simple matter to translate and rotate the side-group atoms from their local coordinate system into the fixed-coordinate system of the entire molecule.

The new value of the transformation at each step along the backbone is determined by the fixed rotation angles and translation distances that are built into the computer program and by the variable angles that must somehow be determined during the running of the program. The principal problem, therefore, is precisely how to provide correct values for the variable angles. A number of investigators are working on this problem in different ways. Before discussing any of these approaches I should emphasize the magnitude of the problem that remains even after one has gone as far as possible in using chemical constraints to reduce the number of variables from several thousand to a few hundred. Because each bond angle must be specified with an accuracy of a few degrees, the number of possible configurations that can result when each angle is varied by a small amount becomes astronomical even for a small protein. Moreover, these small rotations can produce a large effect on the total energy of the structure [see top illustration on preceding page].

One way to understand the difficulty

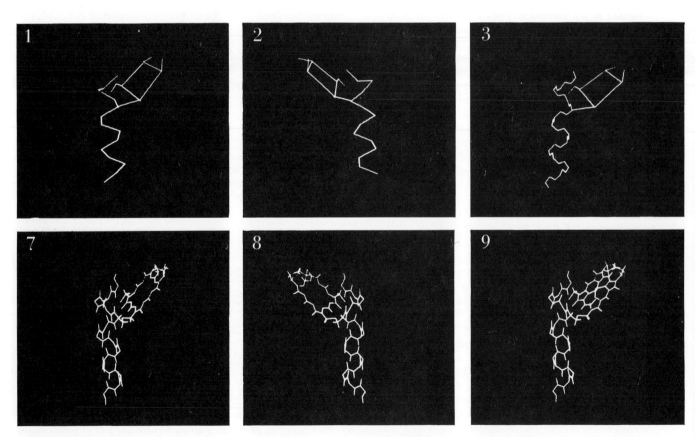

CYTOCHROME C segment seen in the two opening illustrations is shown on this page and the opposite page in the various degrees of detail of which the system is capable. At first only the carbon atoms to which the side groups are attached are displayed, along with the

of finding a configuration of minimum energy is to imagine the problem facing a man lost in a mountainous wilderness in a dense fog. He may know that within a few miles there is an inhabited river valley leading into a calm lake. He may also know that the lake is at the lowest point in the area, but let us assume that he can only determine his own elevation and the slope of the ground in his immediate vicinity. He can walk down whatever hill he is standing on, but this would probably trap him at the bottom of a small valley far from the lake he seeks. In finding a configuration of minimum energy the comparable situation would be getting trapped in a metastable state far from a real energy minimum. Our lost man has only two dimensions to worry about, north-south and east-west; the corresponding problem in a molecule involves several hundred dimensions.

Our approach to this problem has assumed that even sophisticated techniques for energy minimization will not, at least at present, be sufficient to determine the structure of a protein from its amino acid sequence in a fully automatic fashion. We therefore decided to develop programs that would make use of a man-computer combination to do a

kind of model-building that neither a man nor a computer could accomplish alone. This approach implies that one must be able to obtain information from the computer and introduce changes in the way the program is running in a span of time that is appropriate to human operation. This in turn suggests that the output of the computer must be presented not in numbers but in visual form.

I first became aware of the possibilities of using visual output from a computer in a conversation with Robert M. Fano, the director of Project MAC at the Massachusetts Institute of Technology. (MAC stands for multiple-access computer.) It soon became clear that the new types of visual display that had been developed would permit direct interaction of the investigator and a molecular model that was being constructed by the computer. All our subsequent work on this problem has made use of the large computer of Project MAC, which operates on the basis of "time-sharing," or access by many users. The system, developed by Fernando J. Corbató, allows as many as 30 people to have programs running on the computer at the same time. For all practical purposes it seems to each of them that he is alone on the system. A user can have

any of his data in the high-speed memory printed out on his own typewriter, and he can make whatever changes he wants in this stored data. What is more important from our point of view is the ability to make changes in the commands that control the sequential flow of the program itself.

It is true, of course, that one of 30 users has access to a computer that, when it is fully occupied, has only a thirtieth of the speed of the normal machine, but for many problems this is enough to keep the man side of the man-machine combination quite well occupied. The program that acts to supervise the time-sharing system is organized in such a way that no user can interfere with the system or with any other user, and the computer is not allowed to stand idle if the man takes time out to think.

In working with molecular models we are interested in being able to obtain data quickly in order to evaluate the effect of changing the input variables of the program. For any particular molecular configuration the computer can readily supply the positions (in the three-dimensional coordinates x, y and z) of all the atoms. The important question is: What can be done with 5,000 to 10,000 numbers corresponding to the

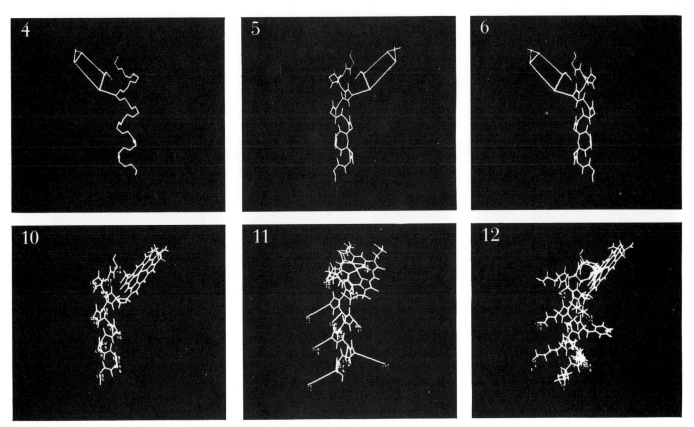

square outline of the heme group connected to this segment (1, 2). The other atoms of the backbone are added (3, 4), then the oxygen and hydrogen atoms (5, 6). The heme group is shown in more detail (7–9), and side groups are named (10) and displayed (11, 12).

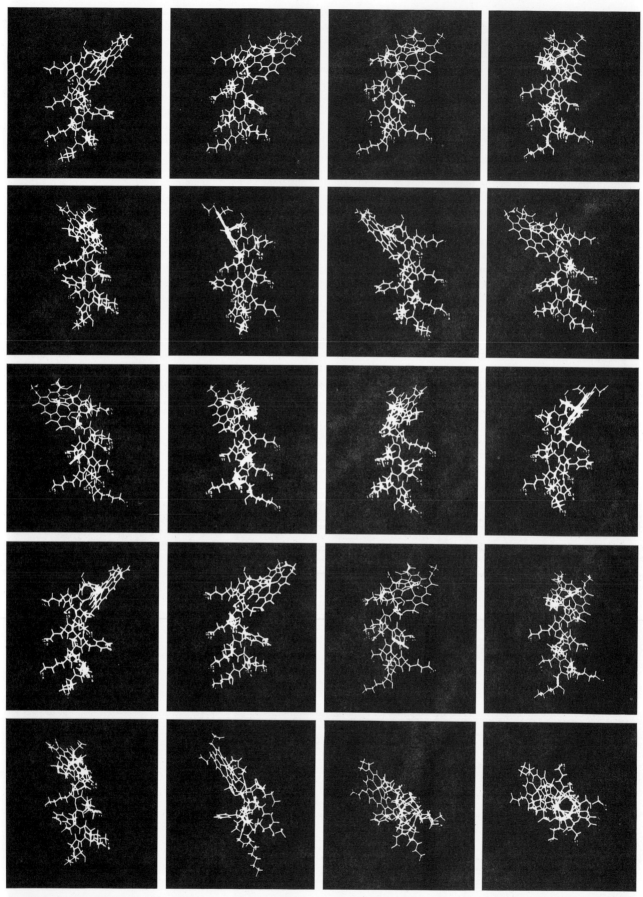

CYTOCHROME HELIX is rotated on the screen (*left to right, top to bottom*), a procedure that makes it possible for the investigator to perceive the three-dimensional arrangement of the atoms. A set of three-dimensional vectors connecting the atoms of the molecule is stored in the computer's high-speed memory. The computer calculates the projection of those vectors on a plane and draws the projected vectors on the screen. The operator controls the rotation of the plane, thus apparently turning the model.

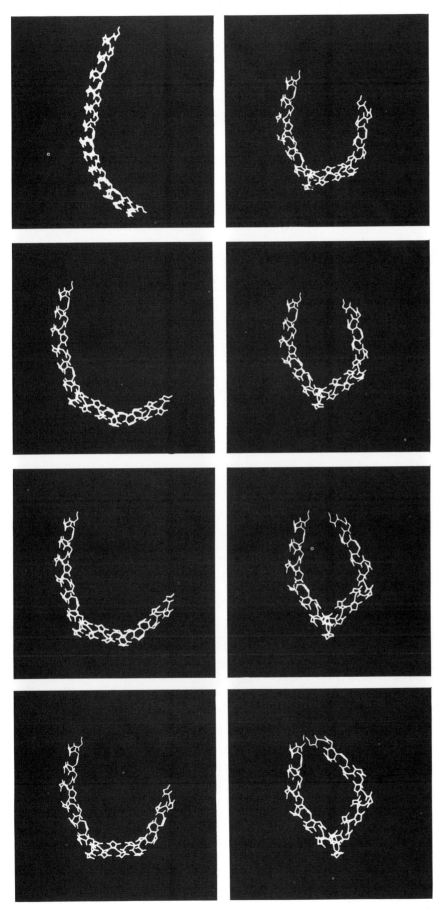

"CLOSING" ROUTINE is applied to a hypothetical peptide chain assumed to consist of several helical sections. The individual sections do not bend, but the rotation angles between sections are changed (*top to bottom, left to right*) to close the chain into a circle.

position of every atom in even a small protein? Obviously if we could formulate specific questions concerning energy, bond angles and lengths, overall shape, density and so on, the computer could calculate the answer and there would be no need for a man ever to look at the numerical values of the coordinates. We realized that our best hope of gaining insight into unexpected structural relations—relations that had not been anticipated—lay in getting the computer to present a three-dimensional picture of the molecule.

Although computer-controlled oscilloscopes have been available for about 10 years, they have been used mainly to display numbers and letters. It is only recently that they have been used to produce the output of computer programs in graphical form. The oscilloscope tube can of course present only a two-dimensional image. It is no great trick, however, to have the computer rotate the coordinates of the molecule before plotting their projection. If this is done, the brain of the human viewer readily constructs a three-dimensional image from the sequential display of two-dimensional images. Such sequential projections seem to be just as useful to the brain as simultaneous stereoscopic projections viewed by two eyes. The effect of rotation obtained from the continuously changing projection nonetheless has an inherent ambiguity. An observer cannot determine the direction of rotation from observation of the changing picture alone. In the Project MAC display system, designed by John Ward and Robert Stotz, the rate of rotation of the picture is controlled by the position of a globe on which the observer rests his hand; with a little practice the coupling between hand and brain becomes so familiar that any ambiguity in the picture can easily be resolved.

In evaluating the energy of a particular configuration of a protein molecule one must add up all the small interactions of atomic groups that contribute to this energy. These must include interactions not only between the different parts of the protein molecule but also between the parts of the protein molecule and the surrounding water molecules. If we are interested in altering the configuration in the direction of lower energy, we must be able to calculate the derivative of each of the energy terms—that is, the direction in which the energy curves slope—as changes are made in each of the rotation angles. Accordingly we must calculate a very large number of interatomic distances and the derivative of these distances with respect to the allowed rotation angle.

The derivatives can be calculated, however, without going through the extended transformation calculations needed to generate the coordinates themselves. The rotation around any chemical bond will cause one part of the molecule to revolve with respect to another. If both members of a pair of atoms are on the same side of the bond being altered, the rotation will not give rise to a change in their distance. If the two atoms are on opposite sides of the rotating bond, one of the atoms will move in a circle around the axis of rotation while the other remains stationary. By analyzing the geometry of this motion we can simplify the derivative calculations to the point where they require very little computation.

Even though each of these derivative calculations can be done in a few hundred microseconds of computer time, there would still be an excessive amount of calculation if it were done for all possible pairs of atoms within the molecule. Fortunately the interactions with which we are concerned are short-range ones, and most of the pairs of atoms are too far apart to contribute appre-

ciably to the overall energy. In order to select out all pairs of atoms that are close to each other, we have developed a procedure called cube-testing. All the space in the region of the molecule is divided into cubes of some predetermined size, let us say five angstroms on an edge (two or three times the typical bond length) and each atom is assigned to a cube. To consider the interactions involving any given atom one need only determine the distance between this atom and all others in the same cube and in the 26 surrounding ones [*see middle illustration on page 2165*]. Although the procedure is still time-consuming, it is much faster than having to do calculations for all possible pairs of atoms in the molecule.

In addition to enabling us to screen the data for close pairs, the cubing procedure provides information about which groups in the protein molecule can interact with the surrounding water molecules. In order to enumerate such interactions, we first define the "insideness" and "outsideness" of the molecule, outsideness meaning that a particular atom or group of atoms is accessible to the surrounding water and insideness that it is not. If we examine the cubing pattern for a particular molecule, an atom on the outside would be in a cube

that is surrounded on one side by filled cubes and on the other by empty ones. In a similar way we can detect holes in the midst of the structure by looking for empty cubes that are surrounded on all sides by filled ones.

By suitable use of derivative calculation and cubing we can alter any configuration of the molecule in the direction of lower energy. This procedure, however, would almost certainly lead to a structure that is trapped in one of the local minima—one of the higher valleys of our wilderness analogy—and may not even be close to the true minimum-energy configuration we are looking for. For a real molecule floating in solution, the local minima would not represent traps because the normal thermal vibration of the molecule and its parts supplies enough energy to move the structure out of any valley that is not a true minimum.

Although there are various ways in which one can use random elements in a computer calculation to simulate thermal vibration, it is our experience that an investigator who is looking at the molecule can frequently understand the reason for the local minimum and by making a small alteration in the structure can return the program to its

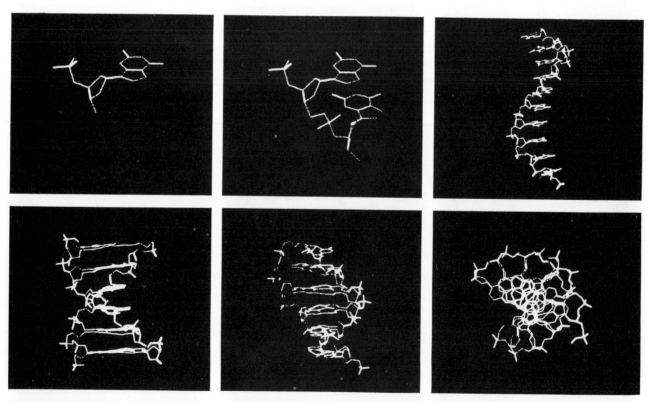

DEOXYRIBONUCLEIC ACID (DNA) is modeled by a program devised by Robert Langridge and Andrew A. MacEwan of the Children's Cancer Research Foundation and Harvard Medical School. This DNA sequence (*left to right, top to bottom*) begins with a single nucleotide: a pentagonal sugar plus a phosphate group and a base. A second nucleotide is added, and then more to make a helical chain that joins with a second chain to form the characteristic double helix. Then the helix is rotated in space.

DISPLAY UNIT designed by John Ward and Robert Stotz has access to the large time-shared central computer at the Massachusetts Institute of Technology. The investigator communicates with the computer by typing commands or punching preset buttons on a keyboard or by pointing with the light pen. He regulates the direction and the speed of rotation of the model by moving the gimbaled control on which his right hand rests.

downhill path. Such alterations can be accomplished in the computer by changing the program in such a way as to introduce pseudo-energy terms that have the effect of pulling on parts of the structure. A few simple subprograms that introduce the appropriate pseudo-energies enable us to do the same kind of pulling and pushing in the computer that we can do with our hands while building actual models.

Pulling a structure by means of these pseudo-energy terms is also useful for building a model that observes all the chemical constraints and at the same time has its atoms as close as possible to the positions indicated by X-ray diffraction studies. In this case the pseudo-energies can be regarded as springs pulling designated atoms to their experimentally determined positions. Such calculations have been carried out by Martin Zwick, a graduate student at M.I.T., in order to make a model of myoglobin fit the configuration determined from X-ray data by John C. Kendrew and Herman Watson at the Laboratory of Molecular Biology in Cambridge. For this type of problem a helpful procedure has been developed by William Davidon of Haverford College. In his program one starts by "walking" in the direction of the steepest slope, but with each successive step one builds up information as to how the slope of the hillside changes.

Once we had produced a computer model of myoglobin, we could ask questions concerning the relative importance of short-range forces acting between various parts of the molecule. There are, for example, Van der Waals forces: electrostatic attractions due to the electric dipoles that all atoms induce in one another when they are close together. There are also electrostatic interactions that arise from the permanent electric dipoles associated with the peptide bonds. The permanent dipole attractions turned out to be larger than we had expected. It is thus possible that the electrostatic interaction between different regions of a protein may play a substantial role in stabilizing its structure. This results in part from the fact that the electric dipoles in an alpha helix are added to one another along the direction of the axis. For this reason two helixes that wind in the same direction will repel each other and two that wind in opposite directions will attract each other. In myoglobin the overall effect is a substantial attractive force. This calculation requires some form of model-building, because the electrically charged regions are associated with the C—O and N—H groups along the backbone, and the hydrogen atom is not detected in the X-ray analysis.

Although the electrostatic interaction energy is of the same order of magnitude as that required to denature a protein, it is probably not the dominant energy for the folding of a protein molecule. The primary source of energy for this purpose probably comes from the interaction of the amino acid side chains and the surrounding water; the electrostatic interactions may do no more than modify the basic structure.

We still have much to learn about the magnitude of the various energy terms involved in holding a protein molecule together. Meanwhile we have been trying to develop our computer technique, using the knowledge we have. Is this knowledge enough to enable us to find the lowest energy state of a protein molecule and to predict its structure in advance of its determination by X-ray analysis?

The answer to this question probably depends on how well we understand what really happens when a protein molecule in a cell folds itself up. Our work has been based on the hypothesis that the folding starts independently in several regions of the protein and that the first structural development is the formation of a number of segments of alpha helix. Our assumption is that these segments then interact with one another to form the final molecular structure. In this method of analyzing the problem the units that have to be handled independently are the helical regions rather than the individual amino acids. Thus the number of independent variables is greatly reduced. The success of the procedure depends, however, on the assumption that we can deduce from the amino acid sequence alone which regions are likely to be helical. It is not necessary, however, that we guess the helical regions correctly the first time; we can see what happens when helical regions are placed in many different parts of the molecule. Several other groups working on this problem are following the hypothesis that the folding proceeds only from the amino end of the protein. Until one of these approaches succeeds in predicting the structure of a protein and having the prediction confirmed by X-ray analysis, we can only consider the different hypotheses as more or less plausible working guides in studying the problem.

It is still too early to evaluate the usefulness of the man-computer combination in solving real problems of molecular biology. It does seem likely, however, that only with this combination can the investigator use his "chemical insight" in an effective way. We already know that we can use the computer to build and display models of large molecules and that this procedure can be very useful in helping us to understand how such molecules function. But it may still be a few years before we have learned just how useful it is for the investigator to be able to interact with the computer while the molecular model is being constructed.

The Author

CYRUS LEVINTHAL is professor of biophysics at the Massachusetts Institute of Technology. His original bent was toward physics; he took a Ph.D. in nuclear physics at the University of California at Berkeley in 1950 and spent seven years in the physics department of the University of Michigan, starting as instructor and leaving as associate professor. In 1957 he began his present work in the biology department of M.I.T. Levinthal did his undergraduate work at Swarthmore College, from which he received a bachelor's degree in 1943.

Bibliography

THE KINETICS OF FORMATION OF NATIVE RIBONUCLEASE DURING OXIDATION OF THE REDUCED POLYPEPTIDE CHAIN. C. B. Anfinsen, E. Haber, M. Sela and F. H. White, Jr., in *Proceedings of the National Academy of Sciences*, Vol. 47, No. 9, pages 1309–1334; September 15, 1961.

THE NATURE OF THE CHEMICAL BOND AND THE STRUCTURE OF MOLECULES AND CRYSTALS: AN INTRODUCTION TO MODERN STRUCTURAL CHEMISTRY. Linus Pauling. Cornell University Press, 1960.

REACTIVATION AND HYBRIDIZATION OF REDUCED ALKALINE PHOSPHATASE. Cyrus Levinthal, Ethan R. Signer and Kathleen Fetherolf in *Proceedings of the National Academy of Sciences*, Vol. 48, No. 7, pages 1230–1237; July, 1962.

STEREOCHEMISTRY OF POLYPEPTIDE CHAIN CONFIGURATIONS. G. N. Ramachandran, C. Ramakrishnan and V. Sasisekharan in *Journal of Molecular Biology*, Vol. 7, No. 1, pages 95–99; July, 1963.

SCIENTIFIC
AMERICAN   June 1966, Vol. 214, No. 6, pp. 74-81   OFFPRINT 1044

THE BLUE-GREEN ALGAE

by Patrick Echlin

These primitive plants more closely resemble bacteria than they do other algae. They live in an extraordinary range of environments, and they have both beneficial and harmful effects in human affairs.

The algae are the simplest members of the plant kingdom, and the blue-green algae are the simplest of the algae. Indeed, the blue-green algae resemble bacteria more closely than they do other forms of algae. By this token they occupy a distinctive niche in the evolutionary order of things. They provide insights into the evolution of bacteria and algae, and also, since they are among the most primitive living cells, into the beginnings of the cell itself. Today, moreover, the blue-green algae have a considerable and increasing economic importance: they have both beneficial and harmful effects on human life.

Most of the blue-green algae are blue-green, but not all; they are found in a wide range of colors. Their name stems from the fact that the first species to be recognized as members of the group were blue-green. A few of the 2,000 species now known live as single cells of microscopic size. The cells of other species gather in colonies but still live essentially as individuals. Most species of blue-green alga, however, are filamentous: their cells are strung together in a hairlike structure. This is the form in which blue-green algae are most likely to be visible to the unaided eye, either as a mosslike growth on land or as a soft mass in water.

Whatever the form, the individual cells of blue-green algae are much alike. Each is surrounded by a gelatinous sheath. Inside the sheath is a thin membrane that encloses the cell's cytoplasm. The cell of a blue-green alga lacks a well-defined nucleus and the elaborate intracellular membranes and separate organelles of cells in advanced plants and animals. In the peripheral parts of the cytoplasm there are, however, complex lamellae, or thin sheets,

that apparently form from the cell membrane [see illustrations on page 2178].

Reproduction in most blue-green algae is a simple and asexual process. The cell merely divides. Some of the filamentous forms reproduce by a breaking of the filament, the two parts of which then grow by cell division. A few species of blue-green alga are able to reproduce by forming spores.

Like most other algae, the blue-greens manufacture their food by photosynthesis. They are distinctive, however, in that their photosynthetic pigments are distributed throughout the peripheral lamellae rather than in discrete bodies such as chloroplasts. A unique feature of certain filamentous species is the tendency to form heterocysts: large colorless cells at irregular intervals along a filament. The function of these cells is uncertain. According to various hypotheses they represent a vestigial reproductive cell, a store of food or a structure associated with either cell division or the formation of internal spores.

The blue-green algae are widely distributed over land and water, often in environments where no other vegetation can exist. They live in water that is salt, brackish or fresh; in hot springs and cold springs, both pure and mineralized; in salt lakes; in moist soils, and in symbiotic or parasitic association with other plants and animals. Most marine forms grow along the shore, fixed to the bottom in the narrow zone between the high and low tidemarks; a few float about as plankton. The largest number of species live in fresh water. Some can be found in fast-moving or turbulent waters, such as the water falling on rocks under a waterfall; others flourish in quiet waters—even in bodies

of water that appear only temporarily.

On land in places of high humidity, such as gullies on the lower slopes of mountains, both tree trunks and rocks may be covered with gelatinous mats of many hues; the mats consist of single-celled blue-green algae. The filamentous algae form a feltlike growth over extensive land areas. Where high temperatures are combined with high humidity, as in the Tropics, the growth can be quite luxurious.

The wide variety of colors among blue-green algae has two main sources: the pigmentation of the gelatinous sheath and the pigmentation within the cell. The sheath, particularly in species that grow on land, is often deeply pigmented. Yellow and brown tints predominate, although shades of red and violet are also seen. The sheath coloration appears to be related to the environment—chiefly to the amount of sunlight received by the algae and to the acidity of their medium.

Within the cell are three pigments that are found in all plants capable of photosynthesis: chlorophyll, carotene and xanthophyll. In addition there are two pigments that are found only in this group of organisms: the blue pigment c-phycocyanin and the red pigment c-phycoerythrin. It is these two pigments that are principally responsible for the group's diverse coloration. The colors range from the red of the species *Oscillatoria cortiana* and *Phormidium persicinum* through the emerald green of the genus *Anacystis* to the near black of some algae that live on rocks. The color of the algae is also dependent on the age and physiological state of the organism. Healthy cultures of *Anacystis montana* are a bright emerald green, whereas an old culture is a dirty yellow. There are even a few members of the

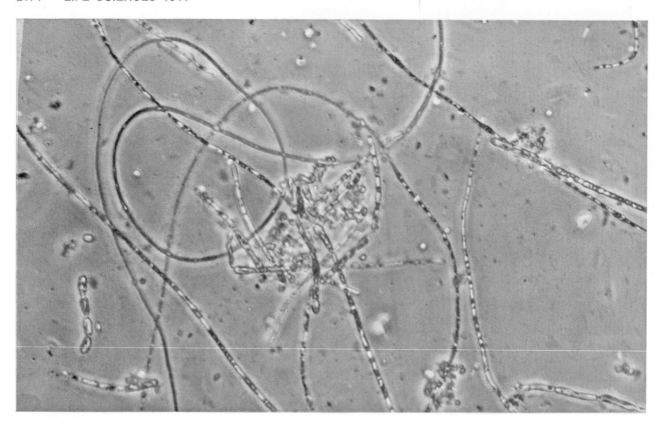

BLUE-GREEN ALGAE of the species *Gloeotrichia echinulata* consist of numbers of individual cells strung together in attenuated filaments radiating from a central point. The enlargement in this photomicrograph is about 150 diameters. Blue-green algae actually appear in a variety of colors. They were named blue-green because the first specimens to be classified were of that color.

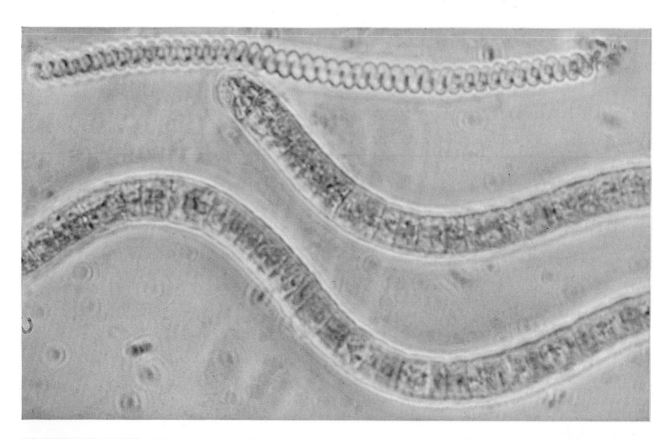

FILAMENTOUS FORMS of blue-green algae also include the species *Spirulina versicolor* (top) and two filaments of the genus *Arthrospira*; the enlargement is approximately 1,500 diameters. *Arthrospira* is one of the blue-green algae responsible for the pink color often seen in flamingos; the birds acquire the color from carotenes in the blue-green algae that are part of their diet.

blue-green group that are colorless; they live in such diverse habitats as the bottom of lakes, the intestines of animals and the human mouth.

Certain forms of blue-green algae have the capacity for changing color in relation to the color of the light that falls on them. The filamentous alga *Oscillatoria sancta* is green in red light, blue-green in yellow-brown light, red in green light and brownish yellow in blue light. Some deep-water algae are red, apparently for the following reason. As sunlight penetrates deeper into water its longer wavelengths, starting with the wavelengths of red light, are progressively absorbed. The last part of the visible spectrum to be absorbed is the blue. Such light could best be utilized for photosynthesis by algae with a preponderance of red pigments.

The capacity of the blue-green algae for adjusting to light of different intensities and colors means they are better adapted than other photosynthetic organisms to utilize the available light. This characteristic probably has much to do with the occurrence of these algae in so many terrestrial and aquatic habitats. Blue-green algae can grow in full

sunlight and in almost complete darkness. In the Jenolan caves of Australia, for example, they grow on moist limestone near incandescent lamps that are lighted for only six hours a week while tourists pass through.

The majority of blue-green algae are aerobic photoautotrophs: their life processes require only oxygen, light and inorganic substances. The process of photosynthesis uses the energy of light to build carbohydrates (and some fats) out of carbon dioxide in the air or the water. The process of respiration then uses oxygen to "burn" these products and supply the energy needed for the rest of the alga's activities. Unlike more advanced organisms, these algae need no substances that have been preformed by other organisms.

A few forms of blue-green algae, such as a species of *Oscillatoria* that is found in mud at the bottom of the Thames, are able to live anaerobically: their life processes do not require free oxygen. They obtain their energy from inorganic compounds such as hydrogen sulfide. Other species, notably some that live in the soil, can grow in the dark if they are

supplied with suitable organic nutrients. Some forms are able to fix atmospheric nitrogen in soluble salts that can then be utilized by the alga itself.

A remarkable feature of blue-green algae in water is their ability to move even though they possess no recognizable locomotory parts such as flagella and cilia. The filamentous forms can move fairly rapidly; the unicellular forms move much more slowly. All the blue-green algae exhibit a gliding movement parallel to the alga's long axis. The movement can be either forward or backward. Sometimes it is accompanied by rotation.

Several mechanisms have been put forward to explain these movements. One currently receiving attention is that the excretion of a mucilaginous substance propels the alga. Other proposed mechanisms involve osmosis, surface tension, the streaming of cytoplasm within the cell and the propagation of rhythmic waves of contraction through the cell. In connection with this last hypothesis a scalloped edge visible in electron micrographs of some species of blue-green algae may be significant. Such an edge could be associated with contractile movement.

Another remarkable feature of the blue-green algae is their ability to withstand environmental extremes such as high and low temperatures and high concentrations of salt. Indeed, blue-green algae are perhaps best known to biologists as inhabitants of hot springs. Most of these "thermal" species live at temperatures of 50 to 60 degrees centigrade (122 to 140 degrees Fahrenheit); a few have been known to exist at temperatures as high as 85 degrees C. (185 degrees F.). Yet most of the thermal blue-green algae can also thrive at normal temperatures. Several species that flourish in my laboratory at the University of Cambridge at a temperature of 15 degrees C. (59 degrees F.) were collected from a hot spring in Yellowstone National Park.

As for the other end of the environmental temperature scale, blue-green algae are found in mountain streams and in Antarctic lakes. Some species live in association with lichens on bare mountain rocks in polar regions, where the surface temperature may vary in a few hours from −60 to +15 degrees C. (−76 to +59 degrees F.). In fact, the only cold environment in which blue-green algae are rare is snow.

About a fifth of all the blue-green algae live in saline environments. A few

ORDER AND FAMILY	GENERA	CHARACTERISTICS
ORDER CHROÖCOCCALES	ANACYSTIS CHROÖCOCCUS GLOEOCAPSA GLOEOTHECE MERISMOPEDIA MICROCYSTIS SYNECHOCOCCUS SYNECHOCYSTIS	Unicellular and free-living, solitary or colonial.
ORDER CHAMAESIPHONALES	CHAMAESIPHON DERMOCARPA	Unicellular and free-living, solitary or colonial. Spore-producing.
ORDER PLEUROCAPSALES	PLEUROCAPSA	Filamentous. Growing on or in rocks.
ORDER NOSTOCALES		Filamentous, simple or branched.
FAMILY OSCILLATORIACEAE	LYNGBYA OSCILLATORIA	Simple filaments. No heterocysts.
FAMILY SCYTONEMATACEAE	PLECTONEMA SCYTONEMA TOLYPOTHRIX	False branching. Generally with heterocysts.
FAMILY RIVULARIACEAE	GLOEOTRICHIA RIVULARIA	False branching. Colonial.
FAMILY NOSTOCACEAE	ANABAENA CYLINDROSPERMUM NOSTOC	Simple filaments.
ORDER STIGONEMATALES	FISCHERELLA STIGONEMA	True branching. Heterocysts.

CLASSIFICATION of blue-green algae according to a system used by many botanists lists them in the division Schizophyta, class Myxophyceae (Cyanophyceae) of the plant kingdom. About 2,000 species of blue-green alga are grouped in the orders and families shown here.

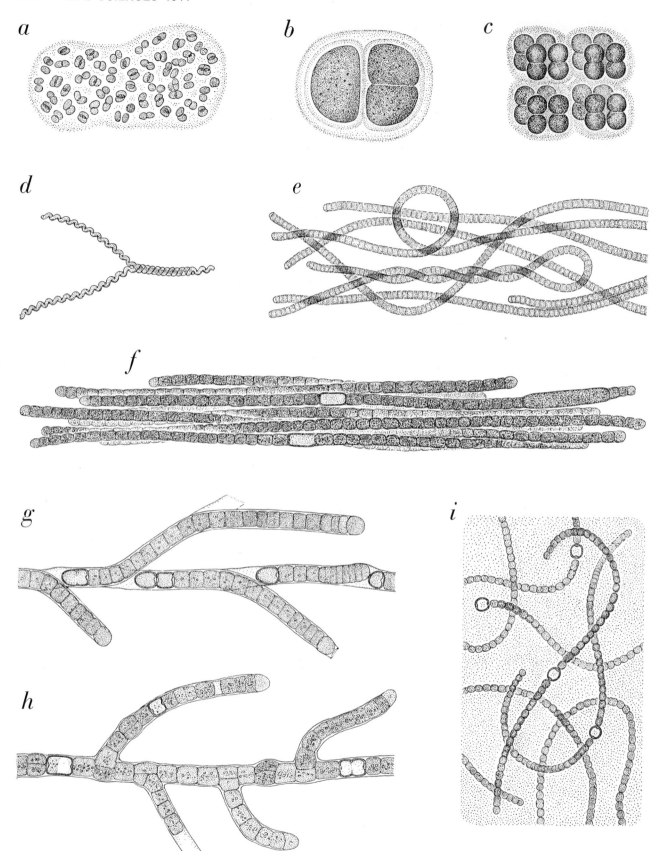

TYPICAL SPECIMENS of blue-green algae include, at top, three of the unicellular and free-living variety: *a, Coccochloris* in a loosely formed colony; *b, Anacystis dimidiata* dividing; *c, Anacystis thermalis* in a compact colony. The remaining examples are of genera in which several cells exist together in a filament: *d, Spirulina,* with two intertwined filaments; *e, Oscillatoria; f, Aphanizomenon,* with two of the large, colorless cells called heterocysts; *g, Tolypothrix,* which is a genus with false branching; *h, Hapalosiphon,* which has true branching; *i, Nostoc* in a gelatinous mass. Each species is represented at an enlargement of about 500 diameters.

species are truly halophilic, or salt-tolerant; such species are found in southern France and in California in brines with a salt concentration as high as 27 percent. (The concentration of salt in seawater is about 3 percent.) An extreme example of high salt tolerance is the single-celled species *Gomphosphaeria,* which grows abundantly in the spring called Bitter Waters in Death Valley. The concentration of magnesium salts there is so high that the mud around the spring is encrusted with them.

From the evolutionary standpoint the algae in general are of interest because of the trends they reveal in the internal organization of the cell and the mechanism of cellular reproduction. The blue-green algae in particular, with their simple cell structure and asexual reproduction, appear to stand in close relation to the first organisms on earth. It is in this context that the similarities between the blue-green algae and the bacteria have intrigued a number of investigators.

Three features that set the blue-green algae and the bacteria apart from all other cellular organisms have been known for some time. These features are the absence of nuclei, the absence of specialized organelles and the absence of sexual reproduction. Citing the absence of certain features from two groups of organisms is, however, a rather negative way of establishing similarity between the groups. With the advances of electron microscopy in recent years it has become possible to examine the fine structure of blue-green algae and bacteria and so to find some positive similarities between them.

One such similarity is a fairly close resemblance between the cell wall of blue-green algae (not the gelatinous sheath) and the cell wall of bacteria [*see illustration on this page*]. In both cases an important component of the cell wall belongs to the class of molecules known as mucopeptides. Another similarity is that in both blue-green algae and the photosynthetic bacteria (as in other photosynthetic organisms) the essential feature of the photosynthetic apparatus is a set of membranes enclosing a space. In the blue-green algae these are the lamellae; in the photosynthetic bacteria they are called the chromatophores.

These similarities and others argue strongly for isolating blue-green algae and bacteria in a group distinct from all other organisms. I would also argue

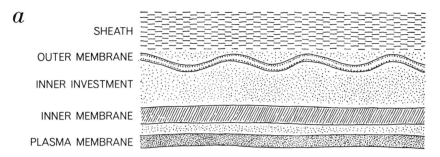

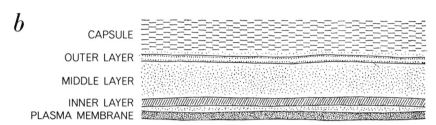

STRUCTURAL RESEMBLANCE between blue-green algae and bacteria is typified by the similarities of their exteriors. At *a* are the sheath and cell wall of a cell of blue-green alga; at *b*, the capsule and wall of a typical bacterium. The particular similarities are in the structure of the walls. In each organism the distance between the outside of the outer membrane or layer and the inside of the inner one is between 200 and 400 angstrom units.

that the blue-green algae and the bacteria have probably descended from the same type of ancestral cell, although here I must rest my case more on speculation than on firm evidence. It is true that there are differences between the two types of organism. Blue-green algae are generally aerobic and photosynthetic and are more complex in form than the bacteria. The bacteria are either aerobic or anaerobic, but they are usually not photosynthetic; they require for their existence substances preformed by other organisms. In cases where bacteria are photosynthetic they differ from blue-green algae in photosynthetic mechanism, particularly in the chemical nature of the pigments.

Still, the similarities are too marked to be overlooked. It is unlikely that so many kindred features would arise independently. This is the root of the argument for a common ancestral cell. The conspicuous differences between the blue-green algae and the bacteria presumably arose at later stages in their evolution.

Perhaps the most important contribution made by the blue-green algae to human affairs lies in the fact that the nitrogen-fixing species increase the fertility of the soil. It is more than likely that this contribution can be enhanced. R. N. Singh of the Banares Hindu University in India has shown that the introduction of blue-green algae to saline and alkaline soils in the province of Uttar Pradesh increases the soils' content of nitrogen and organic matter and also their capacity for holding water. The treatment has so much improved these formerly barren soils that they can now be used to grow crops.

Other studies have shown that blue-green algae can fix enough nitrogen to support a good crop of rice and leave about 70 pounds of nitrogen in each acre after the harvesting of the rice. Astushi Watanabe of the University of Tokyo tested several species of blue-green alga in rice paddies and found that the filamentous form *Tolypothrix tenuis* yielded 1¼ tons of nitrogen per acre per year. Watanabe grew the algae in his laboratory on fine gravel soaked with a culture medium and aerated with air rich in carbon dioxide. The cultures were transferred to the experimental site in plastic bags and then inoculated into it. This kind of inoculation over a period of years increased the nitrogen in the soil by 30 percent and the yield of the rice crop by 20 percent.

Experiments conducted some years ago in Kansas, Oklahoma and Texas by W. E. Booth of the University of Kansas showed that a coating of blue-green algae on prairie soil binds the particles of the soil together, maintains a high water content and reduces erosion. Singh has envisioned the agricultural application of algal "blooms": huge shoals of algae that sometimes form in

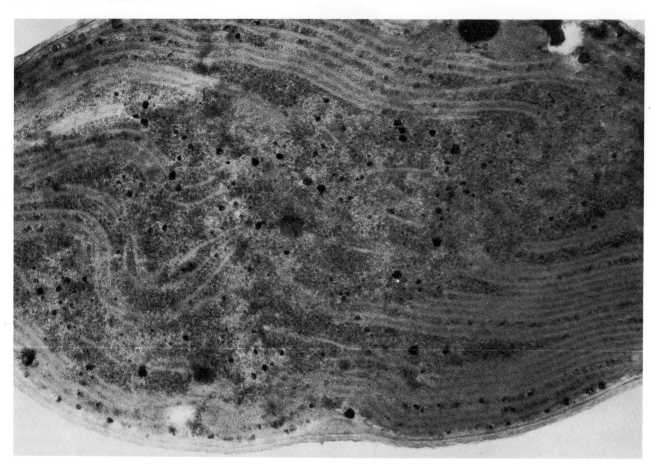

UNICELLULAR BLUE-GREEN ALGA is enlarged 90,000 diameters in this electron micrograph of a specimen of *Anacystis montana*. Like all species of blue-green alga, the cell lacks a well-defined nucleus. A cell of the same species is shown in detail below.

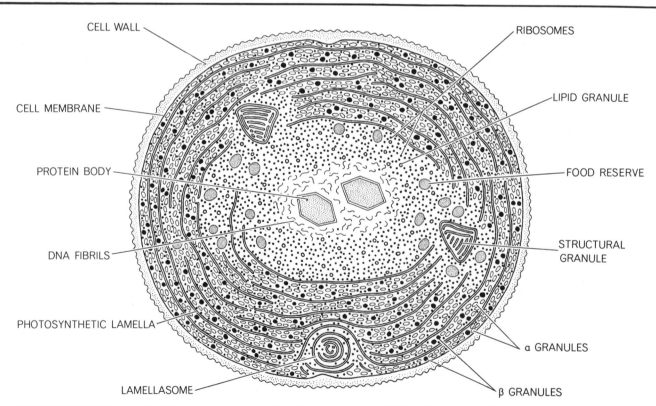

CELL WALL

RIBOSOMES

CELL MEMBRANE

LIPID GRANULE

PROTEIN BODY

FOOD RESERVE

DNA FIBRILS

STRUCTURAL GRANULE

PHOTOSYNTHETIC LAMELLA

α GRANULES

LAMELLASOME

β GRANULES

PRINCIPAL PARTS of a cell of *Anacystis montana* are identified. This genus, like other blue-green algae, lacks the highly specialized structures such as mitochondria and chloroplasts that are found in the cells of higher living forms. The function of many algal structures, including the larger ones, is unknown. Not shown is a gelatinous outer sheath characteristic of the blue-green algae.

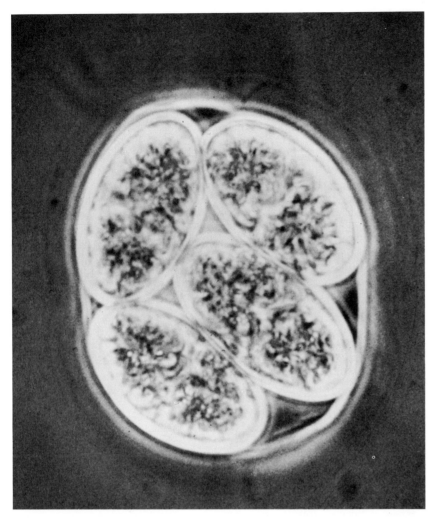

SYMBIOTIC RELATION of blue-green algae and another organism is represented by four cells of *Glaucocystis nostochinearum*, which are enlarged some 2,200 diameters in this photomicrograph. The host cells are a green alga that has lost its chloroplasts. Inside the host cells are filaments of a blue-green alga that apparently function as chloroplasts.

gus receives carbohydrates and perhaps nitrogen compounds from the alga, and the alga is able to survive in otherwise inhospitable environments because of the moist medium for growth provided by the fungus.

Several examples have come to light in which blue-green algae live parasitically within bacteria or other algae (including some blue-green species). I am currently investigating such an organism, *Glaucocystis nostochinearum*. This is a complex of two organisms: the host cell is a green alga that lacks the chlorophyll-containing chloroplasts, and within it are several filaments of a blue-green alga. Apparently the blue-green algae act as chloroplasts for the host cell.

There are many associations between blue-green algae and animals. The exact physiological relation between the partners is not known; presumably the partnership produces an essential substance that neither partner could produce by itself. In associations of this kind it seems likely that the blue-green algae originally entered the host as food but resisted digestion and stayed permanently—even, in the case of simple algae that reproduce by dividing, unto succeeding generations.

Whereas some blue-green algae act to break down rock, the species that live in hot springs actually build rock. This they accomplish by depositing salts of calcium and possibly silica within the gelatinous sheath of the algal cell wall. At Mammoth Hot Springs in Yellowstone National Park, for example, the algae deposit travertine at the rate of two feet a year. The bright colors of the basins and terraces around such hot springs are caused by the algae living in the outer layers.

As one might expect of so large and widely distributed a group of organisms, the blue-green algae have some effects inimical to the interests of man. Today their most harmful effect is undoubtedly the formation of blooms in bodies of water. When these epidemic growths occur in fresh water, they can be hazardous to human health. They choke the intakes of water-supply systems and give the water a disagreeable odor. To make matters worse, the increasing pollution of fresh waters in heavily populated areas favors the growth of algae and not of other organisms. Lake Erie, which once had white beaches and supported a prosperous fishing industry, is now seriously infested with blue-green algae. Sewage,

bodies of water. (The Red Sea, for example, owes its occasional red color to blooms of the blue-green alga *Trichodesmium*.) Singh's proposal is to use blooms as a manure because of their high content of nitrogen and phosphorus. He found that adding dried blooms to soil in which sugarcane was growing substantially increased the crop yield. Periodic applications of fertilizers sufficient to maintain a continuous bloom of algae in fishing lakes in Alabama and Mississippi nourished the large numbers of small animals on which fish feed.

Blue-green algae are often the first plants to colonize bare areas of rock and soil. A dramatic example of such colonization is provided by the island of Krakatoa in Indonesia, which was denuded of all visible plant life by its cataclysmic volcanic explosion of 1883. Filamentous blue-green algae were the first plants to appear on the pumice and

volcanic ash; within a few years they had formed a dark green gelatinous growth. The layer of blue-green algae formed in such circumstances eventually becomes thick enough to provide a soil rich in organic matter for the growth of higher plants. The algae further contribute to soil formation by acting to break down the surface of the rock.

Some of the blue-green algae that live symbiotically with other organisms undoubtedly have an economic impact, but it is difficult to measure. The best-known example of such symbiosis is provided by lichens, which are a combination of a fungus and a blue-green alga. Usually the lichen fungus can grow only if the appropriate alga is present. Lichens, like blue-green algae alone, play an important role in pioneering plant growth on bare rock. The relation between the fungus and the alga is not clearly understood. Presumably the fun-

industrial wastes and an estimated 80 tons a day of phosphates in water running off from farmlands have turned parts of the lake into a vast tank for the culture of algae. The algae rob the water of its oxygen, and the lake becomes incapable of supporting fish life. They also wash onto the beaches and cover them with a malodorous green slime.

The measures needed to ameliorate this problem may cost the states that adjoin the lake up to a billion dollars apiece. The states have to expand sewage plants and establish tighter controls over industrial wastes. They may also have to treat the water in areas where blooms occur with such algicides as copper sulfate, which in concentrations as low as two parts per million prevent all species of blue-green alga from growing.

Under certain circumstances freshwater algae of such genera as *Microcystis, Aphanizomenon* and *Anabaena* can cause death or injury to animals. Cases of human illness associated with blue-green algae are on record, even though forms such as *Oscillospira* and *Anabaenolium* normally reside in the human gastrointestinal tract. Various gastrointestinal, respiratory and skin disorders have been traced to the ingestion or inhalation of blue-green algae or to contact with them. In South Africa in 1943 thousands of cattle and sheep were killed along a dam in the Transvaal, where the reservoir developed a poisonous bloom of *Microcystis*. The toxic substance, which was ingested by the animals when they were watered, was later identified as an alkaloid that affects the liver and central nervous system.

In general the harmful effects of blue-green algae can be controlled. The beneficial effects are open to further development. The time may come, for example, when the pressure of population on food supplies will justify mass cultivation of the blue-green algae, perhaps in conjunction with other algae. At present blue-green algae are seldom eaten by humans. There is, however, a species of *Nostoc* that forms into balls called "water plums," which have a high content of protein and oil and are eaten in parts of China and South America. Most blue-green algae are rather unpalatable, but that difficulty could be overcome by suitable flavorings or by feeding the algae to fish, poultry and cattle destined for human consumption.

The Author

PATRICK ECHLIN is senior assistant in research in the School of Botany of the University of Cambridge. He is also in charge of electron microscopy at the school. Echlin obtained a teacher's certificate from Goldsmith's College of the University of London in 1954 and a bachelor's degree from University College London in 1957. For the next five years he was at the University of Pennsylvania School of Medicine, where he obtained a Ph.D. in medical microbiology in 1961. His research interests include not only algae but also the fine structure and development of pollen. Outside of his work his interests include photography, gourmet cooking, gardening and the camping variety of travel.

Bibliography

PHYSIOLOGY AND BIOCHEMISTRY OF ALGAE. Edited by R. A. Lewin. Academic Press Inc., 1962.

THE RELATIONSHIP BETWEEN BLUE-GREEN ALGAE AND BACTERIA. P. Echlin and I. Morris in *Biological Reviews*, Vol. 40, No. 2, pages 143–187; May, 1965.

THE STRUCTURE AND REPRODUCTION OF THE ALGAE: VOLUME II. F. E. Fritsch. Cambridge University Press, 1965.

SCIENTIFIC
AMERICAN June 1966, Vol. 214, No. 6, pp. 94-100

OFFPRINT 1045

PIGS IN THE LABORATORY

by Leo K. Bustad

Similarities between the physiology of swine and of men suggest that
if pigs were smaller, they would make excellent experimental animals.
The problem of size has now been solved by breeding miniature pigs.

The pig is a greatly underappreciated animal. For thousands of years it has been a mainstay of civilization and a versatile servant of man. It is easily domesticated, and it can be raised in pens or allowed to fend for itself in the field or the woods, since it will eat almost anything, including man's leavings. The pig is the world's most bounteous supplier of meat and fat. What is not commonly realized is that it is capable of serving, and has served, in many capacities besides providing food. It was long employed as a beast of burden. In ancient Egypt it was used for treading seeds into the ground, its small hoofs planting them at the right depth in soft soil. The Polynesians, making use of the pig's sensitive nose, employed it to search out lost burials; other cultures trained the pig to grub for truffles and to retrieve game. In England pigs became popular substitutes for the hunting dog. A celebrated sow named Slut developed such proficiency in hunting that her accomplishments were recorded in 1807 in the periodical *Rural Sports*: "Slut was ... trained ... to find, point and retrieve Game as well as the best Pointer. ... When called to go out Shooting, she would come home off the Forest at full Stretch, and be as elevated as a Dog upon being shown the Gun."

The subject of this article is not, however, the pig's aptitudes or its domestic history; it is the pig as a servant of science. In anatomy and physiology the pig is remarkably like man. Its heart and circulatory system, its diet, its alimentary tract and even its teeth are very similar to those of a human being. Like man, the pig has comparatively little hair on its body. It has a tendency to be sedentary and fat. It develops stomach ulcers and cardiovascular diseases resembling man's. In almost every way the pig offers a closer analogy to man than do those laboratory favorites, the rat and the dog.

The potential usefulness of the pig as an experimental animal was recognized in a general way centuries ago. Leonardo da Vinci studied the cyclic motions of the pig's heart. The 18th-century investigator John Hunter, one of the most brilliant men of medicine Britain has produced, declared the pig to be the most useful of all animals for physiological studies. An anecdote in John Kobler's recently published biography of Hunter (*The Reluctant Surgeon*) has a pig as its hero. The Margrave of Baden Dierlach was stricken with an apparent heart disturbance, and his court physicians decided a poultice should be applied over the heart. They fell into dispute, however, about exactly where the heart was located in the chest. "To settle the issue to the Margrave's satisfaction, they dissected a pig before his eyes in the belief—and it is true—that the situation of a pig's heart is the same as that of a prince's. The Margrave finding this logic admirable, they applied a poultice accordingly a little to the left of his median pectoral line."

Notwithstanding such recommendations, until recently the pig had won no enthusiastic admittance to laboratories. The great Russian physiologist Ivan Pavlov tried experimenting with pigs but gave it up when he found that as soon as a pig was placed on the table it began to squeal at the top of its lungs and squirm so that work was impossible; Pavlov concluded that pigs were inherently hysterical. Work with pigs was handicapped by a general lack of knowledge about the care, feeding and handling (including anesthesia) of these animals in the laboratory. Most forbid-

ding was the pig's size (pigs weigh as much as 800 pounds); there simply was not room for such a subject in most laboratories.

All of this has now changed. Over the past decade several laboratories have succeeded in breeding miniature pigs that grow little larger (150 to 200 pounds) than the average weight of a man. These animals not only are more manageable but also make possible more significant physiological investigations, because they are more closely scaled to the human body. As a result the pig has at last come into its own in biological research. A report by the United Kingdom Agricultural Research Council lists 3,094 publications and current research projects with pigs as the subjects, and the Battelle-Northwest Laboratory of the Atomic Energy Commission has issued a selected list of more than 1,500 articles that have been published in the past five years on studies of pigs in biology and medicine alone.

My interest in pigs goes back to my boyhood on a farm in a Norwegian community in western Washington. I never ceased to be amazed at how much pigs resembled people. They were temperate at the trough, neat and clean if given a chance, dignified in courtship and conjugality. It was as a graduate student at Washington State University in the late 1940's that I developed an enthusiasm for the pig's research possibilities. There, working under Tony J. Cunha and Eugene Ensminger, who introduced me to the use of the pig as an experimental animal, I began with studies of the effects of vitamin deficiencies. In the course of these investigations I attempted the difficult task of raising pigs from birth without their mother, so that we might have subjects uncontaminated by colostrum

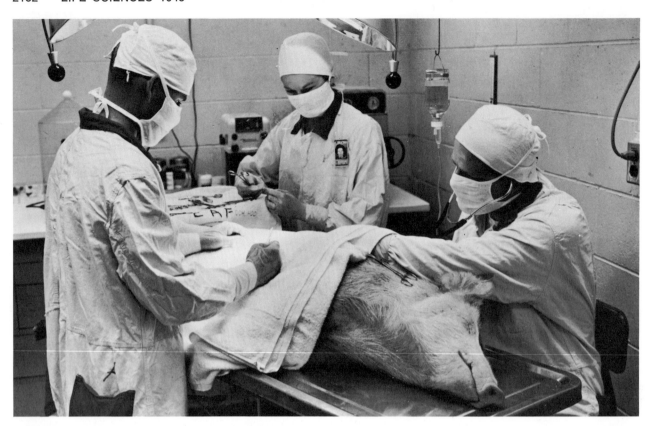

MINIATURE PIG lies anesthetized and ready for surgery after experimental contamination with plutonium at the Battelle-Northwest Laboratory of the Atomic Energy Commission. Here the author and his colleagues bred a strain of miniature pigs for experiments.

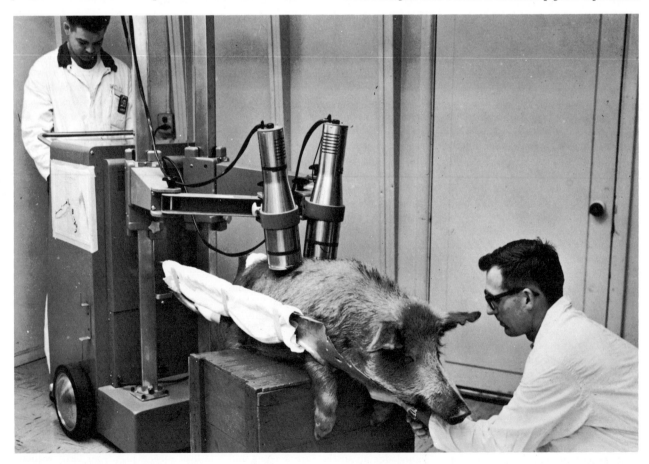

RADIATION DETECTORS are used to study a miniature pig's kidney function after experimental radiation damage. The instrument over each of the pig's kidneys measures the concentration and movement of a substance labeled with a radioactive iodine isotope.

(the milk secreted immediately after delivery). I learned a great deal about pigs as I lived with them night and day for weeks, feeding them around the clock every two or three hours. When I returned some of the piglets to their mother after a few days, they embarrassed me somewhat by squealing and running to me in preference to their mother (in consequence of their early imprinting) whenever they heard me approaching. The experiment, however, succeeded only in breaking up happy pig families (besides putting a severe strain on my own); under the given conditions and in the time allowed I did not manage to keep viable any litter that had been removed at birth from its mother.

Much as I would have liked to continue my work with infant pigs, exploring problems in nutrition, I was more strongly attracted to the field of radiation biology, and so I joined the Hanford Laboratories of the General Electric Company (now the Battelle-Northwest Laboratory); there investigations of the effects of ionizing radiation were being carried out on experimental animals. These studies began with sheep, but we soon extended them to swine, anticipating that the effects on the pig would provide a firmer basis for extrapolation to man. We used a standard breed of swine, called Palouse, that was developed at Washington State University. These animals grew to a weight of between 600 and 800 pounds, even on a restricted diet. They were costly to feed and maintain, were unwieldy and developed arthritis; moreover, their size made it questionable that they could accurately be compared with man. As we ran short of feed, housing and patience we began to wish for a smaller pig.

I learned that a friend from my graduate school days, David England, was conducting a project in breeding a small pig for research purposes at the Hormel Institute of the University of Minnesota. He and his associates William E. Rempel and Almut E. Dettmers had started the crossbreeding program with three wild pig varieties: a guinea hog from Alabama, a wild boar from Catalina Island and a hog from the piney woods of Louisiana. Later a fourth variety, a swine called Ras-N-Lansa from Guam, was introduced. Most recently a white domestic pig, the Tamworth, was bred into the line to give it a light color. The Minnesota group's breeding efforts produced a comparatively small pig (adult weight about 180

pounds) called the Hormel miniature. In the 15 years since they first created this breed they have reduced its weight by roughly a third.

The Hormel Institute provided us with some castrated miniature pigs for experiments. It was the institute's policy at the time not to release any animals in its breeding program that were capable of reproducing. Since we wanted to raise our own miniatures we had to look elsewhere for a breeding stock. We found that the Pitman-Moore Company of Indiana, a veterinary pharmaceutical firm, was breeding another strain of miniature swine from a small, wild Florida hog of mixed ancestry; it was descended from pigs Columbus had brought to the New World and that had interbred with Caribbean swine. The Pitman-Moore Company generously presented the Hanford Laboratories with some of its best stock of this breed. With these animals as the basis, my associates—V. G. Horstman, M. E. Kerr and W. J. Clarke—and I began in 1957 to breed a new strain. We particularly wanted white pigs, to facilitate studies of the effects of radiation on the skin; hence we crossed the Pitman-Moore breed with white swine of the Palouse strain. Later we crossed the offspring with a Labco pig, a sparsely haired, gentle swine from Mexico, and so produced an animal that not only is white but also has a smooth skin with very little hair. The weight of the Hanford miniatures at present runs from 150 to 200 pounds.

From the stocks I have mentioned and from others, several institutions are now engaged in breeding small pigs for research; among them are the Battelle-Northwest Laboratory, the Hormel Institute, the University of Nebraska, the U.S. Food and Drug Administration, the Vita Vet Laboratories, Labco and laboratories in France and Germany. One goal is to produce a pig smaller than a man—about 60 pounds or less—that would require no more space or food than a dog and would be a better subject than the dog for many biological investigations.

Let us review some of the recent research in which pigs have served as the experimental animals. It would take volumes to survey the vast field of these wide-ranging studies; I can only report here the highlights of a few particularly interesting investigations.

Chief among the inquiries in which the pig has been used so far is the study of nutrition. The pig's alimentary tract

and metabolism are so similar to man's that it has yielded a wealth of information bearing on human nutritional problems. The pig provides a standard for the feeding of infants and young children. It has been found that a young pig has more stringent food requirements than a human baby; consequently one can be sure that a diet that provides healthy growth in a piglet will be adequate for a baby. Experiments with pigs have also shed light on the protein-deficiency disease of children called kwashiorkor. Wilson G. Pond and his associates at the Cornell University Graduate School of Nutrition produced the symptoms of this disorder in young pigs by feeding them a low-protein diet containing only 3 percent protein and 20 percent or more of fat. Curiously they found that on the same low ration of protein young pigs did not develop as severe symptoms and showed normal activity if the fat content of the diet was reduced. On the low-protein, high-fat regime infant pigs suffered severe liver damage, anemia, gross edema and in addition permanent losses of learning ability.

Several investigators, among them Jerome C. Pekas of the Battelle-Northwest Laboratory and Donal F. Magee of the Creighton University School of Medicine, have shown that the pig is a particularly convenient animal for studying the functioning of the pancreas and other elements of the digestive system. An operation on the gastrointestinal tract of the pig is the same as the corresponding operation in a human subject; a given dose of a drug or other substance produces very nearly the same degree of response in a pig as it does in a man, and presumably the various digestive juices secreted by the pig are about the same in quantity and composition as those secreted by man. The pig's pancreatic juice is rich in enzymes. Pekas has found that the animal can be excited to a high rate of pancreatic secretion by a continuous infusion of secretin, the pancreas-stimulating hormone. Looking into the functioning of the young pig's pancreas, he has observed that the animal sometimes shows a congenital failing, marked by inefficient metabolism of soybean protein, that parallels a similar disorder in human infants.

Other investigators of the pig's gastrointestinal tract have discovered that it occasionally develops spontaneous ulcers similar to those in man. Experimenters at Purdue University have produced a high incidence of ulcers by

EARLY MINIATURE PIG, bred at the Pitman-Moore division of the Dow Chemical Company, feeds next to a standard Palouse pig, a breed developed at Washington State University that often weighs 800 pounds. A mature miniature pig weighs less than 200 pounds.

HANFORD MINIATURE, also shown with a standard Palouse pig, was bred from Pitman-Moore miniatures, crossed with the Palouse strain to obtain the latter's white color. These pigs are being crossed with a Mexican strain to obtain a more hairless skin.

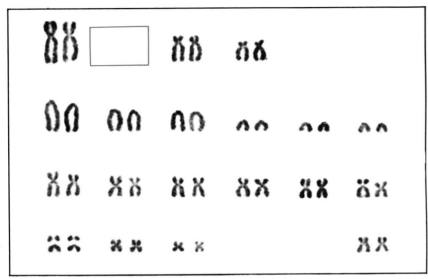

DOMESTICATED PIG has 38 chromosomes, arrayed here in four rows. This and the karyotypes below are from the Agricultural Research Laboratory of the University of Tennessee.

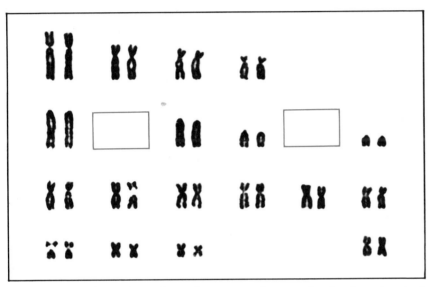

EUROPEAN WILD PIG has only 36 chromosomes. One pair that the domestic animal lacks is in the first row; two present in the domestic are missing in the second row.

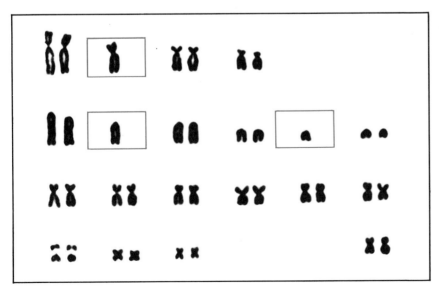

HYBRID PIG has 37 chromosomes. Single chromosomes occupy each of the three karyotype positions in which either the domestic animal or the wild one lacked a pair.

feeding pigs gelatinized cereal products.

In the course of the studies at Washington State University in which we tried but failed to raise pigs from birth without the mother we noticed that the pigs usually succumbed to infection. This fact and other observations suggested to us, as it had to other investigators, that the pig might be a good subject for studies of immunology. In recent years a number of investigators have found that the young pig is indeed uniquely suited for studies of the development of immunity.

A newborn pig has very little gamma globulin (the principal antibody protein) in its serum. Apparently it acquires gamma globulin and other immunoglobulins from its mother's colostrum when it begins to suckle. Diego Segrè of the University of Illinois found that baby pigs deprived of colostrum remained deficient in gamma globulin for weeks and showed little of the normal antibody response to antigens. He concluded that colostrum provides the young with the basis for developing the immune mechanism. Experimenting further, he found that colostrum-deprived baby pigs acquired immunological capability when he injected an antigen together with a small amount of a specific antibody or large amounts of gamma globulin. These results supported the theory that the antigen-antibody complex, rather than the antigen alone, is the usual stimulus for the production of an antibody.

Somewhat different results emerged from experiments by Dennis W. Watson, Y. B. Kim and S. Gaylen Bradley at the University of Minnesota Medical School. They took infant pigs from the mother prematurely by surgery and kept them without colostrum and under germ-free conditions. The piglets proved to be completely free of any detectable immunoglobulins or antibodies. Yet these immunological "virgins," unlike Segrè's, showed an excellent ability to produce antibodies against antigens soon after birth.

The development of the miniature pig proved invaluable for our studies of radiation effects at the Hanford Laboratories. These studies were prompted by the need for detailed information about tolerances and treatment for people exposed to radioactive substances. For such investigation the miniature pig has many useful characteristics as an experimental animal. Its body size and skeletal mass are about the same as man's; its general similarity to human beings in diet and digestion permits meaningful tests of experimental diets; its life-span (15 to 20 years) is long enough to allow measurement of the effects of radiation in shortening life and in causing malignancies.

One of the Hanford investigations, still under way, is exploring the effects of strontium 90, a long-lived and potentially hazardous constituent of nuclear fallout, which is deposited principally in the bones. Strontium 90 at various levels of dosage is fed daily to experimental pigs. Leukemias have already developed in animals receiving the very high levels of dosage in the program. No bone tumors have appeared as yet, but this form of malignancy is known to have a long latent period of development.

Roger McClellan and his associates at Hanford's successor laboratory, Battelle-Northwest, extended the strontium-90 studies to other radioactive substances that could be used in power generators with minimal hazard to man. Power generators of the thermoelectric type with radioactive isotopes as their energy source are being developed for small portable units on the earth and in space. An important factor in determining the safety of such devices is the extent to which the radioactive material in them would be taken up by the body if it were accidentally ingested. McClellan found that when strontium in the form of a titanate is ingested into the pig's digestive tract, less than .5 percent is absorbed into the body. This is only about a tenth of the amount absorbed when more common chemical forms of strontium are ingested. Still smaller is the absorption of the radioactive substances cerium 144 and promethium 147: less than .01 percent of the oral dose of those isotopes is absorbed into the pig's tissues.

Our miniature pigs enabled other investigators at Hanford and Battelle-Northwest to examine the toxic effects of plutonium and to test methods of treatment. It was found that certain chelating agents, including DTPA (diethylenetriaminepentaacetic acid), are effective in helping the body to eliminate plutonium that has been absorbed.

Using a standard breed of pig, the U.S. Navy Radiological Defense Laboratory made detailed tests of the results of high doses of radiation. The investigators found that the 50 percent lethal dose resulting in death within 30 days was 400 roentgens. Surprisingly, they also learned that a sublethal dose endowed pigs with considerable resistance to later heavy exposure. After the animals had received a dose of about 265

roentgens and had been allowed three weeks for partial recovery, it took a dose 70 percent greater than the usual one to cause a 50 percent death rate.

The largest study utilizing swine in radiobiology is one that has been conducted since 1959 at Iowa State University with Atomic Energy Commission support. D. F. Cox and his associates are measuring the effects of radiation on the fertility of male pigs and the genetic effects on their offspring. The standard procedure consists in giving the male's testes an X-ray dose of 300 roentgens and breeding the male later after germ cells subjected to the radiation have developed. As was expected, the irradiation reduces the amount of sperm by about 20 percent; this does not, however, significantly impair the pig's reproductive capacity. So far more than 15,000 baby pigs have been sired by the irradiated males. In one of the breeds under test (the Duroc breed) a peculiar result has been noted: the litters fathered by irradiated males tend to be slightly larger than normal. This result was not observed in the Hampshire breed. No explanation of the phenomenon has yet been found.

The Battelle-Northwest group has studied the effects of radiation on the karyotype (chromosome pattern) by examining the white blood cells of mini-

ature pigs fed radioactive strontium. Investigators in other laboratories have found the pig to be an exceptionally useful animal for analysis of the various forms of chromosome in the cell nucleus. The domestic pig normally has 38 chromosomes—19 pairs. Six of these pairs have characteristic, readily identifiable shapes, and the rest can be classified in small groups. R. A. McFeely of the University of Pennsylvania is making a detailed study of abnormalities in pig chromosomes. This inquiry carries special interest because pigs have an extraordinarily high rate of embryonic death—about 30 to 40 percent—and it is known that chromosome aberrations are sometimes associated with embryonic death in human beings.

Robert Murphree and A. F. McFee of the Agricultural Research Laboratory of the University of Tennessee have found a distinctive complement of chromosomes in a pig resulting from a cross between a domesticated swine and a European wild sow. The parents have 38 and 36 chromosomes respectively, and the offspring turns out to have an odd number: 37. Apparently it is completely fertile, and its chromosome number should be a good marker for research purposes. This case of an odd number of chromosomes is not altogether unique: a cross between two breeds of European ponies has been known to

ADAPTABILITY OF PIGS in experimental situations is shown by the response of a pair of normal pigs, raised from the same litter at the University of Cambridge, to different diets. They are a year old; the larger pig weighs more than 200 pounds, the underfed pig 11 pounds.

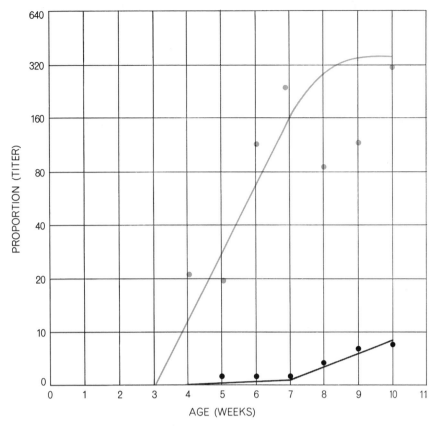

PROTECTIVE ROLE OF COLOSTRUM is demonstrated by the comparative rate of antibody production on the part of two piglets after injections of diphtheria toxin. The normally suckled animal (*color*) quickly produced antibodies but the animal that had been deprived of its mother's colostrum by bottle-feeding from birth (*black*) was a late and low producer.

produce a fertile offspring with 65 chromosomes.

Among the institutions that have used our Hanford miniature pigs for research is the University of Oregon Dental School. There E. B. Jump, M. E. Weaver and their associates have found the animal highly useful for studying dental problems. The pig's teeth are nearly the same size as man's (approximately a fourth larger) and are of the same types, consisting of molars and cutting teeth. Moreover, the general growth pattern is the same: the pig starts with deciduous teeth and sheds them as its permanent teeth develop. Hence the pig's mouth and jaw provide a model that makes possible experimental studies on many of the dental problems of children. Douglas L. Buck and other Oregon investigators have used it to look into the details of tooth growth and development, the basic movements of the teeth in biting and chewing and the functioning of orthodontic appliances.

Probably the field in which the pig will make its greatest contribution to human health and longevity is that of research on the heart and circulatory system. In this area the parallels between the pig and man are striking, to say the least. The pig's rearing as an item for the table has produced an animal that is a counterpart, even a caricature, of the overfed, physically lethargic human population. Coupled with this similarity of nurture and disposition is a porcine cardiovascular system that also is remarkably parallel to the human system. The pig's heart and coronary arteries, unlike the dog's, have much the same pattern as man's. Its blood-clotting mechanism is like that of man.

Investigators have found the pig particularly valuable for the study of atherosclerosis. H. C. Rowsell and his associates at the Ontario Veterinary College have used it to examine the effects of diet. Since the pig likes all man's foods (from peanuts and popcorn to a steady diet of eggs), Rowsell's group has tested pigs with high-cholesterol diets, including foods such as eggs, butter and lard. They find that in pigs such a diet indeed accelerates the development of atherosclerosis, and the signs and symptoms of the disorder are like those in man. Rowsell also used the pig to test anticoagulant drugs administered in certain human cardiovascular diseases. He found that a small dose of dicumarol or heparin was worse than ineffective: it actually had a coagulating effect on the blood. The finding emphasized the importance of proper dosage in the use of these drugs.

D. K. Detweiler and Hans Luginbuhl at the University of Pennsylvania have been analyzing the progressive stages of the development of atherosclerosis. For this purpose they had the good fortune to gain access to a herd of 2,000 breeding sows of various ages that have been raised on garbage (that is, essentially a human diet). In these animals, ranging up to 14 years in age, they have made detailed analyses and tests of the atherosclerotic lesions, the blood vessels and the blood. At Iowa State University, Robert Getty, studying the development of atherosclerosis from another point of view, has found that the characteristic deposits on the artery walls commonly start in the first year of the pig's life and are present in most animals by the second year.

G. D. Lumb and his associates at the Warner-Lambert Research Institute in Canada are studying how blood is supplied to the heart under adverse conditions. It is well known that when the major coronary arteries in man are partly blocked or constricted, this stimulates the development of an auxiliary or substitute circulation to nourish the heart. Lumb's group, using a plastic constrictor to narrow the pig's coronary vessels gradually, demonstrated that the animal, like man, develops a bypass system of circulation. Lumb also found that vessel-dilating drugs could improve the survival of pigs whose coronaries had been occluded.

A joint group at the University of Colorado and Colorado State University (C. A. Maaske, N. H. Booth and T. W. Nielsen) is using the pig to study congestive heart failure, a complex disorder that involves the functioning of the heart as a pump, the mechanisms controlling the heart and secondarily the functioning of the kidneys and lungs. They have found that the pig is a much better subject than the dog for an investigation of this matter. A single operation on the pig's main pulmonary artery produces the symptoms of a gradual development of cardiac failure.

All in all, although the pig is only a newcomer to the laboratories of basic biology, there can be little doubt that it will become, along with the primates, a most important contributor to knowledge about the biology of man.

The Author

LEO K. BUSTAD is director of the radiobiology laboratory and professor of radiation biology in the School of Veterinary Medicine of the University of California at Davis. His degrees include a doctorate in veterinary medicine, which he obtained from Washington State University, and a Ph.D. in physiology from the University of Washington School of Medicine. Before taking his present position he was with the Hanford Laboratories (now the Batelle-Northwest Laboratory), which operate under the sponsorship of the U.S. Atomic Energy Commission. Bustad writes: "Outside of science I am sort of an amateur theologian and am involved locally in a philosophical discussion group and nationally in a retreat center called Holden Village, where I will be the scientist in residence for a short time this summer, addressing the general subject of science and faith. Additionally I have been a member of the board of directors of a social agency concerned with a home for unwed mothers, foster-home care and an adoptive agency. I am also a very amateur bird watcher and gardener."

Bibliography

A History of Domesticated Animals. F. E. Zeuner. Hutchinson of London, 1963.

Pigs from Cave to Corn Belt. Charles Wayland Towne and Edward Norris Wentworth. University of Oklahoma Press, 1950.

A Selected List of References (1960–1965) on Swine in Biomedical Research. J. C. Pekas and L. K. Bustad. Battelle-Northwest, Document BNWL-115, June, 1965.

Swine in Biomedical Research. Edited by L. K. Bustad and R. O. McClellan. Battelle-Northwest, 1966 (in press).

SCIENTIFIC
AMERICAN   August 1966, Vol. 215, No. 2, pp. 13-21   OFFPRINT 1046

THE LAST OF THE GREAT WHALES

by Scott McVay

After bringing two species of great whales in the Antarctic to the
verge of extinction and badly overhunting two others, the whaling
industry is now endangering the last abundant species in the world.

The order Cetacea—the whales—consists of more than 100 species. The 12 largest either were in the past or are now commercially important to man. At one time their oil was valued as a lamp fuel and a high-grade lubricant. Today most whale oil is made into margarine and soap, some whale meat is eaten and the rest of the animal is utilized as feed for domestic animals and fertilizer. Whale hunting is profitable, and as a result a majority of the 12 commercially hunted species have been all but exterminated. In the 18th and 19th centuries the whaling vessels of a dozen nations sailed all the oceans in pursuit of five species of whales. In that period four of the five were hunted almost to the point of extinction; the complete disappearance of these whales during the age of sail was probably prevented only by a slump in the demand for whale oil late in the 19th century. With the age of steam another seven species (which were unsuitable as quarry in the previous era) became the hunted. These species are now also in danger of extinction. It is the purpose of this article to trace the circumstances that have allowed this sorry episode to be repeated in so short a time.

The ultimate fate of the great whales has been a question for more than a century. Herman Melville included such a query among the observations that make his *Moby Dick* an encyclopedia of whales and whaling: "Owing to the al-most omniscient look-outs at the mast-heads of the whale-ships, now penetrating even through Behring's straits, and into the remotest secret drawers and lockers of the world; and the thousand harpoons and lances darting along all the continental coasts; the moot point is, whether Leviathan can long endure so wide a chase, and so remorseless a havoc; whether he must not at last be exterminated from the waters." Melville's conclusion was that Leviathan could endure. This was not unreasonable at the time (1851), when whalers pursued whales in open boats and killed them with lances. The five species of whales that were hunted then included only one from the suborder Odontoceti, or toothed whales; this was the sperm whale (*Physeter catodon*). The other four were baleen whales, of the suborder Mysticeti. These were the bowhead (*Balaena mysticetus*), the two right whales (*Eubalaena glacialis* and *E. australis*) and a lesser cousin, the gray whale (*Eschrichtius glaucus*). All five were hunted because they do not swim too fast to be overtaken by oarsmen and because they float when they are dead.

The bowhead whale and the right whales suffered near extinction. Very few of these once abundant animals have been seen in the past decade. In May, 1963, for example, the Norwegian ship *Rossfjord* was steaming west of the Russian island Novaya Zemlya when a whale with "jaws [that] were extremely curved" was sighted. The event was duly noted in the *Norwegian Whaling Gazette* with the observation that the whale—clearly a right whale—belonged to "a species that the crew had not previously seen."

Today all four of these baleen whales (the gray, the bowhead and both right whales) are nominally protected by international agreement, although three right whales that were sighted in the Antarctic in the early 1960's were promptly killed and processed. Perhaps because of its gregarious way of life, the gray whale has managed a slow recovery from the pressure of hunting. An estimated 6,000 gray whales now migrate annually from the Arctic Ocean to their breeding grounds off the coast of Lower California [see "The Return of the Gray Whale," by Raymond M. Gilmore; SCIENTIFIC AMERICAN, January, 1955]. No one knows today how many (or how few) bowhead and right whales are still alive.

Of the eight great whales that are the quarry of modern whaling fleets, seven belong to the suborder of baleen whales and six of these to the genus *Balaenoptera* [see illustration on next two pages]. The largest of the six is the largest animal known to evolutionary history: the blue whale (*Balaenoptera musculus*). Weighing as much as 25 elephants and attaining a length of as much as 85 feet, this is the true Leviathan. It was known to Melville, who remarked that blue whales (he called them sulfur-bottoms) are seldom seen except in the remoter southern seas and are never chased because they can "run away with rope-walks of line." The modern catcher ship, armed with cannon-launched explosive harpoons, proved to be the blue whale's nemesis. Over the past 60 years antarctic waters have yielded more than 325,000 blue whales, with an aggregate weight in excess of 26 million tons [see "The Blue Whale," by Johan T. Ruud; SCIENTIFIC AMERICAN, December, 1956]. Even though the blue whale is now a rare animal, many of the statistics concerning baleen whales caught in the Antarctic continue to be reckoned in terms of "blue-whale units," as are the whaling nations' annual antarctic quotas.

Five other baleen whales of commercial significance are the finback whale (*Balaenoptera physalus*), the sei whale (*B. borealis*) and three smaller whales: Bryde's whale (*B. edeni*) and the two minke whales (*B. acutorostrata* and *B. bonaerensis*). The finback averages little more than 65 feet in length and yields only 10 tons of oil, compared with the blue whale's 20 tons. Accordingly in terms of blue-whale units it takes two finbacks to equal one blue. The sei is slighter, averaging 55 feet in length. It is comparatively blubber-poor and meat-rich; six sei whales equal one blue-whale unit. Bryde's whale and the minkes, the first averaging 45 feet and the other two 30 feet, are not separately identified in whaling statistics. When taken, they are probably counted as sei whales; they will receive no further mention here.

The remaining baleen whale to be taken commercially is the small but oil-rich humpback whale (*Megaptera novaeangliae*). This animal is shorter than the sei, averaging about 45 feet, but it is so stocky that it yields some eight tons of oil. Two and a half humpbacks thus equal one blue-whale unit. The humpback has evidently never existed in large enough numbers to constitute a major whaling resource. Nonetheless, until recently some 1,000 humpbacks were taken each year.

The eighth and last whale that is hunted today, surprisingly enough, is one that somehow escaped the near extermination that was the lot of the gray, bowhead and right whales in the days of sail. This is the sperm whale, which dives deep to hunt for squid along the ocean floor (its deepest-known dive is about 3,500 feet) and can remain sub-

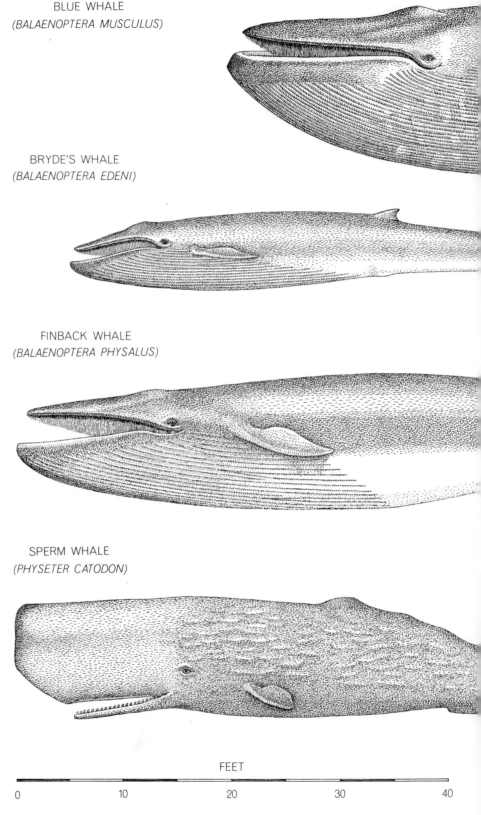

BLUE WHALE
(*BALAENOPTERA MUSCULUS*)

BRYDE'S WHALE
(*BALAENOPTERA EDENI*)

FINBACK WHALE
(*BALAENOPTERA PHYSALUS*)

SPERM WHALE
(*PHYSETER CATODON*)

FEET

0   10   20   30   40

WHALERS' QUARRY TODAY consists mainly of animals of the baleen suborder; six of the seven species are illustrated above. The blue whale, the world's largest animal, is on the verge of extinction, as is the oil-rich humpback. The finback is seriously overhunted and the same fate is befalling the sei whale. Kills of Bryde's whale and two minke whale

SEI WHALE
(*BALAENOPTERA BOREALIS*)

MINKE WHALE
(*BALAENOPTERA ACUTOROSTRATA*)

WHITE WHALE
(*DELPHINAPTERUS LEUCAS*)

NARWHAL
(*MONODON MONOCEROS*)

HUMPBACK WHALE
(*MEGAPTERA NOVAEANGLIAE*)

species (one of which is not illustrated) are not reported by name in the whaling statistics; they are probably counted as sei. As a result their present numbers are unknown. The toothed suborder of whales includes such familiar animals as the porpoises, the dol-phins, the grampus, pothead and the true and false killer whales. Three of the toothed whales are illustrated. Only the largest, the sperm whale, is commercially valued and endangered by overhunt-ing, although the narwhal and white whale are hunted occasionally.

CATCHER VESSEL pitches in a heavy antarctic swell. The stubby device seen silhouetted on the bow platform is the cannon that fires harpoons loaded with explosives. A dead whale, probably a finback, has had its flukes bobbed and is chained by its tail to the ship's side.

merged as long as 90 minutes. The sperm's huge square head contains the largest brain in the animal kingdom: it weighs more than 20 pounds. Sperm whales roam the mid-latitude oceans in groups that whalers call pods, including bulls, cows and calves. Once a year the mature bulls leave the pack and travel to antarctic waters for the summer months. As a result the whaling fleets have an opportunity to kill sperm bulls in the Antarctic and bulls and cows alike during the voyage to and from the fishery.

As the population of baleen whales in antarctic waters has dwindled, the whaling fleets have begun to spend more time in the North Pacific, where the primary quarry is the sperm whale. Every year since 1962 the industry has killed more sperm whales than whales of any other single species; the peak

catch (in 1964) was more than 29,000. Sperm whales are not counted in terms of blue-whale units, and as yet there is no limit on the number that may be taken in any year. The only limitation is on the minimum size of sperm cow that may be killed. The bowhead and the right whales, on the other hand, are supposedly protected everywhere in the world, as are the humpback and the blue whales throughout the Pacific and the humpback south of the Equator around the world.

Before World War II whaling was a *laissez faire* enterprise. Then in the postwar epoch of international cooperation 17 interested nations entered into a convention designed to regulate the whaling industry. In December, 1946, the International Whaling Commission was established as an executive body to

oversee the conservation and sensible utilization of the world's whale resources. The participating nations in the Western Hemisphere were Argentina, Brazil, Canada, Mexico, Panama and the U.S., although only Argentina and Panama were then active in the industry. (Both have since abandoned whaling.) Among the nations of Europe, Denmark, France, Britain, the Netherlands, Norway and the U.S.S.R. were signatories. So were Iceland, South Africa, Australia, New Zealand and Japan. At that time five nations operated factory ships and catcher fleets; today only Japan, Norway and the U.S.S.R. are major whaling nations. The Netherlands and Britain have abandoned their fleets, although the British continue their shore-based antarctic whaling enterprise (which is now conducted jointly with the Japanese) on the subantarctic island of South Georgia.

Since its activation in the fall of 1948 the International Whaling Commission has been charged with such tasks as protecting overexploited whale species, setting minimum-size limits below which various species may not be taken, setting maximum annual catch quotas for the antarctic fishery and designating areas closed to hunting. Although each commissioner is in principle responsible for his nation's observance of the commission's regulations, the commission itself unfortunately has neither inspection nor enforcement powers; any member nation can repudiate or simply ignore the commission's actions. Nonmember nations, of course, are equally unrestricted in their whaling activities. It calls for little political insight to forecast that recommendations made by the nonwhaling members of such a body will be ignored by the whaling members. What comes as a surprise is the fact that both the whaling and the nonwhaling nations on the commission were unresponsive to the significance of the whaling statistics that were presented to them each year during the 1950's.

In the years after World War II the waters of the Antarctic constituted the world's last great whaling ground. Record catches such as the one of 1930–1931 were never repeated, but up to 1950–1951 the whalers killed some 7,000 blue whales each season. The commission's annual quota for the antarctic fishery was 16,000 blue-whale units; the catch of finbacks (at the rate of two for each blue) helped to fulfill the quota. During this period about 18,000 finbacks were killed each season [*see bottom illustration on page 2194*].

As the 1950's progressed, however, an ominous trend was evident. The blue whales were becoming scarce. The blue-whale kill, which totaled only about 5,000 in 1951–1952, fell below 2,000 in 1955–1956 and was down to 1,200 by 1958–1959. To counterbalance the declining catch of blues, the whalers pursued the finbacks more vigorously. By the end of the 1950's, 25,000 or more finbacks were being taken each season. Those familiar with patterns of predation could see that the blue whales were being fished out and were in need of immediate full protection. The finbacks in turn probably could not survive another decade like the preceding one, during which some 240,000 animals had been subtracted from the stock.

By 1960, in spite of continued indifference on the part of the whaling nations, the commission finally decided to undertake some fact-finding. A special three-man committee was assigned the task of assessing the antarctic whale populations, even though an expert as well-regarded as the Dutch cetologist E. J. Slijper declared that the danger of their extinction was "surely remote." The committee was also to recommend any actions necessary to maintain the fishery as a continuing resource. It was agreed that, to avoid bias, the three men should be neither citizens of any nation active in antarctic whaling nor experts on whales. Three specialists in the field of population dynamics were chosen: K. Radway Allen of New Zealand, Douglas G. Chapman of the U.S. and Sidney J. Holt. Although Holt is a British subject, he has the status of an international civil servant by virtue of his employment with the Food and Agriculture Organization of the United Nations. The three men were asked to report their findings to the commission at its annual meeting in 1963.

As the special committee set about its three-year job, the world's whaling fleets continued to kill whales indiscriminately in the antarctic fishery. For the first season following the appointment of the committee the International Whaling Commission failed to set any quota for the antarctic catch. The whaling industry took more than 16,000 units that season, as well as some 4,500 nonquota sperm whales. Within the 16,000 units the catch consisted of 1,740 blue whales (510 more than the previous season) and 27,374 finbacks (a record number for kills of that species). The industry also took 4,310 sei whales, 718 humpbacks and even two

protected right whales that surfaced within range of the gunners.

During the second year of the committee's work the whaling industry did less well in the antarctic fishery. Once again the commission set no quota; the industry only managed to process 15,229 units. A few more sei and sperm whales were killed than during the previous season and another right whale was illegally shot. Among the whales that counted most—the blues and the finbacks—a larger number were immature and the numbers of both were diminishing.

The final season before the committee's report was due (1962–1963) produced a similar record. The commission set a quota of 15,000 blue-whale units. There was a modest increase in the sei and sperm kill but a sharp decline in blue and finback kills. For the first time since World War II the kill of blues fell below 1,000.

In July, 1963, the commission met in London and the special committee presented its report. The committee stated that in the antarctic fishery both the blue whale and the humpback were in serious danger of extermination. It was estimated that no more than 1,950 blue whales—possibly as few as 650—still survived in antarctic waters. The committee also noted that overfishing had reduced the stock of finbacks to approximately 40,000, far below the population level required for a maximum yield. It was recommended that the taking of blues and humpbacks be immediately prohibited and that the annual kill of finbacks be limited to 5,000 or fewer. Elimination of the blue-whale-unit system of accounting and substitution of separate quotas for each whale species was also strongly recommended.

Finally the committee's three members gave the whaling industry a prediction with a clear practical meaning. They forecast that, if unrestricted whaling were permitted in the 1963–1964 season, the industry would not be able

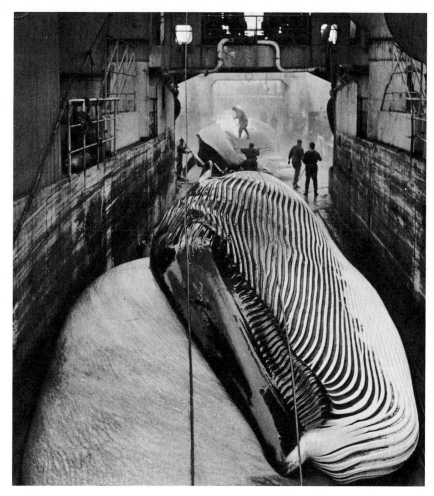

FINBACK WHALE is winched from the sea up the ramp of a factory ship. Its tongue is grotesquely expanded by the action of air that was pumped into the corpse to keep it afloat. On the flensing deck (rear) another whale is having its blubber stripped off for trying out.

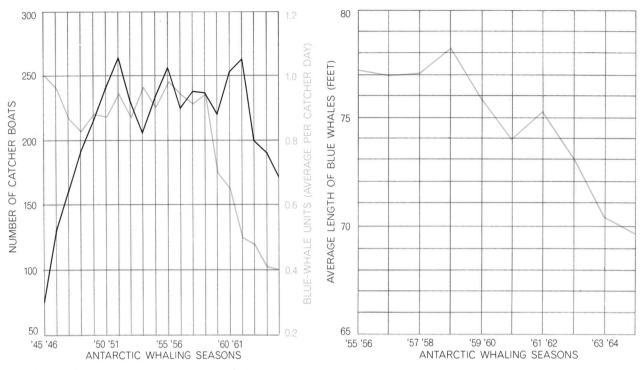

PRODUCTIVITY of the antarctic fishery began a sharp decline in the late 1950's (*color*). The decline, measured in terms of the catch per catcher-day, continued unchecked into the early 1960's although the number of catcher vessels (*black*) remained well above 200.

NINE-SEASON RECORD of the average length of blue whales killed in the Antarctic shows a decline that began in the 1959–1960 season. The average mature female is 77 feet long and a mature male 74 feet. Evidently recent catches have included immature whales.

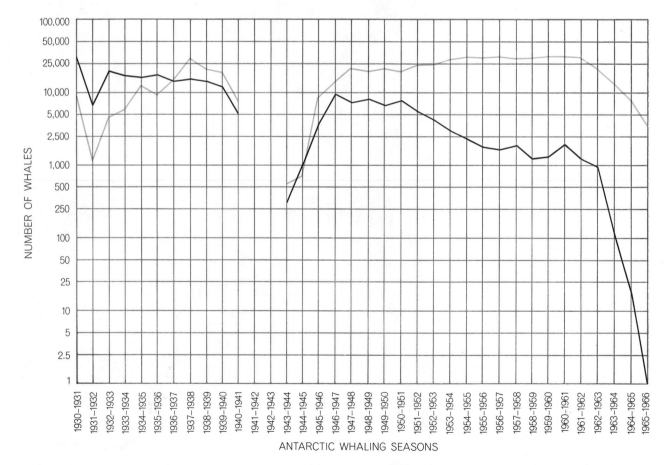

RISE AND FALL in the numbers of blue and finback whales that have been killed in the Antarctic during the past 36 years shows a correlation between the steadily diminishing blue-whale catch dur-ing the 1950's and an increase in the catch of finbacks (*color*). Just as the blue-whale stock dwindled away under the pressure of overhunting, the finback stock is now showing a severe decline.

to harvest more than 8,500 blue-whale units and would slaughter 14,000 finbacks—nearly three times the recommended number—in the process.

The prediction was disregarded. The commission voted a 1963–1964 quota of 10,000 blue-whale units for the antarctic fishery on a motion by the Japanese commissioner that was seconded by the Russian commissioner. In view of the committee's predicted maximum catch this was in effect no quota at all.

As for the committee's other findings, the commission failed to act on some and was lukewarm toward others. In the case of the now economically insignificant humpback the commission could afford to be forthright; that whale was declared protected anywhere in the world south of the Equator. In the case of the blue whale a partial sanctuary was established in all waters south of 40 degrees south latitude except some 3.3 million square miles from 40 to 55 degrees south latitude and from the Greenwich meridian to 80 degrees east longitude. Japanese whalers had taken some 700 small blue whales in this zone during the 1962–1963 season; they considered it too good a hunting ground to be put out of bounds. The suggested elimination of the blue-whale unit and the establishment of species quotas were ignored. The commission added a fourth man (John A. Gulland of Great Britain) to the special committee and asked that a further report be presented in 1964. At that time it was intended to set the antarctic quota at a level in line with the committee's findings.

In 1963 a few members of the commission may have viewed with skepticism the ability of the three committee members to make accurate forecasts of a phenomenon as full of variables and unknowns as the effects of harvesting the antarctic whale stock. If so, the results of the 1963–1964 season settled their doubts. Sixteen factory ships and their catcher fleets worked the fishery; the industry's statistics, weighing such factors as the number of days each catcher was able to spend in hunting, showed that the total effort of the catchers was 91 percent of that during the season of 1962–1963. The number of blue whales killed, however, was the lowest of any season in the industry's history: a mere 112. The committee had predicted a total catch of 8,500 blue-whale units; the fleet managed to process 8,429 units. The committee had predicted that 14,000 finbacks would be killed; the finback toll came to 13,870.

The committee's forecasts thus proved to be highly accurate.

At the commission's 1964 meeting the enlarged committee added the sei whale, formerly the least prized of any in the antarctic fishery, to the list of the overhunted. The committee pointed out that the total sei population had probably never exceeded 60,000, yet more than 20,000 sei had been killed in the course of the four previous seasons. With a whale stock of reasonable size it is a rule of thumb that 10 to 15 percent of the population can be harvested annually without causing a decline. With the expectation that more and more sei whales would be killed each season as the finback population thinned out, the committee anticipated sei kills above the sustainable level in the immediate future. In line with the commission's declared intention of setting quotas according to the committee's findings, it was proposed that the antarctic quota be drastically reduced in three annual steps. A limit of 4,000 units was sought for the 1964–1965 season, a limit of 3,000 units for 1965–1966 and one of 2,000 units for 1966–1967. This degree of restraint, the population experts declared, was necessary merely to hold the number of whales in the Antarctic at the present level. They once more ap-

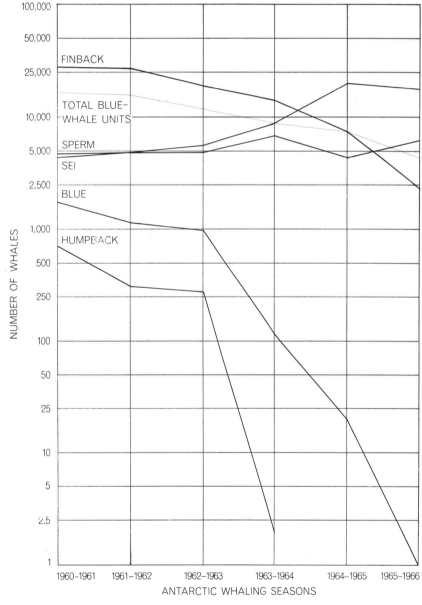

CATCH RECORDS for five species of whales killed in the Antarctic during the past six seasons show that increasing catches of sperm and sei whales have failed to counterbalance the decline in the fishery's productivity. The yield, calculated in blue-whale units (*color*), has dropped from 16,375 units in 1960–1961 to one-quarter of that amount in 1965–1966.

pealed—once more unsuccessfully—for the establishment of species quotas in place of the blue-whale-unit system.

Finally, a new gloomy statistic came before the commission: in 1963, for the first time since modern whaling had begun in the Antarctic, the larger part of the world catch had been taken in other waters. The most heavily fished area had been the North Pacific; most of the whales taken there had been sperm, which continued to be free of quota restrictions. The committee pointed out that this diversion of the industry's effort from the dwindling antarctic whale resource to the North Pacific could have ominous consequences for the sperm-whale stock.

The proposal for a reduced antarctic quota came to a vote in the commission. Japan, the U.S.S.R., Norway and the Netherlands all voted against it; in spite of the commission's declared intent to give substance to the committee's findings, the 1964 meeting adjourned with no commission quota set for the next antarctic season. The four whaling nations subsequently agreed in private that they would limit themselves to 8,000 blue-whale units in the 1964–1965 season, a figure twice the one recommended by the committee.

The 1964–1965 season was disastrous. The industry processed only 7,052 units, more than 10 percent short of its self-established quota. Only 20 blue whales were killed. The finback kill, declining for the fourth successive year, was 7,308 animals, or only a quarter of the 1960–1961 peak. As the committee had anticipated, the industry made up the difference by overkilling sei whales —almost 20,000 of them. In spite of this slaughter and a fairly large nonquota sperm-whale catch, the antarctic fishery for a second year supplied the industry with fewer whales than were taken in other waters.

For the first time since the beginning of the crisis the International Whaling Commission convened a special meeting. At this meeting (in May, 1965) the commission established a quota for the 1965–1966 antarctic season that reflected, at least in part, the committee's concern. The catch, even the whaling nations agreed, should not exceed 4,500 blue-whale units. At the regular June meeting that followed, the reduced quota was approved, and the commission agreed on a plan for further successive reductions of the antarctic fishery's quotas in the seasons to come.

The commission also attempted a first step toward partial protection of the world's sperm-whale stock. Up to that time the only restriction governing sperm kills was that cows less than 38 feet in length should not be taken. In 1964 the worldwide sperm catch had risen to a high of more than 29,000. The fleets en route to and from the Antarctic had killed 4,316 sperm whales. Once they were in the antarctic fishery they had taken 4,211 more; most of the rest had been killed in the North Pacific. In the hope of protecting sperm cows in Temperate Zone waters the commission ordered a worldwide hunting ban in the area between

WORLDWIDE WHALE CATCH during the 40-year period through 1964 exceeded 1.6 million animals. The increase in numbers of whales taken from the 1950's on reflects the antarctic fishery's growing dependence first on finbacks in lieu of blue whales and next on sei whales in lieu of finbacks. From 1963 on the antarctic fishery has provided less than half of the world's whale catch. Figures are from Norway's Bureau of International Whaling Statistics.

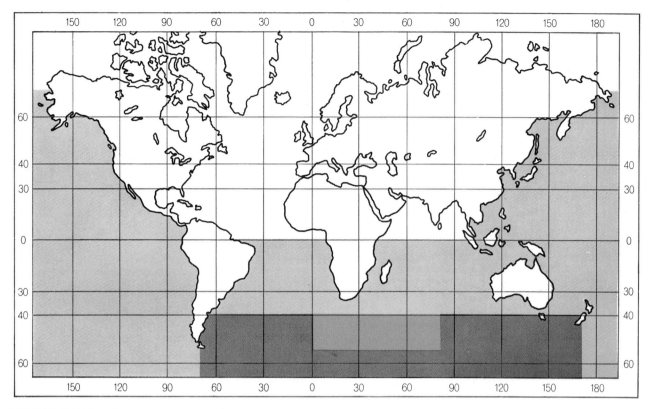

REFUGE AREAS within which designated species of whales are safe from hunting by member nations of the International Whaling Commission have been expanded in recent years. The nearly extinct bowhead and right whales enjoy worldwide protection. The blue and humpback whales are protected throughout the Pacific. The humpback is also protected south of the Equator elsewhere in the world, but the blue whale's protection elsewhere is limited to a zone south of 40 degrees south latitude (*gray area*). Even within this zone of protection 3.3 million square miles of ocean were kept open for blue-whale hunting at the request of Japan until a year ago.

40 degrees north latitude and 40 degrees south latitude. All three whaling nations, however, objected to the commission's order; the ban has simply been ignored. The worldwide sperm catch in 1965 was somewhat lower than in 1964: future catch records will reveal whether or not this drop reflects overkilling.

The imperative need for a reduced antarctic quota was demonstrated clearly enough by the results of the 1965–1966 season. With a quota of 4,500 blue-whale units the antarctic fleets could process only 4,089 units. The finback kill reached a new low, less than 10 percent of the 1960–1961 peak; in spite of protection, one blue whale and one humpback were taken. Again it was the sei whales that bore the brunt of the slaughter, and even their numbers were less than in the previous season. The conclusion was inescapable: The antarctic fishery, with its seasonal yield down to less than 100,000 tons of oil, was no longer economically significant.

Can the antarctic whale fishery ever be restored? Even with the progressively reduced quotas now envisioned it may take 100 years before this resource

recovers to the level of the middle 1950's. Recovery to the levels before World War II, which depended almost exclusively on the blue whale, is improbable. This giant mammal—one of the most remarkable ever to appear on the earth—has probably been reduced in numbers below the level that allows a species to survive; its worldwide population today may well be less than 1,000. Certainly there are 594 fewer blue whales this year than last. Whaling from land stations in Peru and Chile—two nations that are not parties to the international convention—accounted for 449 of these casualties in 1965.

The crucial question today does not concern the antarctic fishery but rather the future of all whaling. Continued overhunting of the finback whale can be expected to do to that species what has already been done to the blue whale. Last year, in addition to the antarctic season's kill of 2,314 finbacks, roughly 4,500 more of these animals were taken in other waters. Throughout the world's oceans today the only great whale that survives in economically significant numbers is the sperm. Yet a measure of the industry's lack of concern for its dwindling resources may be

gained from recent efforts to establish quotas in the North Pacific, where the absence of quotas or restrictions allows hunting all year long. In spite of efforts by Canada and the U.S. the two whaling nations with fleets in the North Pacific—the U.S.S.R. and Japan—could not even agree to restrict the finback kill, let alone that of either sei or sperm.

Each of two past eras of whaling has virtually eradicated its own most highly prized whale species. The bowhead whale and the right whales are monuments to man's thoughtlessness in the days of sail. The blue whale and humpback—and possibly the finback and sei as well—are monuments to an industry's lack of foresight in the days of steam. The whaling nations today face a third and almost certainly a final decision. If essentially unrestricted whaling continues, the only surviving stock of any economic importance—the sperm whale, of whose numbers more than 250,000 have been killed in the past 12 years—is doomed to become a monument to international folly. Only sharply reduced annual harvests and protective regulations that are both enforceable and enforced offer the possibility that the last of the great whales will survive.

The Author

SCOTT McVAY is assistant to the president of Princeton University. Following his graduation from Princeton in 1955 he worked for three years in Berlin as a civilian with Army Intelligence. Then he spent nearly five years as recording secretary of Princeton University and two years as assistant to the director of the Communication Research Institute in Miami. McVay was an English major in college and became interested in whales as a result of reading *Moby Dick*. He has spent much time in reading, correspondence and research on the subject; he writes that what troubles him most is "the prospect that the whales, possessing the largest brains on earth and gloriously unique in the scheme of living things, will be gone from the earth before man may be able to understand them."

Bibliography

CETACEA. William E. Schevill in *The Encyclopedia of the Biological Sciences*, edited by Peter Gray. Reinhold Publishing Corporation, 1961.

MOBY DICK OR THE WHALE. Herman Melville. Garden City Publishing Company, Inc., 1937.

MODERN WHALES, DOLPHINS, AND PORPOISES AS CHALLENGES TO OUR INTELLIGENCE. John C. Lilly in *The Dolphin in History*. The University of California Press, 1963.

WHALES. E. J. Slijper, Basic Books, Inc., Publishers, 1962.

WHALES, DOLPHINS AND PORPOISES. Edited by Kenneth S. Norris. The University of California Press, 1966.

SCIENTIFIC
AMERICAN August 1966, Vol. 215, No. 2, pp. 72-81

OFFPRINT 1047

MAMMALIAN EGGS
IN THE LABORATORY

by R. G. Edwards

The earliest stages of human development may be opened to study
by bringing the eggs of mammals to maturity in a culture medium,
fertilizing them in vivo or in vitro and observing the embryos.

Much of what is known about animal reproduction has been learned from such organisms as the sea urchin and the chicken. This is partly because the eggs of these organisms are readily accessible to observation during such crucial stages of the reproductive process as fertilization and embryonic development. During the past quarter-century the eggs of certain mammals—rodents, rabbits and some farm animals—have become more accessible to study. This increasing availability of mammalian eggs arises largely from advances in knowledge of how ovulation is controlled by hormones. The eggs of man and other primates, however, are still secured very rarely. It has long been recognized by workers in the field that, if a significant number of viable mammalian eggs were available on a regular basis, a host of questions about the early stages of mammalian reproduction would be open to investigation.

Experiments that my colleagues and I have conducted at the University of Cambridge and Johns Hopkins University indicate that such a situation may soon obtain. So far the experiments have been concerned mainly with oocytes, which are immature eggs. In most mammalian species, including man, the female has her full complement of oocytes when she is born. The development of the oocytes into mature eggs ready for fertilization is a long process that goes through many stages. Our experiments have involved removing oocytes from the ovaries of various mammals and stimulating them to proceed to maturity. We have also worked with some human oocytes removed

surgically from women for medical reasons. Our experiments have included the fertilization of some of the animal eggs brought to maturity in vitro and attempts to fertilize the human oocytes. In discussing these experiments it will be useful to begin by describing briefly two of the key processes in the reproduction of mammals and other higher organisms: mitosis and meiosis [see illustration on page 2201].

Mitosis is the name for the processes that take place in most cells (both plant and animal) when the cells reproduce by dividing. The events of mitosis are usually regarded as occurring in four more or less distinct phases: prophase, metaphase, anaphase and telophase. The process can be described simply for a hypothetical organism in which each cell contains four chromosomes: the bodies that carry the cell's genetic information. Two of the chromosomes, say a long one and a short one, were inherited from the mother and two from the father. The two long chromosomes are similar to each other, as are the two short chromosomes. When the members of each pair are matched in this way, they are called homologous chromosomes; the four-chromosome cell would have two pairs of homologous chromosomes. At the beginning of mitosis each chromosome has divided into two strands, which are held together by a central body called the centromere.

In prophase the chromosomes begin to shorten and thicken, and the remarkable structure called the mitotic spindle starts to form. The spindle consists of

fibers in an array resembling the meridian lines of a globe that has been stretched at the poles. In metaphase the centromeres migrate to the equator of the spindle. In anaphase the centromeres divide, and the two daughter centromeres resulting from each division move toward opposite poles of the spindle, pulling their chromosome strands with them. In telophase the separation is complete; the cell divides into two daughter cells, each with a nucleus containing four chromosomes and thus the same complement of genetic information that was contained in the original cell. This completes mitosis; until one of the new cells itself begins mitosis it is said to be in interphase. Toward the end of interphase the chromosomes again divide into two strands.

Meiosis is a special form of mitosis that occurs in the cells that give rise to sperm and eggs. Before the process begins, these cells, like others in the body, are diploid: they have a normal complement of chromosomes. Since mammalian reproduction involves the union of a spermatozoon and an egg, the cells of the offspring would have a double complement of chromosomes if there were not some mechanism by which the spermatozoon and the egg became haploid, meaning that the chromosome complement of each was reduced by half. That mechanism is meiosis. It occurs in two cell divisions, known as meiosis I and meiosis II [see illustration on pages 2202 and 2203].

The prophase of meiosis I is highly specialized and occupies a comparatively long period of time. For these reasons it is subdivided into five stages: lep-

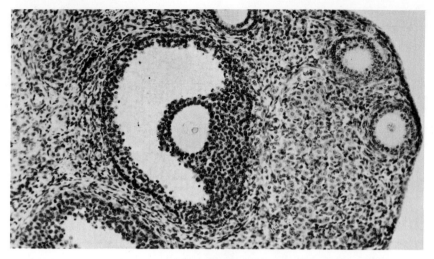

MOUSE OVARY in cross section is enlarged 200 diameters. The light circular areas are oocytes, or immature eggs, enveloped by follicles, which are composed of granulosa cells. The large, light, semicircular area at left center is the antrum, or cavity, of a Graafian follicle; when a follicle has developed to that stage, the oocyte is ready for ovulation.

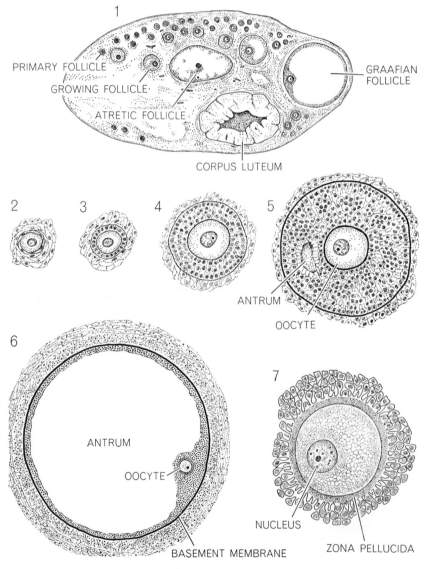

MATURATION OF OOCYTES occurs continually. At top is an ovary with several follicles containing oocytes at various stages of development. At center four stages in the maturation of a follicle are shown. At bottom are a fully grown Graafian follicle (6) and a mature egg (7).

totene, zygotene, pachytene, diplotene and diakinesis. Each relates to the activities of the chromosomes. Essentially what happens in meiosis, as distinct from mitosis, is that the homologous chromosomes pair up and duplicate. At metaphase the homologous pairs line up on the spindle. In anaphase one member of each pair, without splitting, goes to each pole. Thus after the cell divides at telophase each daughter cell has only one member of each pair of homologous chromosomes.

In meiosis II there is no further duplication of chromosomes. The twin-strand chromosomes simply line up on the spindle and separate. When the two cells that resulted from meiosis I divide in meiosis II, each of the four resulting cells has only half the original number of chromosomes. In the case of our hypothetical four-chromosome cell the result of meiosis would be four cells with two chromosomes each. By this process sperm and eggs are made haploid; when they unite through fertilization and begin the mitotic divisions known as cleavage (the first steps in the growth of an embryo), all the resulting cells are diploid.

Let us now examine the normal maturation of a mammalian oocyte. It undergoes the first four stages of the first meiotic division in the ovary of the fetus. In other words, before a female mammal is born her oocytes have completed the leptotene, zygotene and pachytene stages and are well into the diplotene stage. Meiosis halts, however, late in the diplotene stage. At this point a nucleus, called the germinal vesicle, forms in the oocyte.

These developments coincide with the envelopment of the oocyte by an array of cells known as granulosa cells. These gradually form the follicle in which the oocyte will remain enclosed until ovulation. This situation—in which the oocyte is in an arrested state of meiosis, contains a nucleus and is enveloped in a follicle—prevails at the birth of the female and persists during growth to adulthood. During the entire span of this time (up to some 40 years in the human species) the homologous chromosomes remain paired in the germinal vesicle. To many biologists this long period is known as the dictyate stage of oocyte development; others call it the dictyotene stage or the diffuse diplotene stage.

Near puberty many of the oocytes undergo atresia: they degenerate and are resorbed. This process results in a large reduction in the number of oocytes. Those that remain resume their progress toward maturity in the adult ovary. With the onset of puberty, follicles mature in groups during each sexual cycle. The follicles grow by a rapid increase in the number of granulosa and other cells. The oocyte also increases in size, usually before the follicle shows much enlargement; for the time being, however, the oocyte remains in the dictyate stage.

The later stages of follicular growth are characterized by the formation of a cavity, the antrum, in the granulosa layer; the structure is now known as a Graafian follicle. At this stage the follicle is responsive to the hormone called FSH (for follicle-stimulating hormone). FSH is secreted by the anterior part of the pituitary gland during the early part of the sexual cycle and stimulates the final enlargement of the Graafian follicle.

Now the Graafian follicle becomes sensitive to a second pituitary hormone, luteinizing hormone (LH), which has a dual action: it stimulates the oocyte to resume meiosis and it initiates changes in the follicle that lead to ovulation. Under the influence of LH the oocyte completes its first meiotic division, progressing through diakinesis, metaphase, anaphase and telophase. The daughter cells that result from this division are far from identical. One of them, the secondary oocyte, receives a disproportionate share of the original cell's cytoplasm; hence the other, the first polar body, is much smaller.

The second meiotic division begins as soon as the first ends. It reaches metaphase within minutes. Except in a few mammalian species ovulation occurs while the oocyte is in metaphase II.

In the process of ovulation the Graafian follicle fills with fluid, moves toward the surface of the ovary and erupts, releasing the oocyte. The cells of the ruptured follicle are converted to a new structure, the corpus luteum. This is the structure that produces the hormone progesterone, which conditions the walls of the uterus for the development of the fertilized egg.

At this stage meiosis is still not complete. It awaits fertilization in the fallopian tubes. Only when the fertilizing spermatozoon enters the egg is meiosis II ended by the extrusion of the second polar body. The entire process—the first stages of which took place in the fetal ovary, the middle stages in the adult ovary and the final stages in the fallopian tubes after fertilization—is now complete.

In this account of the maturation of a single oocyte the reader may well have lost sight of the setting in which these developments occur. It has been estimated that there are some 500,000 oocytes in the female human fetus, a number vastly exceeding the reproductive needs of the female. Indeed, many mammals shed only one egg during each ovulation. Others—for example mice, rabbits and pigs—produce several eggs in one ovulation, but the number is still tiny in relation to the original population of oocytes. During each sexual cycle FSH stimulates the development of many follicles, but only a few of them progress as far as ovulation. Most of them degenerate, although the oocytes in some of these atretic follicles can complete meiosis as far as metaphase II.

Atresia evidently begins when the amount of FSH becomes insufficient to maintain the growth of all the follicles developing during the female cycle, because if extra FSH is provided by injection, large numbers of follicles continue their growth. In response to LH they will proceed to ovulation.

Treatment with FSH and LH will thus induce the ovulation of large numbers of eggs—several in man, as many as 70 in mice. These eggs can be fertilized, although for many years they were regarded as being somewhat abnormal because a large proportion of the embryos to which they gave rise died during pregnancy. It is now known, primarily from evidence in mice, that such embryos are perfectly capable of normal development provided that the uterus is not overcrowded.

With FSH and LH an experimenter can therefore obtain oocytes from many or all of the Graafian follicles developing during a particular cycle. The method can, however, be laborious and

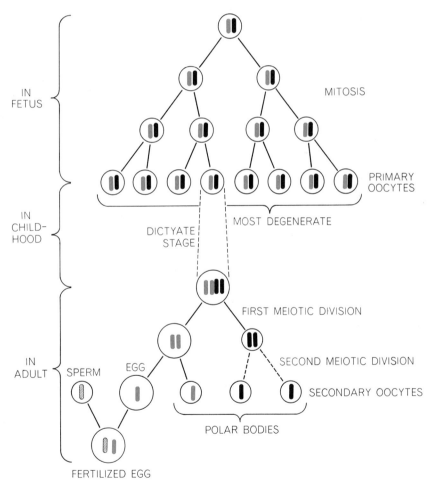

EVOLUTION OF AN EGG is traced through the processes of mitosis and meiosis. The original cell (*top*) is diploid: it has a set of chromosomes from the father (*color*) and one from the mother (*black*). This arrangement is repeated in the daughter cells that result from mitotic divisions to produce oocytes. In meiosis successive divisions produce an egg that is haploid: it has half the normal complement of chromosomes. When the egg and a sperm join to produce fertilization, the resulting cells of the growing embryo are again diploid.

FIRST MEIOTIC DIVISION

PROPHASE

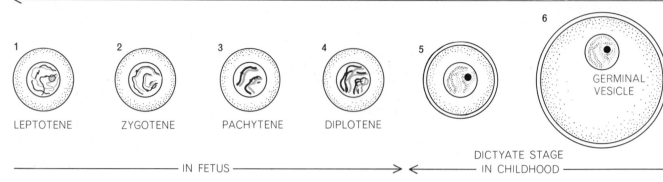

1 — LEPTOTENE   2 — ZYGOTENE   3 — PACHYTENE   4 — DIPLOTENE   5   6 — GERMINAL VESICLE

——— IN FETUS ———→ ←——— DICTYATE STAGE IN CHILDHOOD ———

SECOND MEIOTIC DIVISION

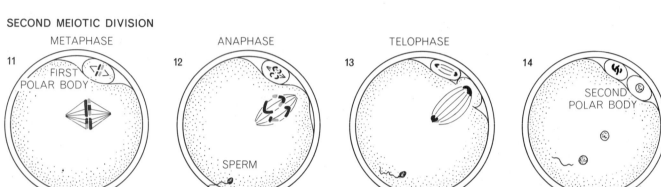

METAPHASE   ANAPHASE   TELOPHASE

11 — FIRST POLAR BODY   12 — SPERM   13   14 — SECOND POLAR BODY

——IN ADULT OVARY——→ OVULATION ←——— FERTILIZATION IN FALLOPIAN TUBE ———

DURATION OF MEIOSIS can be as long as 40 years in human oocytes. Its prophase has a particularly long duration and several chromosomal events; hence it is subdivided into five stages, beginning with leptotene and ending with diakinesis. Homol-ogous, or similar, chromosomes, one (*black*) from the father and one (*color*) from the mother, are paired during much of the process. Meiosis halts late in the diplotene stage and the germinal vesicle appears. Meiosis is resumed in adulthood under the influ-

uncertain. In many species it requires the detailed recording of the female cycle, and in large animals it calls for organizing surgical operations or slaughtering to obtain the eggs from the fallopian tubes. For various reasons it is exceedingly difficult in its application to man. Nonetheless, it is clear that a large

supply of oocytes can be tapped in the ovary at any time during the reproductive life of the female.

Once an experimenter removes an oocyte from its follicle he is confronted by two main problems. First, the oocytes (particularly those taken from atretic or underdeveloped follicles) may

be abnormal. Second, the oocytes will have to be stimulated in some way to complete their meiosis to metaphase II so that they will be comparable to eggs ovulated normally.

The problem of abnormality is manageable. Oocytes from atretic follicles can usually be recognized quickly and

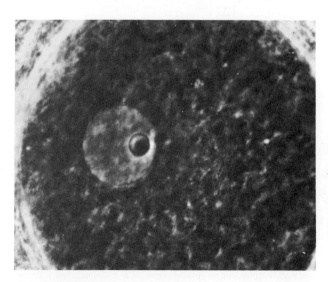

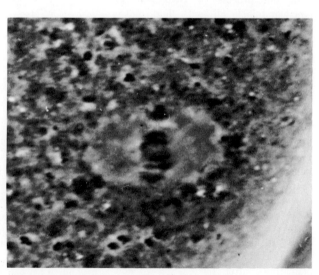

STAGES OF MEIOSIS appear in various oocytes matured in culture. At left is a living monkey oocyte in the dictyate stage; its germinal vesicle, or nucleus (*light circle*), contains a single nucle-olus (*dark circle*). The next photomicrograph shows a living rat oocyte in metaphase I; the light oval area is the spindle, with chromosomes on its equator. The third photomicrograph shows a pig

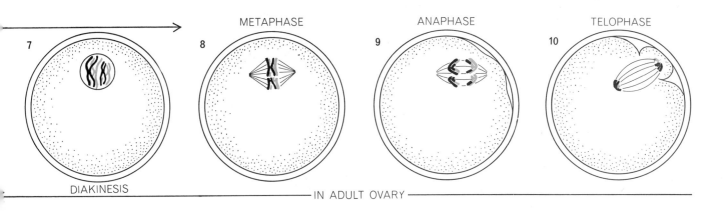

METAPHASE   ANAPHASE   TELOPHASE

DIAKINESIS —————— IN ADULT OVARY ——————

MITOSIS
PROPHASE   METAPHASE   TWO-CELL EMBRYO

———————— CLEAVAGE IN FALLOPIAN TUBE ————————

ence of luteinizing hormone. At the end of meiosis I the cell divides; one of the daughter cells, the secondary oocyte, receives more of the original cell's cytoplasm than the other, the first polar body, and so is larger. Meiosis II begins when the first ends and proceeds quickly to metaphase. At this point ovulation occurs in most mammalian species. The second meiotic division is completed in the fallopian tube after entry of a spermatozoon into the egg. Meiosis thus begins in the fetus and ends long afterward.

excluded from experiments. Underdeveloped follicles either can be recognized or will end up as experimental failures.

An obvious solution to the problem of stimulating oocytes to resume meiosis was to grow them in culture outside the body. A reasonable assumption was that the culture medium would need to contain LH. It turned out, however, that LH was not needed, and the techniques required to induce the resumption of meiosis proved quite simple. Oocytes had only to be removed from the follicles and placed in a standard culture medium for meiosis to recommence in a manner seemingly identical with that in the ovary after stimulation by LH.

These observations were first made in rabbits by Gregory Pincus, now at the Worcester Foundation for Experimental Biology, and his collaborators in 1935. They also made the initial attempts with human oocytes. Our recent work has

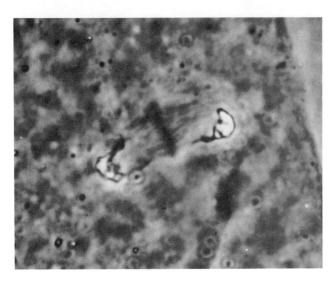

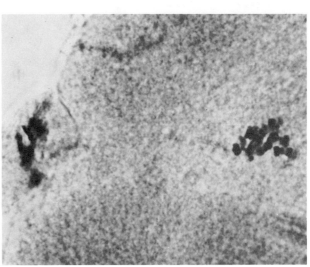

oocyte fixed and stained in telophase I; the dark vertical band is the center of the spindle and the chromosomes have moved to opposite poles. At right is a human oocyte fixed in metaphase II; it has extruded its first polar body (*left*). The chromosomes are the dark structures. The enlargement of each photomicrograph except the third is about 1,200 diameters; that of the third is 2,000.

shown that their method can be applied successfully to the oocytes of many mammalian species.

We first noted that oocytes from mice, rats and hamsters would recommence meiosis in culture. A clear sign of resumed meiosis is a receding of the germinal vesicle; it becomes indistinct as the chromosomes condense. The germinal vesicles of most oocytes in these species regressed after two hours, and meiosis proceeded from diakinesis to metaphase II within 12 hours. These rates are similar to those in the ovary after LH has done its work.

We then assumed (mistakenly) that the oocytes of mammals other than rodents and rabbits would mature after similar periods in culture. When it became clear that in dog, monkey, baboon and human oocytes the germinal vesicle was still intact after as long as 20 hours in culture, we erroneously concluded that oocytes from species with a prolonged sexual cycle required an extra stimulus for the resumption of meiosis. Therefore we added various plant and animal hormones to the culture. They had no effect whatever. Finally we found that by simply extending the period of culture we could induce between 60 and 80 percent of the oocytes from all the animals with which we worked to resume meiosis. In certain species—cow, sheep, monkey and probably baboon (we have had too few baboon oocytes to be sure)—20 to 24 hours passed before the germinal vesicle regressed.

Obviously we had to ensure that the persistence of the germinal vesicle in certain species for as long as 24 hours in vitro mirrored the events in the ovary after stimulation by LH. It was therefore fortunate that Christopher Polge and Ronald Hunter of the British Agricultural Research Council had made detailed estimates of the pig oocyte's meiotic stages in vivo after the pigs had been injected with LH. These estimates showed that the germinal vesicle persisted for 20 to 24 hours after the injection and that meiosis was then resumed. Polge and I examined cultured oocytes and found that they matured at a rate closely comparable to the rate of maturation in the ovary. This was most encouraging to us. If pig oocytes were maturing normally in vitro, we could reasonably conclude that the same was true of oocytes from other species in which there was a long delay before the germinal vesicle regressed.

In all species most oocytes matured to metaphase II. Some oocytes, however, proceeded to anaphase of the first meiotic division and meiosis then halted. The chromosomes failed to segregate along the spindle. The number of oocytes showing this arrest in anaphase was found to depend on the culture medium used. For the most part we now have mediums in which the number of oocytes that fail to reach metaphase II is very small, although in some species—notably the pig and the mouse—we have not fully solved this problem.

A remarkable phenomenon in the culturing of oocytes was that within each species the oocytes matured synchronously, even though they had been taken from females in widely differing stages of the sexual cycle. In other words, it made no difference how near to or far from ovulation an oocyte might have been at the time of removal; once put into the culture medium all the oocytes matured together. As a result of this phenomenon we were able to predict with considerable accuracy the stage of meiosis the oocytes from a particular species of mammal would reach after specific periods in culture. Indeed, by timing the interval between the release of oocytes from their follicles and metaphase II in vitro we can now predict the interval in vivo between the secretion of LH from the pituitary gland and ovulation in cases where this interval is unknown.

Our success with the culturing of oocytes from various experimental and domestic animals presented a major challenge: Would human oocytes respond similarly? After preliminary trials it became abundantly clear they would. In culture the germinal vesicle persisted for 24 hours; the chromosomes condensed at diakinesis between 25 and 28 hours; metaphase I occurred between 26 and 35 hours, and the first polar body was extruded between 36

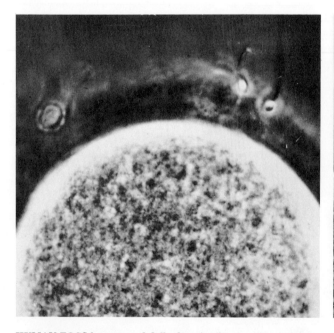
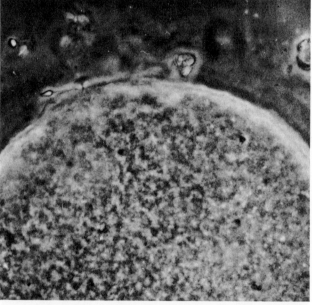

HUMAN EGGS have proved difficult to fertilize in vitro. At left is a human egg with several spermatozoa that have failed to penetrate fully the zona pellucida. In the photomicrograph at right a spermatozoon (*top left*) has passed through the zona pellucida and reached the surface of the egg, but that is inconclusive evidence of fertilization. Some eggs showed other inconclusive evidence of fertilization.

and 43 hours. A large majority of the oocytes examined after 43 hours were in metaphase II and had a polar body.

Even though the oocytes were necessarily taken from women who were ill and undergoing surgery and who were at widely differing stages of the menstrual cycle, approximately 80 percent of the oocytes thus obtained resumed maturation in culture and progressed synchronously through meiosis to metaphase II. From our observations we could therefore estimate that the interval in man between the secretion of LH and ovulation during the menstrual cycle is probably 36 to 43 hours. Moreover, the results showed that we could induce large numbers of oocytes to proceed in culture to the stage where fertilization normally occurs.

Our experiments in the culture of oocytes provide some indications of the mechanisms involved in the normal evolution of oocytes in the ovary. There is evidence that cultured oocytes resume their meiosis when the follicular architecture is destroyed by the rupture of a membrane (variously called the basement membrane or membrana propria) as the oocytes are removed from the ovary. This implies that the intact basement membrane plays a role in restraining the maturation of the oocyte. If it does, that would shed light on several phenomena. For example, in some atretic follicles the oocyte resumes meiosis before the complete degeneration of the follicle. Secondly, the basement membrane is associated with the granulosa cells, and the dictyate stage actually begins when the granulosa cells first enfold the oocyte in the ovary. Moreover, there is evidence that the granulosa cells will begin the changes leading to the formation of a corpus luteum when the follicle is ruptured. It would be most interesting to establish that both of the changes induced in the ovary by LH —the resumption of meiosis in the oocyte and the transformation of a Graafian follicle into a corpus luteum—could be set in motion by rupturing the follicular membrane.

Since it is now possible to induce at will any stage of meiosis between diakinesis and metaphase II, the way is open to investigate how and at what stage chromosome abnormalities arise. In recent years it has been clearly established that in man one such abnormality is associated with mongolism. Many mongoloids have 47 chromosomes per cell instead of the normal 46. The extra chromosome is No. 21, that is,

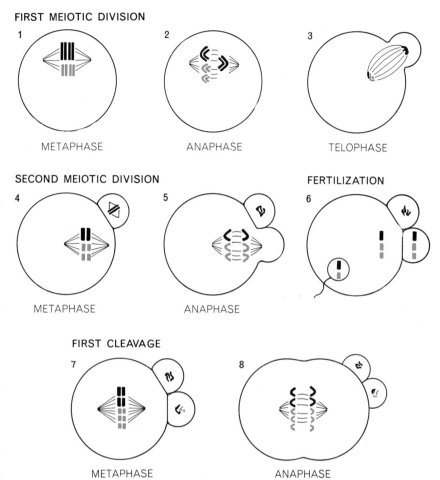

FIRST MEIOTIC DIVISION

METAPHASE   ANAPHASE   TELOPHASE

SECOND MEIOTIC DIVISION   **FERTILIZATION**

METAPHASE   ANAPHASE

FIRST CLEAVAGE

METAPHASE   ANAPHASE

ORIGIN of chromosomal abnormalities such as that leading to mongolism can probably be studied by growing eggs in culture and watching the chromosomes. Such abnormalities might arise in several ways; here paired chromosomes (*color*) fail to separate normally during anaphase I and hence move together to one pole of the spindle. Thus their distribution in the egg and first polar body is faulty and could result in abnormalities after fertilization.

there are three homologous No. 21 chromosomes instead of the two usually found. Mongolism occurs much more frequently among the children of older mothers. Evidently the defect arises early in embryonic development, or perhaps during meiosis in the oocyte. The immediate cause might be an infection.

Several explanations have been put forward to explain the mechanism of this and other chromosomal abnormalities. The reader will recall from the description of meiosis that homologous chromosomes are paired at the beginning of the dictyate stage and should remain paired until meiosis is resumed under the influence of LH. If homologous chromosomes were gradually to separate during the dictyate stage so that they were no longer paired when meiosis was resumed, they would move independently along the spindle at anaphase. Their distribution in the egg and first polar body would become a matter of chance. This failure of the

controlled segregation of the chromosomes would inevitably lead to abnormal karyotypes, or arrays of chromosomes, in some embryos.

Another source of abnormalities might be the nucleolus, the structure that contains much of the ribonucleic acid in the nucleus. Nucleoli are formed from nucleolus-organizer regions in certain chromosomes. The five pairs of human chromosomes carrying nucleolus organizers are involved in a high proportion of chromosomal anomalies. Each of these chromosomes can produce a nucleolus, although in the later stages of maturation an oocyte usually has only one nucleolus because of nucleolar fusion. The close relation of these chromosomes with the nucleolus during the prolonged dictyate stage might lead to abnormal segregation at anaphase. In many of the oocytes that we grew in culture we saw several chromosomes—probably those carrying nucleolus organizers—in intimate association with the nucleolus during diakinesis. In other oocytes all the chromosomes appeared to be associated with the nucleolus or to be sticking together.

Having caused oocytes to mature in culture to the point of development at which fertilization occurs, we decided to see if they could be fertilized. Our technique with animal oocytes was to transfer them into the fallopian tubes of females of the same species. The females were then normally mated.

In earlier work on the rabbit M. C. Chang of the Worcester Foundation for Experimental Biology found that as many as 80 percent of cultured oocytes were fertilized when transferred into a doe. The rate of fetal abnormality, however, was high. Only three normal fetuses and 14 that had died during pregnancy were recovered from 81 oocytes transferred in the experiments.

We worked with the pig oocyte, because it matures at a rate similar to that in man and other large mammals. Our initial attempts produced a high incidence of anomalies. For one thing, large numbers of spermatozoa penetrated the egg instead of the usual one or two [see illustration on page 2199]. In addition there was considerable fragmentation of the eggs. After we had improved this situation by modifying the culture medium the results of fertilization grew progressively better, although many eggs are still anomalous. This result may be partly due to a fact mentioned earlier: that the pig oocyte has a tendency to halt its development in anaphase I. Apparently our conditions of culture are still insufficient for the pig oocyte. So far we have examined all the eggs immediately after fertilization. Our immediate tasks are to improve the culture mediums and to study the further development of fertilized eggs. We have learned already that we can use fluid from the Graafian follicle itself to culture the oocytes.

Since pig ovaries can be obtained easily and cheaply, pig oocytes can be matured and perhaps fertilized in large numbers. On three occasions we have had some 700 pig oocytes maturing synchronously in vitro; we could have had many more. Such large numbers of oocytes should facilitate investigation of the biochemical aspects of early mammalian development.

Among the questions that might be thus elucidated is the matter of where and when DNA and RNA are synthesized. Some evidence suggests that DNA is synthesized during the interphase of each cleavage division of mammalian eggs; there appear to be no large stores of DNA in the cytoplasm. The type of RNA being synthesized probably varies with the stage of development. Large amounts of RNA are found in fully grown follicular oocytes, although it is not certain when the RNA is synthesized. It would be of interest to characterize the types of RNA in mature oocytes and early embryos. Apparently little, if any, "messenger" RNA or protein is synthesized until the early embryonic stage. An intriguing fact is that the earliest evidence of gene action appears in this stage, as does the genetic inactivation of one of the two "X" chromosomes in female embryos. These events suggest that some delicate genetic mechanism has begun to operate.

If rabbit and pig eggs can be fertilized after maturation in culture, presumably human eggs grown in culture could also be fertilized, although obviously it would not be permissible to implant them in a human recipient. We have therefore attempted to fertilize cultured human eggs in vitro. Here we promptly encountered a problem involving what is called capacitation of the spermatozoa. Capacitation, without

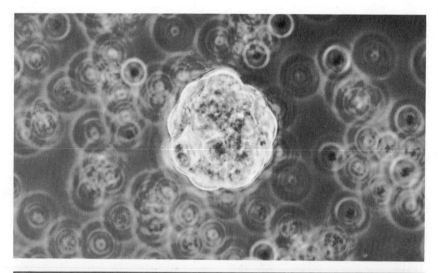

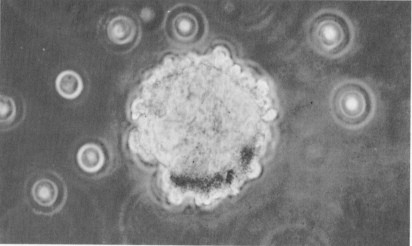

MOUSE EMBRYOS tested for antigens indicate possibilities of the work with eggs. At top is a negative result; red cells fail to adhere to a living embryo. Adherence of red cells to the embryo at bottom is a positive test for an antigen. A distant possibility is detecting female embryos by the presence of sex chromatin in cells excised from living embryos.

PIG EGG was matured in culture and fertilized in the animal. In the photomicrograph on the opposite page a segment of the egg and the zona pellucida, or outer membrane, appears at an enlargement of 1,400 diameters. The small, dark objects in the zona pellucida are sperm heads; the lighter curved lines are trails made by spermatozoa as they penetrated the zona pellucida. Penetration by such a large number of spermatozoa is an unusual condition that appeared in initial experiments with cultured eggs.

which most mammalian eggs cannot be fertilized, is a poorly understood change undergone by spermatozoa in the female reproductive tract. Noncapacitated spermatozoa are unable to penetrate through the zona pellucida: the outer membrane of the egg.

We attempted to overcome this problem by removing the seminal fluid from the spermatozoa, since this fluid is reported to suppress capacitation. Then we added spermatozoa thus treated to 40 oocytes in vitro a few hours before the extrusion of the first polar body. Except in rare cases spermatozoa became attached to but did not penetrate the zona pellucida 24 to 36 hours later [see illustration on page 2204]. Three eggs had two or more nuclei, which might have been a sign of fertilization but was inconclusive evidence. These results were similar to those obtained in earlier attempts by Landrum B. Shettles of the Columbia University College of Physicians and Surgeons. It is undoubtedly significant that when we attempted to

fertilize rabbit and pig eggs in vitro after their maturation in culture, the result was the same: spermatozoa failed to pass. through the zona pellucida, although they did so, often in large numbers, when the oocytes were transferred into a mated recipient.

We accordingly tried to capacitate human spermatozoa. Small pieces of human fallopian tube were added to some cultures, but this brought no increase in fertilization. Next we transferred some oocytes, together with human spermatozoa, into the fallopian tubes of rabbits or monkeys. None of the oocytes were fertilized in the rabbit; those put into monkeys simply disappeared after about 12 hours.

Then we tried placing human spermatozoa in the fallopian tubes or uterus of a rabbit, flushing them out later and adding them to human oocytes in vitro. None of the oocytes were fertilized. Finally, in an attempt to imitate the situation in animals, we took spermatozoa from the uterine cervix of women

10 hours after coitus. The addition of these spermatozoa to human oocytes in vitro produced no fertilization.

So far, then, we have either failed or have at best achieved a very limited success in fertilizing human eggs in vitro. We intend to continue these experiments; the ability to observe cleaving human eggs could be of great medical and scientific value. For example, sterility caused by faulty passage of embryos along the fallopian tube could probably be alleviated by removing oocytes from the ovary, growing and fertilizing them in vitro and then transferring them back into the mother. Another possibility, arising from the number of oocytes that can be obtained from a human ovary (up to 65 in our experiments), is that oocytes and embryos showing anomalies could be eliminated in favor of those developing normally. This achievement might one day permit some choice to be made in the type of offspring born to particular parents.

The Author

R. G. EDWARDS is a research fellow in the physiological laboratory at the University of Cambridge. After graduation from the University College of North Wales he obtained a Ph.D. at the University of Edinburgh, where he began research on embryological and endocrinological genetics in mammals. He left Edinburgh in 1957 to work for a year at the California Institute of Technology, spent five years at the National Institute for Medical Research in London and went to the University of Cambridge in 1963. At intervals he has also worked at the University of Glasgow and at Johns Hopkins University. This summer he is carrying on his research activities at the University of North Carolina School of Medicine.

Bibliography

THE COMPARATIVE BEHAVIOR OF MAMMALIAN EGGS IN VIVO AND IN VITRO, I: THE ACTIVATION OF OVARIAN EGGS. Gregory Pincus and E. V. Enzmann in The Journal of Experimental Medicine, Vol. 62, No. 5, pages 665–675; November 1, 1935.

THE GROWTH, MATURATION AND ATRESIA OF OVARIAN EGGS IN THE RABBIT. G. Pincus and E. V. Enzmann in Journal of Morphology, Vol. 61, No. 2, pages 351–376; September, 1937.

THE MAMMALIAN EGG. Colin R. Austin. Blackwell Scientific Publications, 1961.

PRELIMINARY ATTEMPTS TO FERTILIZE HUMAN OOCYTES MATURED IN VITRO. R. G. Edwards, Roger P. Donahue, Theodore A. Baranki and Howard W. Jones, Jr., in American Journal of Obstetrics and Gynecology, in press.

THE MATURATION OF RABBIT OOCYTES IN CULTURE AND THEIR MATURATION, ACTIVATION, FERTILIZATION AND SUBSEQUENT DEVELOPMENT IN THE FALLOPIAN TUBES. M. C. Chang in The Journal of Experimental Zoology, Vol. 128, No. 2, pages 379–405; March, 1955.

SCIENTIFIC
AMERICAN   May 1961, Vol. 204, No. 5, pp. 135-144   OFFPRINT 1048

TASTE RECEPTORS

by Edward S. Hodgson

In the blowfly the organs of taste are located in hairs on the fly's proboscis. By slipping a slender tubular electrode over such a hair, investigators can learn much about the mechanism of taste in general.

The severed head of a fly, a lump of wax and a minute glass tube filled with salt water were the novel ingredients of the experiment. The other items, including an amplifier, a cathode-ray oscilloscope and a motion-picture camera, were conventional tools for exploring the workings of the nervous system. When this improbable collection was appropriately hooked up, it provided the long-sought means of measuring directly the electrical impulses by which a single taste cell sends a taste sensation to the brain. At last the workings of one of the least understood types of sensory receptor cell could be subjected to direct observation.

Blowflies began losing their heads to such good purpose in 1955, when I collaborated in a study of taste mechanisms with Jerome Y. Lettvin of the Massachusetts Institute of Technology and Kenneth D. Roeder of Tufts University. In our experiments we fastened the fly's head upside down to the lump of wax and subjected the head to slight pressure, causing the proboscis to extend. Then, using a micromanipulator, we could slip the water-filled glass tube over one of the fine sensory hairs on the tip of the proboscis. A silver wire inserted into the other end of the tube connects it with the amplifier and the oscilloscope.

BLOWFLY PROBOSCIS with water-filled glass tube slipped over a single hair (*right*) is in position for experiment. The shiny horizontal object is a staple that keeps the proboscis extended. Part of one of the fly's eyes is just below the staple (*right of center*).

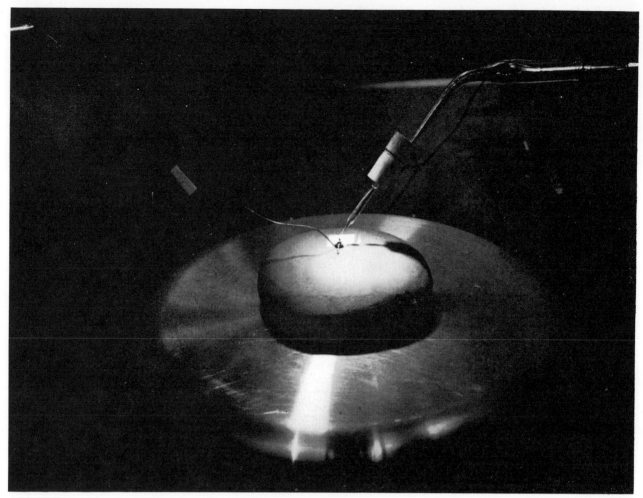

ELECTRICAL CONNECTION carries impulse from taste cells. Blowfly head is on lump of wax. Electrode at right is glass tube filled with salt water. Electrode at left, connected to amplifier, is implanted in severed head to complete the electrical circuit.

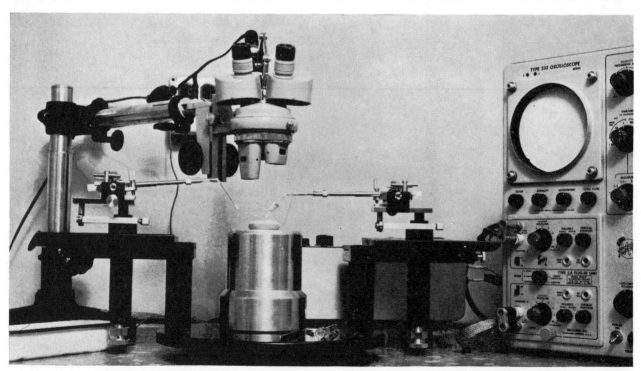

COMPLETE LABORATORY SETUP for measuring impulses from blowfly taste cells includes microscope, micromanipulators *(at left and right of center stand)* and oscilloscope *(right)*. Electrodes that make contact with fly's head are just above lump of wax.

To complete the circuit, another wire from the amplifier is inserted into the fly's head. Contact between the sensory hair and the solution in the tube causes the taste nerve to produce a series of electrical impulses that register as a fleeting trace on the face of the oscilloscope tube. This visible image of the nerve impulse is recorded by the motion-picture camera.

Although the chemical senses—taste and smell—may seem less important than other sensory systems in man, they have always had a central role in the behavior of other animals. Cells particularly sensitive to the chemical environment were among the earliest to appear, no doubt because the murky aquatic environments that were the scene of so much evolutionary history made chemical perception essential for survival. Chemical detectors are found in one of the oldest of multicellular creatures: the jellyfish. In flatworms, the simplest bilaterally symmetrical animals, chemoreceptors on the sides of the head direct the search for food. Knowledge of the operation of these primitive receptors is so meager, however, that the concepts of "smell" and "taste" must be reserved for the animals that evolved later.

When animals emerged from the water, they continued to depend heavily on the chemical senses. In most insects and in many other land animals, taste and smell play a key part in detecting a suitable environment, finding sustenance and initiating reproductive behavior. The chemical senses do much more than provide pleasurable sensations for gourmets: they are essential to the survival of many animal species.

The study of taste and smell not only sheds light on one of the fundamental processes in nature; it also can be of help in combating insects and other pests that share with man a taste for certain foods. By understanding the mechanism of the chemical senses, man may be able to interfere with their operation, to anesthetize them or even to exploit them with chemicals that attract or repel pests.

Quantitative studies of the chemical senses largely awaited the development of equipment sensitive enough to measure nerve impulses. The first such study was made less than three decades ago by E. D. Adrian and C. Ludwig at the University of Cambridge. They recorded impulses from the olfactory stalk of a catfish brain while flushing the fish's nasal sac with fluid from decaying earthworms or from a putre-

fying alligator head. They found that the olfactory nerves carry some impulses even without stimulation. The fluid from decaying meat greatly increases the number of impulses, which signal the brain that food is nearby. Adrian and Ludwig also discovered that the olfactory stalk will not show a response to stimulation twice in quick succession: full sensitivity reappears only after a recovery period. (Nerve physiologists would say that the olfactory system is "slow-adapting.") Subsequent studies have shown that the chemoreceptor systems of most animals, including many only distantly related to the catfish, have the same general characteristics.

From the point of view of the investigator, however, the taste and smell receptors of vertebrate animals usually share certain drawbacks. The actual receptor cells are too small or too inconveniently located to be probed with electrodes; hence recordings of nerve impulses are customarily taken from nerve fibers connected to the receptor cells rather than from the receptors themselves. Since each nerve fiber is connected to several receptor cells, the original messages must be condensed and delayed by the time they reach the recording electrodes. The situation can be further complicated by a layer of mucus over the receptor cell; it is extremely difficult even to estimate the time it takes a stimulating chemical to penetrate the mucus or wash out of it.

The line of investigation that was eventually to lead to the making of direct and convenient contact with single receptor cells began even before the work of Adrian and Ludwig. In the 1920's D. E. Minnich of the University of Minnesota applied a sugar solution to the sensory hairs on the mouth parts of flies and on the feet of butterflies. When the solution touched even a single hair, the proboscis would extend as if the insect were trying to feed. Each hair seemed to be a taste receptor.

More recently V. G. Dethier, working at Johns Hopkins University, dipped the feet of blowflies into a variety of solutions. He observed which solutions caused extension of the proboscis and so was able to compile a long list of molecules that the fly apparently found tasty. By 1950, largely as a consequence of Dethier's work, more was known about the taste receptors of blowflies than about those of any other organism, including man.

The taste hairs of the fly are merely the inert housings of the living taste-receptor cells. By means of microscopic studies of thin sections of the hairs and the surrounding tissue, Dethier found that each sensory hair on the proboscis of the blowfly has three receptor cells at its base. Two of the cells send thin filaments through the hollow shaft of the hair to its tip. Dethier concluded that these two cells are the taste receptors because when he rolled a droplet

LIVING AUSTRALIAN SHEEP BLOWFLY is shown here with proboscis (*between two front legs*) extended. The fly, which lays its eggs on sheep, is a serious pest in Australia.

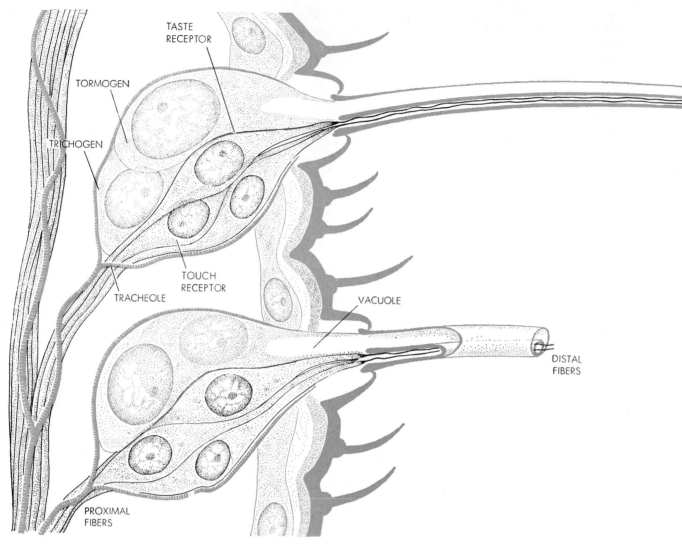

SENSORY HAIR of blowfly proboscis ends in papilla (*far right*) capable of detecting chemicals. A "bag" of cells (*left*) lies at base of each hair. The smaller cells in the bag are the two taste receptors, which send filaments ("*distal fibers*") through hollow hair, and between them is a touch receptor. The tormogen and trichogen are not receptors but give rise to the hair structure. The proximal fibers connect the taste and touch receptors directly with the brain. The entire chemoreception system is shown in black.

of sugar water along the shaft of the hair, the proboscis extended only after the solution had reached the tip. The third receptor cell, which sends no filament into the hair, was found by Myron L. Wolbarsht and Dethier to be a touch receptor, sensitive to the bending of the hair. From each of the three cells an extension goes directly to the brain.

The blowfly's two taste-receptor cells, made accessible to external stimuli by the extension of their sensitive filaments in hairs outside the body, seemed to offer an ideal opportunity for observing the chemoreceptor mechanism. No mucus or saliva flows over the cells. Moreover, the hairs on the end of the proboscis are so far apart that experiments on a single hair do not disturb neighboring hairs.

One important difficulty remained to be overcome: making an electrical connection to detect the nerve impulse. Near the tip of a sensory hair the

filaments from each receptor are only about a ten-thousandth of a millimeter in diameter—too small to generate much voltage or withstand conventional techniques of making electrical connections with cells. At its largest the diameter of the receptor-cell body may be 22 thousandths of a millimeter, but this part of the cell lies buried at the base of the hair, shielded by the tough, nonconducting waxy cuticle of the hair wall and by the surrounding proboscis tissue.

A clue to the technique for making the electrical connection without injuring the delicate receptor cell came from a beautifully simple experiment performed by Eleanor H. Slifer at the State University of Iowa. By dipping hairs on the antenna of a grasshopper into water containing a dye she showed that aqueous solutions penetrate the tips of sensory hairs. These antenna hairs re-

semble in miniature the taste hairs of the blowfly proboscis. Lettvin, Roeder and I guessed that if water passes through the cuticle at the tip of a sensory hair, a solution that conducts electricity might pick up a nerve impulse through the same permeable spot. Perhaps the solution could both stimulate the taste-receptor cell and provide a workable connection between the receptors inside the fly hair and the electrical recording system outside. Thus it was that we performed the experiment described at the beginning of this article.

As we had hoped, the salt water in the tiny glass tube at once stimulated the receptors and conducted a current away from them. Now that we could record messages directly from the taste receptors, we were able to attack the more interesting problem of how the receptors work. Their reactions to various chemical stimuli would, we felt, provide im-

SENSORY PAPILLA

portant clues to the chemical events that generate the electrical impulses in the receptors.

We were especially curious to see if both of the taste receptors in a sensory hair are sensitive to the same kinds of chemical. It quickly became apparent that they are not. Salts, acids, most alcohols and most other compounds, except sugars, elicited electrical impulses with a constant amplitude of about 300 microvolts (300 millionths of a volt). Test solutions of sucrose and many other sugars, mixed with a trace of salt to provide electrical conductivity, elicited predominantly smaller impulses, about 200 microvolts in amplitude. Since a given nerve cell normally produces impulses of only one amplitude, the two distinct amplitudes from the taste hair provided a way to tell the response of one cell from that of the other. Actually the impulse amplitudes varied somewhat in recordings from different hairs, but the impulses of the two taste cells were usually distinguishable.

For easy reference we called the cell producing the larger impulses the "L" receptor and the cell producing the smaller impulses the "S" receptor. Our first generalization was that the S cell appears to be a sugar receptor and the L cell a less specific nonsugar receptor. Since blowflies feed on sugars and avoid most of the chemicals that stimulate the L receptor, the electrical activity of the nerves seemed to match the flies' feeding behavior.

Further work in my laboratory at Columbia University supported the idea that compounds "acceptable" to the fly stimulate the S receptor, whereas "unacceptable" compounds stimulate the L receptor. We found that the electrical recordings from L and S receptors in single hairs correlate well with the proboscis behavior that follows stimulation of single hairs with a droplet of each test solution. For example, fructose and glucose, both sugars that trigger proboscis extension, strongly stimulate S receptors, even when applied in relatively low concentration. Two other sugars, cellobiose and mannose, must be applied in high concentration or to many sensory hairs in order to produce a proboscis response. Correspondingly, they evoke only a few S impulses when observed electrically.

The most striking correlation between taste-receptor activities and behavior occurs with four polyhydric alcohols. All these compounds are composed of exactly the same atoms; only the arrangement of the atoms differs. Sorbitol, dulcitol and mannitol stimulate the L receptor. Inositol, however, strongly stimulates the S receptor; it is also the only one of these alcohols that evokes the feeding response of the proboscis. These reactions indicate that the architecture of a stimulating molecule plays a part in the function of the S receptor, because inositol is the only polyhydric alcohol with a ring-shaped molecule, resembling the sugars we found to be most stimulating.

The selective response of the S receptor suggests that enzymes mediate the chemical reaction that triggers the impulse. These biological catalysts are

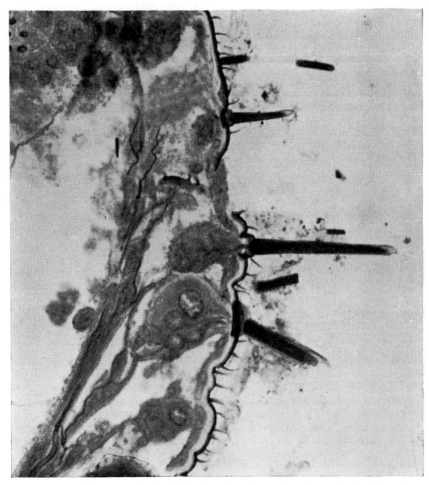

SENSORY HAIRS AND CELLS of blowfly proboscis are shown in section in photomicrograph by V. G. Dethier of University of Pennsylvania. Magnification is 600 diameters.

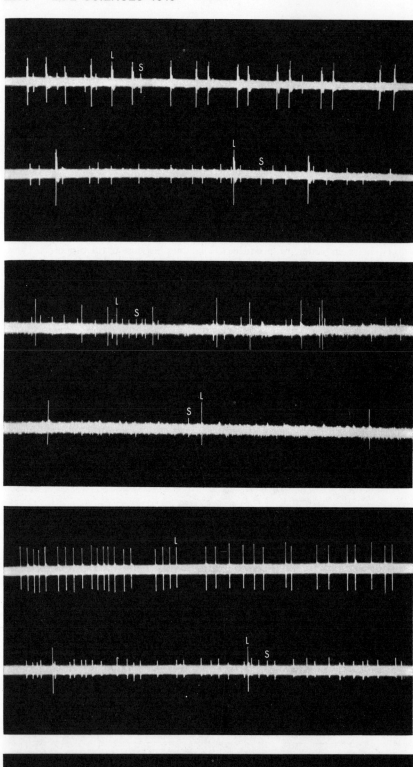

OSCILLOSCOPE TRACES show reactions of taste hairs to various chemicals. Each hair has two receptors, one giving an "L" (large amplitude) response on the oscilloscope, and one giving an "S" (small) response. In top picture top trace resulted from application of the sugar raffinose, which caused many L impulses, while bottom trace shows reaction of same hair to fructose, which caused more S than L impulses. Middle picture shows how another hair reacted to fructose (*top trace*) and to another sugar, ribose (*bottom trace*). Ribose stimulated scarcely any impulses. The bottom pair of traces was made by a third hair exposed to two polyhydric alcohols. The alcohol dulcitol (*top trace*) strongly stimulated L impulses, whereas inositol, made up of same atoms in a different arrangement, primarily stimulated S responses. At bottom is time scale for traces; it has 100 peaks a second.

highly specific in their activity. The far less specific responses of the L receptor, which is stimulated by salts and a variety of other nonsugars, suggest that a different mechanism is involved here. It might be sufficient for ions of the stimulating compounds to become loosely bound to the surface of the L receptor. This possibility is particularly interesting, because the same mechanism has been postulated for the salt-taste receptors in mammals.

Further support for the idea of different mechanisms of S and L activity comes from experiments that Lindsay Barton-Browne and I performed on the Australian sheep blowfly at the Australian National University and at the Australian Commonwealth Scientific and Industrial Research Organization. We were able to measure the time interval between the applications of the stimulus and the first receptor impulse in 141 individual taste-receptor cells. It happens that the oscilloscope beam shows a slight deflection the instant our experimental circuit is closed by contact between the stimulating solution and the sensory hair [*see bottom illustration on opposite page*]. The deflection is followed by a brief interval before the taste cell fires the impulse that goes to the brain. We found that the impulses from the L receptors appear within as little as a millisecond (a thousandth of a second) after a salt solution is applied. With S receptors, however, the delay after contact with a sugar solution is always at least five milliseconds. (These speeds are only a fourth to a 20th as long as those generally observed in experiments with vertebrates, showing again the value of making recordings as close as possible to the site of receptor stimulation.) The sugar molecules would be expected to move slower than the salt ions to the receptor site. Only part of the difference in the response times of S and L receptors can, however, be explained on this basis alone, and some fundamental difference in their mechanism of operation again seems indicated.

Of course, a fly does not normally encounter chemicals in the pure forms employed in our experiments. In nature, feeding behavior may depend on the proportions of L and S impulses reaching the brain. Experiments at Columbia have shown that mixtures seldom produce impulses that are the simple sum of the impulses obtained when the chemicals are tried singly. The addition of sucrose to a solution of sodium chloride, for example, not only activates the S receptor; it also lowers the frequency of the L impulses caused by the salt. This may be due in part to interactions of the ions and molecules in solution. Whatever the mechanism, this effect tends to increase the discrepancy between frequencies of L and S impulses, enhancing the contrast between acceptable and unacceptable chemicals. Thus the fly's taste receptors would signal the brain that a substance is either "very acceptable" or "very unacceptable."

The individual sensory hairs on the fly's mouth parts exhibit further refinements that provide additional information to the brain. Barton-Browne and I found that the receptors in some hairs are slow in responding to stimuli and are relatively inexcitable, while those in other hairs always fire rapidly. Thus strong stimulation that would virtually inactivate the sensitive receptors would still be affecting the less active receptors. The reverse would be true of barely perceptible stimuli.

Temperature changes of less than a degree can also modulate the frequency of firing of some receptors during a period of otherwise regular discharge. This temperature effect is not produced at the tips of the hairs and apparently does not involve the chemosensory processes occurring there. Since the bending of a sensory hair can also provide information about tactile properties of the environment, the range of sensations provided by even a single sensory hair can be wide indeed.

It is amusing to imagine the sensations experienced by the living fly when a taste receptor hair is stimulated in various ways. In contact with heated sirup a single hair might signal not only a strong and acceptable taste but the temperature and stickiness of the sirup as well. Other situations and the sensations they excite are not too difficult to imagine. The wire tapping that brings the nerve impulse to the oscilloscope has probably provided far more accurate information about the fly's taste sensations than could be obtained if the insect could talk.

Although microelectrodes attached to the tip of a fly's taste hairs have revealed a great deal about nerve cells sensitive to chemicals, they have failed to detect one of the very first steps that was expected to occur in the process of tasting: the initial electrical changes that trigger the fly's taste cell to send an impulse to the brain. Recently two Japanese investigators, Hiromichi Morita and Satoru Yamashita of Kyushu University, reached this objective. Through an opening in the side wall of a fly's sen-

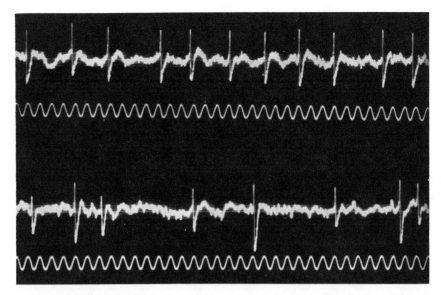

ONLY L FIBER RESPONDS when solution consists of sodium chloride alone (*top*). A much weaker salt solution plus the sugar sucrose causes five S and only three L impulses in same time period (*bottom*). The time scales here contain 100 peaks to the second.

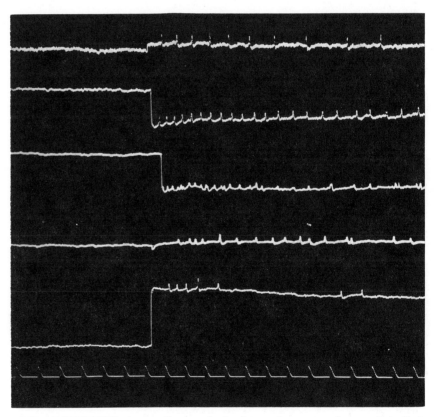

TIME OF RESPONSE after application of stimulus can be seen on these tracings. Each peak on time scale (*bottom*) marks passage of 10 one-thousandths of a second. First deflection of beam indicates application of stimulus. Second deflection is first receptor response. The three top traces show response of L receptors to salt. The two bottom traces, showing response of S receptors to sucrose, illustrate how the S receptor reacts slower.

sory hair they managed to connect a microelectrode to the filaments inside. Before being stimulated, the receptor-cell filaments registered some spontaneous activity like that found by Adrian and Ludwig in the catfish olfactory stalk. More important, Morita and Yamashita

have demonstrated that, upon stimulation, a relatively slow change in electrical potential in the filament precedes and leads to the generation of the brief but much stronger impulse going to the brain. These slow electrical changes occur only in the filaments that lie within

INOSITOL

DULCITOL

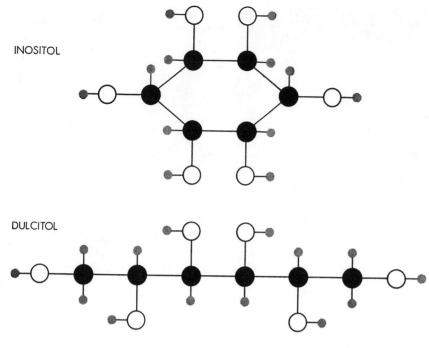

● HYDROGEN

○ OXYGEN

● CARBON

POLYHYDRIC ALCOHOL MOLECULES are made of same atoms in different arrangements. Because of its ring structure, which resembles that of stimulating sugars, inositol evokes feeding response in blow-flies. Dulcitol, which has no ring, tends instead to repel the fly.

the shaft of the sensory hair and are elicited by chemical reaction with the stimulating chemical. They correspond to the "generator" potentials observed in other receptor cells, which cause the main bodies of the cells to fire impulses into the central nervous sys-tem [see "Biological Transducers, by Werner R. Loewenstein; SCIENTIFIC AMERICAN Offprint 70]. Further study of these generator potentials in taste-receptor cells will undoubtedly lead to a more complete description of the mechanisms of the chemical senses.

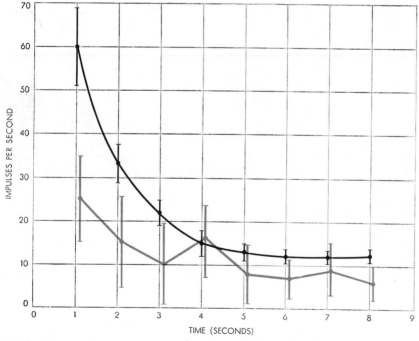

TASTE CELLS "ADAPT" to stimulus by decreasing number of impulses sent to brain. L receptor (*black line*) sends more impulses than S receptor (*color*) and rate decreases faster. The vertical lines indicate the range of impulses found in repeated tests on one hair.

The Author

EDWARD S. HODGSON is professor of zoology at Columbia University. He was born in Wilmington, Del., in 1928 and received his B.S. from Allegheny College at the age of 18. He did graduate work in sensory physiology under V. G. Dethier at Johns Hopkins University, acquired a Ph.D. in biology at that institution in 1951 and joined the faculty of Columbia later the same year. The research discussed in the present article was begun at Tufts University, where Hodgson worked for a year in the laboratory of Kenneth D. Roeder.

Bibliography

CHEMORECEPTOR MECHANISMS. V. G. Dethier in *Molecular Structure and Functional Activity of Nerve Cells,* edited by R. G. Grenell and L. J. Mullins, pages 1–30. American Institute of Biological Sciences, 1956.

ELECTROPHYSIOLOGICAL STUDIES OF ARTHROPOD CHEMORECEPTION. III: CHEMORECEPTORS OF TERRESTRIAL AND FRESH-WATER ARTHROPODS. Edward S. Hodgson in *Biological Bulletin,* Vol. 115, No. 1, pages 114–125; August, 1958.

PROBLEMS IN INVERTEBRATE CHEMORECEPTION. Edward S. Hodgson in *The Quarterly Review of Biology,* Vol. 30, No. 4, pages 331–347; December, 1955.

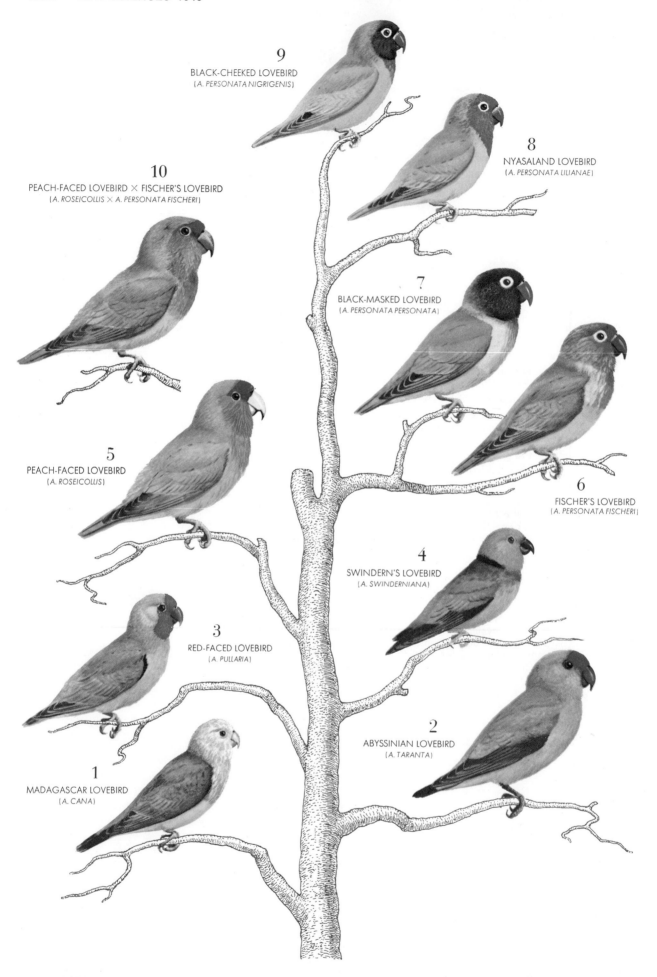

9
BLACK-CHEEKED LOVEBIRD
(A. PERSONATA NIGRIGENIS)

8
NYASALAND LOVEBIRD
(A. PERSONATA LILIANAE)

10
PEACH-FACED LOVEBIRD × FISCHER'S LOVEBIRD
(A. ROSEICOLLIS × A. PERSONATA FISCHERI)

7
BLACK-MASKED LOVEBIRD
(A. PERSONATA PERSONATA)

5
PEACH-FACED LOVEBIRD
(A. ROSEICOLLIS)

6
FISCHER'S LOVEBIRD
(A. PERSONATA FISCHERI)

4
SWINDERN'S LOVEBIRD
(A. SWINDERNIANA)

3
RED-FACED LOVEBIRD
(A. PULLARIA)

2
ABYSSINIAN LOVEBIRD
(A. TARANTA)

1
MADAGASCAR LOVEBIRD
(A. CANA)

SCIENTIFIC
AMERICAN   January 1962, Vol. 206, No. 1, pp. 88-98   OFFPRINT 1049

THE BEHAVIOR OF LOVEBIRDS

by William C. Dilger

The nine members of the genus Agapornis have different rituals for
such activities as nest building. These differences shed light on
the evolution of lovebirds and on the role of heredity in behavior.

All lovebirds display the behavior that gives them their anthropomorphic common name. They pair early, and once pairs are formed they normally endure for life. The partners exhibit their mutual interest with great constancy and in a variety of beguiling activities. For the student of the evolution of animal behavior the lovebirds have special interest. The genus comprises nine forms (species or subspecies). They show a pattern of differentiation in their behavior that corresponds to their differentiation in color and morphology. By comparative study of their behavior, therefore, one can hope to reconstruct its evolution and to observe how natural selection has brought about progressive variations on the same fundamental scheme.

Together with my colleagues in the Laboratory of Ornithology at Cornell University, I have been studying both the constants and the variables in lovebird behavior for the past five years. It is not too difficult to duplicate in the laboratory the basic features of the lovebirds' natural African environment, so the birds thrive in captivity. Our work has covered all the lovebirds except Swindern's lovebird; we have not been able to obtain any specimens of this species. Our findings in two areas—sexual behavior and the defense and construction of the nest—have been particularly fruitful, be-

cause in these areas the evolutionary changes in lovebird behavior stand out in sharp relief.

Lovebirds constitute the genus *Agapornis,* and are members of the parrot family. Their closest living relatives are the hanging parakeets of Asia (the genus *Loriculus*). Three species of lovebird— the Madagascar lovebird, the Abyssinian lovebird and the red-faced lovebird—resemble the hanging parakeets and differ from all other lovebirds in two major respects. The males and females of these three species differ in color and are easily distinguishable from each other. The male and female of the other lovebirds are the same color. In these three species the primary social unit is the pair and its immature offspring. The other lovebirds are highly social and tend to nest in colonies. In these respects, then, the Madagascar lovebird, the Abyssinian lovebird and the red-faced lovebird most closely resemble the ancestral form, and the other lovebirds are more divergent.

Our study of interspecies differentiation of behavior has begun to reveal the order in which the other species arrived on the scene. Next after the three "primitive" species is Swindern's lovebird. Then comes the peach-faced lovebird and finally the four subspecies of *Agapornis personata,* commonly referred to as the white-eye-ringed forms: Fischer's lovebird, the black-masked lovebird, the Nyasaland lovebird and the black-cheeked lovebird. There are significant differences in behavior between the peach-faced lovebird and the four white-eye-ringed forms.

Perhaps the sharpest contrasts in behavior are those that distinguish the three primitive species from the species that evolved later. Even the common generic characteristic of pairing at an

early age shows changes between the two groups that must be related to their contrasting patterns of life—nesting in pairs as opposed to nesting in colonies. Among the primitive species pair formation takes place when the birds are about four months old. At that time they are entirely independent of their parents and have already developed adult plumage. In the more recently evolved species, the colonial nesting pattern of which offers them access to their contemporaries virtually from the moment of their birth, pair formation takes place even earlier: the birds are about two months old and still have their juvenile plumage.

Among all the lovebird species pair formation is a rather undramatic event. Unpaired birds seek out the company of other unpaired birds and test them, as it were, by attempting to preen them and otherwise engage their interest. Couples quickly discover if they are compatible, and generally it takes no more than a few hours to establish lifelong pairs.

When the paired birds reach sexual maturity, their behavior with respect to each other becomes much more elaborate. This behavior as a whole is common to all lovebirds, and some activities are performed in the same way by all. Other activities, however, are not, and they show a gradation from the most primitive forms to the most recently evolved ones. One constant among all species is the female's frequent indifference to, and even active aggression against, the male each time he begins to woo her. Another is the essential pattern of the male's response—a combination of fear, sexual appetite, aggression and consequent frustration. Primarily motivated by both fear and sexual appetite, the male makes his first approach to his mate by sidling toward and then away from

NINE FORMS OF LOVEBIRD, as well as one hybrid (*top left*), are shown on the opposite page. They are arranged in their apparent order of evolution. The hybrid was bred in the laboratory for experiments on the inheritance of behavior. The letter *A.* at the beginning of each of the Latin species names stands for the genus *Agapornis.*

her while turning about on his perch. This switch-sidling, as it is called, is common to all species.

Two forms of male behavior initially associated with frustration, on the other hand, show a distinct evolutionary progression. The first of these activities is called squeak-twittering. Among the three primitive species—the Madagascar lovebird, the Abyssinian lovebird and the red-faced lovebird—the male utters a

series of high-pitched vocalizations when the female thwarts him by disappearing into the nest cavity. The sounds are quite variable in pitch and purity of tone and have no recognizable rhythm. In the more recently evolved species—the peach-faced and the four white-eye-ringed forms—squeak-twittering is rather different. The sound is rhythmic, purer in tone and less variable in pitch. Nor does it occur only when the female has

turned her back on the male and entered the nest cavity. The male usually vocalizes even when the female is present and gives no indication whatever of thwarting him. Squeak-twittering has undergone a progressive change not only in its physical characteristics but also in the context in which it appears.

A similar evolution toward more highly ritualized behavior has occurred in another sexual activity, displacement

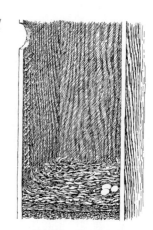

BEHAVIOR OF MADAGASCAR LOVEBIRD is outlined. Both sexes engage in courtship feeding (*a*). Accompanying head bobs are rapid and trace small arc (*b*). Nest materials, generally bark and leaves, are carried several pieces at a time and tucked among

BEHAVIOR OF PEACH-FACED LOVEBIRD suggests higher evolutionary stage. Only males perform courtship feeding; females fluff their feathers during this ritual (*a*). Slower head bobs trace wider arc (*b*). Nest materials, also bark and leaves, are

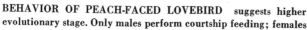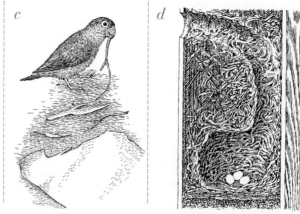

BEHAVIOR OF FISCHER'S LOVEBIRD indicates a further evolution. Courtship feeding (*a*), mobbing (*e*) and bill-fencing (*f*) are performed much as they are by the peach-faced lovebird. But other kinds of behavior are significantly different. Head bobs

scratching. This response derives from the habit, common to all species, of scratching the head with the foot when frustrated. Among the three primitive species displacement scratching is still close to its origins. Only two things distinguish it from ordinary head-scratching: its context and the fact that it is always performed with the foot nearest the female. Purely practical considerations govern this behavior: the male already has that foot raised preparatory to mounting his mate. In the more recently evolved species, displacement scratching has become primarily a form of display. Its progressive emancipation from the original motivation with which it is associated becomes more and more apparent as one observes it in the species from the peach-faced lovebird through the white-eye-ringed forms. Among all these the scratching is far more rapid and perfunctory than it is among the primitive species. Nor is it uniformly directed at the feathered portions of the head. In the peach-faced lovebird it is sometimes directed at the bill instead, and among the Nyasaland and black-cheeked lovebirds it is nearly always so directed. Moreover, these species use the far foot as well as the near one in displacement scratching; among the Nyasaland and black-cheeked lovebirds one is

e

f

all feathers of the body (*c*). Short strips are used to make an unshaped nest pad (*d*). The young join the mother in cavity-

defense display (*e*). In *f* birds show threat and appeasement display. It usually averts combat; if it fails, the birds fight furiously.

e

f

carried several at a time in back plumage (*c*); long strips are used to make a well-shaped nest (*d*). Birds join in "mobbing" to

protect nest (*e*). Bill-fencing (*f*) has a display function. It never leads to real harm; the birds bite only their opponents' toes.

e

f

(*b*) are still slower and trace an even wider arc. Nest materials are carried in the bill, one piece at a time (*c*); twigs as well

as strips of bark and leaf are used. This permits construction of an elaborate covered nest, entered through a tunnel (*d*).

used as often as the other. Finally, as in the case of squeak-twittering, which is often performed at the same time as displacement scratching among these species, the display occurs even when the female does not seem to be thwarting her mate.

All species engage in courtship feeding: the transfer of regurgitated food from one member of the pair to the other. In the three primitive species the female often offers food to her mate. This behavior has never been observed among the peach-faced and white-eye-ringed forms; here courtship feeding seems exclusively a male prerogative.

One can also discern an evolutionary progression in the manner in which the birds carry out the rather convulsive bobbing of the head associated with the act of regurgitation that immediately precedes courtship feeding. Among the primitive species these head-bobbings describe a small arc, are rapid and numerous and are usually followed by rather prolonged bill contacts while the food is being transferred. In the other forms the head-bobbings are slower, fewer in number and trace a wider arc; the bill contacts usually last for only a short time. Moreover, among the more recently evolved forms head-bobbing has become pure display; it is no longer accompanied by the feeding of the female. Unlike the females of the primitive lovebird species, which have no special display activity during courtship feeding, the females of the more recently evolved species play a distinctly ritualized role. They ruffle their plumage throughout the entire proceeding.

Females of all species indicate their fluctuating readiness to copulate by subtle adjustments of their plumage, particularly the feathers of the head. The more the female fluffs, the readier she is, and the more the male is encouraged. Finally she will solicit copulation by leaning forward and raising her head and tail. Females of the primitive species do not fluff their plumage during copulation; females of the more recently evolved species do. This is undoubtedly related to the morphological differences among the lovebirds. Since males and females of the more recently evolved species have the same coloring and patterning, the females must reinforce their mates' recognition of them, both in courtship and in copulation, by some behavioral means.

Although the forms of precopulatory behavior seem to be innate among all species, learning appears to play a major role in producing the changes that occur as the members of a pair become more familiar with each other. Newly formed pairs are rather awkward. The males make many mistakes and are frequently threatened and thwarted by their mates. After they have had a few broods, however, and have acquired experience, they become more expert and tend more and more to perform the right activity at the right time. As a result the female responds with aggression far less often, and the male engages more rarely in the displays that are associated with frustration and thwarting. Squeak-twittering and displacement scratching in particular become less frequent. Switch-sidling is still performed, but with a perceptibly diminished intensity. Altogether precopulatory bouts become less protracted. In spite of the male's reduced activity, the female seems to become receptive fairly quickly.

Disagreements among members of the same species are handled in quite different ways by those lovebirds that nest in pairs and those that nest colonially. Among the less social primitive species an elaborate pattern of threat and appeasement display has developed. For example, a formalized series of long, rapid strides toward an opponent signalizes aggression; a ruffling of the feathers, fear and the wish to escape. The loser in a bout of posturing may indicate submission by fleeing or by remaining quiet, turning its head away from its opponent and fluffing its plumage. By means of this code the birds can communicate rather exact items of information as to their readiness to attack or to flee. As a result actual fights seldom occur. When they do, however, the birds literally tear each other apart.

The peach-faced lovebird and the white-eye-ringed forms, which nest colonially, are thrown in contact with members of their own species much more often. This is undoubtedly related to the fact that they have developed a ritualized form of display fighting that goes far beyond a mere code of threat and appeasement and that replaces serious physical conflict. Display fighting among these more recently evolved species consists primarily of bill-fencing. The two birds parry and thrust with their bills and aim sharp nips at each other's toes.

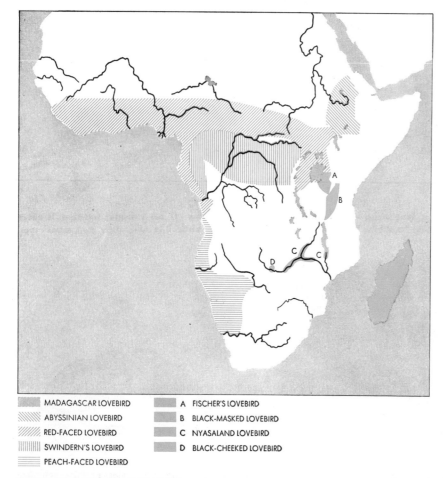

▨ MADAGASCAR LOVEBIRD	A FISCHER'S LOVEBIRD
▧ ABYSSINIAN LOVEBIRD	B BLACK-MASKED LOVEBIRD
▨ RED-FACED LOVEBIRD	C NYASALAND LOVEBIRD
▥ SWINDERN'S LOVEBIRD	D BLACK-CHEEKED LOVEBIRD
▤ PEACH-FACED LOVEBIRD	

DISTRIBUTION OF LOVEBIRDS is shown on this map of Africa and the island of Madagascar. All nine of the lovebird species and subspecies inhabit different areas.

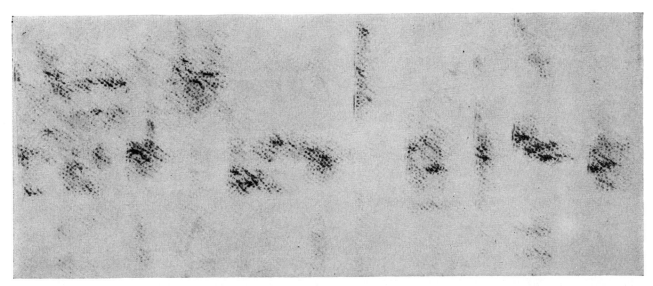

SQUEAK-TWITTERING in male Madagascar lovebird is seen on sound spectrogram. The horizontal axis represents time; the vertical axis, frequency. Uneven distribution of spots along both axes shows an arhythmic quality and a wide variation in pitch.

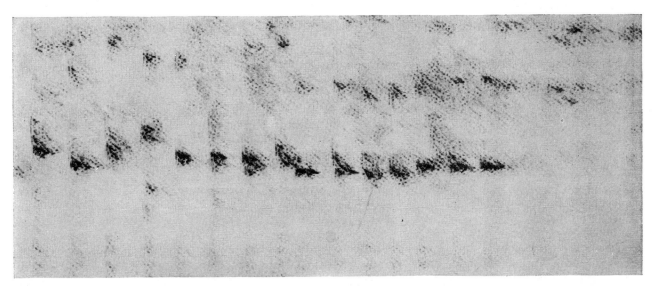

SOUND SPECTROGRAM of squeak-twittering in peach-faced lovebird shows greater rhythmicity and less variation in pitch. In Madagascar lovebird behavior is displayed only when female thwarts male. In peach-faced lovebird this is not always the case.

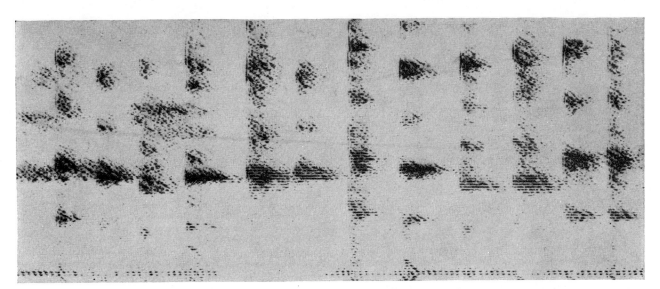

FURTHER EVOLUTION in squeak-twittering is seen in behavior of Nyasaland lovebird. Sounds are very rhythmic and show almost no variation in pitch; wide vertical distribution of spots reflects the large number of harmonics contained in the monotonous note.

The toe is the only part the birds ever bite, and the inhibition against biting a member of the same species in any other place seems to be, like bill-fencing itself, an innate pattern. Though bill-fencing appears to be innate, it must be perfected by learning. The colonial nesting pattern offers young birds considerable practice with their contemporaries, and they quickly become skilled.

If lovebirds have had experience in rearing their own young, they will not rear the young of those other forms that have a natal down of a different color. On the other hand, a female that is given the egg of such a form at the time of her first egg-laying will rear the bird that emerges. Indeed, if a peach-faced lovebird has her first experience of motherhood with a newly hatched Madagascar lovebird, she will thereafter refuse to raise her own offspring. The down of the peach-faced lovebird's newly hatched

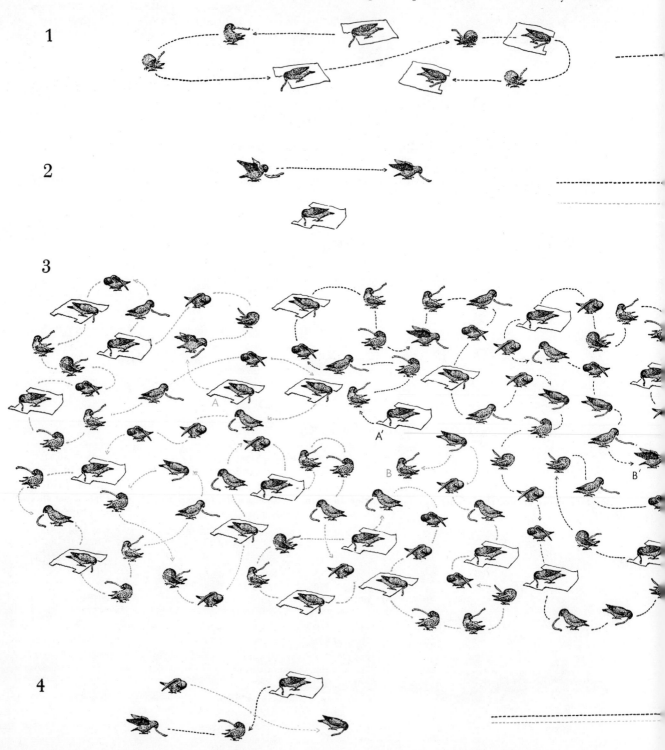

HYBRID LOVEBIRD inherits patterns for two different ways of carrying nest-building materials. From the peach-faced lovebird (1) it inherits patterns for carrying strips several at a time, in feathers. From Fischer's lovebird (2) it inherits patterns for carrying strips one at a time, in the bill. When the hybrid first begins to build a nest (3), it acts completely confused. Colored lines from A to B and black lines from A' to B' indicate the number of activities necessary for it to get two strips to the nest site, a feat achieved only when the strips are carried singly, in the bill. It takes three years before the bird perfects its bill-carrying behavior (4),

young (like the down of the white-eye-ringed forms) is red, and the down of newly hatched Madagascar, Abyssinian and red-faced lovebirds is white.

Unlike most of the other members of

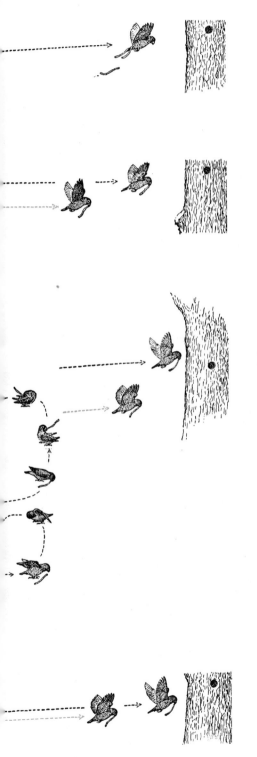

and even then it makes efforts to tuck its nest materials in its feathers. As the bird gains experience it becomes more and more proficient in this activity, which, however, never results in successful carrying.

the parrot family, which simply lay their eggs in empty cavities, all lovebird species make nests. The red-faced lovebird constructs its nest in a hole it digs in the hard, earthy nests certain ants make in trees. All other species, however, make their nests in pre-existing cavities, which are usually reached through small entrances. The nests of the Madagascar lovebird, the Abyssinian lovebird and the red-faced lovebird are quite simple, consisting essentially of deposits of soft material on the cavity floor. These three species have developed an elaborate cavity-defense display. The moment an intruder appears, the female ruffles her feathers, partly spreads her wings and tail and utters a rapid series of harsh, buzzing sounds. If the intruder persists, she will suddenly compress her plumage, utter a piercing yip and lunge toward it. She does not bite, but she gives every indication of being about to do so. Her older offspring may join her at this time, ruffling their feathers and making grating sounds.

The effect of this performance is quite startling; it can even give pause to an experienced investigator! The Madagascar lovebird, the most primitive of all the species, is the quickest to engage in the cavity-defense display and is the only species we have seen carry the display through both stages. A stronger stimulation is necessary before the Abyssinian lovebird engages in this behavior, and we have not seen the bird go any further than ruffling its body plumage and making the harsh, rasping sounds.

The white-eye-ringed lovebirds build rather elaborate nests, consisting of a roofed chamber at the end of a tunnel within the cavity. This fact and their strongly social nature combine to make their response to a threat to their nests different from the response of the primitive species. They have no cavity-defense displays at all. If a predator actually reaches the cavity, the birds within it will either cower or, if possible, flee through the entrance. But if the predator, encouraged by this show of fear, enters the cavity, it is likely to find that its troubles have just begun. It faces a journey down a narrow tunnel, defended at the end by a bird with a powerful and sharp bill. Moreover, a predator is seldom allowed to come close to the cavity. As soon as it is seen approaching, the entire colony engages in a form of behavior called mobbing: holding their bodies vertically, the birds beat their wings rapidly and utter loud, high-pitched squeaks. The sight and sound of a whole flock mobbing is quite impressive and probably serves to deter many

would-be predators.

All female lovebirds prepare their nest materials in much the same way: by punching a series of closely spaced holes in some pliable material such as paper, bark or leaf. The material is held between the upper and lower portions of the bill, which then works like a train conductor's ticket punch. The pieces cut out in this way vary in size and shape among the various lovebirds. So do the forms of behavior that now ensue.

The three primitive species and the peach-faced lovebird tuck the pieces they have cut into the feathers of their bodies and fly off with them. The Madagascar lovebird, the Abyssinian lovebird and the red-faced lovebird use very small bits of material. (This is one of the reasons their nests are so unstructured.) The entire plumage of the bird is erected as it inserts the six to eight bits of material in place and remains erect during the whole operation. The peach-faced lovebird cuts strips that are considerably longer. (This permits the more elaborate structuring of its cuplike nest.) Indeed, the strips are so long that they can be carried only in the feathers of the lower back. These are the feathers erected when the strips are tucked in, and the feathers are compressed after each strip is inserted. The peach-faced lovebird loses about half of its cargo before it gets to its nest site; either pieces fall out while others are being cut or tucked in, or they fall out while the bird is flying. The lovebirds that use smaller bits of nest material are more successful in carrying them.

Carrying nest material in the feathers is unique to these birds and the related hanging parakeets. What is more, speculation about its origin must begin with the fact that no other parrots (with one unrelated exception) build nests at all. It is almost certain that this behavior arose from fortuitous occurrences associated with two characteristic parrot activities: chewing on bits of wood, bark and leaf to keep the bill sharp and properly worn down; and preening, which serves to keep the plumage clean and properly arranged. Some parrots that do not build nests will accidentally leave bits of the material in their feathers when they proceed directly from chewing to preening. Such oversights almost certainly initiated the evolution of the habit of carrying nest materials in the feathers.

The four white-eye-ringed forms are completely emancipated from this ancestral pattern. Fischer's lovebird, the black-masked lovebird, the Nyasaland lovebird and the black-cheeked lovebird all carry their nest materials as do most birds—in their bills. They lose little material in the process of carrying, and they pick up twigs in addition to cutting strips of pliable material. With these materials, they can build their characteristically elaborate nests.

Although the peach-faced lovebird normally carries its nest-building material in its feathers, on about 3 per cent of its trips it carries material in its bill. This peculiarity suggested an experiment. We mated the peach-faced lovebird with Fischer's lovebird (the birds hybridize readily in captivity) to see what behavior would show up in the hybrids. In confirmation of the thesis that patterns of carrying nest materials are primarily innate, the hybrid displays a conflict in behavior between the tendency to carry material in its feathers (inherited from the peach-faced lovebird) and the tendency to carry material in its bill (inherited from Fischer's lovebird).

When our hybrids first began to build their nests, they acted as though they were completely confused. They had no difficulty in cutting strips, but they could not seem to determine whether to carry them in the feathers or in the bill. They got material to the nest sites only when they carried it in the bill, and in their first effort at nest building they did carry in their bills 6 per cent of the time. After they had cut each strip, however, they engaged in behavior associated with tucking. Even when they finally carried the material in the bill, they erected the feathers of the lower back and rump and attempted to tuck. But if they were able to press the strips into their plumage—and they were not always successful in the attempt—they could not carry it to the nest site in that fashion. Every strip dropped out.

Two months later, after they had become more experienced, the hybrids carried many more of their nest strips in their bills—41 per cent, to be exact. But they continued to make the movements associated with the intention to tuck: they erected their rump plumage and turned their heads to the rear, flying away with material in their bills only after attempting to tuck.

After two more months had passed they began to learn that strips could be picked up in the bill and carried off with a minimum of prior abortive tucking. But it took two years for them to learn to diminish actual tucking activity to any great extent, and even then they continued to perform many of the movements associated with tucking.

Today the hybrids are behaving, by and large, like Fischer's lovebird, the more recently evolved of their two parents. Only infrequently do they attempt to tuck strips into their plumage. But it has taken them three years to reach this stage—evidence of the difficulty they experience in learning to use one innate pattern at the expense of another, even though the latter is never successful. Moreover, when they do carry out the activities associated with tucking, they perform them far more efficiently than they did at first. Evidently this behavior need not achieve its normal objective in order to be improved.

So far our hybrids have proved to be sterile and therefore unable to pass on their behavior to a second generation. Even in the first generation, however, one can see the ways in which nature interweaves innate and learned elements to produce the behavior characteristic of a species. Further comparative studies can add much to our understanding not only of the behavior of lovebirds but also of the behavior of all vertebrates, including man.

———— STRIPS CARRIED IN BILL
- - - - - INTENTION MOVEMENTS TO CARRY IN BILL
———— STRIPS TUCKED (NEVER CARRIED)
- - - - - INTENTION MOVEMENTS TO TUCK
          IRRELEVANT ACTIVITIES

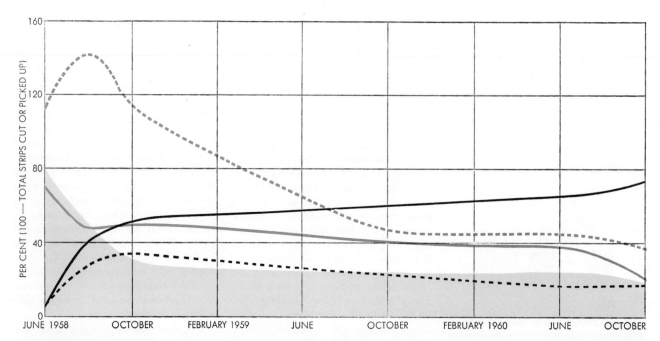

CONFLICTING PATTERNS of carrying nest-building materials are inherited by a hybrid lovebird, produced by mating the peach-faced and Fischer's lovebirds. The hybrid's behavior is charted here for a period of almost three years. As the bird progressively learns to carry nest materials as Fischer's lovebird does, the number of irrelevant movements and inappropriate activities decreases.

The Author

WILLIAM C. DILGER is assistant director of the Laboratory of Ornithology at Cornell University and head of the laboratory's research program. Dilger began his undergraduate studies at Cornell following the end of World War II, in which he had served as a combat and reconnaissance photographer with the Second Air Command Group in the Southeast Asia theater. He received his B.S. from Cornell in 1949, became curator of birds the same year and acquired his Ph.D. in 1955. Though trained primarily in evolutionary biology and vertebrate Zoology, Dilger notes that he has "always been interested in living, whole animals." Dilger taught comparative anatomy and general zoology at St. Lawrence University for a year and then returned to Cornell in 1956.

Bibliography

THE COMPARATIVE ETHOLOGY OF THE AFRICAN PARROT GENUS AGAPORNIS. William C. Dilger in *Zeitschrift für Tierpsychologie*, Vol. 17, No. 6, pages 649–685; 1960.

THE EVOLUTION OF BEHAVIOR IN GULLS. N. Tinbergen in *Scientific American*, Vol. 203, No. 6, pages 118–130; December, 1960.

SOME RECENT TRENDS IN ETHOLOGY. R. A. Hinde in *Psychology: A Study of a Science*, Vol. 2, edited by Sigmund Koch, pages 561–610. McGraw-Hill Book Company, Inc., 1959.

THE STUDY OF INSTINCT. N. Tinbergen. Oxford University Press, 1951.

SCIENTIFIC
AMERICAN   July 1953, Vol. 189, No. 1, pp. 73-78

OFFPRINT 1050

THE DESERT RAT

by Knut and Bodil Schmidt-Nielsen

A remarkable little animal can live in an environment such as Death Valley on dry food and no water at all. It is only recently that this physiological mystery has been solved.

THERE IS a common impression that no higher animal can live long without drinking water. Certainly this is true of man and many other mammals; we need water at frequent intervals, and in a very hot, dry desert a man without water cannot last more than a day or so. An animal such as the camel can survive somewhat longer, but sooner or later it too must drink to refill its supply.

Yet we know that the waterless desert is not uninhabited. Even in desert areas with no visible drinking water within scores of miles, one will often find a fairly rich animal life. How do these animals get the water they must have to live? The body of a desert mammal has about the same water content (65 per cent of body weight) as that of a drinking animal, and it generally has no more tolerance to desiccation of the tissues, sometimes less. For many desert animals the answer is simple: they get their water in their food. These animals live on juicy plants, one of the most important of which is cactus. The pack rat, for example, eats large quantities of cactus pulp, which is about 90 per cent water. Thus it is easy to account for the survival of animals in areas where cacti and other water-storing plants are available.

There are, however, animals which can live in areas altogether barren of juicy vegetation. An outstanding example is a certain general type of desert rodent which is found in all the major desert areas of the world—in Africa, in Asia, in Australia and in the southwestern U. S. Although the rats of this type seem to have evolved independently in the several areas and are not related to one another, all of them are similar in appearance and habits and all seem to be able to live with a minimum of water. How they do so has long been a puzzle to biologists.

During the past few years we have investigated intensively a rodent of this type—the so-called kangaroo rat that lives in deserts of the U. S. Southwest. In a field laboratory in Arizona and in biological laboratories at Swarthmore College, Stanford University and the University of Cincinnati we have studied the kangaroo rat's habits and physiology, and we now have a good understanding of how this rodent is able to get along on a diet so dry that other animals would soon die of thirst.

THE LITTLE kangaroo rat is not actually related to the kangaroo, though it looks a great deal like one. It hops along on long hind legs, and it has a long, strong tail which it uses for support and steering. It lives in a burrow in the ground by day and comes out for food only at night. The animal thrives in the driest regions, even in the bare sand dunes of Death Valley. Water to drink, even dew, is rarely available in its natural habitat. The kangaroo rat apparently has only a short range of movement—not more than a few hundred yards—and

BANNERTAILED KANGAROO RAT (*Dipodomys spectabilis*) from the Santa Rita Range of Arizona is photographed in the laboratory. It is called the kangaroo rat because of its powerful hind legs and long tail.

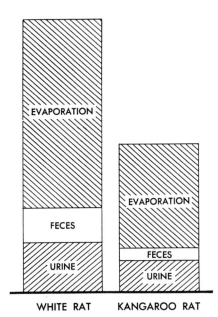

WATER LOSSES of the kangaroo rat (*right*) and the white rat (*left*) are compared at zero humidity.

therefore does not leave its dry area to find juicy plants. Stomach analyses have shown that it seldom or never consumes any succulent vegetation. Its food consists of seeds and other dry plant material. In the laboratory it will live indefinitely without water and with no other food but dry barley seeds.

The first question to be answered was whether the kangaroo rat stores water in its body to carry it over long dry periods. It was found that the animal's water content was always about the same (some 65 per cent of body weight), in the rainy season or the dry season, or after it had been kept on dry food in the laboratory for several weeks. During eight weeks on nothing but dry barley in the laboratory some of the animals increased their body weight, and their water percentage was as high as at the beginning of the experiment; they had actually increased the total amount of water in their bodies. Furthermore, kangaroo rats which were

given watermelon as well as barley to eat showed no higher water percentage in their bodies than animals maintained on a dry diet. They must therefore have eliminated the excess of water at the same rate as it was taken in. Altogether the experiments made clear that the kangaroo rat does not store water or live through dry periods at the expense of its body water.

There is only one way the kangaroo rat can get any substantial amount of water on its dry diet. That is by oxidizing its food. The oxidation of hydrogen or a substance containing hydrogen always forms water. Obviously the amount of water an animal forms in its metabolism will depend upon the hydrogen content of its food. The amount is simply a matter of chemistry and is the same in all animals. Oxidation of a gram of carbohydrate (starch or sugar) yields .6 of a gram of water; of a gram of fat, 1.1 grams of water; of a gram of protein, .3 of a gram of water. Protein produces relatively little water because a considerable part of its hydrogen is not oxidized but is excreted with nitrogen as urea.

Now the experimental diet of dry barley on which the kangaroo rats lived yields 54 grams of water for each 100 grams of barley (dry weight) consumed. If there is any moisture in the air, the barley will also contain a little absorbed water—about 13 grams per 100 grams when the relative humidity is 50 per cent at 75 degrees Fahrenheit. The kangaroo rat consumes 100 grams of barley in a period of about five weeks. Thus during that period its total intake of water is between 54 and 67 grams, depending on atmospheric conditions.

THIS is an astonishingly small amount of water for an animal of its size to subsist on. It can maintain its water balance only if its water losses are correspondingly small. The next step, therefore, was to find out how the animal manages to keep its water loss so low, if indeed it does. We proceeded to measure its losses of water through the three

routes by which an animal eliminates water; in the urine, in the feces and by evaporation from the skin and the respiratory passages.

There is an animal, the African lungfish, which can get along for long periods without excreting any urine at all. When the stream or pond in which it is living dries up, it burrows into the mud and stays there until the next rain. The eminent authority on the kidney, Homer W. Smith; SCIENTIFIC AMERICAN Offprint 37], has found that during this time the urea content of the fish's blood may rise to the extravagant level of 4 per cent. Can the kangaroo rat similarly accumulate waste products and avoid urinating during a dry spell? We investigated and found that it could not: the urea and salt content of its blood did not rise when it was on a dry diet or fall when it had a moist diet. And it continued on its dry diet to excrete urea as usual.

However, we learned that it could get rid of its waste products with a very small output of water. The kangaroo rat has an amazingly efficient kidney. The concentration of urea in its urine can be as high as 24 per cent, whereas in man the maximum is about 6 per cent. Thus the kangaroo rat needs only about one fourth as much water to eliminate a given amount of urea as a man would. Its excretion of salts is similarly efficient. The animal can excrete urine about twice as salty as sea water!

The reason that a human being cannot tolerate drinking sea water is that the body is dehydrated in the process of getting rid of the salts. The saltiness of the kangaroo rat's urine suggested that this animal might be able to drink sea water and get a net water gain from it. Of course it was not easy to induce the kangaroo rat, which normally does not drink, to imbibe sea water. But we were able to make it do so by feeding it a high protein diet (soy beans) which formed very large amounts of urea and forced the rat to drink to avoid dehydration. The animal's kidney proved able to excrete both the excess of urea and the salts in the sea water. Drinking sea water actually enabled the animal to maintain its water balance. So far as is known, no other mammal can drink sea water with impunity.

From the known efficiency of the kangaroo rat's kidney we calculated that the animal uses 13 grams of water to excrete the waste products formed from 100 grams of dry barley. Measurement of the water content of its feces, which are exceptionally dry, showed that it loses about three grams of water by this route in metabolizing 100 grams of dry barley. There remained, then, the question of how much water the kangaroo rat loses by evaporation.

Very little escapes through its skin. Rodents have no sweat glands except on the toe pads, and the kangaroo rat has

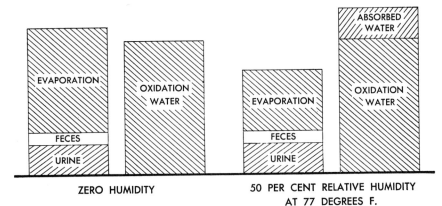

WATER BALANCE of the kangaroo rat is shown under two different conditions of humidity. The first and third bars indicate water loss; the second and fourth, water gain. The term "absorbed water" refers to water in food.

fewer sweat glands than most rats. All mammals lose a little water from the skin even where there are no sweat glands, and there is reason to believe that the kangaroo rat suffers less loss by this route than other mammals. It does, however, lose a considerable amount of water by evaporation from its respiratory tract. In the extremely dry desert air this loss could be serious. At zero humidity the loss by evaporation from the skin and respiratory tract would amount to some 44 grams of water during the five weeks in which the rat metabolizes 100 grams of barley. At a relative humidity of 50 per cent and a temperature of 75 degrees the loss by evaporation would be about 25 grams.

W E CAN NOW add up the balance sheet of the kangaroo rat's water intake and outgo. At zero humidity its total intake on a diet of dry barley would be 54 grams, and the total loss would be 61 grams (14 in the urine, 3 in the feces and 44 by evaporation). At 50 per cent relative humidity at 75 degrees the intake would be 67 grams and the outgo only 43 grams. Thus it seems clear that the kangaroo rat cannot survive on a barley diet in completely dry air, for under those conditions it has a water deficit in spite of its marvelous mechanisms for water conservation. Actual tests showed that the minimum atmospheric conditions under which the animal can maintain its water balance on the dry diet is 10 to 20 per cent relative humidity at 75 degrees.

The desert atmosphere is often somewhat drier than this, but the explanation of the kangaroo rat's survival is that it is a night animal. During the day it stays in its burrow, where the air is always a little more humid than outside, even when the soil seems to be completely dry. To measure the temperature and humidity in the burrow we used a tiny

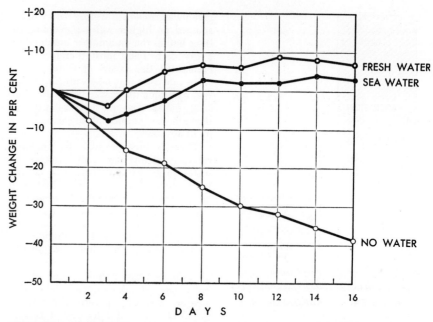

WEIGHT CHANGES of kangaroo rats fed either fresh water, sea water or no water showed that they could drink sea water without ill effects. Although kangaroo rats normally drink no water, they were induced to do so by a protein-rich diet that required water for the excretion of urea.

instrument which included a humidity-sensitive hair hygrometer. The instrument makes a record on a smoked glass disk, which can be read afterward under a microscope. The recorder was tied to the rat's tail, and the animal dragged it into the burrow. It was secured by a thin wire so that the animal could not run away with the instrument. After 12 hours we opened the burrow and read the record. We found that in early summer in the Arizona desert the relative humidity inside the kangaroo rat's burrows ranged from 30 to 50 per cent, and the temperature from about 75 to 88 degrees. At night, in the desert outside the burrows, the relative humidity varied from 15 to 40 per cent and the temperature from about 60 to 75 degrees. The protection

of the burrow by day provides just enough margin to enable the kangaroo rat to maintain its water balance and live in the driest of our deserts.

The same protection allows the kangaroo rat to survive the desert heat. A mammal such as man avoids overheating only by evaporating large quantities of water. The kangaroo rat cannot do this, nor can it tolerate a body temperature of much more than 100 degrees. It does not sweat or increase evaporation from its respiratory passages by panting, as a dog does. If it were exposed to the daytime heat in the desert, it would soon perish. The adaptations that permit it to thrive in the hot desert are its nocturnal habits and its extraordinary facilities for water conservation.

The Authors

KNUT and BODIL SCHMIDT-NIELSEN have collaborated in investigating the physiology of desert mammals. Knut was born in Trondheim, Norway, in 1915 and educated at the universities of Oslo and Copenhagen. At Copenhagen he studied with August Krogh, Nobel laureate in physiology and medicine, and received a doctorate of philosophy in 1946. While at Copenhagen he married his mentor's daughter Bodil. She was born in Copenhagen in 1918, holds a dental degree and Ph.D., and has done much work in general physiology. The Schmidt-Nielsens came to the U. S. in 1946 and have successively been on the faculties of Swarthmore College, Stanford University and the University of Cincinnati. They are now at Duke University, Knut as professor of zoology and Bodil as an assistant professor. Both members of this husband-and-wife team hold Guggenheim Fellowships for a study of water metabolism in camels.

Bibliography

THE WATER ECONOMY OF DESERT MAMMALS. Bodil and Knut Schmidt-Nielsen in *The Scientific Monthly*, Vol. 69, No. 3; September, 1949.

SCIENTIFIC
AMERICAN December 1959, Vol. 201, No. 6, pp. 152-162   OFFPRINT 1051

DIFFERENTIATION IN SOCIAL AMOEBAE

by John Tyler Bonner

Certain amoebae gather to form a mass of spores and a stalk. The way
in which spore cells and stalk cells segregate may shed light on how
the cells of many-celled organisms differentiate into various types.

Recently I was asked to talk to two visiting Russian university rectors (both biologists) about the curious organisms known as slime molds. Communication through the interpreter was somewhat difficult, but my visitors obviously neither knew nor really cared what slime molds were. Then, without anticipating the effect, I wrote on the blackboard the words "social amoebae," a title I had used for an article about these same organisms some years ago [see "The Social Amoebae," by John Tyler Bonner; SCIENTIFIC AMERICAN, June, 1949]. The Russians were electrified with delight and curiosity. I described how individual amoebae can come together under certain conditions to form a multicellular organism, the cells moving into their appropriate places in the organism and differentiating to divide the labor of reproduction. Soon both of my guests were beaming, evidently pleased that even one-celled animals could be so sophisticated as to form collectives.

Of course there are other reasons why slime molds hold the interest of biologists. The transformation of free-living, apparently identical amoebae into differentiated cells, members of a larger organism, presents some of the same questions as the differentiation of embryonic cells into specialized tissues. In the budding embryo, moreover, cells go through "morphogenetic movements" which seemingly parcel them out to their assigned positions in the emergent organism. The only difference is that the simplicity of the slime molds provides excellent material for experiments.

The slime-mold amoebae, inhabitants of the soil, do their feeding as separate, independent individuals. Flowing about on their irregular courses they engulf bacteria, in the manner of our own

amoeboid white blood cells. At this stage they reproduce simply by dividing in two. Once they have cleared the food away, wherever they are fairly dense, the amoebae suddenly flow together to central collection points. There the cells, numbering anywhere from 10 to 500,000, heap upward in a little tower which, at least in the species *Dictyostelium discoideum*, settles over on its side and crawls about as a tiny, glistening, bullet-shaped slug, .1 to two millimeters long. This slug has a distinct front and hind end (the pointed end is at the front) and leaves a trail of slime as it moves. It is remarkably sensitive to light and heat; it will move toward a weak source of heat or a light as faint as the dial of a luminous wrist watch. As the slug migrates, the cells in the front third begin to look different from the cells in the two thirds at the rear. The changes are the early signs of differentiation; eventually all the hind cells turn into spores—the seeds for the next generation—and all the front cells cooperate to make a slender, tapering stalk that thrusts the mass of spores up into the air.

To accomplish this transformation the slug first points its tip upward and stands on end. The uppermost front cells swell with water like a bit of froth and become encased in a cellulose cylinder which is to form the stalk. As new front cells arrive at the frothy tip of the stalk they add themselves to its lengthening structure and push it downward through the mass of hind-end cells below. When this process, like a fountain in reverse, has brought the stalk into contact with the surface, the continued upward migration of pre-stalk cells heightens the stalk lifting the presumptive spore cells up into the air. Each amoeba in the spore mass now encases itself in cellu-

lose and becomes a spore. The end result is a delicate tapering shaft capped by a spherical mass of spores. When the spores are dispersed (by water or by contact with some passing creature such as an insect or a worm), each can split open to liberate a tiny new amoeba.

What mechanism brings the independent slime-mold amoebae together in a mass? More than a decade ago we found that they are attracted by the gradient of a substance which they themselves produce. In our early experiments we were unable to obtain cell-free preparations of this substance (which we named acrasin); cells actively secreting it were always necessary to start an aggregation. Later B. M. Shaffer of the University of Cambridge got around this barrier in an ingenious experiment. He took water that had been near acrasin-producing cells (but was itself free of cells) and applied it to the side of a small agar block placed on top of some amoebae. The amoebae momentarily streamed toward the side where the concentration of acrasin was higher. Shaffer found that the water must be used immediately after it is collected in order to achieve this effect, and that it must be applied repeatedly. He therefore concluded that acrasin loses its potency rapidly at room temperature. The loss of potency, he showed, is caused by enzymes that are secreted by the amoebae along with acrasin; when he filtered the fluid through a cellophane membrane to hold back the large enzyme molecules, he was able to secure a stable preparation of acrasin. Presumably the enzymes serve to clear the environment of the substance and so enhance the establishment of a gradient in the concentration of acrasin when it is next secreted. Maurice Sussman and his

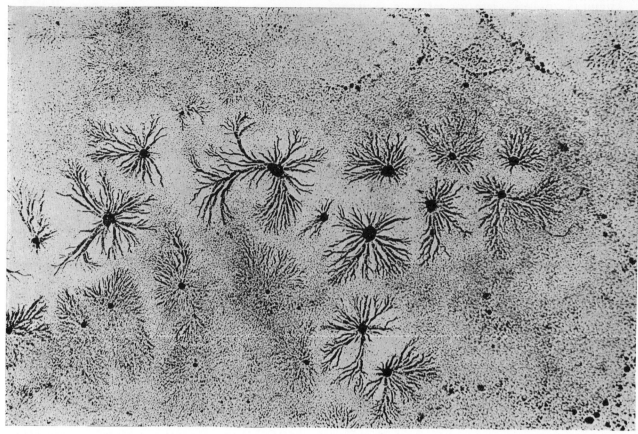

AGGREGATING AMOEBAE of *Dictyostelium discoideum* move in thin streams toward central collection points. Each of the centers comprises thousands of cells. This photograph and facing one were made by Kenneth B. Raper of the University of Wisconsin.

co-workers at Brandeis University in Waltham, Mass., have confirmed Shaffer's work and are now attempting the difficult task of fractionating and purifying acrasin, steps leading toward its identification.

Meanwhile Barbara Wright of the National Institutes of Health in Bethesda dropped a bombshell. She discovered that urine from a pregnant woman could attract the amoebae under an agar block just as acrasin does. The active compo-

nents of the urine turned out to be steroid sex hormones. This does not necessarily mean that acrasin is such a steroid. Animal embryologists were thrown off the track for years when they found that locally applied steroids induce the further development of early embryos. Only after much painful confusion did it become clear that steroids do not act directly on the embryo, but stimulate the normal induction substance. We must therefore consider the

possibility that the steroids act in a similarly indirect manner on the amoebae. The purification of acrasin will, we hope, soon settle the question.

From observations of the cells during aggregation, Shaffer has come to the interesting conclusion that the many incoming amoebae are not responding to one large gradient of acrasin but to relays of gradients. That is, a central cell will release a puff of acrasin that produces a small gradient in its immediate

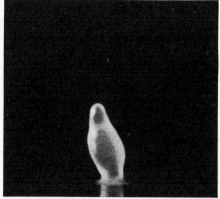

DEVELOPMENT OF THE FRUITING BODY of a slime mold is shown in this series of photographs made at half-hour intervals. At far left the tip cells are starting to form a stalk. In the next two pictures the stalk has pushed down through the mass to the

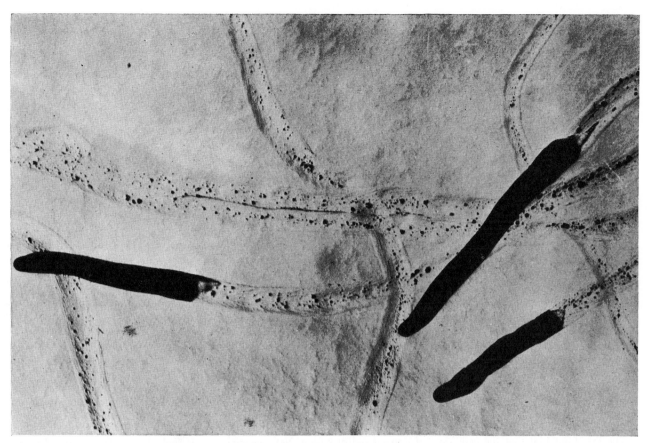

MIGRATING SLUGS of *Dictyostelium discoideum* leave trails of slime behind them as they move. The photographs in this article appear in *The Cellular Slime Molds*, by John Tyler Bonner, and are reproduced with permission of Princeton University Press.

vicinity. The surrounding cells become oriented, and now produce a puff of their own. This new puff orients the cells lying just beyond, and in this way a wave of orientation passes outward. Time-lapse motion pictures show the amoebae moving inward in waves, which could well represent the relay system. If this interpretation is sound, then the rapid breakdown of acrasin by an enzyme plainly serves to clear the slate after each puff in preparation for

the next. The cells do not depend entirely on acrasin for orientation; once they are in contact they tend to stick to one another and the pull-tension of one guides the cells that follow. This is a special case of contact guidance, a phenomenon well known in the movements of embryonic cells of higher animals.

After the amoebae have gathered together, what determines their position within the bullet-shaped slug?

One might assume that the cells that arrive at the center of the heap automatically become the tip of the slug, and that the last cells to come in from the periphery make up the hind end. If this were the case, chance alone would determine whether a cell is to become a front-end cell and enter into the formation of the stalk, or a hind-end cell and become a spore. If, on the other hand, the cells rearrange themselves as they organize into a slug, then it is conceiv-

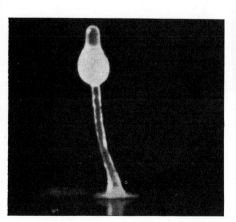

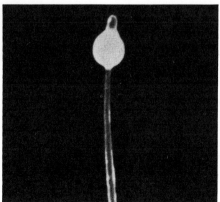

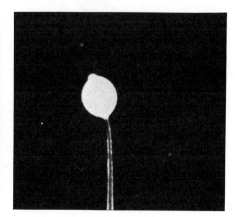

surface and is starting to lift the cell mass. In the fourth picture the spores have formed their cellulose coats, making the ball more opaque. In the last two pictures the spore mass moves up to the very top of the stalk, as the stalk itself becomes still longer.

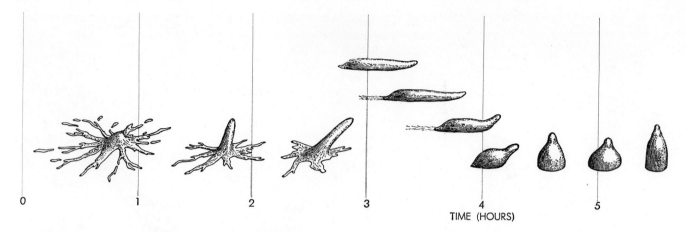

TIME (HOURS)

LIFE CYCLE OF A SLIME MOLD, typified by *Dictyostelium discoideum*, involves the aggregation of free-living amoebae into a unified mass (*first three drawings*), then the formation of a slug which moves about for a time (*next four drawings*) and finally

able that the front end might contain selected cells, differing in particular ways from those in the hind end. I am embarrassed to say that in 1944 I presented some evidence to support the idea that their chance position was the determining factor—evidence that, as will soon be clear, was inadequate. It is some comfort, however, that I was able to rectify the error myself.

The first faint hint that the cells do redistribute themselves in the slug stage came when we repeated some experiments first done by Kenneth B. Raper of the University of Wisconsin. We stained some slugs with harmless dyes and then grafted the hind half of a colored slug onto the front half of an unstained slug. The division line remained sharp for a

number of hours, just as Raper had previously observed. But later we noticed that a few stained cells were moving forward into the uncolored part of the slug. In the reverse graft, with the front end stained, a similar small group of colored cells gradually migrated toward the rear end of the slug. Still, the number of cells involved was so small that it could hardly be considered the sign of a major redistribution. Next we tried putting some colored front-end cells in the hind end of an intact slug. The result was a total surprise: now the colored cells rapidly moved to the front end, traveling as a band of color up the length of the slug.

Here was a clear demonstration that the cells do rearrange themselves in the

slug and that there is a difference between the cells at the front and hind ends. The difference between front-end and hind-end cells—whatever its nature—was confirmed in control experiments in which we grafted front-end cells to the front ends of the slugs and hind-end cells to the hind ends; in each case the cells maintained their positions.

It looked as if front-end cells were selected by their speed; the colored cells simply raced from the rear end to the front. When we placed hind-end cells in the front end, they traveled to the rear, outpaced by the faster-moving cells, which again assumed their forward positions. We tried to select fast cells and slow cells over a series of genera-

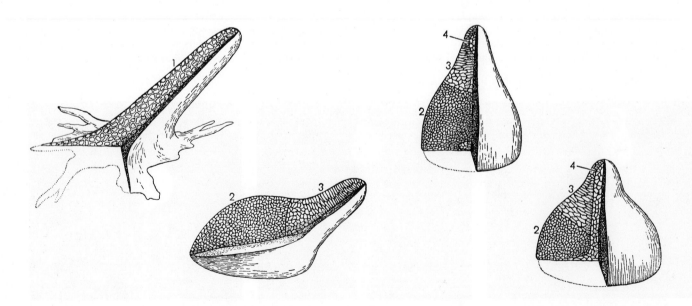

CUTAWAY DRAWINGS of five stages show how the cells change. At the end of aggregation all cells appear the same (1), but in the slug they are of two types (2 and 3). The cells near the tip (3) gradually turn into stalk cells (4) and move down inside the

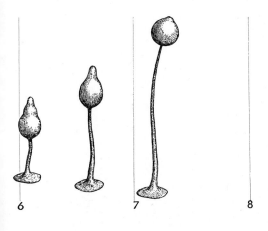

the development of a fruiting body (*last six drawings*). Times are only approximate.

tions to see if speed was a hereditary trait, but after selection the cultures showed no differences from one another or from the parent stock.

Quite by accident a new bit of evidence turned up in an experiment designed for totally independent reasons. Instead of using the fully formed slug we stained amoebae colonies in the process of aggregation and made grafts at this stage by removing the center of the stained group and replacing it with a colorless center, or vice versa. In either case the resulting slug was always uniformly colored, indicating a rapid reassortment of the cells during the formation of the slug.

The evidence for a rearrangement of

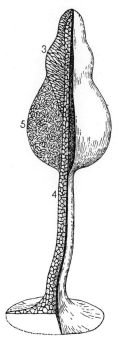

mass. The others (2) become spores (5) as the growing stalk lifts them into the air.

cells was becoming impressive, but I felt uneasy about the reliability of tests with dyes because such tests had led me into my earlier error. We needed to confirm our results by a different method.

At about this time M. F. Filosa, who was working in our laboratory on his doctoral dissertation, discovered that many of our amoeba cultures contained more than one genetic type. By isolating and cultivating single cells of each type he was able to obtain pure strains that displayed various recognizable abnormalities—in the way they aggregated, in the shape of their slugs or in the form of their spore masses [*see illustration on page 2238*]. Discovery of these strains furnished natural "markers" for identifying and following cells.

Of course there remained one technical problem: How could the individual cells be identified? Fortunately Raper had shown some time earlier that each fragment of a slug that has been cut into pieces will form a midget fruiting body. Spores derived from the several fragments can then be cultured individually. The amoeba from each spore will give rise to many daughter amoebae which can be scored for mutant or normal characteristics as they proceed to form slugs and fruiting bodies.

In one experiment we started with a culture of cells in the free-living feeding stage, into which was mixed 10 to 15 per cent of mutant cells. If we were to find a higher concentration of one type of cell in one part of the resulting slug, then we could conclude that there had been a rearrangement. We allowed the cells to form a slug and cut it up into three parts. Upon culturing the individual spores produced by each part, we found that the hind third had 36 per cent mutant cells, the middle third 6 per cent and the front third 1 per cent. Nothing could be more clear-cut; obviously the cells sort themselves out in a way that brings the normal cells to the front end of the slug. In another experiment, with a larger percentage of mutant cells in the mixture, hind and middle fractions contained 91 per cent mutant cells, and the front end only 66 per cent. Further experiments, including some with other species of slime mold, all led to the same conclusion. During the process of slug formation some cells are more likely to reach the front end than others, and the position of a cell in the slug does not merely depend upon its chance position before aggregation.

One must assume that certain cells move to the front because they travel the fastest, while the other, slower cells are

SPHERICAL MASSES OF SPORES of the social amoeba *Dicty-ostelium discoideum* are held aloft by stalks composed of other amoebae of the same species. When the spores are dispersed, each can liberate a new amoeba. The stalks are about half an inch high.

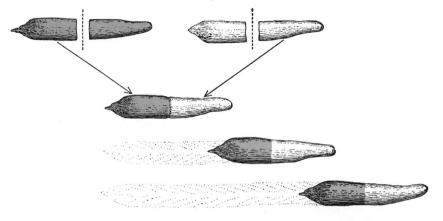

GRAFTED SLUG composed of the hind end of a stained slug and the front end of an unstained slug retains a sharp line of demarcation between the parts even after several hours.

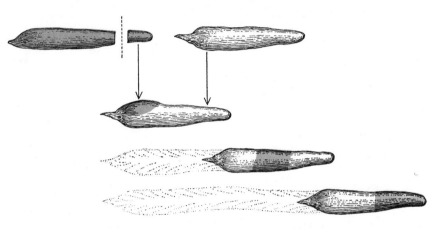

COLORED TIP taken from a stained slug can be inserted into the hind part of an intact slug. The colored cells then move forward as a band until they again are at the front tip.

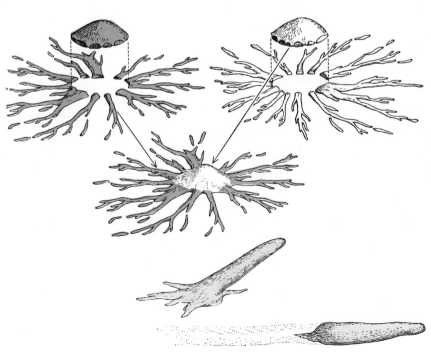

COLORED AGGREGATE in which the center has been replaced by a colorless center produces a uniformly colored slug, indicating that the cells are rearranged as the slug forms. The experiment illustrated in these drawings was originally performed by Kenneth B. Raper.

fastest, while the other, slower cells are left behind in the rear end of the slug. Considering the different fates of the front and rear cells, however, it is natural to wonder whether there are any other discernible differences between the front and hind cells. Size is one of the easiest qualities to measure, and comparison of spores from the front and rear portions showed that cells of the front segment are larger. From this it might be concluded that the fastest cells are the largest. But size is related to many other factors; some evidence indicates that cells in the front end divide less frequently than those in the hind regions, and this could affect their size. The possibility of a correlation between size and speed can only be settled by further experiment and observation.

But one fact is inescapable. The cells that tend to go forward are not identical with those that lag behind. Do the differences ultimately determine which cells become stalk cells and which will be spores? The most obvious deduction is that among feeding amoebae roughly a third are presumptive stalk cells, and the rest are predestined to be spores. This interpretation is clearly false, however, because then it would be impossible to explain how a single fragment of a cut-up slug can produce a perfect miniature fruiting body. The cells in the hind piece, which would normally yield spores, recover from the surgery that isolates them from the large slug, and one third of these presumptive spore cells proceed to form the midget stalk. This remarkable accommodation to a new situation is also exhibited by many types of cells in embryos and in animals capable of regenerating limbs and organs.

A more reasonable way to explain the relation between sorting-out and differentiation is to visualize the aggregating amoebae as having all shades of variation in characteristics between the extremes found at the ends of the slug. As they form a slug the cells place themselves in such an order that from the rear to the front they display a gradual increase in speed, in size and perhaps in other properties not yet measured. Thus each fragment of a cut-up slug retains a small gradient of these properties. It is conceivable that the gradient, set up in the process of cell rearrangement, actually controls the chain of events that leads the front cells to form a stalk and the hind cells to become spores. For the present, however, this is only conjecture.

At this point let me emphasize that the sorting-out process is not unique to slime molds. Recently A. A. Moscona of the University of Chicago and others have found that if the tissues of various embryos or simple animals are separated into individual cells, the cells can come together and sort themselves out [see "Tissues from Dissociated Cells," by A. A. Moscona; SCIENTIFIC AMERICAN, May, 1959]. For instance, if separate single pre-cartilage cells are mixed with pre-muscle cells, the cartilage cells will aggregate into a ball and ultimately form a central mass of cartilage surrounded by a layer of muscle. By marking the cells in a most ingenious way Moscona showed that there was no transformation of pre-cartilage cells into muscle cells or vice versa; each cell retained its original identity but moved to a characteristic location. In animals, then, sorting-out appears to be a general phenomenon when the cells are artificially dissociated. Since the movement in slime molds is part of their normal development, this raises the challenging question whether such sorting-out occurs in the normal development of animal embryos as well.

One must concede that slime-mold amoebae do profit by collectivization: the aggregate can do things the individuals cannot accomplish alone. In the amoebae's society, however, all are not created equal; some rise to the top and others lag behind. And then there is this distressing moral: Those that go forward with such zest to reach the fore are rewarded with sacrifice and destruction as stalk cells. It is the laggards that they lift into the air which survive to propagate the next generation.

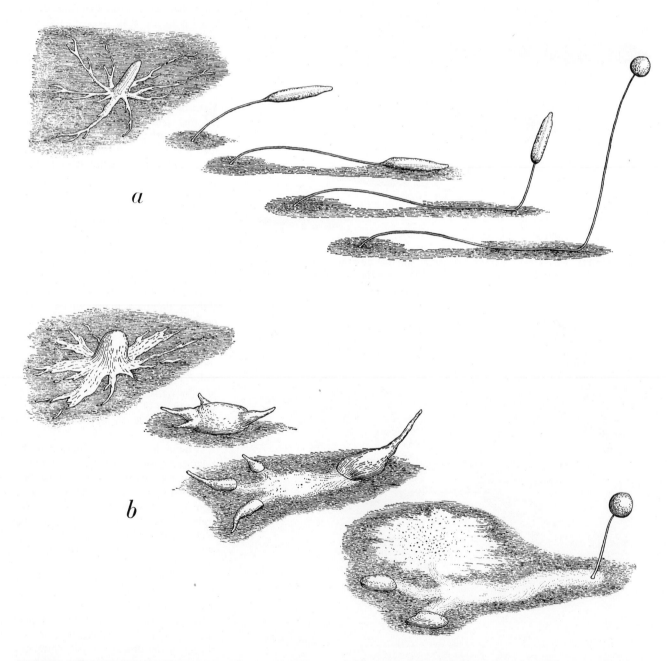

NORMAL AND MUTANT STRAINS of *Dictyostelium mucoroides* are contrasted in these drawings. The normal form (*a*) aggregates in thin streams, and its slug remains anchored by a thin stalk. The "MV" mutant (*b*) aggregates in broad streams and produces a starfish-like slug which then breaks up into smaller slugs. The stalk of the mutant is usually shorter than that of normal strain.

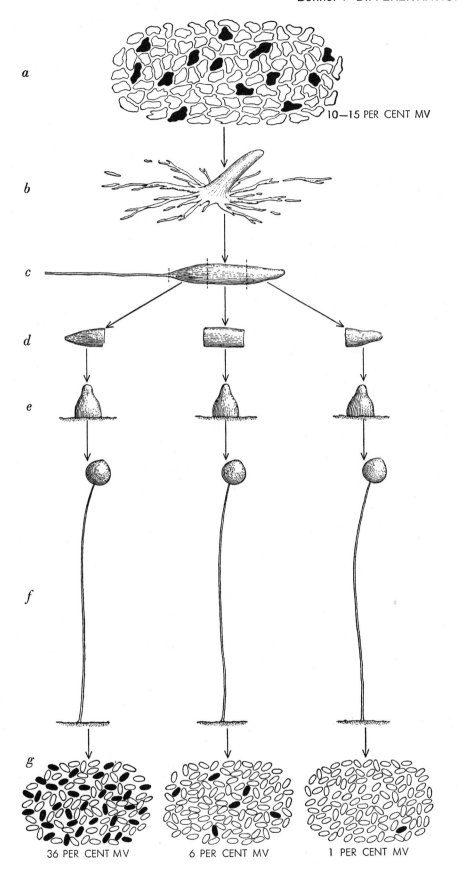

a   10—15 PER CENT MV

b

c

d

e

f

g   36 PER CENT MV   6 PER CENT MV   1 PER CENT MV

REDISTRIBUTION OF CELLS was proved in an experiment in which MV mutant cells (*black*) were randomly mixed with normal cells at feeding stage (*a*). The cells aggregated (*b*), and the resulting slug (*c*) was cut into three parts (*d*). Each part produced a fruiting body (*e* and *f*). Spores of each were then identified (*g*) by culturing them separately. The concentration of mutant cells was markedly higher in spores from the hind part of the slug.

The Author

JOHN TYLER BONNER is professor of biology at Princeton University. He was born in New York City in 1920 and took his degrees at Harvard University. During World War II he did research in the Aero Medical Laboratory at Wright Field, and afterward was a junior fellow at Harvard. Bonner joined the faculty at Princeton in 1947. He started his research on social amoebae as an undergraduate under William H. Weston, and has been studying these life forms ever since. This is his fifth article for SCIENTIFIC AMERICAN.

Bibliography

THE CELLULAR SLIME MOLDS. John Tyler Bonner. Princeton University Press, 1959.

EVIDENCE FOR THE SORTING OUT OF CELLS IN THE DEVELOPMENT OF THE CELLULAR SLIME MOLDS. John Tyler Bonner in *Proceedings of the National Academy of Sciences*, Vol. 45, No. 3, pages 379-384; March, 1959.

SCIENTIFIC AMERICAN October 1966, Vol. 215, No. 4, pp. 55-62

OFFPRINT **1052**

THE GENETIC CODE: III

by F. H. C. Crick

The central theme of molecular biology is confirmed by detailed knowledge of how the four-letter language embodied in molecules of nucleic acid controls the 20-letter language of the proteins.

The hypothesis that the genes of the living cell contain all the information needed for the cell to reproduce itself is now more than 50 years old. Implicit in the hypothesis is the idea that the genes bear in coded form the detailed specifications for the thousands of kinds of protein molecules the cell requires for its moment-to-moment existence: for extracting energy from molecules assimilated as food and for repairing itself as well as for replication. It is only within the past 15 years, however, that insight has been gained into the chemical nature of the genetic material and how its molecular structure can embody coded instructions that can be "read" by the machinery in the cell responsible for synthesizing protein molecules. As the result of intensive work by many investigators the story

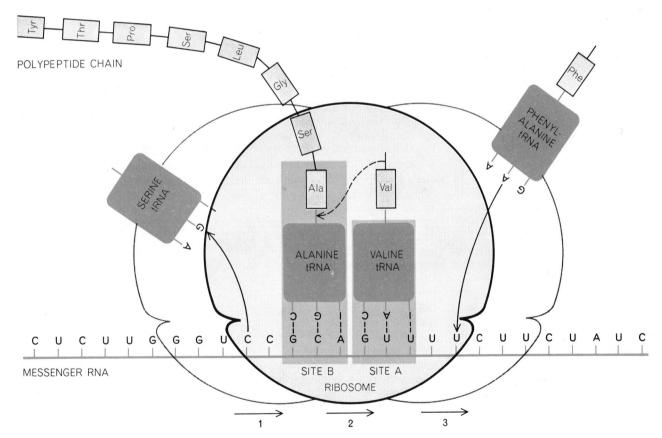

SYNTHESIS OF PROTEIN MOLECULES is accomplished by the intracellular particles called ribosomes. The coded instructions for making the protein molecule are carried to the ribosome by a form of ribonucleic acid (RNA) known as "messenger" RNA. The RNA code "letters" are four bases: uracil (U), cytosine (C), adenine (A) and guanine (G). A sequence of three bases, called a codon, is required to specify each of the 20 kinds of amino acid, identified here by their abbreviations. (A list of the 20 amino acids and their abbreviations appears on the next page.) When linked end to end, these amino acids form the polypeptide chains of which proteins are composed. Each type of amino acid is transported to the ribosome by a particular form of "transfer" RNA (tRNA), which carries an anticodon that can form a temporary bond with one of the codons in messenger RNA. Here the ribosome is shown moving along the chain of messenger RNA, "reading off" the codons in sequence. It appears that the ribosome has two binding sites for molecules of tRNA: one site (A) for positioning a newly arrived tRNA molecule and another (B) for holding the growing polypeptide chain.

AMINO ACID	ABBREVIATION
ALANINE	Ala
ARGININE	Arg
ASPARAGINE	AspN
ASPARTIC ACID	Asp
CYSTEINE	Cys
GLUTAMIC ACID	Glu
GLUTAMINE	GluN
GLYCINE	Gly
HISTIDINE	His
ISOLEUCINE	Ileu
LEUCINE	Leu
LYSINE	Lys
METHIONINE	Met
PHENYLALANINE	Phe
PROLINE	Pro
SERINE	Ser
THREONINE	Thr
TRYPTOPHAN	Tryp
TYROSINE	Tyr
VALINE	Val

TWENTY AMINO ACIDS constitute the standard set found in all proteins. A few other amino acids occur infrequently in proteins but it is suspected in each case that they originate as one of the standard set and become chemically modified after they have been incorporated into a polypeptide chain.

of the genetic code is now essentially complete. One can trace the transmission of the coded message from its original site in the genetic material to the finished protein molecule.

The genetic material of the living cell is the chainlike molecule of deoxyribonucleic acid (DNA). The cells of many bacteria have only a single chain; the cells of mammals have dozens clustered together in chromosomes. The DNA molecules have a very long backbone made up of repeating groups of phosphate and a five-carbon sugar. To this backbone the side groups called bases are attached at regular intervals. There are four standard bases: adenine (A), guanine (G), thymine (T) and cytosine (C). They are the four "letters" used to spell out the genetic message. The exact sequence of bases along a length of the DNA molecule determines the structure of a particular protein molecule.

Proteins are synthesized from a standard set of 20 amino acids, uniform throughout nature, that are joined end to end to form the long polypeptide

chains of protein molecules [*see illustration at left*]. Each protein has its own characteristic sequence of amino acids. The number of amino acids in a polypeptide chain ranges typically from 100 to 300 or more.

The genetic code is not the message itself but the "dictionary" used by the cell to translate from the four-letter language of nucleic acid to the 20-letter language of protein. The machinery of the cell can translate in one direction only: from nucleic acid to protein but not from protein to nucleic acid. In making this translation the cell employs a variety of accessory molecules and mechanisms. The message contained in DNA is first transcribed into the similar molecule called "messenger" ribonucleic acid—messenger RNA. (In many viruses—the tobacco mosaic virus, for example—the genetic material is simply RNA.) RNA too has four kinds of bases as side groups; three are identical with those found in DNA (adenine, guanine and cytosine) but the fourth is uracil (U) instead of thymine. In this first transcription of the genetic message the code letters A, G, T and C in DNA give rise respectively to U, C, A and G. In other words, wherever A appears in DNA, U appears in the RNA transcription; wherever G appears in DNA, C appears in the transcription, and so on. As it is usually presented the dictionary of the genetic code employs the letters found in RNA (U, C, A, G) rather than those found in DNA (A, G, T, C).

The genetic code could be broken easily if one could determine both the amino acid sequence of a protein and the base sequence of the piece of nucleic acid that codes it. A simple comparison of the two sequences would yield the code. Unfortunately the determination of the base sequence of a long nucleic acid molecule is, for a variety of reasons, still extremely difficult. More indirect approaches must be used.

Most of the genetic code first became known early in 1965. Since then additional evidence has proved that almost all of it is correct, although a few features remain uncertain. This article describes how the code was discovered and some of the work that supports it.

Scientific American has already presented a number of articles on the genetic code. In one of them ["The Genetic Code," Offprint 123] I explained that the experimental evidence (mainly indirect) suggested that the code was a triplet code: that the bases on the messenger RNA were read three at a time and that each group corresponded to a

particular amino acid. Such a group is called a codon. Using four symbols in groups of three, one can form 64 distinct triplets. The evidence indicated that most of these stood for one amino acid or another, implying that an amino acid was usually represented by several codons. Adjacent amino acids were coded by adjacent codons, which did not overlap.

In a sequel to that article ["The Genetic Code: II," Offprint 153] Marshall W. Nirenberg of the National Institutes of Health explained how the composition of many of the 64 triplets had been determined by actual experiment. The technique was to synthesize polypeptide chains in a cell-free system, which was made by breaking open cells of the colon bacillus (*Escherichia coli*) and extracting from them the machinery for protein synthesis. Then the system was provided with an energy supply, 20 amino acids and one or another of several types of synthetic RNA. Although the exact sequence of bases in each type was random, the proportion of bases was known. It was found that each type of synthetic messenger RNA directed the incorporation of certain amino acids only.

By means of this method, used in a quantitative way, the *composition* of many of the codons was obtained, but the *order* of bases in any triplet could not be determined. Codons rich in G were difficult to study, and in addition a few mistakes crept in. Of the 40 codon compositions listed by Nirenberg in his article we now know that 35 were correct.

The Triplet Code

The main outlines of the genetic code were elucidated by another technique invented by Nirenberg and Philip Leder. In this method no protein synthesis occurs. Instead one triplet at a time is used to bind together parts of the machinery of protein synthesis.

Protein synthesis takes place on the comparatively large intracellular structures known as ribosomes. These bodies travel along the chain of messenger RNA, reading off its triplets one after another and synthesizing the polypeptide chain of the protein, starting at the amino end (NH$_2$). The amino acids do not diffuse to the ribosomes by themselves. Each amino acid is joined chemically by a special enzyme to one of the codon-recognizing molecules known both as soluble RNA (sRNA) and transfer RNA (tRNA). (I prefer the latter designation.) Each tRNA molecule has its own triplet of bases, called an anticodon, that recognizes the relevant codon on the messenger RNA by pairing bases with it [*see illustration on page 2241*].

Leder and Nirenberg studied which amino acid, joined to its tRNA molecules, was bound to the ribosomes in the presence of a particular triplet, that is, by a "message" with just three letters. They did so by the neat trick of passing the mixture over a nitrocellulose filter that retained the ribosomes. All the tRNA molecules passed through the filter except the ones specifically bound to the ribosomes by the triplet. Which they were could easily be decided by using mixtures of amino acids in which one kind of amino acid had been made artificially radioactive, and determining the amount of radioactivity absorbed by the filter.

For example, the triplet GUU retained the tRNA for the amino acid valine, whereas the triplets UGU and UUG did not. (Here GUU actually stands for the trinucleoside diphosphate GpUpU.) Further experiments showed that UGU coded for cysteine and UUG for leucine.

Nirenberg and his colleagues synthesized all 64 triplets and tested them for their coding properties. Similar results have been obtained by H. Gobind Khorana and his co-workers at the University of Wisconsin. Various other groups have checked a smaller number of codon assignments.

Close to 50 of the 64 triplets give a clearly unambiguous answer in the binding test. Of the remainder some evince only weak binding and some bind more than one kind of amino acid. Other results I shall describe later suggest that the multiple binding is often an artifact of the binding method. In short, the binding test gives the meaning of the majority of the triplets but it does not firmly establish all of them.

The genetic code obtained in this way, with a few additions secured by other methods, is shown in the table below. The 64 possible triplets are set out in a regular array, following a plan

SECOND LETTER

FIRST LETTER | THIRD LETTER

	U	C	A	G	
U	UUU ⎫ Phe UUC ⎭ UUA ⎫ Leu UUG ⎭	UCU ⎫ UCC ⎪ Ser UCA ⎪ UCG ⎭	UAU ⎫ Tyr UAC ⎭ UAA OCHRE UAG AMBER	UGU ⎫ Cys UGC ⎭ UGA ? UGG Tryp	U C A G
C	CUU ⎫ CUC ⎪ Leu CUA ⎪ CUG ⎭	CCU ⎫ CCC ⎪ Pro CCA ⎪ CCG ⎭	CAU ⎫ His CAC ⎭ CAA ⎫ GluN CAG ⎭	CGU ⎫ CGC ⎪ Arg CGA ⎪ CGG ⎭	U C A G
A	AUU ⎫ AUC ⎪ Ileu AUA ⎭ AUG Met	ACU ⎫ ACC ⎪ Thr ACA ⎪ ACG ⎭	AAU ⎫ AspN AAC ⎭ AAA ⎫ Lys AAG ⎭	AGU ⎫ Ser AGC ⎭ AGA ⎫ Arg AGG ⎭	U C A G
G	GUU ⎫ GUC ⎪ Val GUA ⎪ GUG ⎭	GCU ⎫ GCC ⎪ Ala GCA ⎪ GCG ⎭	GAU ⎫ Asp GAC ⎭ GAA ⎫ Glu GAG ⎭	GGU ⎫ GGC ⎪ Gly GGA ⎪ GGG ⎭	U C A G

GENETIC CODE, consisting of 64 triplet combinations and their corresponding amino acids, is shown in its most likely version. The importance of the first two letters in each triplet is readily apparent. Some of the allocations are still not completely certain, particularly for organisms other than the colon bacillus (*Escherichia coli*). "Amber" and "ochre" are terms that referred originally to certain mutant strains of bacteria. They designate two triplets, UAA and UAG, that may act as signals for terminating polypeptide chains.

that clarifies the relations between them.

Inspection of the table will show that the triplets coding for the same amino acid are often rather similar. For example, all four of the triplets starting with the doublet AC code for threonine. This pattern also holds for seven of the other amino acids. In every case the triplets XYU and XYC code for the same amino acid, and in many cases XYA and XYG are the same (methionine and tryptophan may be exceptions). Thus an amino acid is largely selected by the first two bases of the triplet. Given that a triplet codes for, say, valine, we know that the first two bases are GU, whatever the third may be. This pattern is true for all but three of the amino acids. Leucine can start with UU or CU, serine with UC or AG and arginine with CG or AG. In all other cases the amino acid is uniquely related to the first two bases of the triplet. Of course, the converse is often not true. Given that a triplet starts with, say, CA, it may code for either histidine or glutamine.

Synthetic Messenger RNA's

Probably the most direct way to confirm the genetic code is to synthesize a messenger RNA molecule with a strictly defined base sequence and then find the amino acid sequence of the polypeptide produced under its influence. The most extensive work of this nature has been done by Khorana and his colleagues. By a brilliant combination of ordinary chemical synthesis and synthesis catalyzed by enzymes, they have made long RNA molecules with various repeating sequences of bases. As an example, one RNA molecule they have synthesized has the sequence UGUG-UGUGUGUG.... When the biochemical machinery reads this as triplets the message is UGU–GUG–UGU–GUG.... Thus we expect that a polypeptide will be produced with an alternating sequence of two amino acids. In fact, it was found that the product is Cys–Val–Cys–Val.... This evidence alone would not tell us which triplet goes with which amino acid, but given the results of the binding test one has no hesitation in concluding that UGU codes for cysteine and GUG for valine.

In the same way Khorana has made chains with repeating sequences of the type XYZ... and also XXYZ.... The type XYZ...would be expected to give a "homopolypeptide" containing one amino acid corresponding to the triplet XYZ. Because the starting point is not clearly defined, however, the homopolypeptides corresponding to YZX... and ZXY... will also be produced. Thus

poly-AUC makes polyisoleucine, polyserine and polyhistidine. This confirms that AUC codes for isoleucine, UCA for serine and CAU for histidine. A repeating sequence of four bases will yield a single type of polypeptide with a repeating sequence of four amino acids. The general patterns to be expected in each case are set forth in the table on this page. The results to date have amply demonstrated by a direct biochemical method that the code is indeed a triplet code.

Khorana and his colleagues have so far confirmed about 25 triplets by this method, including several that were quite doubtful on the basis of the binding test. They plan to synthesize other sequences, so that eventually most of the triplets will be checked in this way.

The Use of Mutations

The two methods described so far are open to the objection that since they do not involve intact cells there may be some danger of false results. This objection can be met by two other methods of checking the code in which the act of protein synthesis takes place inside the cell. Both involve the effects of genetic mutations on the amino acid sequence of a protein.

It is now known that small mutations are normally of two types: "base substitution" mutants and "phase shift" mutants. In the first type one base is changed into another base but the total number of bases remains the same. In the second, one or a small number of bases are added to the message or subtracted from it.

There are now extensive data on base-substitution mutants, mainly from studies of three rather convenient proteins: human hemoglobin, the protein of tobacco mosaic virus and the A protein of the enzyme tryptophan synthetase obtained from the colon bacillus. At least 36 abnormal types of human hemoglobin have now been investigated by many different workers. More than 40 mutant forms of the protein of the tobacco mosaic virus have been examined by Hans Wittmann of the Max Planck Institute for Molecular Genetics in Tübingen and by Akita Tsugita and Heinz Fraenkel-Conrat of the University of California at Berkeley [see "The Genetic Code of a Virus," by Heinz Fraenkel-Conrat; SCIENTIFIC AMERICAN Offprint 193]. Charles Yanofsky and his group at Stanford University have characterized about 25 different mutations of the A protein of tryptophan synthetase.

RNA BASE SEQUENCE	READ AS	AMINO ACID SEQUENCE EXPECTED
(XY)ₙ ...	X Y X | Y X Y | X Y X | Y X Y ...	αβαβ
(XYZ)ₙ ...	X Y Z | X Y Z | X Y Z ...	ααα
...	Y Z X | Y Z X | Y Z X ...	βββ
...	Z X Y | Z X Y | Z X Y ...	γγγ
(XXYZ)ₙ ...	X X Y Z | X X Y Z | X X Y Z ...	αβγδαβγδ
(XYXZ)ₙ ...	X Y X Z | X Y X Z | X Y X Z ...	αβγδαβγδ

VARIETY OF SYNTHETIC RNA's with repeating sequences of bases have been produced by H. Gobind Khorana and his colleagues at the University of Wisconsin. They contain two or three different bases (X, Y, Z) in groups of two, three or four. When introduced into cell-free systems containing the machinery for protein synthesis, the base sequences are read off as triplets (middle) and yield the amino acid sequences indicated at the right.

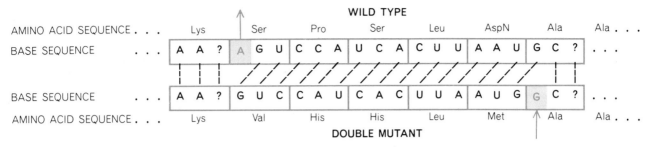

| AMINO ACID SEQUENCE... | Lys | Ser | Pro | Ser | Leu | AspN | Ala | Ala ... |

BASE SEQUENCE ... A A ? A G U C C A U C A C U U A A U G C ? ...

BASE SEQUENCE ... A A ? G U C C A U C A C U U A A U G G C ? ...

| AMINO ACID SEQUENCE... | Lys | Val | His | His | Leu | Met | Ala | Ala ... |

DOUBLE MUTANT

"PHASE SHIFT" MUTATIONS help to establish the actual codons used by organisms in the synthesis of protein. The two partial amino acid sequences shown here were determined by George Streisinger and his colleagues at the University of Oregon. The sequences are from a protein, a type of lysozyme, produced by the bacterial virus T4. A pair of phase-shift mutations evidently removed one base, A, and inserted another, G, about 15 bases farther on. The base sequence was deduced theoretically from the genetic code.

The remarkable fact has emerged that in every case but one the genetic code shows that the change of an amino acid in a polypeptide chain could have been caused by the alteration of a single base in the relevant nucleic acid. For example, the first observed change of an amino acid by mutation (in the hemoglobin of a person suffering from sickle-cell anemia) was from glutamic acid to valine. From the genetic code dictionary on page 2243 we see this could have resulted from a mutation that changed either GAA to GUA or GAG to GUG. In either case the change involved a single base in the several hundred needed to code for one of the two kinds of chain in hemoglobin.

The one exception so far to the rule that all amino acid changes could be caused by single base changes has been found by Yanofsky. In this one case glutamic acid was replaced by methionine. It can be seen from the genetic code dictionary that this can be accomplished only by a change of *two* bases, since glutamic acid is encoded by either GAA or GAG and methionine is encoded only by AUG. This mutation has occurred only once, however, and of all the mutations studied by Yanofsky it is the only one not to back-mutate, or revert to "wild type." It is thus almost certainly the rare case of a double change. All the other cases fit the hypothesis that base-substitution mutations are normally caused by a single base change. Examination of the code shows that only about 40 percent of all the possible amino acid interchanges can be brought about by single base substitutions, and it is only these changes that are found in experiments. Therefore the study of actual mutations has provided strong confirmation of many features of the genetic code.

Because in general several codons stand for one amino acid it is not possible, knowing the amino acid sequence, to write down the exact RNA base sequence that encoded it. This is unfortunate. If we know which amino acid is changed into another by mutation, however, we can often, given the code, work out what that base change must have been. As an example, glutamic acid can be encoded by GAA or GAG and valine by GUU, GUC, GUA or GUG. If a mutation substitutes valine for glutamic acid, one can assume that only a single base change was involved. The only such change that could lead to the desired result would be a change from A to U in the middle position, and this would be true whether GAA became GUA or GAG became GUG.

It is thus possible in many cases (not in all) to compare the nature of the base change with the chemical mutagen used to produce the change. If RNA is treated with nitrous acid, C is changed to U and A is effectively changed to G. On the other hand, if double-strand DNA is treated under the right conditions with hydroxylamine, the mutagen acts only on C. As a result some C's are changed to T's (the DNA equivalent of U's), and thus G's, which are normally paired with C's in double-strand DNA, are replaced by A's.

If 2-aminopurine, a "base analogue" mutagen, is added when double-strand DNA is undergoing replication, it produces only "transitions." These are the same changes as those produced by hydroxylamine—plus the reverse changes. In almost all these different cases (the exceptions are unimportant) the changes observed are those expected from our knowledge of the genetic code.

Note the remarkable fact that, although the code was deduced mainly from studies of the colon bacillus, it appears to apply equally to human beings and tobacco plants. This, together with more fragmentary evidence, suggests that the genetic code is either the same or very similar in most organisms.

The second method of checking the code using intact cells depends on phase-shift mutations such as the addi-

tion of a single base to the message. Phase-shift mutations probably result from errors produced during genetic recombination or when the DNA molecule is being duplicated. Such errors have the effect of putting out of phase the reading of the message from that point on. This hypothesis leads to the prediction that the phase can be corrected if at some subsequent point a nucleotide is deleted. The pair of alterations would be expected not only to change two amino acids but also to alter all those encoded by bases lying between the two affected sites. The reason is that the intervening bases would be read out of phase and therefore grouped into triplets different from those contained in the normal message.

This expectation has recently been confirmed by George Streisinger and his colleagues at the University of Oregon. They have studied mutations in the protein lysozyme that were produced by the T4 virus, which infects the colon bacillus. One phase-shift mutation involved the amino acid sequence ...Lys—Ser—Pro—Ser—Leu—AspN—Ala—Ala—Lys.... They were then able to construct by genetic methods a double phase-shift mutant in which the corresponding sequence was ...Lys—Val—His—His—Leu—Met—Ala—Ala—Lys....

Given these two sequences, the reader should be able, using the genetic code dictionary on page 2243, to decipher uniquely a short length of the nucleic acid message for both the original protein and double mutant and thus deduce the changes produced by each of the phase-shift mutations. The correct result is presented in the illustration above. The result not only confirms several rather doubtful codons, such as UUA for leucine and AGU for serine, but also shows which codons are actually involved in a genetic message. Since the technique is difficult, however, it may not find wide application.

Streisinger's work also demonstrates what has so far been only tacitly as-

ANTICODON	CODON
U	A G
C	G
A	U
G	U C
I	U C A

"WOBBLE" HYPOTHESIS has been proposed by the author to provide rules for the pairing of codon and anticodon at the *third* position of the codon. There is evidence, for example, that the anticodon base I, which stands for inosine, may pair with as many as three different bases: U, C and A. Inosine closely resembles the base guanine (G) and so would ordinarily be expected to pair with cytosine (C). Structural diagrams for standard base pairings and wobble base pairings are illustrated at the bottom of this page.

sumed: that the two languages, both of which are written down in a certain direction according to convention, are in fact translated by the cell in the same direction and not in opposite directions. This fact had previously been established, with more direct chemical methods, by Severo Ochoa and his colleagues at the New York University School of Medicine. In the convention, which was adopted by chance, proteins are written with the amino (NH_2) end on the left. Nucleic acids are written with the end of the molecule containing

a "5 prime" carbon atom at the left. (The "5 prime" refers to a particular carbon atom in the 5-carbon ring of ribose sugar or deoxyribose sugar.)

Finding the Anticodons

Still another method of checking the genetic code is to discover the three bases making up the anticodon in some particular variety of transfer RNA. The first tRNA to have its entire sequence worked out was alanine tRNA, a job done by Robert W. Holley and his collaborators at Cornell University [see "The Nucleotide Sequence of a Nucleic Acid," by Robert W. Holley; SCIENTIFIC AMERICAN Offprint 1033]. Alanine tRNA, obtained from yeast, contains 77 bases. A possible anticodon found near the middle of the molecule has the sequence IGC, where I stands for inosine, a base closely resembling guanine. Since then Hans Zachau and his colleagues at the University of Cologne have established the sequences of two closely related serine tRNA's from yeast, and James Madison and his group at the U.S. Plant, Soil and Nutrition Laboratory at Ithaca, N.Y., have worked out the sequence of a tyrosine tRNA, also from yeast.

A detailed comparison of these three sequences makes it almost certain that the anticodons are alanine–IGC, serine–IGA and tyrosine–GΨA. (Ψ stands for pseudo-uridylic acid, which can form the same base pairs as the base uracil.) In addition there is preliminary evidence from other workers that an anticodon for valine is IAC and an anticodon for phenylalanine is GAA.

All these results would fit the rule that the codon and anticodon pair in an antiparallel manner, and that the pairing in the first two positions of the codon is of the standard type, that is, A pairs with U and G pairs with C. The pairing in the third position of the codon is more complicated. There is now good experimental evidence from both Nirenberg and Khorana and their co-workers that one tRNA can recognize several codons, provided that they differ only in the last place in the codon. Thus Holley's alanine tRNA appears to recognize GCU, GCC and GCA. If it recognizes GCG, it does so only very weakly.

The "Wobble" Hypothesis

I have suggested that this is because of a "wobble" in the pairing in the third place and have shown that a reasonable theoretical model will explain many of the observed results. The suggested rules for the pairing in the third position of the anticodon are presented in the table at the top of this page, but this theory is still speculative. The rules for the first two places of the codon seem reasonably secure, however, and can be used as partial confirmation of the genetic code. The likely codon-anticodon pairings for valine, serine, tyrosine, alanine and phenylalanine satisfy the standard base pairings in the first two places and the wobble hypothesis in the third place [see illustration on page 2247].

Several points about the genetic code remain to be cleared up. For example, the triplet UGA has still to be allocated.

GUANINE   CYTOSINE   GUANINE   URACIL

STANDARD AND WOBBLE BASE PAIRINGS both involve the formation of hydrogen bonds when certain bases are brought into close proximity. In the standard guanine-cytosine pairing (*left*) it is believed three hydrogen bonds are formed. The bases are shown as they exist in the RNA molecule, where they are attached to 5-carbon rings of ribose sugar. In the proposed wobble pairing (*right*) guanine is linked to uracil by only two hydrogen bonds. The base inosine (I) has a single hydrogen atom where guanine has an amino (NH_2) group (*broken circle*). In the author's wobble hypothesis inosine can pair with U as well as with C and A (*not shown*).

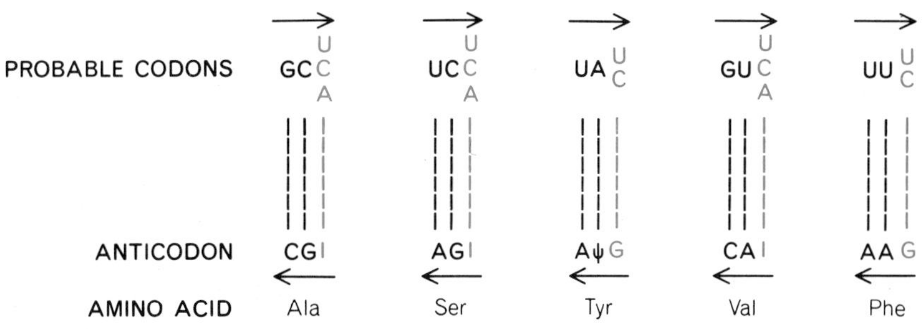

The punctuation marks—the signals for "begin chain" and "end chain"—are only partly understood. It seems likely that both the triplet UAA (called "ochre") and UAG (called "amber") can terminate the polypeptide chain, but which triplet is normally found at the end of a gene is still uncertain.

The picturesque terms for these two triplets originated when it was discovered in studies of the colon bacillus some years ago that mutations in other genes (mutations that in fact cause errors in chain termination) could "suppress" the action of certain mutant codons, now identified as either UAA or UAG. The terms "ochre" and "amber" are simply invented designations and have no reference to color.

A mechanism for chain initiation was discovered fairly recently. In the colon bacillus it seems certain that formylmethionine, carried by a special tRNA, can initiate chains, although it is not clear if all chains have to start in this way, or what the mechanism is in mammals and other species. The formyl group (CHO) is not normally found on finished proteins, suggesting that it is probably removed by a special enzyme. It seems likely that sometimes the methionine is removed as well.

It is unfortunately possible that a few codons may be ambiguous, that is, may code for more than one amino acid. This is certainly not true of most codons. The present evidence for a small amount of ambiguity is suggestive but not conclusive. It will make the code more difficult to establish correctly if ambiguity can occur.

Problems for the Future

From what has been said it is clear that, although the entire genetic code

CODON-ANTICODON PAIRINGS take place in an antiparallel direction. Thus the anticodons are shown here written backward, as opposed to the way they appear in the text. The five anticodons are those tentatively identified in the transfer RNA's for alanine, serine, tyrosine, valine and phenylalanine. Color indicates where wobble pairings may occur.

is not known with complete certainty, it is highly likely that most of it is correct. Further work will surely clear up the doubtful codons, clarify the punctuation marks, delimit ambiguity and extend the code to many other species. Although the code lists the codons that *may* be used, we still have to determine if alternative codons are used equally. Some preliminary work suggests they may not be. There is also still much to be discovered about the machinery of protein synthesis. How many types of tRNA are there? What is the structure of the ribosome? How does it work, and why is it in two parts? In addition there are many questions concerning the control of the rate of protein synthesis that we are still a long way from answering.

When such questions have been answered, the major unsolved problem will be the structure of the genetic code. Is the present code merely the result of a series of evolutionary accidents, so that the allocations of triplets to amino acids is to some extent arbitrary? Or are there

profound structural reasons why phenylalanine has to be coded by UUU and UUC and by no other triplets? Such questions will be difficult to decide, since the genetic code originated at least three billion years ago, and it may be impossible to reconstruct the sequence of events that took place at such a remote period. The origin of the code is very close to the origin of life. Unless we are lucky it is likely that much of the evidence we should like to have has long since disappeared.

Nevertheless, the genetic code is a major milestone on the long road of molecular biology. In showing in detail how the four-letter language of nucleic acid controls the 20-letter language of protein it confirms the central theme of molecular biology that genetic information can be stored as a one-dimensional message on nucleic acid and be expressed as the one-dimensional amino acid sequence of a protein. Many problems remain, but this knowledge is now secure.

The Author

F. H. C. CRICK is a molecular biologist who works for the British Medical Research Council's Laboratory of Molecular Biology at the University Postgraduate Medical School in Cambridge. He was originally a physicist but turned to basic research on the structure of viruses, collagen and the nucleic acids. He is best known for putting forward (with James D. Watson) the idea that the molecule of the genetic material deoxyribonucleic acid (DNA) is a double helix; for work on the structure of DNA, Crick, Watson and M. H. F. Wilkins jointly received the Nobel prize for physiology and medicine in 1962.

Bibliography

THE GENETIC CODE, VOL. XXXI: 1966 COLD SPRING HARBOR SYMPOSIA ON QUANTITATIVE BIOLOGY. Cold Spring Harbor Laboratory of Quantitative Biology, in press.

MOLECULAR BIOLOGY OF THE GENE. James D. Watson. W. A. Benjamin, Inc., 1965.

RNA CODEWORDS AND PROTEIN SYNTHESIS, VII: ON THE GENERAL NATURE OF THE RNA CODE. M. Nirenberg, P. Leder, M. Bernfield, R. Brimacombe, J. Trupin, F. Rottman and C. O'Neal in *Proceedings of the National Academy of Sciences*, Vol. 53, No. 5, pages 1161–1168; May, 1965.

STUDIES ON POLYNUCLEOTIDES, LVI: FURTHER SYNTHESES, IN VITRO, OF COPOLYPEPTIDES CONTAINING TWO AMINO ACIDS IN ALTERNATING SEQUENCE DEPENDENT UPON DNA-LIKE POLYMERS CONTAINING TWO NUCLEOTIDES IN ALTERNATING SEQUENCE. D. S. Jones, S. Nishimura and H. G. Khorana in *Journal of Molecular Biology*, Vol. 16, No. 2, pages 454–472; April, 1966.

SCIENTIFIC AMERICAN   October 1966, Vol. 215, No. 4, pp. 78-84   OFFPRINT 1053

NIGHT BLINDNESS

by John E. Dowling

It has long been known that poor vision in dim light can be improved with vitamin A. Experiments with rats have now clarified exactly what it is the vitamin does.

Night blindness—insensitivity of the eye to dim light—is one of the oldest diseases known to man, and a cure for the disease has also been known since early times. Medical papyruses of ancient Egypt prescribed the eating of raw liver as a specific for restoring night vision. Early in this century investigators identified the curative factor in liver as vitamin A. Beginning in the 1930's, George Wald of Harvard University and other workers went on to elucidate in detail the critical role played by vitamin A in vision [see "Eye and Camera," by George Wald; SCIENTIFIC AMERICAN Offprint 46].

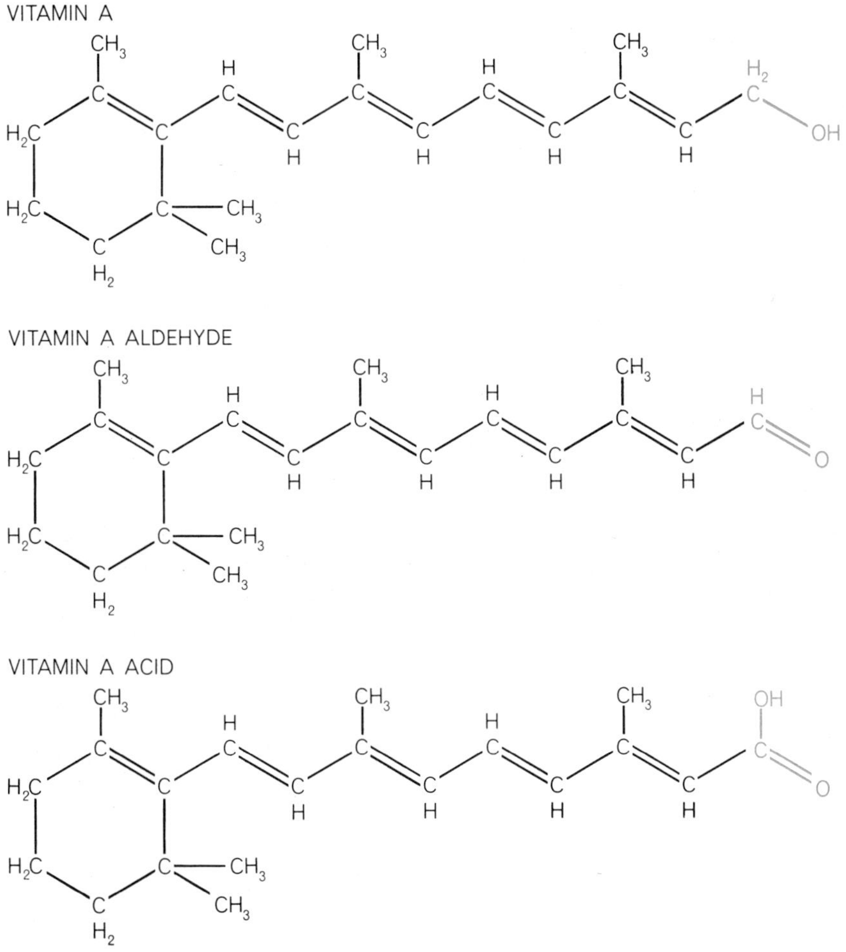

In his classic study Wald showed that the visual pigment in the rods, the retinal cells responsible for vision in dim light, is a complex called rhodopsin that consists of the aldehyde form of vitamin A (also called retinene and retinaldehyde) joined to a large protein molecule named opsin. This pigment, on absorbing light, initiates excitation of the rod cell. The absorption of light also splits the rhodopsin molecule into vitamin A aldehyde and opsin, and the pigment is thereby "bleached" from purplish red to yellow. The chemical conversion of the vitamin A aldehyde into vitamin A can also be detected by a marked change in the color of the retina from yellow to white.

It then became evident that a deficiency of vitamin A would prevent rod cells from synthesizing sufficient rhodopsin and thus would produce night blindness. It has since been shown that a deficiency of the vitamin also reduces the sensitivity of the retinal cone cells, which serve for vision in ordinary light (such as daylight), because vitamin A is necessary for the synthesis of their visual pigments. The loss of cone sensitivity, however, is not usually great enough to be noticed in daylight; it is only in the faint light of nighttime that a person deficient in vitamin A becomes blind.

Soon after Wald's discovery investigators proceeded to test the visual effects of vitamin A deficiency, and of treatments with the vitamin, on human volunteers. Two puzzling findings emerged. Although some of the subjects who were fed an A-deficient diet showed signs of night blindness within a few days, others retained their normal visual sensitivity for months or even

VITAMIN A

VITAMIN A ALDEHYDE

VITAMIN A ACID

CHEMICAL STRUCTURES of three different molecular forms of vitamin A are depicted here; the parts of the molecules that differ are in color. The aldehyde form of vitamin A combines with a large protein molecule (opsin) to form a complex (rhodopsin) that is the visual pigment in the rods, the retinal cells responsible for vision in dim light. Vitamin A acid keeps rats healthy but is not converted into vitamin A or vitamin A aldehyde in rat tissues.

years. Secondly, of those who developed night blindness, some quickly recovered normal vision after vitamin A was restored to their diet, but in others the recovery was slow and occasionally was not complete even many months later. Not surprisingly, in view of the latter finding, the experiments with human subjects were discontinued.

A search began for possible explanations of these curious results. Thomas Moore of the Dunn Nutritional Laboratory in Cambridge, England, discovered one significant clue: adult human beings vary considerably in the amount of reserve vitamin A stored in their liver. Consequently a person with a large reserve might show no signs of deficiency for months after going on an A-deficient diet, whereas one with little storage of the vitamin would show effects almost immediately.

The second question—why some affected persons responded promptly to treatment with vitamin A while others did not—was less easy to answer. There were one or two suggestive findings. In the 1930's Katherine Tansley of University College London and others had found in experiments with animals that the visual cells in the retina degenerated when the animals were kept on an A-deficient diet for a prolonged period. More recently Ruth Hubbard of Harvard learned that opsin is rather unstable compared with rhodopsin. It seemed, therefore, that in the absence of a supply of vitamin A aldehyde for re-forming rhodopsin, opsin might break down with a consequent degeneration of the visual cell.

It was in the light of these findings that, as a student in Wald's laboratory at Harvard, I undertook a study of nutritional night blindness. As our experimental animal we used the rat, the retina of which contains mostly rod cells. We began by measuring the depletion of vitamin A, rhodopsin and opsin from the animal's body when it was fed a diet deficient in the vitamin. The results ran true to our expectations. First the animal drew on the store of vitamin A in its liver; in young rats this supply lasted about three to four weeks, and during that time the vitamin level in the animal's blood and the levels of rhodopsin and opsin in the retina remained normal. After the vitamin A reserve in the liver was used up the level of the vitamin in the blood fell precipitously. Within a few days the level of rhodopsin in the eye also began to decline; two to three weeks later the opsin level began to fall.

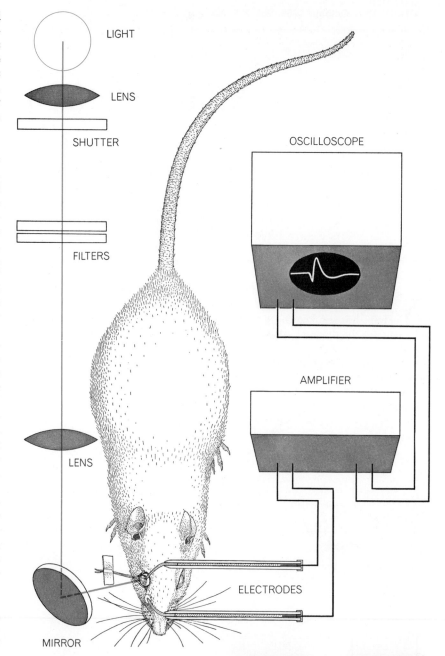

LIGHT

LENS

SHUTTER

FILTERS

OSCILLOSCOPE

AMPLIFIER

LENS

ELECTRODES

MIRROR

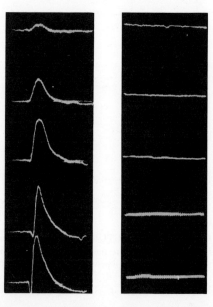

ELECTRORETINOGRAM (ERG) is used by the author to measure the visual sensitivity of rats' eyes to flashes of light of varying intensity. The optical system delivers a flash of light lasting a fiftieth of a second to the eye of an anesthetized rat. Cotton-wick electrodes inserted in the ends of glass pipettes filled with salt solution are placed on the edge of the cornea and on a shaved area of the cheek (the same as if the electrode were placed on the back of the eye). The eye's electrical response to a flash of light is amplified and recorded on an oscilloscope. Visual sensitivity is determined by the threshold of light intensity to which the eye will respond with a minimum ERG. The two sets of oscilloscope traces at right show the ERG responses of a normal rat (left) and a rat that has been on a vitamin-A-deficient diet for 10 months (right). The second rat is blind. Its loss of visual sensitivity increased exponentially, or at a logarithmic rate.

How did this depletion correlate with the animal's vision? As a measure of its visual sensitivity we resorted to the electroretinogram (ERG), a gross electrical response of the retina to a flash of light. Cotton-wick electrodes are placed on the eye of the anesthetized animal, and the eye's electrical response to a flash of light is amplified and recorded on an oscilloscope. The eye's sensitivity is determined by the threshold of light intensity to which it will respond with a minimum ERG.

During the first three to four weeks of a rat's subsistence on the vitamin-A-deficient diet, while the rhodopsin level in the eye remained normal, there was no detectable loss of visual sensitivity. By the fifth week, with a decline in the rhodopsin level, the ERG response also began to decline: it took more light to evoke the minimal electrical reaction. By the eighth week, when the rhodopsin level had dropped to 15 to 20 percent of normal, the ERG threshold had risen by a factor of almost 1,000, that is, the light intensity had to be 1,000 times stronger to produce a response. In general, as the rhodopsin level fell, the loss of visual sensitivity increased exponentially, or at a logarithmic rate.

Up to this point there was apparently no permanent damage to the eye. The retina could be restored to yield a normal ERG response within a few days simply by giving the rat a large dose of vitamin A. Thus the eye's loss and recovery of sensitivity was uncomplicated, in the sense that it paralleled the usual behavior of the organ in adapting to the dark after adapting to bright light. We found, by using the ERG test, that during the process of dark adaptation the sensitivity of the rat's eye bears a loga-

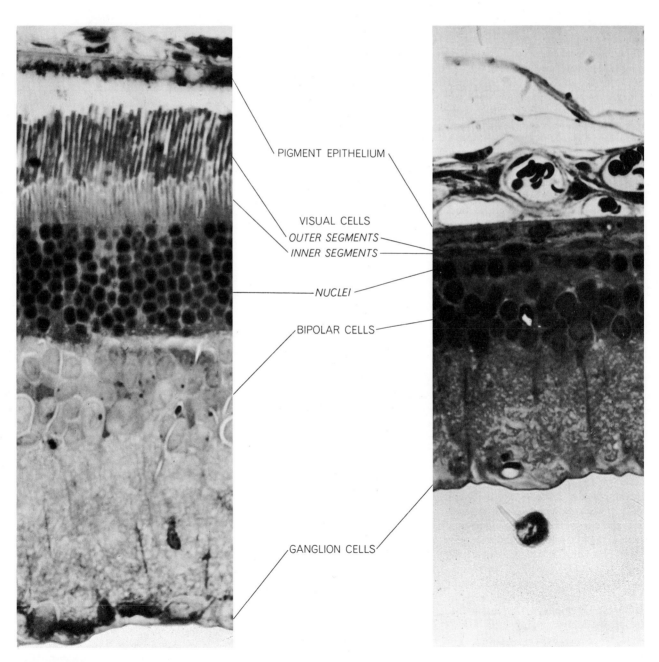

PIGMENT EPITHELIUM

VISUAL CELLS
OUTER SEGMENTS
INNER SEGMENTS

NUCLEI

BIPOLAR CELLS

GANGLION CELLS

VISUAL CELLS in a rat's retina degenerate when the animal is kept on a vitamin-A-deficient diet for a prolonged period of time. The retina shown in cross section at left is from a normal rat. The retina at right is from a totally blind rat that had been on a vitamin-A-deficient diet for 10 months. Its visual cells had been almost completely destroyed and could not have been regenerated later.

rithmic relation to the rhodopsin level, just as it does when the rhodopsin level is depleted by vitamin A deficiency. W. A. H. Rushton of the University of Cambridge has found that a similar relation between the logarithm of visual sensitivity and pigment concentration holds during the dark adaptation of the rods and cones in the human eye [see "Visual Pigments in Man," by W. A. H. Rushton; SCIENTIFIC AMERICAN Offprint 139].

What happens when the rat is kept on a vitamin-A-deficient diet beyond eight weeks? Investigation of the visual effects here runs into a serious difficulty: the problem of keeping the animal alive. Vitamin A is essential for maintaining epithelial tissues throughout the body, and a severe, prolonged deficiency will destroy the animal's health and eventually kill it. After eight to nine weeks on an A-deficient diet rats lose weight drastically, have difficulty breathing and become highly susceptible to infection; usually they do not survive beyond 10 to 12 weeks on such a diet. Fortunately we found a way to circumvent this difficulty. It was suggested by certain experiments reported by Moore in his superb book *Vitamin A,* published in 1957. Moore noted that two Dutch organic chemists, J. F. Arens and D. A. Van Dorp, had made the finding that a compound called vitamin A acid, which apparently was not converted into vitamin A in the tissues of rats, was highly effective in keeping the animals healthy. This looked like a possible answer to our problem. Perhaps we could maintain rats on the vitamin A acid and observe a decline in their vision because they lacked the vitamin itself.

This was, indeed, the way the experiment turned out. On a diet deficient in vitamin A but with a supplement of the acid, rats grew normally and remained generally healthy but became severely night-blind. After about two months on the deficient diet the visual cells in their retinas began to degenerate, and this breakdown was correlated with a loss of opsin from the retina. By about the tenth month the visual cells were almost completely destroyed. At that point the animals were totally blind; their eyes gave no ERG response to light at any intensity. Treatment with doses of vitamin A failed to restore sight to the animals. Visual cells, like other cells in the nervous system, cannot be regenerated once they are lost.

Before full destruction of the cells

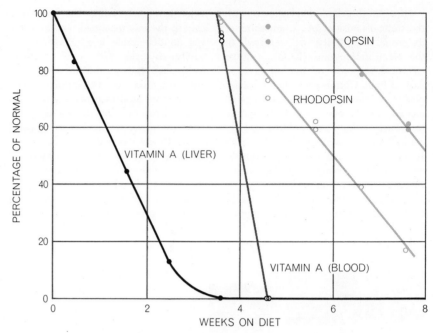

PROGRESSIVE DEPLETION of vitamin A, rhodopsin and opsin in the body of a rat fed a diet deficient in vitamin A is represented in this graph. The rat first drew on the store of vitamin A in its liver; in young rats this supply lasted about three to four weeks, and during that time the vitamin level in the animal's blood and the levels of rhodopsin and opsin in the retina remained normal. After the vitamin A reserve in the liver was used up the level of vitamin in the blood fell precipitously. Within a few days the level of rhodopsin in the eye also began to decline; two or three weeks later the opsin level began to fall.

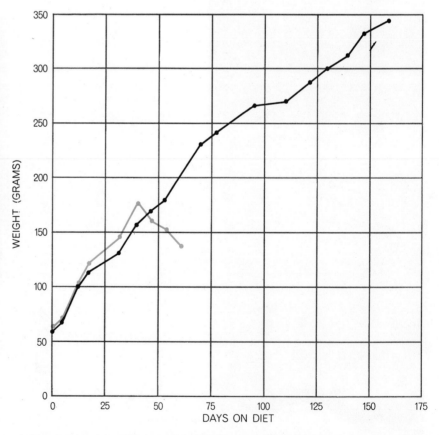

SUPPLEMENT OF VITAMIN A ACID given to a rat on a vitamin-A-deficient diet enabled the rat to grow normally and remain healthy while becoming severely night-blind (*black curve*). A rat on an identical diet without the vitamin A acid died (*colored curve*).

occurs, some recovery is possible. If a rat is given vitamin A at the six-month stage, for example, when the visual cells are only partly damaged, it can regenerate missing cell structures and regain a certain degree of night vision [see illustration below]. The ERG response of such an animal, however, is only about half the size of the normal ERG, which suggests that probably about half of the visual cells in the retina were lost beyond repair.

The breakdown of the A-deprived visual cell begins in the outer part of the cell, which contains the visual pigment. A study with the electron microscope that I carried out with Ian Gibbons at Harvard showed that the disks in the outer region, which give the cell its rod shape, swell and break apart into vesicles and tubules [see upper illustration on page 2255]. The outer structure of the cell later loses its rod shape and becomes a spherical blob. Eventually it disappears altogether. If the animal is treated with vitamin A therapy while the inner part of the cell is still intact, it will regenerate the outer structure in a manner that is strikingly sim-ilar to the growth of an embryonic visual cell during its normal development [see lower illustration on page 2255]. Cilia-like structures grow out from the cell interior, slowly enlarge and become filled with membrane-covered disks that are characteristic of the outer part of the visual cell. The process of regeneration takes about two weeks, the same length of time the normal embryonic visual cell takes to differentiate its outer structure.

After the studies of nutritional night blindness, Richard L. Sidman of the Harvard Medical School and I decided to look into the hereditary forms of night blindness. In man the most common of these inherited disorders is the disease known as retinitis pigmentosa. The genetic disorder cannot be attributed to any shortcoming in the diet, yet it shows striking similarities to nutritional night blindness. The eye gradually loses visual sensitivity, the visual cells degenerate and eventually complete blindness results. The parallel to the progressive blinding that results from vitamin A deficiency is so close that it seemed the inherited disorder might be due to a genetic defect in the metabolism of vitamin A or the synthesis of the visual pigments. Sidman and I undertook to investigate this hypothesis.

Our experimental subject, as before, was the rat. In this animal the inherited disease is carried by a recessive gene, and the disorder (called inherited retinal dystrophy) shows itself only in individuals that have received the defective gene from both parents. The disease begins to show its effects at about the 18th day of the young animal's life; tests by means of the ERG disclosed that its visual sensitivity gradually declines until by the age of 60 days the ERG response has disappeared. We reasoned that if the defect was related to vitamin A metabolism or rhodopsin synthesis, the decline in visual sensitivity should be paralleled by a decline in the rhodopsin content of the visual cells. To our great surprise we found that there was actually an *increase* of the rhodopsin level in the animals' eyes during the early stages of the disease. Rats with the inherited night blindness had much

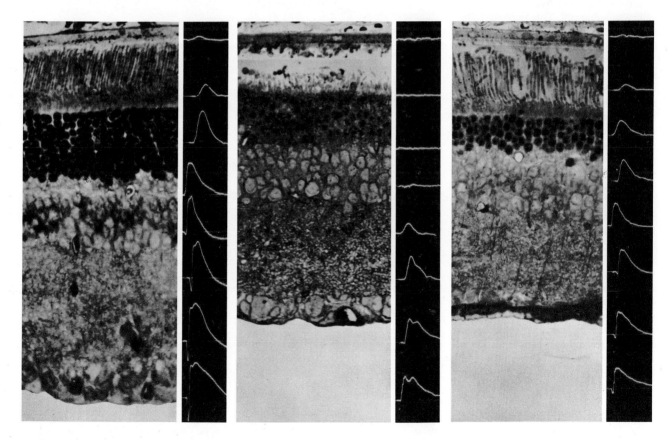

RECOVERY FROM NIGHT BLINDNESS is represented here in two different ways. The micrographs show cross sections of the retinas of a normal rat (left), a severely night-blind rat fed a vitamin-A-deficient diet with a vitamin-A-acid supplement for approximately six and a half months (center) and a partially recov-ered rat fed the identical vitamin-deficient, acid-supplemented diet for six and a half months and then given vitamin A for another 16 days (right). The accompanying ERG responses show that only about half of the normal ERG potential is recovered, which suggests that about half of the visual cells at right were lost.

more rhodopsin than is ever found in normal animals!

Along with the excess of rhodopsin there was a considerable overdevelopment of the outer structure of the visual cells. In a rat with the inherited disease this zone at 22 days of age, for example, was almost twice as large as it is in the normal eye [*see top illustration at right*]. It was divided into two layers: an inner layer containing structures in the normal rodlike form and an outer layer filled with spiral-shaped bodies instead of disks. It appeared that the diseased retinas produced an overabundance of material that formed distorted structures.

Evidently the inherited disease arises from some failure of metabolic control. In any event, the cause of the blindness is so unrelated to the simple case of vitamin A deficiency that we could see there was little hope of finding a simple cure in the form of therapeutic feeding. One of our observations, however, opened up an interesting new line of investigation. We found that when animals with the inherited disease were kept in darkness or dim light, the accumulation of rhodopsin in their visual cells was enhanced. This suggested that the progress of the disease might be influenced by the amount of light to which the eye was exposed.

To test this idea we reared groups of rats bearing the genetic defect under different conditions: one group was kept in darkness or in dim light 24 hours a day, the other was kept in the ordinary daily cycle of alternating daylight and darkness. The rats kept in darkness showed a much slower deterioration of visual sensitivity than those that were exposed to normal light. At the age of 60 days, when the latter animals had lost all sensitivity to light, the animals that had been kept in the dark still showed a considerable ERG response to light. In fact, they continued to give an ERG response up to the age of 120 days. Microscopic examination of the retinas also showed that the degeneration of the visual cells proceeded more slowly in the animals kept in darkness.

This finding led us to ask the question of what effect prolonged exposure to bright light might have on the normal eye. During World War II, Selig Hecht of Columbia University and his co-workers demonstrated that daily exposure to several hours of bright sunlight on the beach slightly impaired the dark-adapting abilities of human subjects. The effects were cumulative, and after several such sessions of expo-

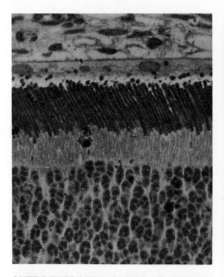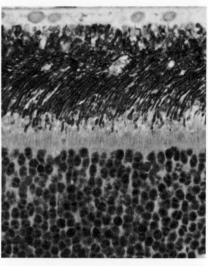

OVERDEVELOPED OUTER SEGMENTS of the visual cells in a 22-day-old rat with an inherited form of night blindness known as a retinal dystrophy (*right*) are almost twice as large as the outer segments in the eye of a normal 22-day-old rat (*left*). The inherited disease, which apparently arises from some failure of metabolic control, is also characterized by a decrease in ERG response and an increase in the rhodopsin content of the visual cells.

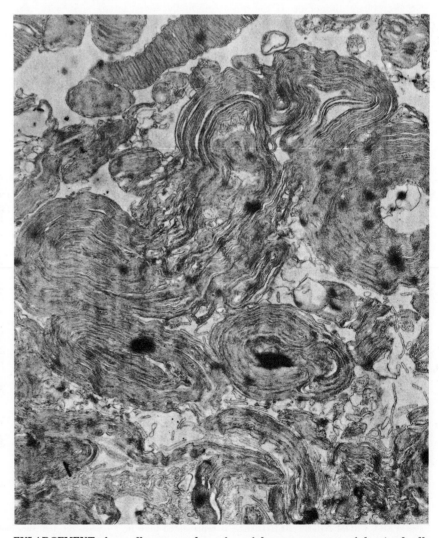

ENLARGEMENT of a small area near the surface of the outer segments of the visual cells in a rat with inherited night blindness reveals the spiral-shaped bodies that characterize this layer. The distorted structures appear to be formed by an overabundance of material produced by the diseased retina. An inner layer containing disks in the normal rodlike form (*not shown in this electron micrograph*) underlies the layer of distorted retinal structures.

sure it took the subjects several days to recover their normal capacities for dark adaptation. In the laboratory where I am now working, at the Wilmer Ophthalmological Institute of the Johns Hopkins University School of Medicine, Robert Mittenthal and I recently conducted a similar experiment on rats. We found that albino rats with normal vision that were kept around the clock in light of ordinary brightness (two 75-watt fluorescent lamps) developed severe night blindness after only three to five days of exposure to this light. These animals, given long periods (up to three months) of dark adaptation afterward, recovered very little of their normal sensitivity to light, according to ERG measurements. The visual cells in their retinas were almost completely destroyed by several days of constant exposure to light. Werner K. Noell of the State University of New York at Buffalo School of Medicine has reported similar results in experiments he conducted with both pigmented and albino rats: short periods of exposure to bright light destroyed the visual cells in his animals also.

Probably the lighting to which human beings are customarily exposed rarely produces any permanent damage to normal eyes. It seems possible, however, that people with inherited night blindness (such as retinitis pigmentosa) or other retinal diseases may be more sensitive to excessive light. Thus the possibility exists—and it is well worth testing—that wearing dark glasses, particularly in bright light, may be helpful to such persons, much as dim light prolongs visual responses in rats with inherited blindness.

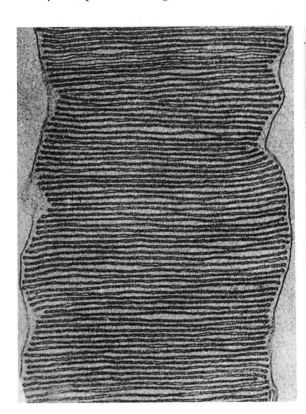

DEGENERATION of the outer segments of the rods in a rat's retina is the first stage in the breakdown of a vitamin-A-deprived visual cell. The electron micrograph at left shows the disks, enlarged about 45,000 diameters, in the outer region that give the normal cell its rod shape. In the electron micrograph of an A-deficient cell at right the disks, enlarged about 30,000 diameters, are swollen and broken apart into vesicles and tubules. The outer structure has consequently lost its rod shape and become a spherical blob.

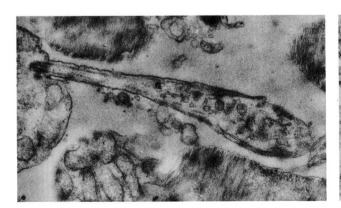

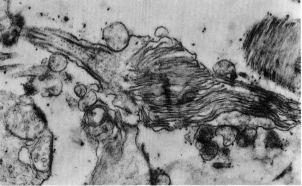

REGENERATION of the outer segments of a rod is possible if the animal is treated with vitamin A therapy while the internal part of the cell is still intact. The regeneration of the outer structure, which takes about two weeks, is strikingly similar to the growth of an embryonic visual cell during its normal development. Cilia-like structures grow out from the cell interior and form disks enclosed in membranes (electron micrograph at right). In both electron micrographs the outer segments of the rod are to the right.

The Author

JOHN E. DOWLING is associate professor of biology at the Wilmer Ophthalmological Institute of the Johns Hopkins University School of Medicine. After graduation from Harvard College in 1957 he spent two years at the Harvard Medical School; he then switched to biology and obtained a Ph.D. from Harvard in 1961. He taught in the Harvard department of biology until 1964, when he went to Johns Hopkins. Dowling writes: "A major goal of our group at Hopkins is to correlate structure and function in the vertebrate retina. In particular I have worked extensively on problems of visual adaptation, and most recently on the synaptic organization of the retina as revealed by electron microscopy."

Bibliography

THE BIOLOGICAL FUNCTION OF VITAMIN A ACID. John E. Dowling and George Wald in *Proceedings of the National Academy of Sciences*, Vol. 46, No. 5, pages 587–616; May 15, 1960.

INHERITED RETINAL DYSTROPHY IN THE

SCIENTIFIC AMERICAN   October 1966, Vol. 215, No. 4, pp. 104-113   OFFPRINT **1054**

THE NAVIGATION OF PENGUINS

by John T. Emlen and Richard L. Penney

The Adélie penguin travels hundreds of miles from its breeding grounds over virtually featureless land and water and returns to the same nest. How it does so is investigated by experiment.

It has long been known that the domesticated pigeon can find its way home after having been transported to a strange location, and experiments conducted in recent years have shown that a number of wild bird species possess the same ability. A series of experiments conducted recently in Antarctica has demonstrated that one wild bird's ability to travel almost straight across hundreds of miles of featureless antarctic landscape depends on a "clock" and a "compass" working in combination. The experiments were conducted with a flightless bird, the Adélie penguin (*Pygoscelis adeliae*). Their results may help to answer the question that inevitably arises in discussions of bird navigation: How do the animals do it? In this article we shall relate why both an unusual field area and an unusual bird were selected for the experiments, relate the outcome of our studies and conclude with a summary of the questions concerning bird navigation to which there now appear to be complete or partial answers.

Early in the nesting season of 1959 five adult male Adélie penguins were captured and banded at an Adélie rookery near Wilkes Station in Antarctica and flown 1,200 miles to McMurdo Sound. The birds were then released; in effect they were being asked if they could find their way home. The majority answer was yes: when the Wilkes rookery penguin population assembled the following spring, three of the five kidnapped males waddled up the beach from the sea to establish their claim at the very nesting sites from which they had been so abruptly taken 10 months earlier. By what route they had traveled home no one knows, but their performance added the Adélie penguin to the

lengthening list of bird species able to navigate over long distances. The achievement has an extra dimension; most bird navigators fly, but the penguins had walked, tobogganed on their bellies or swum the entire way.

The observation that migratory birds return to the same nesting sites year after year almost always raises questions that are phrased in terms of how the migrants find their home. The late Gustav Kramer's discovery that captive birds could orient themselves by means of the sun was hailed as a major research breakthrough at the time of his first experiments in Germany 15 years ago. Here was a new insight into a compass-like mechanism that might explain birds' navigational abilities. As Kramer and others pointed out, however, neither bird nor man nor any other animal is able to find the way home from a strange place with the aid of a compass alone. A man who undertakes true bicoordinate navigation needs both a compass and the equivalent of a map on which both his present position and his destination are located; at the very least a bird needs some kind of information about its position with respect to home at some point during its journey. Nonetheless, many investigators who are attempting to discover the cues that may tell navigating birds the direction of home have begun to wonder if the birds have access to such information after all.

One of the more troublesome problems connected with studies of bird navigation gave us a reason for selecting Antarctica as an experimental site. This is the difficulty involved in keeping track of experimental birds and recording their performance. If a bird is placed

in a circular cage during its migrating season, it will provide information on some aspects of orientation. But if the bird is released from the cage in the hope of obtaining more information, control of the experiment flies out the window with the bird. Although free-flight experiments making use of birds fitted with telemetering devices that radio their position are currently yielding interesting results, at the time our antarctic experiments were undertaken the advantages offered by a flightless bird that travels overland in an environment free of obstacles and disturbances were compelling.

In addition to being a slow enough traveler on land to be followed easily, the Adélie penguin has a number of other assets as an experimental animal. First, it is a migratory bird with a demonstrated homing ability; each spring and fall Adélies travel hundreds of miles between the outer fringe of the antarctic pack ice and their rookeries on the coast of the continent. Second, it thrives in subzero weather and shuns all food for weeks on end during the nesting season. Third, it is abundant and easily captured at its rookeries. Fourth, because its normal range is along the coastal fringe of the continent, individual birds are not likely to be familiar with any landmarks in inland areas. Finally, the Adélie's back is broad, black and conspicuous in the polar snowscape, and on most snow surfaces its tracks can be followed and charted in detail [see illustration on page 2263].

The experimental advantages of Antarctica itself, in addition to its vast stretches of generally featureless interior, include 24-hour daylight during the summer season. Furthermore, the meridians of longitude come closer and closer together until they meet at the South Pole; therefore a comparatively short journey east or west along the coast may cover dozens of degrees of longitude. With the excellent facilities provided by the Navy and the scientific-support arm of the Antarctic Research Program, it was possible to move captured penguins readily to locales many miles and many degrees of longitude distant from their home.

The subjects in most of our tests came from a thriving Adélie rookery at Cape Crozier, where some 300,000 birds gather each nesting season. We netted and moved the penguins 20 at a time to our test areas. There they were banded (on the wing) and housed in pits excavated in the snow until it was their turn to be tested. Our principal test site was located in the middle of the 150,000-square-mile Ross Ice Shelf, some 180 miles southeast of Cape Crozier, at a point where the 180th meridian and the 80th parallel of south latitude intersect. Here a featureless white landscape stretches northward

105 miles to the Ross Sea and extends unchanged even farther southward and eastward. Only to the west is the flat terrain eventually broken by glacier-crowned mountain ranges, and these were out of sight 180 miles from our camp. Although the snow surface close at hand is wrinkled by irregular wind furrows, the distant line where sky and land meet is monotonously level.

In order to record the direction in which the penguins traveled when they were released we set up three tall tripods so that they formed the points of

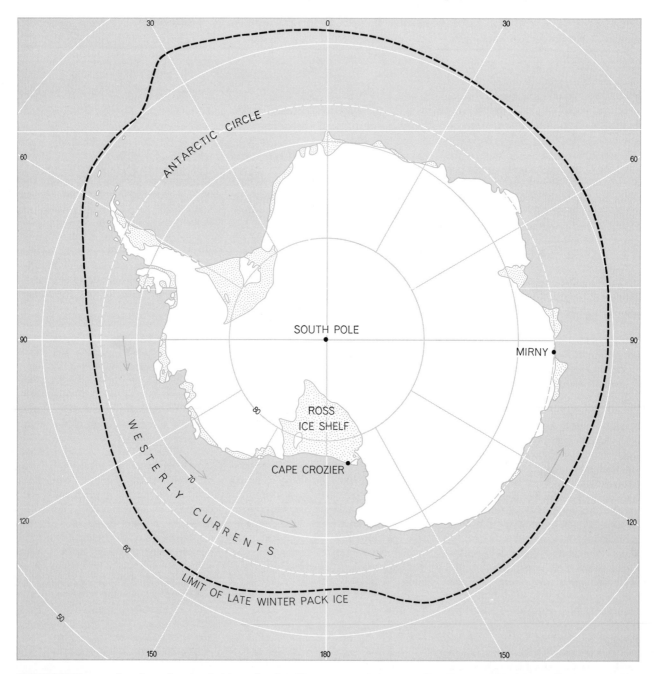

ANTARCTICA was selected as a location for the authors' studies both because Adélie penguins are hardy and accomplished migrants and because moving captive birds a comparatively short distance to the east or west placed them in a completely novel environ- ment that contained a minimum of familiar navigation cues. Each fall the birds travel from any one of a number of coastal rookeries such as Cape Crozier north to the open water along the edge of the pack ice. When spring comes, they return to their home rookeries.

an equilateral triangle 200 meters on a side. A surveyor's transit was placed at the top of each tripod. At the midpoint of the triangular area we dug a small release pit with a cover that could be pulled clear with a tug on a length of cord that extended to an inconspicuous white shelter some distance away. When all was in readiness, we would remove a bird from its storage pit, put it in the release pit and set the cover in place. We then retired to our shelter and pulled the cord; the bird promptly jumped up to the surface, ready either to travel or, as sometimes happened, to lie down and go to sleep.

Usually the newly freed bird would make a few short dashes in various directions and then stand and peer at the limited scenery: the three transit tripods, our shelter and the antarctic sun. After a few minutes the bird would set off again, this time in a definite direction from which it rarely veered. Every five minutes two observers would take simultaneous azimuth readings, using the two transits that were best situated for the purpose. These readings enabled us to plot the bird's course over a distance of one to three miles and usually for 20 to 40 minutes, by which time our subject would have disappeared over the horizon [see top illustration at right]. Sometimes we extended the record by following a bird's tracks for as many as 16 miles from the release site. We also fitted a few penguins with radio transmitters and recorded their direction of travel for 50 miles or so. The bulk of our most useful data, however, was obtained by visually tracking 174 penguins during the first one to three miles of their journey. Most of our subjects polar summer, when the sun neither rises nor sets, almost all its motion is azimuthal. To hold a constant course while one's "sun compass" swings around the horizon calls for continuous access to information on the passage of time, yet we found that the penguins were not affected by the sun's shifting azimuth. Birds that were released early in the morning set off northward, even though at that time a northerly heading was about 90 degrees to the left of the sun; at noon their northward departure was straight toward the sun; in the afternoon they still headed north, although by then such a heading was about 90 degrees to the right of the sun. Moreover, once the birds selected a course, they showed no tendency to fix on and follow the sun in its inexorable counterclockwise march along the horizon. This ability to be guided by the sun

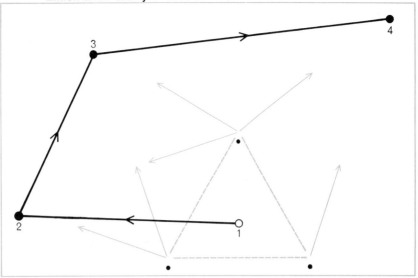

TRACKING SYSTEM required visual checks on the position of each bird at five-minute intervals after it was released from a pit located at the midpoint of an equilateral triangle with sides 200 meters long (1). A transit was located at each point of the triangle; readings from the two best-situated instruments (arrows) allowed the bird's position to be recorded until it vanished over the horizon. Some birds were subsequently tracked as far as 16 miles across the snow. A few birds fitted with radio transmitters were monitored up to 50 miles.

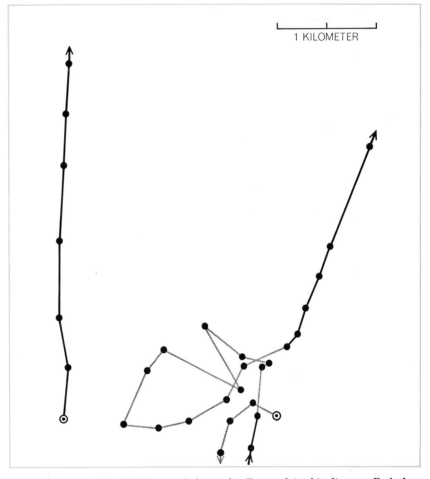

CLEAR AND CLOUDY SKIES caused the tracks illustrated in this diagram. Each dot represents the position of an Adélie penguin at five-minute intervals following its release (bull's-eye). In sunlight one bird (left) started on and held to a straight course until out of sight. Released under a cloudy sky, a second bird (right) headed the opposite way (gray line) but reappeared (black) when the sky cleared. More clouds left the bird moving at random until sunlight again headed it on much the same course as the first bird's.

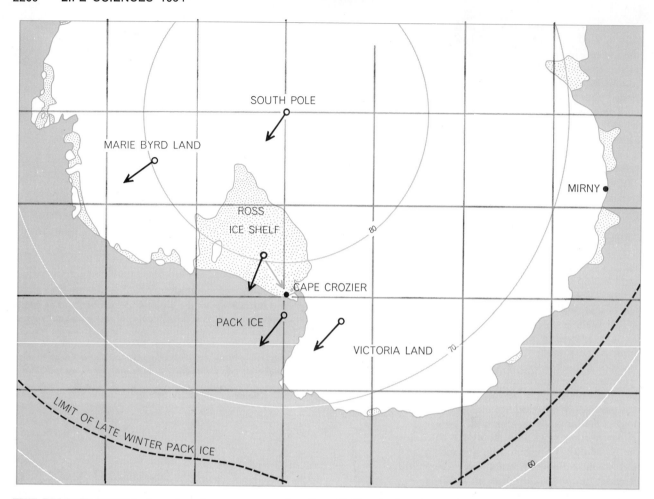

FIVE RELEASE POINTS, situated to the east, west, north and south of Cape Crozier, were used by the authors for their tests. Regardless of where they were released, birds from Cape Crozier all chose escape routes that were roughly parallel and approximately north-northeast with respect to a north-south line passing through Cape Crozier (*black arrows and gray grid*). When birds from the Russian antarctic station of Mirny were transported to the Ross Ice Shelf and released, they first chose escape routes almost perpendicular to those of Cape Crozier birds (*colored arrow*). When plotted with respect to a north-south line passing through Mirny, this heading also proved to be north-northeast. Other penguins from Mirny, kept on the Ross Ice Shelf for a few weeks, readjusted their "biological clock." When released, they chose the same general escape direction taken by the birds from the Cape Crozier rookery.

and yet to compensate for changes in its azimuthal position with the passage of time is the strongest kind of evidence that the Adélie penguins possess the timing mechanism commonly called a "biological clock."

Although the penguins' general heading after release was northward, it could more accurately be described as north-northeasterly rather than due north. Some considerations of polar geography are a necessary preliminary to discussion of this point. When one is standing on the South Pole, all true compass directions are north. In polar areas, therefore, it is useful to forget about true compass headings and instead to calculate directions on the basis of a rectangular grid. Such grids take the meridian on which the user is located as their central vertical line. In the illustration above, for example, the grid is oriented to the meridian that runs from the South Pole through the Cape Crozier rookery. Analyzing the penguins'

travel directions in terms of this grid, we found that no matter where birds from Cape Crozier were set free they all set off in much the same north-northeast direction. This meant, of course, that they seldom headed for "home" at all. When Cape Crozier penguins were released on the Ross Ice Shelf or at Byrd Station, which are to the east of Cape Crozier, their heading pointed them far to the right of a homing course; when released in Victoria Land, to the west, their heading was about 90 degrees to the left of home. As for the penguins we released on the pack ice some 125 miles offshore, they set off on a north-northeast heading that took them directly away from the Cape Crozier rookery.

The fact that all the Cape Crozier birds, wherever they were released, pursued essentially parallel courses regardless of the actual direction of their home rookery is further evidence that the cue that guided all the birds was far more

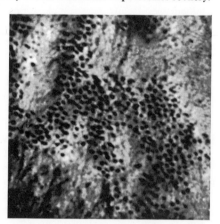

PENGUIN ROOKERY at Cape Crozier in Antarctica has a summer population of some 300,000 Adélie penguins. The aerial photograph on the opposite page shows a part of the rookery; each of the black dots is the shadow of single or paired birds. The area indicated in color is shown enlarged above. Most of the birds used in the authors' studies of penguin navigation were adult or juvenile inhabitants of the rookery at Cape Crozier.

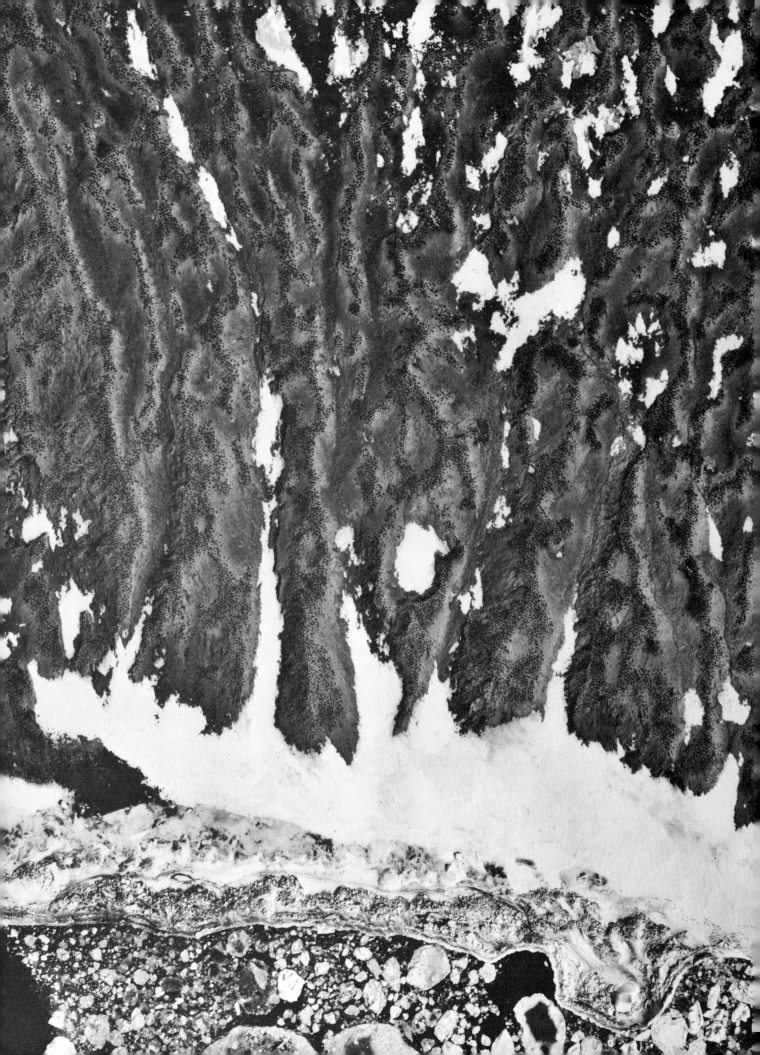

POSITION READING is taken by a member of the authors' party, who stands atop a stepladder in the middle of the Ross Ice Shelf. The escape paths pursued by 54 penguins released during clear weather varied from a straight line by a factor of less than 1 percent.

ESCAPING PENGUIN ignores another bird's path as it heads across the Ross Ice Shelf. Adélie penguins travel two to three miles per hour; the fastest did eight miles per hour.

remote than anything connected with their home or, for that matter, with any localized terrestrial cue. The sun, some 93 million miles away, was their compass, and they could use it unerringly because their biological clocks served to correct for its azimuthal changes. At the same time, it was clear that the Cape Crozier penguins did not head for home. Their movements were oriented in terms of a common direction of escape rather than an approach toward a common goal.

The cooperation of our Russian colleagues at Mirny, 2,000 miles and 90 degrees of longitude away, enabled us to make a further test of our conclusion. Forty Adélie penguins were captured at Mirny and flown to the Ross Ice Shelf. When we released 20 of them, the birds set off north-northeast, but north-northeast only with respect to a grid centered on their home meridian at Mirny. Their actual course with respect to the local grid was northwest, so that their route lay almost at right angles to that of the Cape Crozier penguins.

What functional explanation can be found, in terms of survival value, for the generally northward escape route taken by the Adélie penguins we captured at various rookeries? Northward, to be sure, is always seaward in Antarctica; an attractively simple explanation is that movement northward would carry a lost penguin along the shortest route to the sea—the species' only source of food. There is also another consideration. For migratory birds such as the Adélie penguin a sun compass "set" to a home meridian would tend to reduce lateral dispersal of any one rookery's population and ensure that the same group of penguins returned from the fringes of the pack ice to the same stretch of coast each year. Indeed, the home meridian—regarded as a reasonably broad corridor with one end in the coastal rookery and the other in the food-rich waters at the edge of the pack ice—may be what "home" is to an Adélie penguin. The bird's annual movements inward or outward along the corridor could be the result of physiologically controlled negative or positive responses to the same basic orientation cue or cues.

What accounts for the slight but unmistakable easterly vector that turns the outward journey from true north to north-northeast? At the end of our first season's work in Antarctica we were prepared to dismiss it as a chance variation. Further and stronger evidence of the easterly vector gathered in 1964

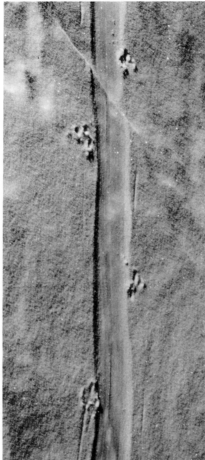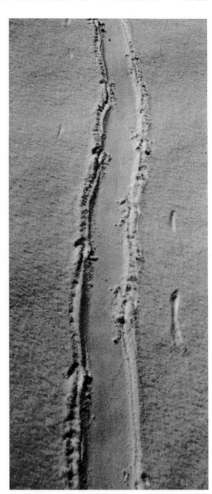

PENGUIN'S PROGRESS on land can vary from a brisk waddle (*left*), in which the bird's oscillating tail leaves a serpentine track in the snow, to a swift tobogganing, sometimes propelled by the feet alone (*center*) and sometimes assisted by wing strokes (*right*).

made it impossible to ignore. One possible answer suggests itself at present: The coastal currents in both the Cape Crozier and the Mirny areas are westerly. A penguin adrift on the offshore pack ice would be slowly carried westward out of its home zone unless it compensated by moving to the east from time to time. Similarly, a bird moving from the coast to the outer fringe of the pack ice would be borne toward the west if its line of march were true north instead of north-northeast. One observation that lends weight to our suggestion that the easterly vector is a compensation for westerly coastal currents is that the Mirny birds released on the Ross Ice Shelf showed a stronger easterly bias than the Cape Crozier birds released there. The westerly currents off the Mirny coast are known to run strong.

The contrast between the escape headings chosen by Cape Crozier and Mirny birds immediately raises two questions. It seems safe to assume that a penguin's ability to select an escape direction when transferred to a strange environment is something innate. But what about the specific direction selected? Is this innately determined or is it a function of the environment in which the bird was raised? And can external influences alter the setting of the bird's compass?

We decided to see what information the escape behavior of two-month-old, inexperienced penguins might provide concerning the first of these questions. We captured a number of Cape Crozier chicks, some near the nests where they had been hatched and others on the beach that borders the rookery. When they were released on the Ross Ice Shelf, all of them headed off generally north-northeast on a straight course, although they showed somewhat greater variations in their selection of departure directions than did the adult Adélies.

The chicks' possession of a directional preference cannot, however, be taken as proof that the response is innate in the species. From the day they emerge from their eggs the Adélie penguins at

Cape Crozier look down a steep slope that faces the Ross Sea to the northeast. Below, adult penguins are constantly entering and leaving the water, returning with food for the ravenous chicks (who, when their hunger is unsatisfied, will often pursue a parent part of the way back to the water). The same north-easterly direction is the one in which the chicks themselves will move once they become independent of the nesting area. North-northeast thus becomes a significant direction to the birds as they mature. It seems plausible that such an upbringing, in which the topographic cues that come to mean "seaward" are constantly associated with the celestial cues that represent north-northeast, might allow the celestial cues to persist and function in situations where the topographic ones are no longer available.

As for the second question, we would have found it surprising if our birds had proved impervious to the environmental influences that are known to reset the biological clocks of many Temperate Zone animals within a period of a week or so. Yet, compared with the day-and-night cycle of the Temperate Zone, the cues available in the continuous daylight of the antarctic summer are notably weak ones. To put the matter to a test we kept the remaining 20 of the 40 birds from Mirny penned under the open sky on the Ross Ice Shelf for periods that ranged from 18 to 27 days. These birds had arrived with their clock synchronized to a time zone some 88 degrees to the west (equivalent to the six-hour time difference between London and New Orleans). At the end of their three- to four-week detention the 20 Mirny birds selected local north-northeast as their departure direction. Their clock—and thus their compass—had been reset; the resetting turned them 55 degrees to the right and pointed them in the same general escape direction as the one selected by the "local" Cape Crozier birds.

This finding leaves us in something of a dilemma. If all the Adélie penguins in the Antarctic can reset their clock as easily as the 20 birds from Mirny did, our earlier speculation that a constant local escape orientation would be useful in maintaining population-specific coastal zones may not be warranted. Any birds that wandered toward the lateral boundary of their population's corridor would be in danger of adapting to the new conditions there. The unifying interrelation of breeding grounds and feeding area that is provided by a common compass setting would therefore be lost to them. For the moment we can only suggest that unconfined birds may not reset their clock as readily as birds that are artificially detained do.

We have seen that the Adélie penguin can navigate with the sun as a directional cue and with an inherent timing mechanism as compensation for the sun's position changes from hour to hour. We have also seen that the consistent escape direction chosen by released birds is a northerly one that under normal circumstances would possess considerable survival value by leading a lost bird to the nearest feeding ground at sea. Unfortunately these two observations tell us little about the question that faced us at the outset: How do the birds find their way home? The fact that so many of our experimental subjects did reach their home rookeries indicates that Adélie penguins possess something by way of navigational equipment in addition to the sun-compass orientation they demonstrated during the release experiments. Cape Crozier birds released on the Ross Ice Shelf consistently headed far to the right of their true homeward direction, but at least half of them were back at Cape Crozier within 25 days. Of the 20 Cape Crozier birds we turned loose on the pack ice many miles offshore, 15 were back home within two weeks even though all had started off in exactly the opposite direction. How did the three birds from Wilkes Station and at least two of the birds from Mirny find their way home over thousands of intervening miles in time for the next nesting season? For that matter, how do millions of Adélie penguins do much the same thing in their annual migrations?

We can only speculate that a homing bird must receive new information at some point on its long trek. We suspect that the birds receive this new information when they reach the point at which open water enables them to swim and feed after a long period of deprivation. What a homing bird does and what cues it uses at this or any other critical point in its travels, however, are unknown. A simple 180-degree reversal in direction of travel, still depending on the sun compass, would be a maneuver useful to a penguin that had finally penetrated to the seaward fringe of the pack ice. Birds within 75 miles or so of the coast might also make use of visual cues such as the 13,000-foot peak of Mount Erebus on Ross Island. But at this stage in our investigations it is fruitless to speculate further.

To sum up, we have shown that the Adélie penguin uses a sun compass for orientation when released in a strange environment. We surmise that the same sun compass may guide the birds back from the open water to their breeding grounds after some other as yet undetermined cue or cues have reversed their direction of travel. A number of questions remain to be answered. We may, however, already have the answer to one of them. The antarctic winter is the season during which Adélie penguins spend their time away from land; when they leave the polar ocean at all, they perch on the ceaselessly shifting and drifting floes of the offshore pack ice. The antarctic winter is also a time of nearly total darkness, just as summer is a time of 24-hour-long daylight. How do these competent little navigators keep track of their position during the long dark period? We suspect that in the Adélie penguins' winter habitat the sun's brief appearance low on the horizon each noon is a strong enough cue to keep the birds' sun compass correctly set throughout the long polar night.

The Authors

JOHN T. EMLEN and RICHARD L. PENNEY are respectively professor of zoology at the University of Wisconsin and an investigator at the Institute for Research in Animal Behavior, which is sponsored jointly by Rockefeller University and the New York Zoological Society. Emlen was graduated from Haverford College in 1931 and obtained a Ph.D. in ornithology from Cornell University in 1934. He spent some years as a biologist with the U.S. Department of Agriculture and as a research associate at Johns Hopkins University before going to the University of Wisconsin in 1946. In addition to his work with penguins he has studied social and population control in gulls, swallows, blackbirds, mice, squirrels and bats and made special studies of gorillas, bison and porpoises. Penney took a bachelor's degree at St. Olaf College in 1957 and a doctorate in zoology at the University of Wisconsin in 1963. He was a postdoctoral fellow and assistant professor at Johns Hopkins before going to his present position in May. Penney says he is a "hobbyist carpenter, gun collector and outdoorsman."

Bibliography

BIRD NAVIGATION. G. V. T. Matthews. Cambridge University Press, 1955.

CURRENT PROBLEMS IN BIRD ORIENTATION. Klaus Schmidt-Koenig in *Advances in the Study of Behavior: Vol. I*, edited by Daniel S. Lehrman, Robert A. Hinde and Evelyn Shaw. Academic Press, 1965.

LONG-DISTANCE ORIENTATION. G. Kramer in *Biology and Comparative Physiology of Birds: Vol. II*, edited by A. J. Marshall. Academic Press, 1961.

SCIENTIFIC AMERICAN   November 1966, Vol. 215, No. 5, pp. 78-90   OFFPRINT **1055**

THE THREE-DIMENSIONAL STRUCTURE OF AN ENZYME MOLECULE

by David C. Phillips

The arrangement of atoms in an enzyme molecule has been worked out for the first time. The enzyme is lysozyme, which breaks open cells of bacteria. The study has also shown how lysozyme performs its task.

One day in 1922 Alexander Fleming was suffering from a cold. This is not unusual in London, but Fleming was a most unusual man and he took advantage of the cold in a characteristic way. He allowed a few drops of his nasal mucus to fall on a culture of bacteria he was working with and then put the plate to one side to see what would happen. Imagine his excitement when he discovered some time later that the bacteria near the mucus had dissolved away. For a while he thought his ambition of finding a universal antibiotic had been realized. In a burst of activity he quickly established that the antibacterial action of the mucus was due to the presence in it of an enzyme; he called this substance lysozyme because of its capacity to lyse, or dissolve, the bacterial cells. Lysozyme was soon discovered in many tissues and secretions of the human body, in plants and most plentifully of all in the white of egg. Unfortunately Fleming found that it is not effective against the most harmful bacteria. He had to wait seven years before a strangely similar experiment revealed the existence of a genuinely effective antibiotic: penicillin.

Nevertheless, Fleming's lysozyme has proved a more valuable discovery than he can have expected when its properties were first established. With it, for example, bacterial anatomists have been able to study many details of bacterial structure [see "Fleming's Lysozyme," by Robert F. Acker and S. E. Hartsell; SCIENTIFIC AMERICAN, June, 1960]. It has now turned out that lysozyme is the first enzyme whose three-dimensional structure has been

determined and whose properties are understood in atomic detail. Among these properties is the way in which the enzyme combines with the substance on which it acts—a complex sugar in the wall of the bacterial cell.

Like all enzymes, lysozyme is a protein. Its chemical makeup has been established by Pierre Jollès and his colleagues at the University of Paris and by Robert E. Canfield of the Columbia University College of Physicians and Surgeons. They have found that each molecule of lysozyme obtained from egg white consists of a single polypeptide chain of 129 amino acid subunits of 20 different kinds. A peptide bond is formed when two amino acids are joined following the removal of a molecule of water. It is customary to call the portion of the amino acid in-

corporated into a polypeptide chain a residue, and each residue has its own characteristic side chain. The 129-residue lysozyme molecule is cross-linked in four places by disulfide bridges formed by the combination of sulfur-containing side chains in different parts of the molecule [see illustration on opposite page].

The properties of the molecule cannot be understood from its chemical constitution alone; they depend most critically on what parts of the molecule are brought close together in the folded three-dimensional structure. Some form of microscope is needed to examine the structure of the molecule. Fortunately one is effectively provided by the techniques of X-ray crystal-structure analysis pioneered by Sir Lawrence Bragg and his father Sir William Bragg.

ALA	ALANINE	GLY	GLYCINE	PRO	PROLINE
ARG	ARGININE	HIS	HISTIDINE	SER	SERINE
ASN	ASPARAGINE	ILEU	ISOLEUCINE	THR	THREONINE
ASP	ASPARTIC ACID	LEU	LEUCINE	TRY	TRYPTOPHAN
CYS	CYSTEINE	LYS	LYSINE	TYR	TYROSINE
GLN	GLUTAMINE	MET	METHIONINE	VAL	VALINE
GLU	GLUTAMIC ACID	PHE	PHENYLALANINE		

TWO-DIMENSIONAL MODEL of the lysozyme molecule is shown on the opposite page. Lysozyme is a protein containing 129 amino acid subunits, commonly called residues (*see key to abbreviations above*). These residues form a polypeptide chain that is cross-linked at four places by disulfide (−S−S−) bonds. The amino acid sequence of lysozyme was determined independently by Pierre Jollès and his co-workers at the University of Paris and by Robert E. Canfield of the Columbia University College of Physicians and Surgeons. The three-dimensional structure of the lysozyme molecule has now been established with the help of X-ray crystallography by the author and his colleagues at the Royal Institution in London. A painting of the molecule's three-dimensional structure is on pages 2268 and 2269. The function of lysozyme is to split a particular long-chain molecule, a complex sugar, found in the outer membrane of many living cells. Molecules acted upon by enzymes are known as substrates. The substrate of lysozyme fits into a cleft, or pocket, formed by the three-dimensional structure of the lysozyme molecule. In the two-dimensional model on the opposite page the amino acid residues that line the pocket are shown in dark green.

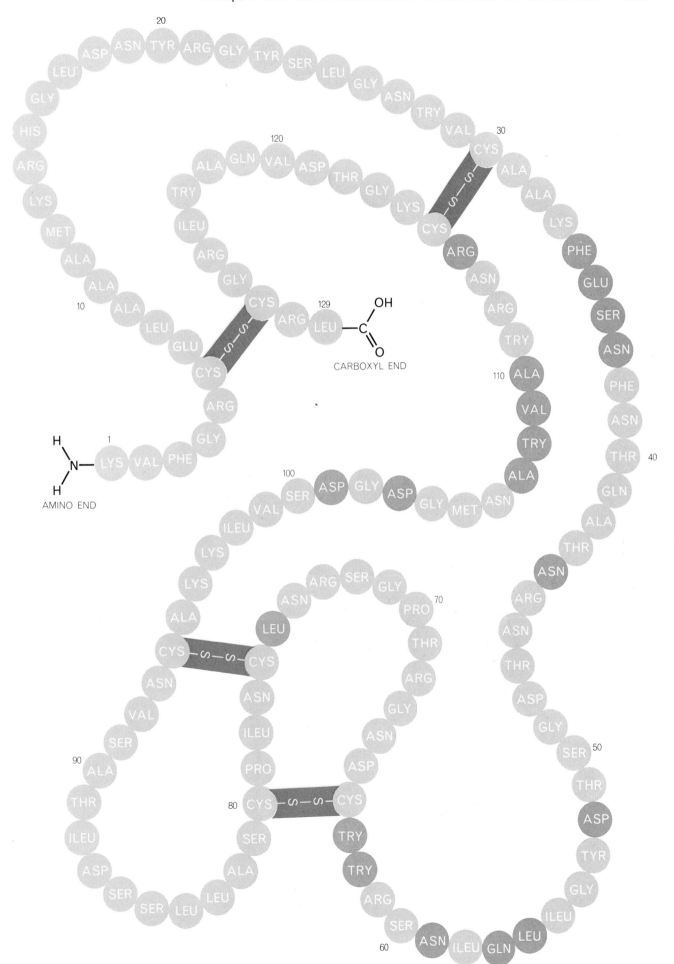

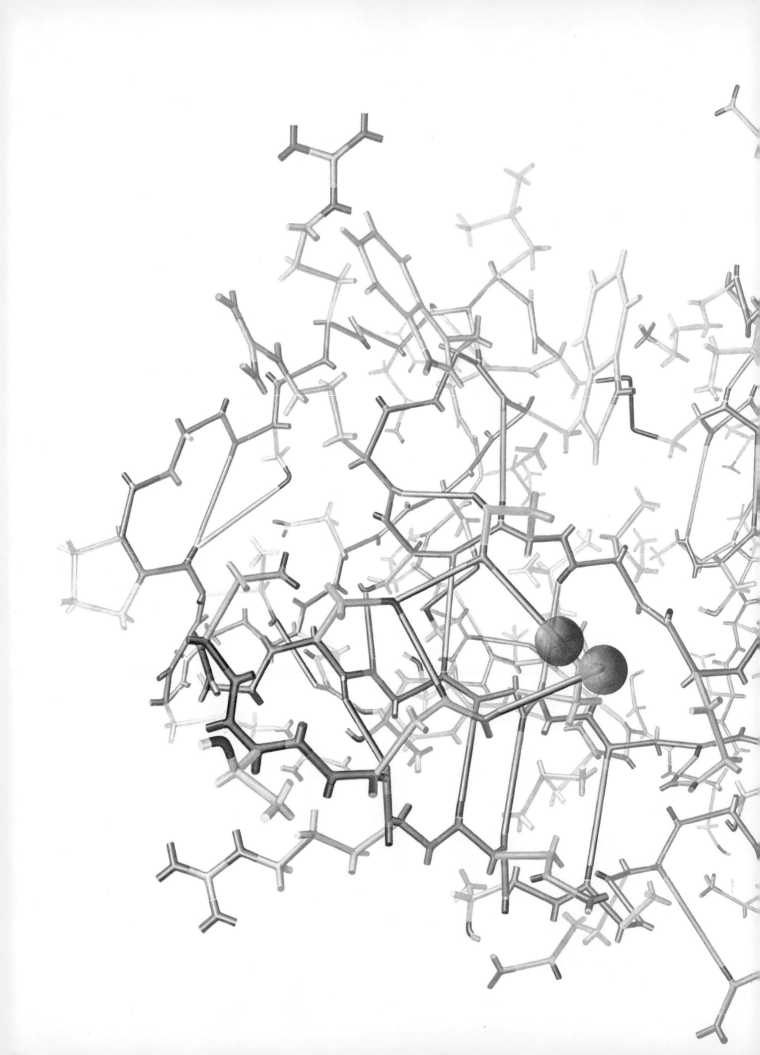

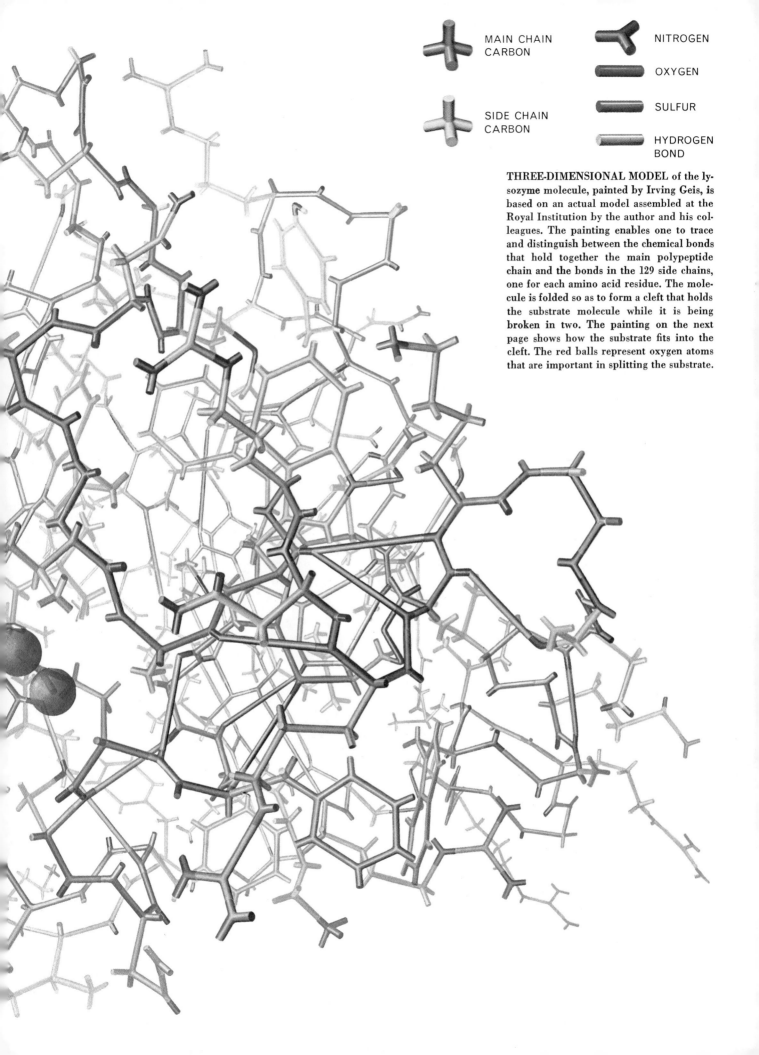

MAIN CHAIN CARBON

SIDE CHAIN CARBON

NITROGEN

OXYGEN

SULFUR

HYDROGEN BOND

THREE-DIMENSIONAL MODEL of the lysozyme molecule, painted by Irving Geis, is based on an actual model assembled at the Royal Institution by the author and his colleagues. The painting enables one to trace and distinguish between the chemical bonds that hold together the main polypeptide chain and the bonds in the 129 side chains, one for each amino acid residue. The molecule is folded so as to form a cleft that holds the substrate molecule while it is being broken in two. The painting on the next page shows how the substrate fits into the cleft. The red balls represent oxygen atoms that are important in splitting the substrate.

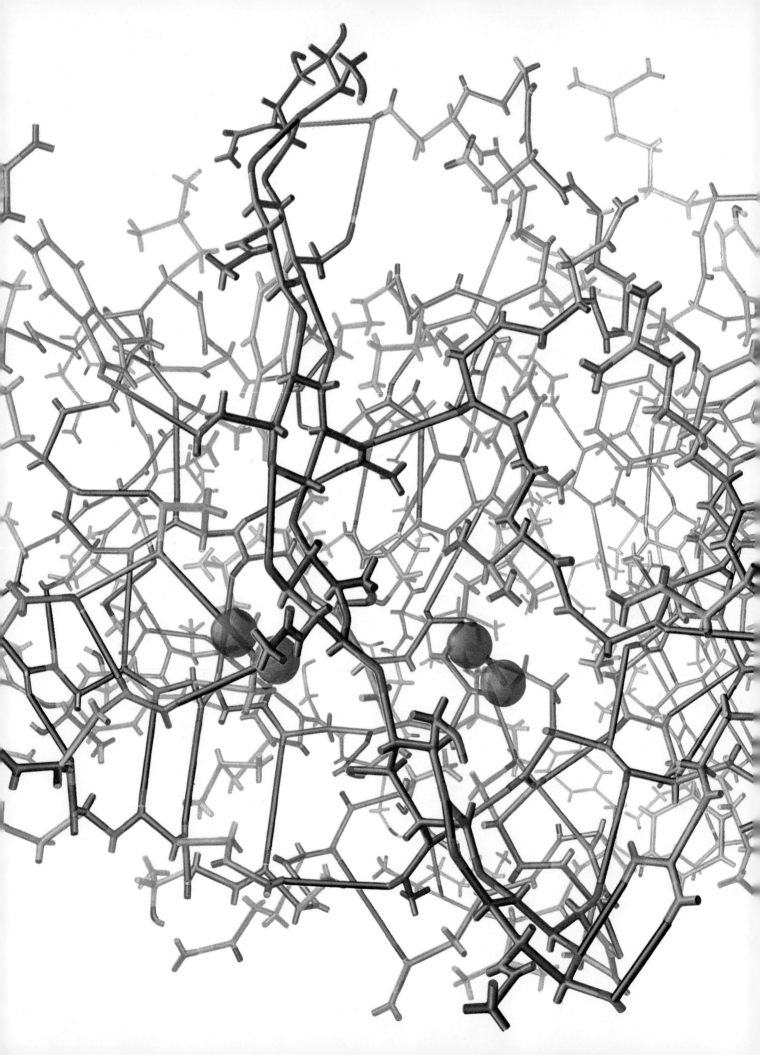

The difficulties of examining molecules in atomic detail arise, of course, from the fact that molecules are very small. Within a molecule each atom is usually separated from its neighbor by about 1.5 angstrom units (1.5×10^{-8} centimeter). The lysozyme molecule, which contains some 1,950 atoms, is about 40 angstroms in its largest dimension. The first problem is to find a microscope in which the atoms can be resolved from one another, or seen separately.

The resolving power of a microscope depends fundamentally on the wavelength of the radiation it employs. In general no two objects can be seen separately if they are closer together than about half this wavelength. The shortest wavelength transmitted by optical microscopes (those working in the ultraviolet end of the spectrum) is about 2,000 times longer than the distance between atoms. In order to "see" atoms one must use radiation with a much shorter wavelength: X rays, which have a wavelength closely comparable to interatomic distances. The employment of X rays, however, creates other difficulties: no satisfactory way has yet been found to make lenses or mirrors that will focus them into an image. The problem, then, is the apparently impossible one of designing an X-ray microscope without lenses or mirrors.

Consideration of the diffraction theory of microscope optics, as developed by Ernst Abbe in the latter part of the 19th century, shows that the problem can be solved. Abbe taught us that the formation of an image in the microscope can be regarded as a two-stage process. First, the object under examination scatters the light or other radiation falling on it in all directions, forming a diffraction pattern. This pattern arises because the light waves scattered from different parts of the object combine so as to produce a wave of large or small amplitude in any direction

according to whether the waves are in or out of phase—in or out of step—with one another. (This effect is seen most easily in light waves scattered by a regularly repeating structure, such as a diffraction grating made of lines scribed at regular intervals on a glass plate.) In the second stage of image formation, according to Abbe, the objective lens of the microscope collects the diffracted waves and recombines them to form an image of the object. Most important, the nature of the image depends critically on how much of the diffraction pattern is used in its formation.

X-Ray Structure Analysis

In essence X-ray structure analysis makes use of a microscope in which the two stages of image formation have been separated. Since the X rays cannot be focused to form an image directly, the diffraction pattern is recorded and the image is obtained from it by calculation. Historically the method was not developed on the basis of this reasoning, but this way of regarding it (which was first suggested by Lawrence Bragg) brings out its essential features and also introduces the main difficulty of applying it. In recording the intensities of the diffracted waves, instead of focusing them to form an image, some crucial information is lost, namely the phase relations among the various diffracted waves. Without this information the image cannot be formed, and some means of recovering it has to be found. This is the well-known phase problem of X-ray crystallography. It is on the solution of the problem that the utility of the method depends.

The term "X-ray crystallography" reminds us that in practice the method was developed (and is still applied) in the study of single crystals. Crystals suitable for study may contain some

10^{15} identical molecules in a regular array; in effect the molecules in such a crystal diffract the X radiation as though they were a single giant molecule. The crystal acts as a three-dimensional diffraction grating, so that the waves scattered by them are confined to a number of discrete directions. In order to obtain a three-dimensional image of the structure the intensity of the X rays scattered in these different directions must be measured, the phase problem must be solved somehow and the measurements must be combined by a computer.

The recent successes of this method in the study of protein structures have depended a great deal on the development of electronic computers capable of performing the calculations. They are due most of all, however, to the discovery in 1953, by M. F. Perutz of the Medical Research Council Laboratory of Molecular Biology in Cambridge, that the method of "isomorphous replacement" can be used to solve the phase problem in the study of protein crystals. The method depends on the preparation and study of a series of protein crystals into which additional heavy atoms, such as atoms of uranium, have been introduced without otherwise affecting the crystal structure. The first successes of this method were in the study of sperm-whale myoglobin by John C. Kendrew of the Medical Research Council Laboratory and in Perutz' own study of horse hemoglobin. For their work the two men received the Nobel prize for chemistry in 1962 [see "The Three-dimensional Structure of a Protein Molecule," by John C. Kendrew, SCIENTIFIC AMERICAN Offprint 121, and "The Hemoglobin Molecule," by M. F. Perutz, SCIENTIFIC AMERICAN Offprint 196].

Because the X rays are scattered by the electrons within the molecules, the image calculated from the diffraction pattern reveals the distribution of electrons within the crystal. The electron density is usually calculated at a regular array of points, and the image is made visible by drawing contour lines through points of equal electron density. If these contour maps are drawn on clear plastic sheets, one can obtain a three-dimensional image by assembling the maps one above the other in a stack. The amount of detail that can be seen in such an image depends on the resolving power of the effective microscope, that is, on its "aperture," or the extent of the diffraction pattern that has been included in the formation of the image. If the waves diffracted through sufficiently high angles are included

MODEL OF SUBSTRATE shows how it fits into the cleft in the lysozyme molecule. All the carbon atoms in the substrate are shown in purple. The portion of the substrate in intimate contact with the underlying enzyme is a polysaccharide chain consisting of six ringlike structures, each a residue of an amino-sugar molecule. The substrate in the model is made up of six identical residues of the amino sugar called N-acetylglucosamine (NAG). In the actual substrate every other residue is an amino sugar known as N-acetylmuramic acid (NAM). The illustration is based on X-ray studies of the way the enzyme is bound to a trisaccharide made of three NAG units, which fills the top of the cleft; the arrangement of NAG units in the bottom of the cleft was worked out with the aid of three-dimensional models. The substrate is held to the enzyme by a complex network of hydrogen bonds. In this style of model-making each straight section of chain represents a bond between atoms. The atoms themselves lie at the intersections and elbows of the structure. Except for the four red balls representing oxygen atoms that are active in splitting the polysaccharide substrate, no attempt is made to represent the electron shells of atoms because they would merge into a solid mass.

(corresponding to a large aperture), the atoms appear as individual peaks in the image map. At lower resolution groups of unresolved atoms appear with characteristic shapes by which they can be recognized.

The three-dimensional structure of lysozyme crystallized from the white of hen's egg has been determined in atomic detail with the X-ray method by our group at the Royal Institution in Lon-

don. This is the laboratory in which Humphry Davy and Michael Faraday made their fundamental discoveries during the 19th century, and in which the X-ray method of structure analysis was developed between the two world wars by the brilliant group of workers led by William Bragg, including J. D. Bernal, Kathleen Lonsdale, W. T. Astbury, J. M. Robertson and many others. Our work on lysozyme was begun in 1960

when Roberto J. Poljak, a visiting worker from Argentina, demonstrated that suitable crystals containing heavy atoms could be prepared. Since then C. C. F. Blake, A. C. T. North, V. R. Sarma, Ruth Fenn, D. F. Koenig, Louise N. Johnson and G. A. Mair have played important roles in the work.

In 1962 a low-resolution image of the structure was obtained that revealed the general shape of the molecule and

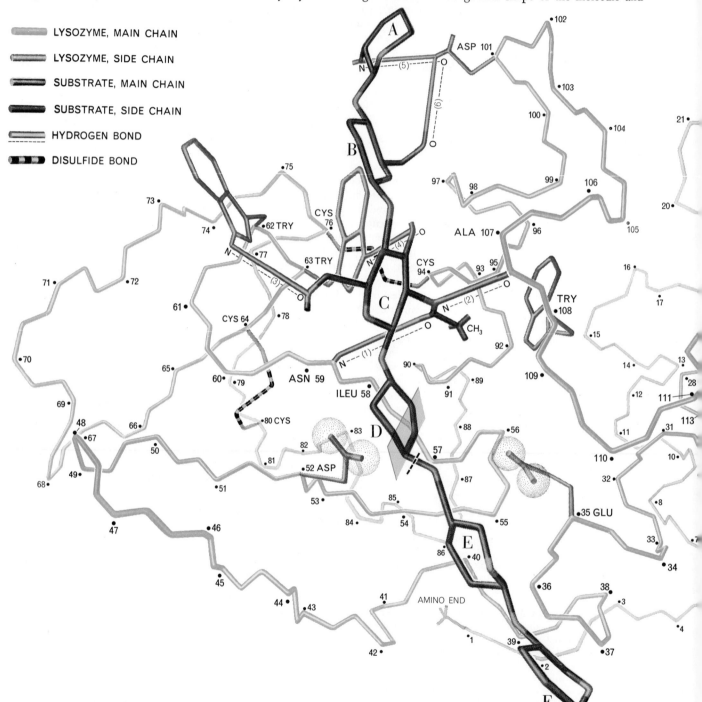

MAP OF LYSOZYME AND SUBSTRATE depicts in color the central chain of each molecule. Side chains have been omitted except for those that produce the four disulfide bonds clipping the lysozyme molecule together and those that supply the terminal connections for hydrogen bonds holding the substrate to the lysozyme. The top three rings of the substrate (A, B, C) are held to the underlying enzyme by six principal hydrogen bonds, which are identified by number to key with the description in the text. The lyso-

showed that the arrangement of the polypeptide chain is even more complex than it is in myoglobin. This low-resolution image was calculated from the amplitudes of about 400 diffraction maxima measured from native protein crystals and from crystals containing each of three different heavy atoms. In 1965, after the development of more efficient methods of measurement and computation, an image was calculated

on the basis of nearly 10,000 diffraction maxima, which resolved features separated by two angstroms. Apart from showing a few well-separated chloride ions, which are present because the lysozyme is crystallized from a solution containing sodium chloride, the two-angstrom image still does not show individual atoms as separate maxima in the electron-density map. The level of resolution is high enough, however, for many of the groups of atoms to be clearly recognizable.

The Lysozyme Molecule

The main polypeptide chain appears as a continuous ribbon of electron density running through the image with regularly spaced promontories on it that are characteristic of the carbonyl groups (CO) that mark each peptide bond. In some regions the chain is folded in ways that are familiar from theoretical studies of polypeptide configurations and from the structure analyses of myoglobin and fibrous proteins such as the keratin of hair. The amino acid residues in lysozyme have now been designated by number; the residues numbered 5 through 15, 24 through 34 and 88 through 96 form three lengths of "alpha helix," the conformation that was proposed by Linus Pauling and Robert B. Corey in 1951 and that was found by Kendrew and his colleagues to be the most common arrangement of the chain in myoglobin. The helixes in lysozyme, however, appear to be somewhat distorted from the "classical" form, in which four atoms (carbon, oxygen, nitrogen and hydrogen) of each peptide group lie in a plane that is parallel to the axis of the alpha helix. In the lysozyme molecule the peptide groups in the helical sections tend to be rotated slightly in such a way that their CO groups point outward from the helix axes and their imino groups (NH) inward.

The amount of rotation varies, being slight in the helix formed by residues 5 through 15 and considerable in the one formed by residues 24 through 34. The effect of the rotation is that each NH group does not point directly at the CO group four residues back along the chain but points instead between the CO groups of the residues three and four back. When the NH group points directly at the CO group four residues back, as it does in the classical alpha helix, it forms with the CO group a hydrogen bond (the weak chemical bond in which a hydrogen atom acts as a

bridge). In the lysozyme helixes the hydrogen bond is formed somewhere between two CO groups, giving rise to a structure intermediate between that of an alpha helix and that of a more symmetrical helix with a three-fold symmetry axis that was discussed by Lawrence Bragg, Kendrew and Perutz in 1950. There is a further short length of helix (residues 80 through 85) in which the hydrogen-bonding arrangement is quite close to that in the three-fold helix, and also an isolated turn (residues 119 through 122) of three-fold helix. Furthermore, the peptide at the far end of helix 5 through 15 is in the conformation of the three-fold helix, and the hydrogen bond from its NH group is made to the CO three residues back rather than four.

Partly because of these irregularities in the structure of lysozyme, the proportion of its polypeptide chain in the alpha-helix conformation is difficult to calculate in a meaningful way for comparison with the estimates obtained by other methods, but it is clearly less than half the proportion observed in myoglobin, in which helical regions make up about 75 percent of the chain. The lysozyme molecule does include, however, an example of another regular conformation predicted by Pauling and Corey. This is the "antiparallel pleated sheet," which is believed to be the basic structure of the fibrous protein silk and in which, as the name suggests, two lengths of polypeptide chain run parallel to each other in opposite directions. This structure again is stabilized by hydrogen bonds between the NH and CO groups of the main chain. Residues 41 through 45 and 50 through 54 in the lysozyme molecule form such a structure, with the connecting residues 46 through 49 folded into a hairpin bend between the two lengths of comparatively extended chain. The remainder of the polypeptide chain is folded in irregular ways that have no simple short description.

Even though the level of resolution achieved in our present image was not enough to resolve individual atoms, many of the side chains characteristic of the amino acid residues were readily identifiable from their general shape. The four disulfide bridges, for example, are marked by short rods of high electron density corresponding to the two relatively dense sulfur atoms within them. The six tryptophan residues also were easily recognized by the extended electron density produced by the large double-ring structures in their

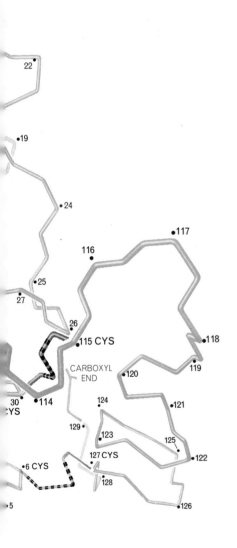

zyme molecule fulfills its function when it cleaves the substrate between the *D* and the *E* ring. Note the distortion of the *D* ring, which pushes four of its atoms into a plane.

FIRST 56 RESIDUES in lysozyme molecule contain a higher proportion of symmetrically organized regions than does all the rest of the molecule. Residues 5 through 15 and 24 through 34 (*right*) form two regions in which hydrogen bonds (*gray*) hold the residues in a helical configuration close to that of the "classical" alpha helix. Residues 41 through 45 and 50 through 54 (*left*) fold back against each other to form a "pleated sheet," also held together by hydrogen bonds. In addition the hydrogen bond between residues 1 and 40 ties the first 40 residues into a compact structure that may have been folded in this way before the molecule was fully synthesized (*see illustration at the bottom of these two pages*).

liquid. Such "polar" side chains are hydrophilic—attracted to water; they are found in aspartic acid and glutamic acid residues and in lysine, arginine and histidine residues, which have basic side groups. On the other hand, most of the markedly nonpolar and hydrophobic side chains (for example those found in leucine and isoleucine residues) are shielded from the surrounding liquid by more polar parts of the molecule. In fact, as was predicted by Sir Eric Rideal (who was at one time director of the Royal Institution) and Irving Langmuir, lysozyme, like myoglobin, is quite well described as an oil drop with a polar coat. Here it is important to note that the environment of each molecule in the crystalline state is not significantly different from its natural environment in the living cell. The crystals themselves include a large proportion (some 35 percent by weight) of mostly watery liquid of crystallization. The effect of the surrounding liquid on the protein conformation thus is likely to be much the same in the crystals as it is in solution.

It appears, then, that the observed conformation is preferred because in it the hydrophobic side chains are kept out of contact with the surrounding liquid whereas the polar side chains are generally exposed to it. In this way the system consisting of the protein and the solvent attains a minimum free energy, partly because of the large number of favorable interactions of like groups within the protein molecule and between it and the surrounding liquid, and partly because of the relatively high disorder of the water molecules that are in contact only with other polar groups of atoms.

Guided by these generalizations, many workers are now interested in the possibility of predicting the conforma-

side chains. Many of the other residues also were easily identifiable, but it was nevertheless most important for the rapid and reliable interpretation of the image that the results of the chemical analysis were already available. With their help more than 95 percent of the atoms in the molecule were readily identified and located within about .25 angstrom.

Further efforts at improving the accuracy with which the atoms have been located is in progress, but an almost complete description of the lysozyme molecule now exists [*see illustration on pages 2268 and 2269*]. By studying it

and results of further experiments we can begin to suggest answers to two important questions: How does a molecule such as this one attain its observed conformation? How does it function as an enzyme, or biological catalyst?

Inspection of the lysozyme molecule immediately suggests two generalizations about its conformation that agree well with those arrived at earlier in the study of myoglobin. It is obvious that certain residues with acidic and basic side chains that ionize, or dissociate, on contact with water are all on the surface of the molecule more or less readily accessible to the surrounding

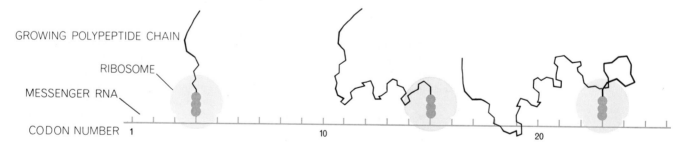

FOLDING OF PROTEIN MOLECULE may take place as the growing polypeptide chain is being synthesized by the intracellular particles called ribosomes. The genetic message specifying the amino acid sequence of each protein is coded in "messenger" ribonucleic acid (RNA). It is believed several ribosomes travel simultaneously along this long-chain molecule, reading the message as they go.

tion of a protein molecule from its chemical formula alone [see "Molecular Model-building by Computer," by Cyrus Levinthal; SCIENTIFIC AMERICAN Offprint 1043]. Exploring all possible conformations in the search for the one of the lowest free energy seems likely, however, to remain beyond the power of any imaginable computer. On a conservative estimate it would be necessary to consider some 10^{129} different conformations for the lysozyme molecule in any general search for the one with minimum free energy. Since this number is far greater than the number of particles in the observable universe, it is clear that simplifying assumptions will have to be made if calculations of this kind are to succeed.

The Folding of Lysozyme

For some time Peter Dunnill and I have been trying to develop a model of protein-folding that promises to make practicable calculations of the minimum energy conformation and that is, at the same time, qualitatively consistent with the observed structure of myoglobin and lysozyme. This model makes use of our present knowledge of the way in which proteins are synthesized in the living cell. For example, it is well known, from experiments by Howard M. Dintzis and by Christian B. Anfinsen and Robert Canfield, that protein molecules are synthesized from the terminal amino end of their polypeptide chain. The nature of the synthetic mechanism, which involves the intracellular particles called ribosomes working in collaboration with two forms of ribonucleic acid ("messenger" RNA and "transfer" RNA), is increasingly well understood in principle, although the detailed environment of the growing protein chain remains unknown. Nevertheless,

it seems a reasonable assumption that, as the synthesis proceeds, the amino end of the chain becomes separated by an increasing distance from the point of attachment to the ribosome, and that the folding of the protein chain to its native conformation begins at this end even before the synthesis is complete. According to our present ideas, parts of the polypeptide chain, particularly those near the terminal amino end, may fold into stable conformations that can still be recognized in the finished molecule and that act as "internal templates," or centers, around which the rest of the chain is folded [see illustration at bottom of these two pages]. It may therefore be useful to look for the stable conformations of parts of the polypeptide chain and to avoid studying all the possible conformations of the whole molecule.

Inspection of the lysozyme molecule provides qualitative support for these ideas [see top illustration on opposite page]. The first 40 residues from the terminal amino end form a compact structure (residues 1 and 40 are linked by a hydrogen bond) with a hydrophobic interior and a relatively hydrophilic surface that seems likely to have been folded in this way, or in a simply related way, before the molecule was fully synthesized. It may also be important to observe that this part of the molecule includes more alpha helix than the remainder does.

These first 40 residues include a mixture of hydrophobic and hydrophilic side chains, but the next 14 residues in the sequence are all hydrophilic; it is interesting, and possibly significant, that these are the residues in the antiparallel pleated sheet, which lies out of contact with the globular submolecule formed by the earlier residues. In the light of our model of protein fold-

ing the obvious speculation is that there is no incentive to fold these hydrophilic residues in contact with the first part of the chain until the hydrophobic residues 55 (isoleucine) and 56 (leucine) have to be shielded from contact with the surrounding liquid. It seems reasonable to suppose that at this stage residues 41 through 54 fold back on themselves, forming the pleated-sheet structure and burying the hydrophobic side chains in the initial hydrophobic pocket.

Similar considerations appear to govern the folding of the rest of the molecule. In brief, residues 57 through 86 are folded in contact with the pleated-sheet structure so that at this stage of the process—if indeed it follows this course—the folded chain forms a structure with two wings lying at an angle to each other. Residues 86 through 96 form a length of alpha helix, one side of which is predominantly hydrophobic, because of an appropriate alternation of polar and nonpolar residues in that part of the sequence. This helix lies in the gap between the two wings formed by the earlier residues, with its hydrophobic side buried within the molecule. The gap between the two wings is not completely filled by the helix, however; it is transformed into a deep cleft running up one side of the molecule. As we shall see, this cleft forms the active site of the enzyme. The remaining residues are folded around the globular unit formed by the terminal amino end of the polypeptide chain.

This model of protein-folding can be tested in a number of ways, for example by studying the conformation of the first 40 residues in isolation both di-

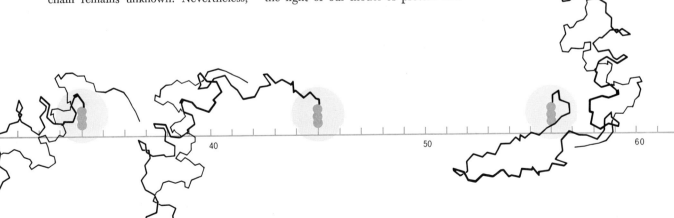

Presumably the messenger RNA for lysozyme contains 129 "codons," one for each amino acid. Amino acids are delivered to the site of synthesis by molecules of "transfer" RNA (*dark color*). The illustration shows how the lysozyme chain would lengthen as a ribosome travels along the messenger RNA molecule. Here, hypothetically, the polypeptide is shown folding directly into its final shape.

rectly (after removal of the rest of the molecule) and by computation. Ultimately, of course, the model will be regarded as satisfactory only if it helps us to predict how other protein molecules are folded from a knowledge of their chemical structure alone.

The Activity of Lysozyme

In order to understand how lysozyme brings about the dissolution of bacteria we must consider the structure of the bacterial cell wall in some detail. Through the pioneer and independent studies of Karl Meyer and E. B. Chain, followed up by M. R. J. Salton of the University of Manchester and many others, the structures of bacterial cell walls and the effect of lysozyme on them are now quite well known. The important part of the cell wall, as far as lysozyme is concerned, is made up of glucose-like amino-sugar molecules linked together into long polysaccharide chains, which are themselves cross-connected by short lengths of polypeptide chain. This part of each cell wall probably forms one enormous molecule—a "bag-shaped macromolecule," as W. Weidel and H. Pelzer have called it.

The amino-sugar molecules concerned in these polysaccharide structures are of two kinds; each contains an acetamido (—NH·CO·CH$_3$) side group, but one of them contains an additional major group, a lactyl side chain [see illustration below]. One of these amino sugars is known as N-acetylglucosamine (NAG) and the other as N-acetylmuramic acid (NAM). They occur alternately in the polysaccharide chains, being connected by bridges that include an oxygen atom (glycosidic linkages) between carbon atoms 1 and 4 of consecutive sugar rings; this is the same linkage that joins glucose residues in cellulose. The polypeptide chains that cross-connect these polysaccharides are attached to the NAM residues through the lactyl side chain attached to carbon atom 3 in each NAM ring.

Lysozyme has been shown to break the linkages in which carbon 1 in NAM is linked to carbon 4 in NAG but not the other linkages. It has also been shown to break down chitin, another common natural polysaccharide that is found in lobster shell and that contains only NAG.

Ever since the work of Svante Arrhenius of Sweden in the late 19th century enzymes have been thought to work by forming intermediate compounds with their substrates: the substances whose chemical reactions they catalyze. A proper theory of the enzyme-substrate complex, which underlies all present thinking about enzyme activity, was clearly propounded by Leonor Michaelis and Maude Menton in a remarkable paper published in 1913. The idea, in its simplest form, is that an enzyme molecule provides a site on its surface to which its substrate molecule can bind in a quite precise way. Reactive groups of atoms in the enzyme then promote the required chemical reaction in the substrate. Our immediate objective, therefore, was to find the structure of a reactive complex between lysozyme and its polysaccharide substrate, in the hope that we would then be able to recognize the active groups of atoms in the enzyme and understand how they function.

Our studies began with the observation by Martin Wenzel and his colleagues at the Free University of Berlin that the enzyme is prevented from functioning by the presence of NAG itself. This small molecule acts as a competitive inhibitor of the enzyme's activity and, since it is a part of the large substrate molecule normally acted on by the enzyme, it seems likely to do this by binding to the enzyme in the way that part of the substrate does. It prevents the enzyme from working by preventing the substrate from binding to the enzyme. Other simple amino-sugar molecules, including the trisaccharide made of three NAG units, behave in the same way. We therefore decided to study the binding of these sugar molecules to the lysozyme molecules in our crystals in the hope of learning something about the structure of the enzyme-substrate complex itself.

My colleague Louise Johnson soon found that crystals containing the sugar molecules bound to lysozyme can be prepared very simply by adding the sugar to the solution from which the lysozyme crystals have been grown and in which they are kept suspended. The small molecules diffuse into the protein crystals along the channels filled with water that run through the crystals. Fortunately the resulting change in the crystal structure can be studied quite simply. A useful image of the electron-density changes can be calculated from

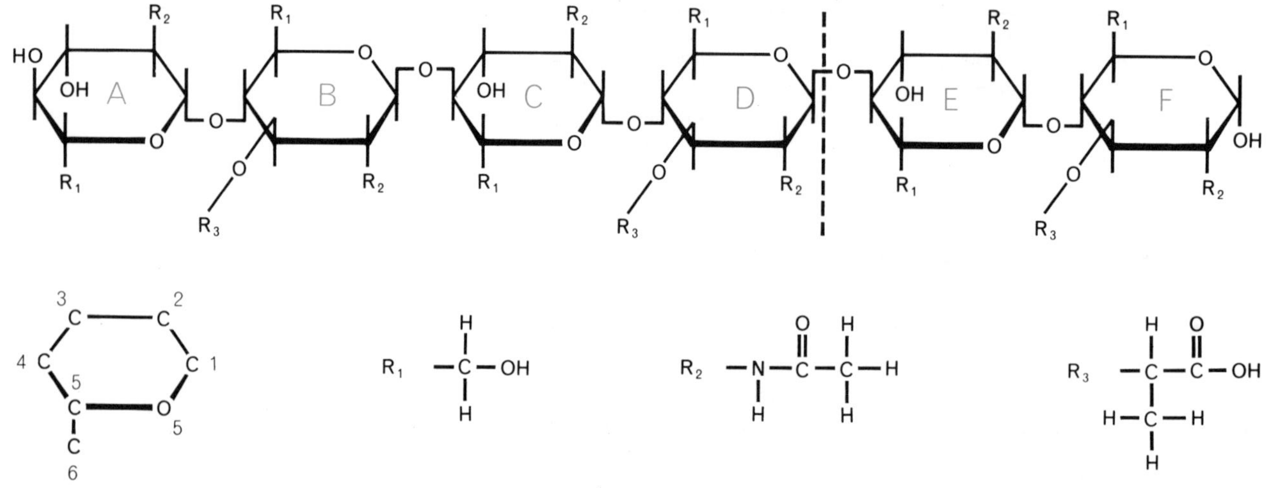

POLYSACCHARIDE MOLECULE found in the walls of certain bacterial cells is the substrate broken by the lysozyme molecule. The polysaccharide consists of alternating residues of two kinds of amino sugar: N-acetylglucosamine (NAG) and N-acetylmuramic acid (NAM). In the length of polysaccharide chain shown here A, C and E are NAG residues; B, D, and F are NAM residues. The inset at left shows the numbering scheme for identifying the principal atoms in each sugar ring. Six rings of the polysaccharide fit into the cleft of the lysozyme molecule, which effects a cleavage between D and E (see illustration on pages 2272 and 2273).

measurements of the changes in amplitude of the diffracted waves, on the assumption that their phase relations have not changed from those determined for the pure protein crystals. The image shows the difference in electron density between crystals that contain the added sugar molecules and those that do not.

In this way the binding to lysozyme of eight different amino sugars was studied at low resolution (that is, through the measurement of changes in the amplitude of 400 diffracted waves). The results showed that the sugars bind to lysozyme at a number of different places in the cleft of the enzyme. The investigation was hurried on to higher resolution in an attempt to discover the exact nature of the binding. Happily these studies at two-angstrom resolution (which required the measurement of 10,000 diffracted waves) have now shown in detail how the trisaccharide made of three NAG units is bound to the enzyme.

The trisaccharide fills the top half of the cleft and is bound to the enzyme by a number of interactions, which can be followed with the help of the illustration on pages 2272 and 2273. In this illustration six hydrogen bonds, to be described presently, are identified by number. The most critical of these interactions appear to involve the acetamido group of sugar residue C [third from top], whose carbon atom 1 is not linked to another sugar residue. There are hydrogen bonds from the CO group of this side chain to the main-chain NH group of amino acid residue 59 in the enzyme molecule [bond No. 1] and from its NH group to the main-chain CO group of residue 107 (alanine) in the enzyme molecule [bond No. 2]. Its terminal CH_3 group makes contact with the side chain of residue 108 (tryptophan). Hydrogen bonds [No. 3 and No. 4] are also formed between two oxygen atoms adjacent to carbon atoms 6 and 3 of sugar residue C and the side chains of residues 62 and 63 (both tryptophan) respectively.* Another hydrogen bond [No. 5] is formed between the acetamido side chain of sugar residue A and residue 101 (aspartic acid) in the enzyme molecule. From residue 101 there is a hydrogen bond [No. 6] to the oxygen adjacent to carbon atom 6 of sugar residue B. These polar interactions are supplemented by a large number of nonpolar interactions that are more difficult to summarize briefly. Among the more important nonpolar interactions, however, are those between sugar residue B and the ring system of residue

62; these deserve special mention because they are affected by a small change in the conformation of the enzyme molecule that occurs when the trisaccharide is bound to it. The electron-density map showing the change in electron density when tri-NAG is bound in the protein crystal reveals clearly that parts of the enzyme molecule have moved with respect to one another. These changes in conformation are largely restricted to the part of the enzyme structure to the left of the cleft, which appears to tilt more or less as a whole in such a way as to close the cleft slightly. As a result the side chain of residue 62 moves about .75 angstrom toward the position of sugar residue B. Such changes in enzyme conformation have been discussed for some time, notably by Daniel E. Koshland, Jr., of the University of California at Berkeley, whose "induced fit" theory of the enzyme-substrate interaction is supported in some degree by this observation in lysozyme.

The Enzyme-Substrate Complex

At this stage in the investigation excitement grew high. Could we tell how the enzyme works? I believe we can. Unfortunately, however, we cannot see this dynamic process in our X-ray images. We have to work out what must happen from our static pictures. First of all it is clear that the complex formed by tri-NAG and the enzyme is not the enzyme-substrate complex involved in catalysis because it is stable. At low concentrations tri-NAG is known to behave as an inhibitor rather than as a substrate that is broken down; clearly we have been looking at the way in which it binds as an inhibitor. It is noticeable, however, that tri-NAG fills only half of the cleft. The possibility emerges that more sugar residues, filling the remainder of the cleft, are required for the formation of a reactive enzyme-substrate complex. The assumption here is that the observed binding of tri-NAG as an inhibitor involves interactions with the enzyme molecule that also play a part in the formation of the functioning enzyme-substrate complex.

Accordingly we have built a model that shows that another three sugar residues can be added to the tri-NAG in such a way that there are satisfactory interactions of the atoms in the proposed substrate and the enzyme. There is only one difficulty: carbon atom 6 and its adjacent oxygen atom in sugar residue D make uncomfortably close contacts

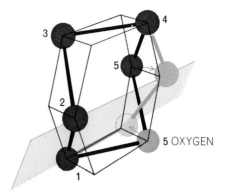

"CHAIR" CONFIGURATION (gray) is that normally assumed by the rings of amino sugar in the polysaccharide substrate. When bound against the lysozyme, however, the D ring is distorted (color) so that carbon atoms 1, 2 and 5 and oxygen atom 5 lie in a plane. The distortion evidently assists in breaking the substrate below the D ring.

with atoms in the enzyme molecule, unless this sugar residue is distorted a little out of its most stable "chair" conformation into a conformation in which carbon atoms 1, 2 and 5 and oxygen atom 5 all lie in a plane [see illustration above]. Otherwise satisfactory interactions immediately suggest themselves, and the model falls into place.

At this point it seemed reasonable to assume that the model shows the structure of the functioning complex between the enzyme and a hexasaccharide. The next problem was to decide which of the five glycosidic linkages would be broken under the influence of the enzyme. Fortunately evidence was at hand to suggest the answer. As we have seen, the cell-wall polysaccharide includes alternate sugar residues of two kinds, NAG and NAM, and the bond broken is between NAM and NAG. It was therefore important to decide which of the six sugar residues in our model could be NAM, which is the same as NAG except for the lactyl side chain appended to carbon atom 3. The answer was clear-cut. Sugar residue C cannot be NAM because there is no room for this additional group of atoms. Therefore the bond broken must be between sugar residues B and C or D and E. We already knew that the glycosidic linkage between residues B and C is stable when tri-NAG is bound. The conclusion was inescapable: the linkage that must be broken is the one between sugar residues D and E.

Now it was possible to search for the origin of the catalytic activity in the neighborhood of this linkage. Our task was made easier by the fact that John A.

Rupley of the University of Arizona had shown that the chemical bond broken under the influence of lysozyme is the one between carbon atom 1 and oxygen in the glycosidic link rather than the link between oxygen and carbon atom 4. The most reactive-looking group of atoms in the vicinity of this bond are the side chains of residue 52 (aspartic acid) and residue 35 (glutamic acid).

One of the oxygen atoms of residue 52 is about three angstroms from carbon atom 1 of sugar residue D as well as from the ring oxygen atom 5 of that residue. Residue 35, on the other hand, is about three angstroms from the oxygen in the glycosidic linkage. Furthermore, these two amino acid residues have markedly different environments. Residue 52 has a number of polar neighbors and appears to be involved in a network of hydrogen bonds linking it with residues 46 and 59 (both asparagine) and, through them, with residue 50 (serine). In this environment residue 52 seems likely to give up a terminal hydrogen atom and thus be negatively charged under most conditions, even when it is in a markedly acid solution, whereas residue 35, situated in a nonpolar environment, is likely to retain its terminal hydrogen atom.

A little reflection suggests that the concerted influence of these two amino

acid residues, together with a contribution from the distortion to sugar residue D that has already been mentioned, is enough to explain the catalytic activity of lysozyme. The events leading to the rupture of a bacterial cell wall probably take the following course [see illustration on this page].

First, a lysozyme molecule attaches itself to the bacterial cell wall by interacting with six exposed amino-sugar residues. In the process sugar residue D is somewhat distorted from its usual conformation.

Second, residue 35 transfers its terminal hydrogen atom in the form of a hydrogen ion to the glycosidic oxygen, thus bringing about cleavage of the bond between that oxygen and carbon atom 1 of sugar residue D. This creates a positively charged carbonium ion (C^+) where the oxygen has been severed from carbon atom 1.

Third, this carbonium ion is stabilized by its interaction with the negatively charged aspartic acid side chain of residue 52 until it can combine with a hydroxyl ion (OH^-) that happens to diffuse into position from the surrounding water, thereby completing the reaction. The lysozyme molecule then falls away, leaving behind a punctured bacterial cell wall.

It is not clear from this description that the distortion of sugar residue D plays any part in the reaction, but in fact it probably does so for a very interesting reason. R. H. Lemieux and G. Huber of the National Research Council of Canada showed in 1955 that when a sugar molecule such as NAG incorporates a carbonium ion at the carbon-1 position, it tends to take up the same conformation that is forced on ring D by its interaction with the enzyme molecule. This seems to be an example, therefore, of activation of the substrate by distortion, which has long been a favorite idea of enzymologists. The binding of the substrate to the enzyme itself favors the formation of the carbonium ion in ring D that seems to play an important part in the reaction.

It will be clear from this account that although lysozyme has not been seen in action, we have succeeded in building up a detailed picture of how it may work. There is already a great deal of chemical evidence in agreement with this picture, and as the result of all the work now in progress we can be sure that the activity of Fleming's lysozyme will soon be fully understood. Best of all, it is clear that methods now exist for uncovering the secrets of enzyme action.

CARBON
OXYGEN
HYDROGEN

A
B
C
D
E

R₁ R₂ R₁ R₁ R₂ R₁ R₁ R₂

ASP 52
LYSOZYME, MAIN CHAIN
O^- O^-
C^+
OH⁻
H^+
O^-
H^+
O^-
WATER MOLECULE
GLU 35
LYSOZYME, MAIN CHAIN

SPLITTING OF SUBSTRATE BY LYSOZYME is believed to involve the proximity and activity of two side chains, residue 35 (glutamic acid) and residue 52 (aspartic acid). It is proposed that a hydrogen ion (H^+) becomes detached from the OH group of residue 35 and attaches itself to the oxygen atom that joins rings D and E, thus breaking the bond between the two rings. This leaves carbon atom 1 of the D ring with a positive charge, in which form it is known as a carbonium ion. It is stabilized in this condition by the negatively charged side chain of residue 52. The surrounding water supplies an OH^- ion to combine with the carbonium ion and an H^+ ion to replace the one lost by residue 35. The two parts of the substrate then fall away, leaving the enzyme free to cleave another polysaccharide chain.

The Author

DAVID C. PHILLIPS is professor of molecular biophysics at the University of Oxford. After taking bachelor's and doctor's degrees at the University of Wales, he worked at the National Research Laboratories in Ottawa for four years, investigating with X rays the structure of small organic molecules. From 1956 until this year he was at the Royal Institution in London, working with Sir Lawrence Bragg, J. C. Kendrew, M. F. Perutz and others on X-ray analysis of protein structures. Phillips writes that his nonprofessional interests include "reading (mainly history), growing vegetables and talking with children."

Bibliography

Biosynthesis of Macromolecules. Vernon M. Ingram. W. A. Benjamin, Inc., 1965.

Introduction to Molecular Biology. G. H. Haggis, D. Michie, A. R. Muir, K. B. Roberts and P. M. B. Walker. John Wiley & Sons, Inc., 1964.

The Molecular Biology of the Gene. J. D. Watson. W. A. Benjamin, Inc., 1965.

Protein and Nucleic Acids: Structure and Function. M. F. Perutz. American Elsevier Publishing Company, Inc., 1962.

Structure of Hen Egg-White Lysozyme: A Three-Dimensional Fourier Synthesis at 2 A. Resolution. C. C. F. Blake, D. F. Koenig, G. A. Mair, A. C. T. North, D. C. Phillips and V. R. Sarma in Nature, Vol. 206, No. 4986, pages 757–763; May 22, 1965.

SCIENTIFIC
AMERICAN November 1966, Vol. 215, No. 5, pp. 94-104   OFFPRINT 1056

THE AGING GREAT LAKES

by Charles F. Powers and Andrew Robertson

Like all other lakes, they are subject to physical and biological
processes that will eventually result in their extinction. These
processes, however, are being accelerated by human activities.

The five Great Lakes in the heart-land of North America constitute the greatest reservoir of fresh water on the surface of the earth. Lake Superior, with an area of 31,820 square miles (nearly half the area of New England), is the world's largest fresh-water lake; Lake Huron ranks fourth in the world, Lake Michigan fifth, Lake Erie 11th and Lake Ontario 13th. Together the five lakes cover 95,200 square miles and contain 5,457 cubic miles of water. They provide a continuous waterway into the heart of the continent that reaches nearly 2,000 miles from the mouth of the St. Lawrence River to Duluth at the western tip of Lake Superior.

The Great Lakes are obviously an inestimable natural resource for the development of the U.S. and Canada. They supply vast amounts of water for various needs: drinking, industrial uses and so forth. They serve as a transportation system linking many large inland cities to one another and to the sea. Their falls and rapids generate huge supplies of hydroelectric power. Their fish life is a large potential source of food. And finally, they serve as an immense playground for human relaxation, through boating, swimming and fishing.

The settlements and industries that have grown up around this attractive resource are already very substantial. Although less than 3.5 percent of the total U.S. land area lies in the Great Lakes basin, it is the home of more than 13.5 percent of the nation's population (and about a third of Canada's population). In the southern part of the basin, from Milwaukee on the west to Quebec on the east, is a string of cities that is approaching the nature and dimensions of a megalopolis. Many economists believe the Great Lakes region is likely to become the fastest-growing area in the U.S. Their forecast is based mainly on the fact that whereas most other regions of the country are experiencing increasing shortages of water, the Great Lakes area enjoys a seemingly inexhaustible supply.

Unfortunately the forecast is now troubled by a large question mark. The viability of this great water resource is by no means assured. Even under natural conditions the life of an inland lake is limited. It is subject to aging processes that in the course of time foul its waters and eventually exhaust them. The Great Lakes are comparatively young, and their natural aging would not be a cause for present concern, since the natural processes proceed at the slow pace of the geological time scale. The aging of these lakes is now being accelerated tremendously, however, by man's activities. Basically the destructive agent is pollution. The ill effect of pollution is not limited to the circumstance that it renders the waters unclean. Pollution also hastens the degeneration and eventual extinction of the lakes as bodies of water.

These conclusions are based on recent extensive studies of the Great Lakes by a number of universities and governmental agencies in the U.S. and Canada. Employing various research techniques, including those of oceanography, the studies have produced new basic knowledge about the natural history and ecology of the Great Lakes and recent major changes that have occurred in them.

The natural aging of a lake results from a process called "eutrophication," which means biological enrichment of its water. A newly formed lake begins as a body of cold, clear, nearly sterile water. Gradually streams from its drainage basin bring in nutrient substances, such as phosphorus and nitrogen, and the lake water's increasing fertility gives rise to an accumulating growth of aquatic organisms, both plant and animal. As the living matter increases and organic deposits pile up on the lake bottom, the lake becomes smaller and shallower, its waters become warmer, plants take root in the bottom and gradually take over more and more of the space, and their remains accelerate the filling of the basin. Eventually the lake becomes a marsh, is overrun by vegetation from the surrounding area and thus disappears.

As a lake ages, its animal and plant life changes. Its fish life shifts from forms that prefer cold water to those that do better in a warmer, shallower environment; for example, trout and whitefish give way to bass, sunfish and perch. These in turn are succeeded by frogs, mud minnows and other animals that thrive in a marshy environment.

The natural processes are so slow that

PROCESS OF EXTINCTION that is the destiny of all lakes is seen in action in the aerial photograph on the opposite page. Cattaraugus Creek, a stream that forms the boundary between Erie and Chautauqua counties in New York, enters Lake Erie at this point southwest of Buffalo. (North is to the right.) The stream is not polluted but it carries silt and nutrients. The silt acts to fill the lake; the nutrients feed various forms of plant life that encroach on the shallows and add to the accumulation of bottom deposits. The aging process, which eventually converts every lake into dry land, is greatly accelerated when, as in the case of America's Great Lakes, human and industrial wastes are added to the normal runoff load.

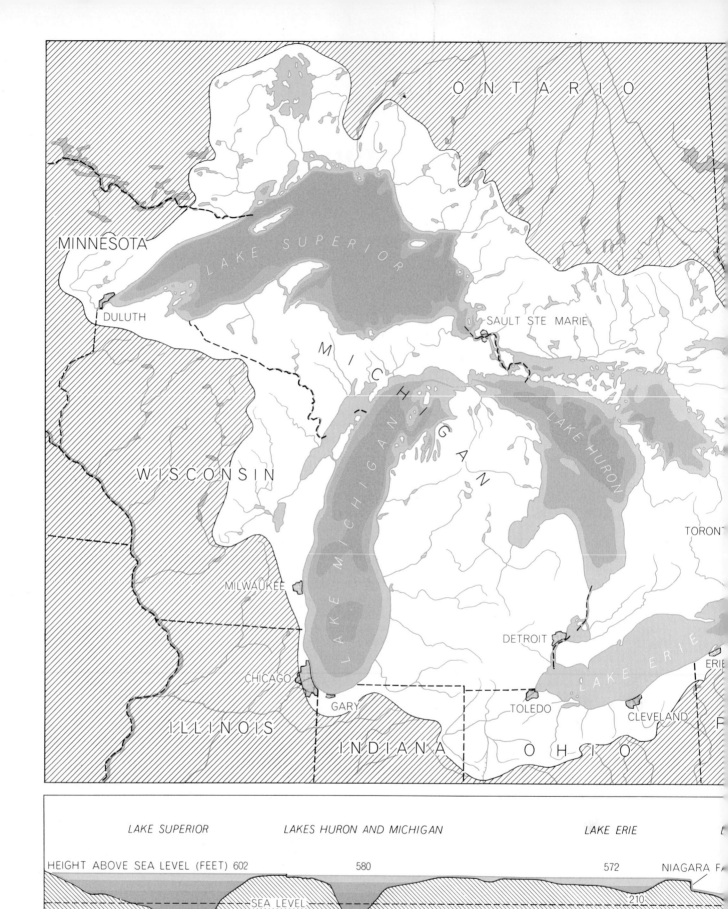

AMERICAN GREAT LAKES comprise the world's largest freshwater reservoir. Their drainage area (*white*) is not big enough to counteract the loss of lake water through discharge and evaporation but the lakes' level is kept stable by the inflow of groundwater and capture of the rain and snow that fall on 95,200 square miles of water surface. Superior (*left*) is the deepest of the five and Erie the shallowest (*vertical scale of profile is exaggerated*). Erosion will have destroyed the escarpment forming Niagara Falls 25,000

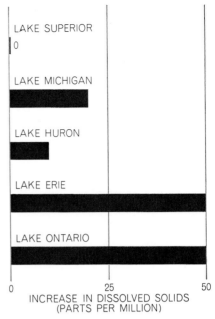

INDEX OF POLLUTION is provided by the extent to which the lakes' content of dissolved solids has increased in the past 50 years. Lake Superior shows no increase, and the modest increase for Lake Huron is attributable to its receipt of Lake Michigan water, which is more heavily polluted. Lake Erie's major cities and its small volume of water account for its rising solids content. Lake Ontario's pollution is a combination of what is received from Lake Erie and what the cities along its shores contribute.

the lifetime of a lake may span geological eras. Its rate of aging will depend on physical and geographic factors such as the initial size of the lake, the mineral content of the basin and the climate of the region. The activities of man can greatly accelerate this process. Over the past 50 years it has become clear that the large-scale human use of certain lakes has speeded up their aging by a considerable factor. A particularly dramatic example is Lake Zurich in Switzerland: the lower basin of that lake, which receives large amounts of human pollution, has gone from youth to old age in less than a century. In the U.S. similarly rapid aging has been noted in Lake Washington at Seattle and the Yahara lake chain in Wisconsin.

When the European explorers of North America first saw the Great Lakes, the lakes were in a quite youthful stage: cold, clear, deep and extremely pure. In the geological sense they are indeed young—born of the most recent ice age. Before the Pleistocene their present sites were only river valleys. The advancing glaciers deepened and enlarged these valleys; after the glaciers began to retreat some 20,000 years ago the scoured-out basins filled with the melting water. The succeeding advances and retreats of the ice further deepened and reshaped the lakes until the last melting of the ice sheet left them in their present form.

The land area drained by the Great Lakes (194,039 square miles) is relatively small: it is only about twice the area of the lakes themselves, whereas the ratio for most other large lakes is at least six to one. The drainage alone is not sufficient to replace the water lost from the Great Lakes by evaporation and discharge into the ocean by way of the St. Lawrence. Thanks to their immense surface area, however, their capture of rainfall and snowfall, supplemented by inflow of groundwater, maintains the lakes at a fairly stable level. The level varies somewhat, of course, with the seasons (it is a foot to a foot and a half higher in summer than in winter) and with longer-range fluctuations in rainfall. Prolonged spells of abnormal precipitation or drought have raised or lowered the level by as much as 10 feet, thereby causing serious flooding along the lake shores or leaving boat moorings high and dry.

The five lakes differ considerably from one another, not only in surface area but also in the depth and quality of their waters. Lake Superior averages

487 feet in depth, whereas shallow Lake Erie averages only 58 feet. There is also a large difference in the lakes' altitude: Lake Superior, at the western end, stands 356 feet higher above sea level than Lake Ontario at the eastern extreme. Most of the drop in elevation occurs in the Niagara River between Lake Erie and Lake Ontario. At Niagara Falls, where the river plunges over the edge of an escarpment, the drop is 167 feet. This escarpment, forming a dam across the eastern end of Lake Erie, is continuously being eroded away, and it is estimated that in 25,000 years it will be so worn down that Lake Erie will be drained and become little more than a marshy stream.

The lakes are all linked together by a system of natural rivers and straits. To this system man has added navigable canals that today make it possible for large ocean-going ships to travel from the Atlantic to the western end of Lake Superior. Hundreds of millions of tons of goods travel up and down the Great Lakes each year, and on the U.S. side alone there are more than 60 commercial ports. The Sault Ste Marie Canal (the "Soo"), which connects Lake Su-

years from now; Lake Erie will then empty, leaving little more than a marshy stream to channel water from the upper lakes into Lake Ontario and on to the Atlantic Ocean.

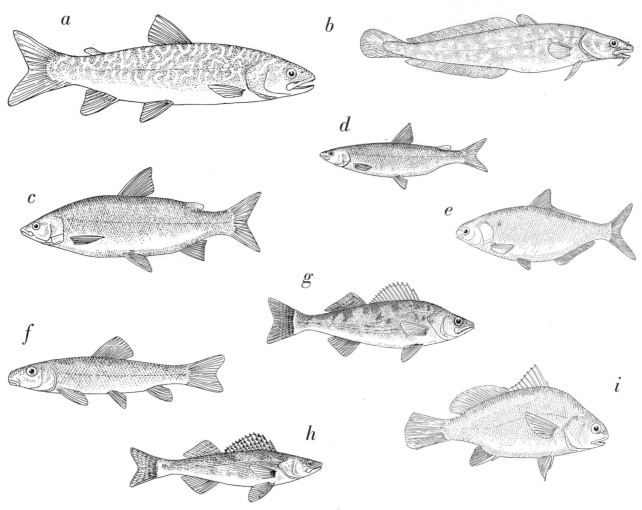

OLDER FISH POPULATION of the Great Lakes includes seven fishes that have nearly disappeared in the past two decades. Among them are the lakes' two largest species, the lake trout (*a*) and the burbot (*b*), and four smaller but economically important fishes, the whitefish (*c*), its close relative the chub, or lake herring (*d*), the walleye (*g*) and its close relative the blue pike (*not illustrated*). All six, as well as the sucker (*f*), have been victims of the parasitic sea lamprey, a fish that was confined to Lake Ontario until completion of the Welland Canal in 1932. Other indigenous fishes illustrated are the gizzard shad (*e*), the sauger (*h*) and the sheepshead (*i*).

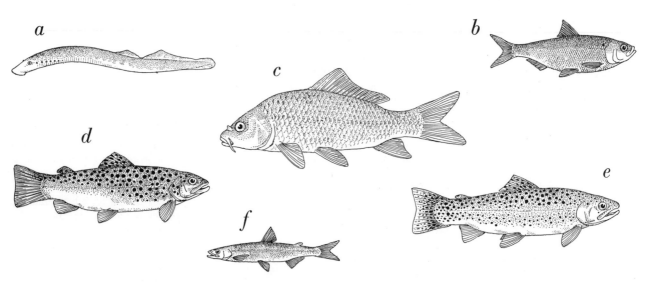

INTRUSIVE FISH POPULATION, responsible for disrupting the previous ecological balance of the four upper Great Lakes, are of two classes: those introduced by man and those that have entered on their own. The lamprey (*a*) is one of the voluntary intruders, as is the alewife (*b*), which also entered the upper lakes from Lake Ontario via the Welland Canal. Not a predator of adult fishes, the alewife nonetheless threatens the indigenous fish population. It feeds on these fishes' eggs and also consumes much of the other available food. Species introduced by man are the European carp (*c*) and brown trout (*d*), the rainbow trout (*e*) and the smelt (*f*).

perior and Lake Huron, carries a greater annual tonnage of shipping than the Panama Canal. Other major man-made links in the system are the Welland Canal, which bypasses the Niagara River's falls and rapids to connect Lake Erie and Lake Ontario, and the recently completed St. Lawrence Seaway, which makes the St. Lawrence River fully navigable from Lake Ontario to the Atlantic Ocean.

One of the first signs that man's activities might have catastrophic effects on the natural resources of the Great Lakes came as an inadvertent result of the building of the Welland Canal. The new channel allowed the sea lamprey of the Atlantic, which had previously been unable to penetrate any farther than Lake Ontario, to make its way into the other lakes. The lamprey is a parasite that preys on other fishes, rasping a hole in their skin and sucking out their blood and other body fluids. It usually attacks the largest fish available. By the 1950's it had killed off nearly all the lake trout and burbot (a relative of the cod that is also called the eelpout) in Lake Huron, Lake Michigan and Lake Superior. The lamprey then turned its attention to smaller species such as the whitefish, the chub (a smaller relative of the whitefish), the blue pike, the walleye and the sucker. Its depredations not only destroyed a large part of the fishing industry of the Great Lakes but also brought radical changes in the ecology of these lakes.

Since the late 1950's U.S. and Canadian agencies have been carrying on a determined campaign to eradicate the lamprey, using a specific larvicide to kill immature lampreys in streams where the species spawns [see "The Sea Lamprey," by Vernon C. Applegate and James W. Moffett; SCIENTIFIC AMERICAN, April, 1955]. This program has succeeded in cutting back greatly the lamprey population in Lake Superior; it is now being applied to the streams feeding into Lake Michigan and will be extended next to Lake Huron. Efforts have already been started to reestablish a growing lake-trout population in Lake Superior.

Meanwhile a second invader that also penetrated the lakes through the Welland Canal has become prominent. This fish is the alewife, a small member of the herring family. The alewife, which ranges up to about nine inches in length, does not attack adult fishes, but it feeds on their eggs and competes with their young for food. In the past decade it has

multiplied so rapidly that it is now the dominant fish species in Lake Huron and Lake Michigan and seems to be on the way to taking over Lake Superior.

Recently attempts have been made to convert the alewives from a liability to an asset. The Pacific coho, or silver salmon, has been introduced into Lake

Superior and Lake Michigan on an experimental basis. This fish should thrive feeding on the alewife and yet be protected from its depredations, because the eggs and young of the coho are found in tributary streams the alewives do not frequent. Other fishes such as the Atlantic striped bass are being con-

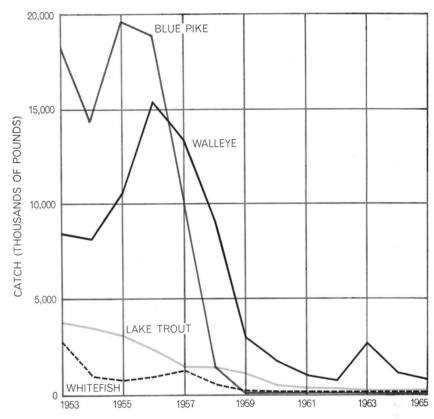

STEADY DROP in productivity of the Great Lakes commercial fisheries is reflected in the numbers of three species taken in Lake Erie (*black*) and one taken in Lake Superior (*color*) between 1953 and 1965. The lake-trout catch in Lake Michigan once rivaled Lake Superior's; from 1941 through 1946 it averaged more than six million pounds. The decline then began to be significant. Within a decade the Lake Michigan fishery ceased to yield lake trout.

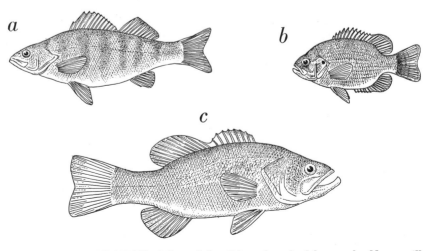

SUCCESSOR POPULATION of Great Lakes fishes when the lakes reach old age will probably include species that inhabit the lakes' shallow waters today. Among these are the yellow perch (*a*), the kind of sunfish known as rock bass (*b*) and the largemouth bass (*c*).

sidered for introduction to supplement the coho.

The introduction of a new fish into a lake is always an unpredictable matter. It may, as in the accidental admission of the lamprey and the alewife, disrupt the ecological balance with disastrous results. Even when the introduction is made intentionally with a favorable prognosis, it frequently does not work out according to expectations. The carp, prized as a food fish in many countries of Europe, was stocked in the Great Lakes many years ago and has established itself in all the lakes except Lake Superior. Commercial and sport fishermen in these lakes, however, have come to regard the carp as a nuisance. North Americans generally consider it inedible, chiefly because they have not learned how to prepare and cook it prop-

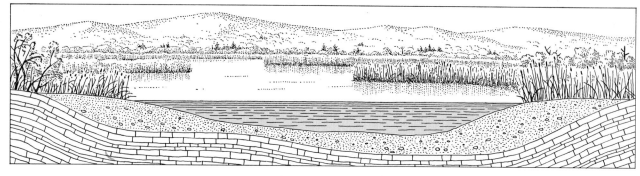

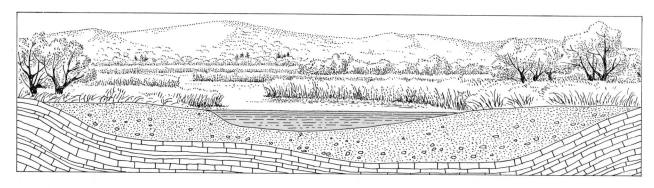

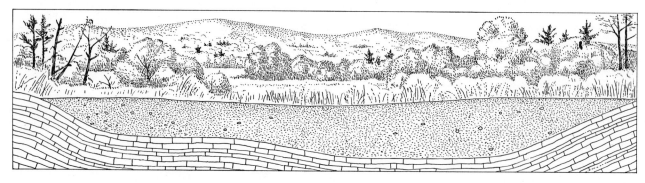

OBLITERATION of a lake is a process that starts at the edge of the water (*top*): a few bog-adapted conifers rise in a forest of hardwoods. Next the debris of shallow-water plants turns the lake margin into marsh that is gradually invaded by mosses and bog plants, bog-adapted bushes and trees such as blueberry and willow, and additional conifers. Eventually the lake, however deep, is entirely filled with silt from its tributaries and with plant debris. In the final stage (*bottom*) the last central bog soon grows up into forest.

erly. On the other hand, the smelt, introduced into the upper lakes from Lake Ontario early in this century, has become prized by fishermen and is taken in large numbers in the Great Lakes today. What effect it will eventually have on the ecology of the lakes remains to be seen.

The Great Lakes are so young that, biologically speaking, they must be considered in a formative stage. So far only a few species of fishes have been able to invade them and adapt to their specialized environment, particularly in their deep waters. As time goes on, more species will arrive in the lakes and evolve into forms specially adapted to the environmental conditions. Lake Baikal in Siberia, a very large and ancient body of fresh water, offers a good illustration of such a history: it has developed a well-diversified and distinctive population of aquatic animals including a freshwater seal. As diversity in the Great Lakes increases, it will become less and less likely that the arrival or disappearance of one or two species (such as the lake trout and burbot) will result in any profound alteration of the ecological balance.

Pollution, however, is a decidedly different factor. Its effects are always drastic—and generally for the worse. This is clearly evident in Lake Erie, the most polluted of the Great Lakes. The catch of blue pike from this lake dropped from 18,857,000 pounds in 1956 to less than 500 pounds in 1965, and that of the walleye fell from 15,405,000 pounds in 1956 to 790,000 pounds in 1965. There was also a sharp decline in lake herring, whitefish and sauger (a small relative of the walleye). While these most desirable fishes decreased, there were rises in the catch of sheepshead (the freshwater drum), carp, yellow perch and smelt. Other signs in the lake gave evidence of an environment increasingly unfavorable for desirable fish; among these were the severe depletion of oxygen in the bottom waters, the disappearance of mayfly larvae (a fish food), which used to be extremely abundant in the shallow western end of the lake, and spectacular growths of floating algae—a certain sign of advanced age in a lake.

Lake Erie receives, to begin with, the grossly polluted water of the Detroit River, into which 1.6 billion gallons of waste are discharged daily from the cities and industries along the riverbanks. To this pollution an enormous amount is added by the great urban and

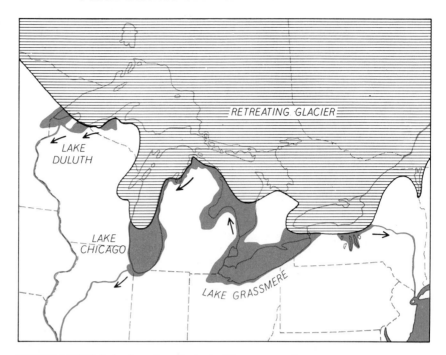

YOUNG LAKES drained southward, via the Mississippi to the west and the Mohawk and Hudson to the east, during the last glacial retreat of the Pleistocene some 10,000 years ago.

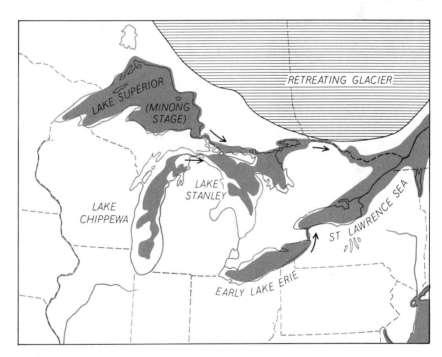

MATURING LAKES altered the southward drainage pattern and began to channel their waters eastward into the prehistoric St. Lawrence Sea as the glacial retreat continued.

industrial complex around the lake itself. A recent study of the Detroit River by the U.S. Public Health Service showed that its waters contain large quantities of sewage bacteria, phenols, iron, oil, ammonia, chlorides, nitrogen compounds, phosphates and suspended solids. Similar waste materials are discharged into the lake by the steel, chemical, refining and manufacturing plants along the lake. Pollution is par-

ticularly serious in Lake Erie because of the lake's shallowness; its volume of water is too small to dilute the pollutants effectively. Over the past 50 years the concentrations of major contaminants in the Lake Erie waters have increased sharply.

Many of the industrial wastes, notably phenols and ammonia, act as poisons to the fish and other animal life in the lake. Solid material settles to the bottom and smothers bottom-dwelling organisms. Moreover, some of the solids decompose and in doing so deplete the water of one of its most vital constituents: dissolved oxygen. Algae, on the other hand, thrive in the polluted waters, particularly since the sewage wastes contain considerable amounts of the plant-fertilizing elements nitrogen and phosphorus. The algae contribute to the depletion of oxygen (when they die and decay), give the lake water disagreeable tastes and odors and frustrate the attempts of water-purifying plants to filter the water.

In addition to Lake Erie, the southern end of Lake Michigan has also become seriously polluted. Interestingly the city of Chicago, the dominant metropolis of this area, apparently does not contribute substantially to the lake pollution; it discharges its sewage into the Mississippi River system instead of the lake. The main discharge into Lake Michigan comes from the large industrial concentration—steel mills, refineries and other establishments—clustered along its southern shores. The Public Health Service has found that the lake water in this area contains high concentrations of inorganic nitrogen, phosphate, phenols and ammonia.

Apart from the southern end, most of the water of Lake Michigan is still of reasonably good quality. In Lake Ontario, although it receives a considerable discharge of wastes, the situation is not yet as serious as in Lake Erie because Ontario's much larger volume of water provides a higher dilution factor. Lake Huron, bordered by a comparatively small population, so far shows only minor pollution effects, and Lake Superior almost none. Nevertheless, the growth of the entire region and the spreading pollution of the lakes and their tributary waters make the long-range outlook disquieting. Already the quality of the waters over a considerable portion of the lake system has greatly deteriorated, and many bathing beaches must be closed periodically because of pollution.

It is clear that in less than 150 years man has brought about changes in the Great Lakes that probably would have taken many centuries under natural conditions. These changes, shortening the usable life of the lakes, seem to be accumulating at an ever increasing rate. We still know far too little about the complicated processes that are under way or about what measures are necessary to conserve this great continental resource. Obviously the problem calls for much more study and for action that will not be too little and too late. No doubt the Great Lakes will be there for a long time to come; they are not likely to dry up in the foreseeable future. But it will be tragic irony if one day we have to look out over their vast waters and reflect bitterly, with the Ancient Mariner, that there is not a drop to drink. To realize that this is not an unthinkable eventuality we need only remind ourselves of the water crisis in New York City, where water last year had to be drastically rationed while billions of gallons in the grossly polluted Hudson River flowed uselessly by the city.

The Authors

CHARLES F. POWERS and ANDREW ROBERTSON are respectively associate research oceanographer and assistant research limnologist with the Great Lakes Research Division of the University of Michigan. Powers received a bachelor's degree in zoology at the University of North Carolina in 1950; while there he developed an interest in water environments. As a graduate student at Cornell University, where he obtained a Ph.D. in 1955, he concentrated on oceanography but also gave attention to limnology and ichthyology. His primary interest is the Great Lakes, but he has also worked on the ecological aspects of small marshes and on coastal oceanography and estuarine processes. Robertson, who majored in chemistry at the University of Toledo, received master's and doctor's degrees in zoology from the University of Michigan.

Bibliography

EUTROPHICATION OF THE ST. LAWRENCE GREAT LAKES. Alfred M. Beeton in *Limnology and Oceanography,* Vol. 10, No. 2, pages 240–254; April, 1965.

GEOLOGY OF THE GREAT LAKES. Jack L. Hough. University of Illinois Press, 1958.

GREAT LAKES BASIN. Edited by Howard J. Pincus. American Association for the Advancement of Science, Publication No. 71. The Horn-Shafer Company, 1962.

GREAT LAKES: SPORT FISHING FRONTIER. Howard A. Tanner in *Michigan Conservation,* Vol. 34, No. 6, pages 2–9; November–December, 1965.

THE ST. LAWRENCE GREAT LAKES. Alfred M. Beeton and David C. Chandler in *Limnology in North America,* edited by David G. Frey. The University of Wisconsin Press, 1963.

SPECIAL NOTE TO TEACHERS: Each article in this volume, plus more than 660 others, is available as a separate, self-bound SCIENTIFIC AMERICAN Offprint. Offprints may be ordered in any combination and in any quantity. Teachers who want to adopt articles for their courses, therefore, can ensure that each student has his own set. Students' sets are collated by the publisher before shipment.

SCIENTIFIC AMERICAN November 1966, Vol. 215, No. 5, pp. 118-124   OFFPRINT 1057

ACETABULARIA: A USEFUL GIANT CELL

by Aharon Gibor

This marine alga grows to a length of an inch but has only one
cell and one nucleus. It is therefore almost ideal for studying
the relations between the nucleus and other parts of the cell.

One of the outstanding problems of biology is the clarification of the subtle relations between the nucleus of the living cell and its surrounding cytoplasm. If a biologist could design an ideal cell for the purpose of looking into this problem, he would probably specify properties remarkably like those of *Acetabularia,* a tropical seaweed that is sometimes called the mermaid's wineglass because of its graceful shape. *Acetabularia,* which is classified among the green algae, is a single-celled organism that grows more or less vertically to a length of several centimeters. Its nucleus is invariably located at the bottom. Hence the experimenter can easily separate nucleus and cytoplasm to see how they fare independently and what happens when they are put back together in various ways.

Experiments with *Acetabularia* have already yielded considerable information about relations between the nucleus and the cytoplasm. The work has been done mostly in the laboratories of Joachim Hämmerling at the Max Planck Institute for Marine Biology in Wilhelmshaven and of Jean Brachet at the Free University of Brussels. Recently the organism has attracted interest in a number of laboratories in the U.S. With the advances that are occurring in the techniques of cell biology, the experiments now under way with *Acetabularia* promise further disclosures about the roles played by the components of the cell in the cell's activity.

The group of plants in which *Acetabularia* is classified, along with the other green algae, is the order Siphonales. Members of the order are distinguishable by a kind of growth called "coenocytic," a term derived from two Greek words translated roughly as "common-celled." The body of such a

plant is made up of an elongated and branched filament. No cross walls separate the filament into individual cells; the cytoplasm is thus continuous throughout the plant. Most plants of the order contain many nuclei and the smaller cell bodies called plastids and

mitochondria. The family Dasycladaceae, to which *Acetabularia* belongs, is further characterized by the development of specialized branches that at their apexes become the reproductive organs of the plant.

Hämmerling, studying the life history

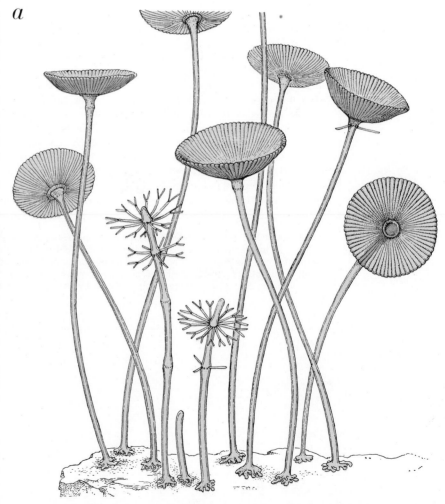

a

VIEWS OF *ACETABULARIA* at increasing enlargements begin (*a*) with a representation
of *A. mediterranea* in its natural habitat. The cap (*b*) consists of rays that at maturity develop cysts as shown in one ray at right. The rhizoid (*c*) attaches the organism to a rock

of *Acetabularia*, discovered that the organism differs from other plants of the order Siphonales in a most important feature. In *Acetabularia* the nucleus does not divide during the period in which the cell grows. In other words, the cell contains a single nucleus during the entire period of growth.

Another feature of the plant is that the end containing the nucleus develops a special structure called the rhizoid. This structure serves to attach the cell to a solid object, usually a rock. (The natural habitat of *Acetabularia* is a shallow tropical sea with a rocky bottom.)

At the top of the cell a second special structure called the cap develops at about the time the growth of the cell ends. The cap matures to become the reproductive organ of the cell. Only when this happens does the nucleus begin to divide. Until that time the organism can be regarded as a giant single cell. Once the division of the nucleus starts, the plant becomes similar

to all other coenocytic algae of the order Siphonales.

A further relevant characteristic of *Acetabularia* is apparent when the cell is cut or bruised. The cell rapidly seals off the damaged portion, heals and proceeds to regenerate a new part. If an immature cap is cut from the top of the stalk, for example, a new cap develops in its place.

The value of the regenerative cap to the experimenter is enhanced by the fact that nature has provided several species of *Acetabularia*. The Mediterranean species, *A. mediterranea*, has a cap that looks like a small umbrella with a smooth rim. The species *A. crenulata*, found in the Caribbean, has a cap that looks like several small bananas arranged radially at the tip of the cell. Since the appearance of each cap is so distinctive the experimenter can readily see the effect of transferring a nucleus from one species to another.

In sum, four properties give *Acetabularia* its remarkable value as an experi-

mental organism: (1) the delay in the division of the nucleus until the cell has attained its full size and the cap has matured, (2) the location of the nucleus in a particular and recognizable region of the cell, (3) the difference in the caps of different species and (4) the organism's capacity for regenerating parts. These properties have lent themselves admirably to the examination of the influence of the nucleus on the development of the cytoplasm and the influence of the cytoplasm on processes in the nucleus.

The nucleus of a cell in any organism is known to carry genetic information in its chromosomes. Yet the translation of the information into the orderly development of a cell from an immature state to a mature one is not all accomplished by the nucleus. Indeed, the genetic information in the nucleus represents only a potential. An intricate mechanism regulates the realization of the potential; by means of the mecha-

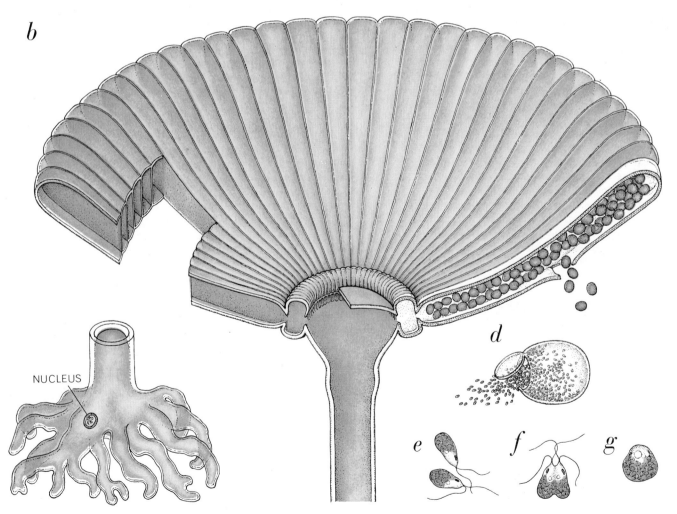

b

NUCLEUS

d

e   *f*   *g*

and also is the site of the nucleus. The rhizoid and cap are enlarged 20 diameters. At *d* is a ripe cyst, enlarged some 150 diameters, from which gametes, or mature germ cells, are emerging. A gamete fuses with another gamete (*e–g*) to give rise to a zygote, which is the immature cell that will grow into a new *Acetabularia*. The enlargement of the drawings *e, f* and *g* is about 1,000 diameters.

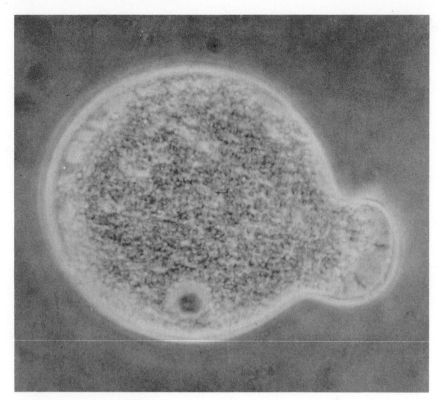

YOUNG CELL of *Acetabularia* contains a prominent nucleus, which is the dark spot at bottom. The rest of the material in the cell is cytoplasm. This cell is in the early stage of growth and has just begun to develop a stalk. The enlargement is about 2,000 diameters.

nism different genes are perhaps activated to function at different times. It is evident from numerous experiments that the process involves both commands from the nucleus to the cytoplasm and commands from the cytoplasm to the nucleus.

Before the unique properties of *Acetabularia* could be exploited in order to explore the details of the nuclear-cytoplasmic interaction, the first workers in the field had to study the organism's life cycle intensively in the laboratory to familiarize themselves with its normal events. The study proved to be difficult. It is not easy to take algae from a marine environment and maintain them in the laboratory, particularly when, as in the case of *Acetabularia*, the nutritional requirements of the organism are not known.

When Hämmerling began his studies, he was associated with the laboratory of the late Max Hartmann at the Kaiser Wilhelm Institute in Berlin. The laboratory was trying to maintain various species of marine algae. In time the workers at the laboratory developed a special culture medium—the Erd-Schreiber medium—in which many delicate algae seemed to thrive. The secret of the medium was the addition to seawater of a special brew prepared by cooking a particular kind of garden soil for many hours. With the Erd-Schreiber medium Hämmerling was able to domesticate *Acetabularia* and establish the details of its life cycle.

Hämmerling found that a mature cap develops cysts that are the key to reproduction [*see illustration on preceding two pages*]. Each cyst contains several nuclei, many chloroplasts and mitochondria and other materials that can form a new cell. The reproductive process begins when the cap releases the cysts, which germinate to produce the gametes, or mature germ cells. Two gametes meet and fuse to form a zygote that immediately begins to grow and develop. It takes about 60 days for the cell to grow to the stalklike stage that precedes the formation of a cap.

With the life cycle established Hämmerling was ready to begin his experiments. One of the first questions he considered was whether or not an *Acetabularia* cell could continue to live and function without its nucleus. It was easy to remove the nucleus by cutting off the rhizoid. Cells thus enucleated continued to grow in length and eventually developed a typical cap. Of course, such a cap would not mature to produce ripe cysts because no nuclei were present. An enucleated cell would, however, remain alive and active for several months.

It therefore appeared that the growth of the cell and even the development of a complex structure such as the cap were independent of the nucleus. Elaborations of the experiment showed that the independence was somewhat conditional. The fact that an enucleated cell can both grow and develop new structures proved to arise from the accumulation in the cell of substances that originated in the nucleus.

The experiment that led to this conclusion can be summarized as follows. If the top segment of a cell is cut off, that segment continues to grow in length; it also develops a cap. The bottom segment of the cell, which contains the nucleus, can regenerate a complete and normal cell [*see top illustration on opposite page*]. The middle segment of the cell, however, lacks the ability to increase in length or regenerate a cap.

The next step was to remove a small top segment of a complete plant but to delay cutting off a middle segment for several days. If the middle segment was then separated from the bottom segment, it was found to have acquired the capacity to grow and to form a cap. Evidently the middle segment acquired the properties of growth and cap-forming because it was attached to the rhizoidal segment, which contained the nucleus.

One naturally asks next if the acquired properties of the middle segment arose from the nucleus. The question was answered affirmatively by an experiment in which a nucleus was squeezed out of a cell, washed to remove most of the adhering cytoplasm and then transplanted into the isolated middle section of another cell. New growth began several days later.

Here was a finding of considerable importance. It implied that the nucleus produces a diffusible substance that migrates and concentrates in the top region of the cell. The substance controls the ability of the cell to grow and to develop a cap. It is a stable substance and can remain active for many days.

Another important observation came from the transfer of a nucleus to the middle section of a stalk. New rhizoids developed in the vicinity of the transplanted nucleus. The implication is that the position of the nucleus in the cell establishes a polarity in the cell; the rhizoid always develops near the nucleus and the cap develops at the point farthest from the nucleus. Since one type of message clearly concentrates at one end of a cell and another

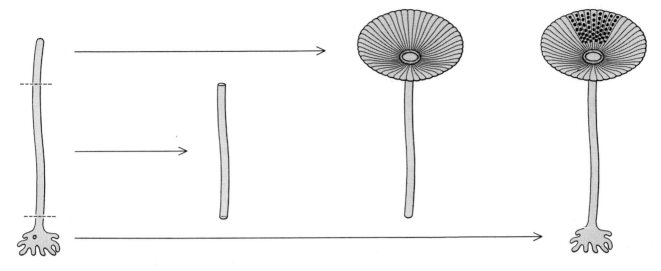

CUTTING EXPERIMENTS show the effect of the nucleus on the growth of a cell of *Acetabularia*. A young plant (*left*) is cut in two places. The middle section remains alive but does not grow. The tip develops a cap. The base develops into a fully mature cell.

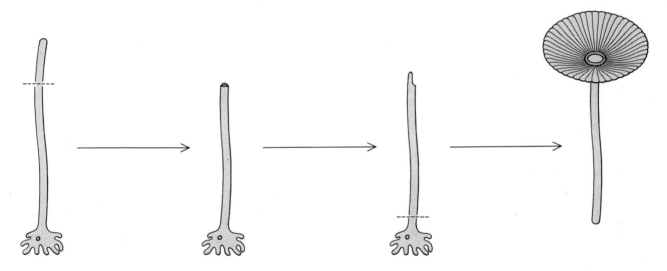

FURTHER CUTTING introduces a time factor. The tip of a cell is cut off (*left*) and the remaining part is left alone for several days. Then it is cut in two. Its top part, which was originally the middle section, has acquired from the nucleus the ability to develop.

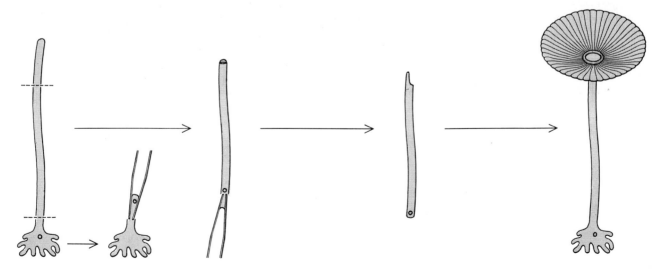

TRANSPLANTATION OF NUCLEUS into what was originally the middle section of a cell of *Acetabularia* is accomplished by pipette. Segment receiving the nucleus begins to show growth after several days and eventually develops into a mature cell (*right*).

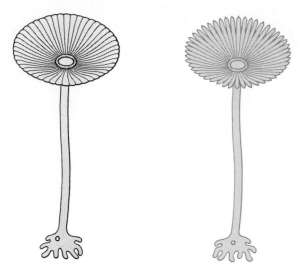
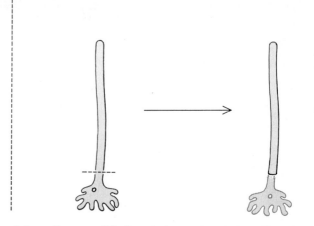
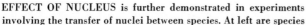

EFFECT OF NUCLEUS is further demonstrated in experiments involving the transfer of nuclei between species. At left are species of *A. mediterranea* (*black*) and *A. crenulata* (*color*). The cell of *mediterranea* is cut in two and the rhizoid, containing the nucleus,

type concentrates at the other end, it is evident that messages do not simply diffuse out of the nucleus. They are also spatially organized in the cytoplasm.

It soon became apparent that the diffusible message from the nucleus carries specific genetic information. This fact was demonstrated when a nucleus of one species was introduced into an enucleated cell of another species. The cap that eventually developed was typical of the species of the transplanted nucleus [*see illustration at top of these two pages*].

In some cases, when the enucleated cell was well developed and apparently contained a considerable amount of the diffusible message from its own nucleus, the first cap to develop after the implantation of a foreign nucleus showed characteristics intermediate between the two species. If such a hybrid cap was removed, however, the cap that then developed was typical of the kind found on the species from which the nucleus came. Here was a clear demonstration that the genetic factors in the nucleus determine the ultimate form of the cell. Moreover, the nucleus exercises its control by secreting diffusible messages into the cytoplasm; the messages thereupon migrate to the region of the cell where the information they bear will be utilized.

What is the chemical nature of the diffusing message? Indirect evidence suggests that here, as in all other mechanisms of genetic information that have been studied, molecules of ribonucleic acid (RNA) function in the transfer of information from the deoxyribonucleic acid (DNA) of the genes into protein enzymes. Three kinds of indirect evidence implicated RNA in the mature

cell of *Acetabularia*. First, if an enucleated top segment was treated with ultraviolet light, which is known to damage nucleic acids, the segment lost its ability to grow. Second, treatment of such a segment with ribonuclease, an enzyme that specifically breaks down molecules of RNA, also prevented growth. Finally, antibiotics such as actinomycin, which inhibit the synthesis of the kind of RNA called messenger RNA, curtailed the accumulation of growth-initiated substances in decapitated cells that still had their nuclei.

The experiments I have described owe their success to the remarkable hardiness of the *Acetabularia* nucleus. Such a nucleus can be taken out of the cell, washed repeatedly in a sucrose solution and then reimplanted in a cell without loss of viability. In contrast, transplantations of the nuclei of amoebae or other animal cells must be performed in such a way that the nucleus is never exposed to the culture medium.

As a result of the experiments with the nuclei of *Acetabularia,* the genetic role of the nucleus was considerably clarified. The experiments showed that the nucleus, by its production of messenger RNA, makes possible the vegetative growth of the cell and its differentiation into a rhizoid at one end and a cap at the other. The next question to be asked concerned the cytoplasm. Does it have some control over the development and function of the nucleus? Several experiments provided an affirmative answer to the question.

One line of experimentation was based on the fact that the nucleus of a cell with a developing cap is quite large. The experiments involved decapitating

such cells. Invariably the result was that the nucleus shrank to a fraction of its former size. Hämmerling was able to keep such cells growing for several years, repeatedly removing the cap and thus apparently rejuvenating the nucleus.

In other experiments a mature cap was grafted onto the top of a young cell. The result was an early onset of nuclear divisions in the still small nucleus [*see illustration at bottom of these two pages*]. Both sets of experiments lead to the inference that cytoplasmic factors govern the developmental state of the nucleus. When a cap is fully developed, it signals the nucleus at the other pole of the cell to start dividing. What the signal may be is unknown.

A straightforward way of studying the nature of the substances that might affect a nucleus or cytoplasm is to add

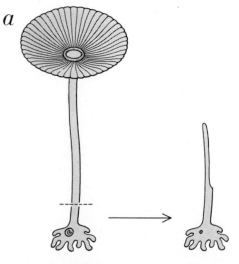

EFFECT OF CYTOPLASM on the nucleus appears in two experiments. If a mature cap

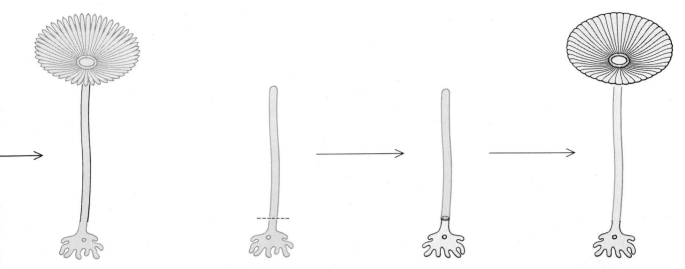

is removed. Then a rhizoid from a cell of *crenulata* is grafted onto the *mediterranea* stem. Eventually the stem develops a cap charac-

teristic of the *crenulata* species. A comparable result occurs (*far right*) when a *mediterranea* rhizoid is put on a *crenulata* stem.

known substances to a culture medium containing cells. If an additive of known properties produces results similar to those produced naturally by the unknown substance, the experimenter has a clue to the properties of the unknown substance. To be meaningful, however, such experiments should be performed on cultures that are free of bacteria, since any added organic substance is more likely to be used or changed by the actively metabolizing microorganisms than by the relatively sluggish alga.

In recent years my colleagues at Rockefeller University and I have been able to obtain and grow cultures of bacteria-free *Acetabularia*. With them we undertook first to find what organic growth factors are needed by intact cells. We found that thiamine (vitamin B_1) can replace the soil extract in the Erd-Schreiber medium. Another factor,

perhaps vitamin B_{12}, is usually supplied in sufficient quantities in natural seawater but must be added if artificial seawater is used.

Pure cultures have also enabled us to settle a long debate concerning the presence of DNA in organelles, or intracellular bodies, other than the nucleus. Organelles such as mitochondria and chloroplasts can be isolated from disrupted cells, and their composition can then be determined. Since the quantity of DNA in organelles thus obtained is very small, it must be determined that the DNA does not come from broken nuclei or contaminating bacteria.

Our technique for determining if chloroplasts of *Acetabularia* contained DNA was to remove nuclei from uninfected cells by cutting off the rhizoid

ends. From the stalks that remained we isolated chloroplasts. We found that the chloroplasts indeed contained small but significant amounts of DNA.

Furthermore, we were able to show that the DNA of the chloroplasts is synthesized even in the absence of the nucleus. We did so by growing enucleated cells in a radioactive environment. Afterward we isolated chloroplasts from the cells; radioactive DNA was found in the chloroplasts. The experiment indicated that the chloroplasts may possess a degree of genetic autonomy.

Recently we have found that we can prepare very small droplets of *Acetabularia* cytoplasm [*see bottom illustration on next page*]. The droplets continue to live and grow in vitro. We call the droplets cytoplasts. They represent an intermediate system between the complex intact cell and the completely disorga-

b

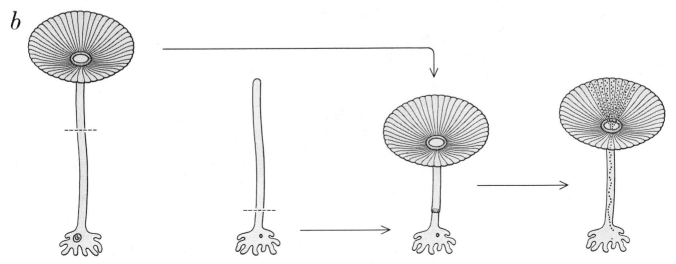

is removed from a cell, such as the *A. mediterranea* shown at *a*, the nucleus, which was previously well developed, shrinks markedly.

If a developed cap is transferred to a young rhizoid (*b*), the nuclear divisions characteristic of a mature rhizoid soon start.

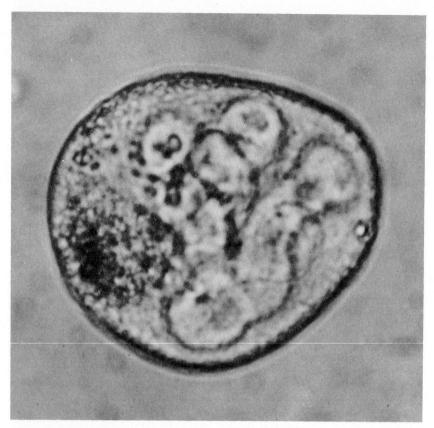

ISOLATED NUCLEUS of a cell of *Acetabularia* can be used for experiments in transplantation. A normal nucleus is 100 to 200 microns (thousandths of a millimeter) in diameter.

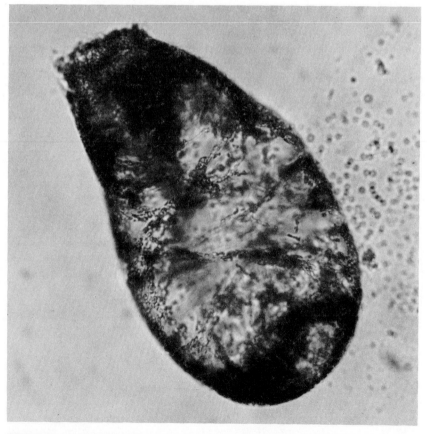

DROPLET OF CYTOPLASM without a nucleus can be used to study function of such cytoplasmic bodies as chloroplasts and mitochondria. This synthetic cell is called a cytoplast.

nized homogenized cell preparations commonly studied by biochemists interested in the function of the various components of cells. A typical cytoplast is surrounded by a membrane and contains many chloroplasts and mitochondria. The cytoplasm in it exhibits for several weeks the streaming, or continuous motion, characteristic of living cytoplasm.

We hope the cytoplasts will provide suitable simplified material for further studies of nuclear-cytoplasmic relations. We wonder, for example, if we could induce a cytoplast to develop a new cell wall and to differentiate further if we supplied it with appropriate messenger RNA. If such a cytoplast could be made to grow, could we simplify conditions still further and grow isolated organelles such as chloroplasts and mitochondria outside the cell? The ability to do so would make it possible to establish and to study in detail the degree of independence of different components of a cell.

Another interesting contribution to fundamental biological problems from studies of *Acetabularia* is the recent finding by Hans Schweiger and his colleagues at the Max Planck Institute in Wilhelmshaven that the nucleus plays a role in setting the cell's "clock." Schweiger established different photosynthetic rhythms in *Acetabularia* cells grown under various regimes of light and darkness. When nuclei were transferred between *Acetabularia* cells that differed in the timing of their photosynthetic activity, it was discovered that the introduced nucleus caused a shift in the rhythm of the cytoplasm. Although photosynthesis is a process that is restricted to the chloroplasts, the experiments show that it is somehow regulated by the nucleus. Further work with *Acetabularia* should shed more light on the still poorly understood phenomenon of biological clocks.

Some of the other unique properties of *Acetabularia* await further exploitation. The messages of the nucleus are conveyed to specific parts of the cytoplasm. What organizes their distribution? The cytoplasm influences divisions of the nucleus. What is the nature of the cytoplasmic message to the nucleus? The nuclear divisions in the rhizoid of *Acetabularia* are separated in time and space from the organization of the cytoplasm and membranes around nuclei in the ripe cap to form cysts. What would study of the separation reveal about cell division?

The Author

AHARON GIBOR is assistant professor of biochemistry and cell physiology at Rockefeller University. A native of Israel, he studied at an agricultural high school and engaged in farming until the age of 21, when he decided to continue his education. He came to the U.S. in 1947 to study agriculture at the University of California at Berkeley, but he soon shifted to biochemistry. With work on algae he received a Ph.D. from Stanford University in 1955. After a few years as a biologist with the Department of Fish and Game in Alaska he went to Rockefeller University, where his work was concerned with fundamental relations between the components of living cells. "For my studies I prefer to draw from the rich variety of algal forms available in nature," he writes, "since finding the right organism for tackling a biological problem is probably the most important step toward the solution of the problem." Gibor adds that when he has the time he likes to "read novels, particularly science fiction novels."

Bibliography

DETERMINATION AND REALIZATION OF MORPHOGENESIS IN ACETABULARIA. Günther Werz in *Brookhaven Symposia in Biology*, No. 18, pages 185–203; Brookhaven National Laboratory, 931 (C-44), 1965.

ENDOGENOUS CIRCADIAN RHYTHM IN CYTOPLASM OF ACETABULARIA: INFLUENCE OF THE NUCLEUS. E. Schweiger, H. G. Wallraff, H. G. Schweiger in *Science*, Vol. 146, No. 3644, pages 658–659; October 30, 1964.

NUCLEO-CYTOPLASMIC INTERACTIONS. J. Hämmerling in *Annual Review of Plant Physiology: Vol. XIV*. Annual Reviews, Inc., 1963.

NUCLEOCYTOPLASMIC INTERACTIONS IN UNICELLULAR ORGANISMS. J. Brachet in *The Cell, Vol. II: Cells and Their Component Parts*, edited by Jean Brachet and Alfred E. Mirsky. Academic Press, 1961.

SURVIVING CYTOPLASTS IN VITRO. Aharon Gibor in *Proceedings of the National Academy of Sciences*, Vol. 54, No. 6, pages 1527–1531; December, 1965.

SCIENTIFIC
AMERICAN   December 1966, Vol. 215, No. 6, pp. 32-39   OFFPRINT **1058**

THE GENETIC CONTROL OF
THE SHAPE OF A VIRUS

by Edouard Kellenberger

The protein shell of a virus is an assembly of subunits. In simple
viruses the subunits themselves may specify the shape of the shell.
Complex viruses seem to be formed on an interior core, or scaffold.

Living things are enormously diverse in form, but form is remarkably constant within any given line of descent: pigs remain pigs and oak trees remain oak trees generation after generation. The morphological character—the form—of a species is inherited, and this hereditary information must surely be contained in the genes; indeed, genes that determine morphological traits have been identified in many plants and animals. So far, however, little is known about how these genes carry out their morphopoietic, or form-making, function. For the general study of the morphopoietic function a particularly suitable group of organisms is the viruses: a virus has shape (a precisely defined shell of protein) and hereditary information (a core of nucleic acid) and not much else. Among viruses the bacteriophages, the viruses that infect bacteria, are especially convenient subjects of investigation because their genetics is accessible to manipulation and experimentation. In the past decade a number of investigations, in our laboratory at the University of Geneva and in many other laboratories, have been directed at trying to learn how viruses control the process by which they assemble themselves in characteristic shapes.

As viruses go, bacteriophages have a rather complicated structure, so I shall first describe some simpler viruses. One of the simplest is the virus that causes the mosaic disease of tobacco, and this virus is the only one that has been taken apart and then reassembled in the test tube [see "Rebuilding a Virus," by Heinz Fraenkel-Conrat; SCIENTIFIC AMERICAN Offprint 9]. The to-bacco mosaic virus has the form of a rod: a cylindrical assembly of protein subunits with a long molecule of ribonucleic acid (RNA) inside the cylinder. Treatment with acetic acid separates the virus into an RNA molecule and some 2,000 protein subunits. When the protein fraction is spun in an ultracentrifuge or otherwise analyzed, it is found to be homogeneous, that is, all the protein subunits are alike. If this fraction is in solution under the appropriate ionic and temperature conditions, rods form that are nearly indistinguishable from the active virus particles. Apparently the protein subunits can assemble themselves into these geometrically defined rods without any outside help; the subunit contains all the information needed to build the rod.

Such self-assembly of identical subunits is not hard to understand. Imagine a two-dimensional array of identical subunits [see top illustration, page 2300]. The shape of these imaginary subunits is such that they can assemble only into a ring of a certain size, even though each subunit is asymmetric and its shape is unrelated to that of the ring. Such subunits are said to have a stringent fit; they are fully shape-specifying and cannot join to form any shape other than the specified ring. Similarly, three-dimensional subunits can be imagined that will assemble into cylindrical or spherical shells [see bottom illustration on pages 2300 and 2301]. In each case the shape of subunits is fully shape-specifying, so that each set can make only a single geometric structure of a fully determined shape and size. Note, however, that in the two cylinders illustrated the difference between the shapes of the subunits

is very slight. This implies that a single subunit might be designed that could give rise to both cylinders. Such subunits would not be fully shape-specifying; some outside influence—even if it were only chance—would have to determine which kind of assembly was to prevail. This theoretical prediction has been verified for the tobacco mosaic virus: the reassembled rods can exist in either a helical or a "stacked disk" form.

Here I should point out that any geometric model of subunit assembly is somewhat naïve. A protein molecule consists of amino acid units arranged in a linear sequence according to information in the genes. Each chain (the primary structure) is coiled into a complex three-dimensional shape, and often chains are combined (the secondary and tertiary structure). The resulting molecule is not a sharp-edged geometric object but an assembly of curved, sausagelike elements, and its fitting properties depend not only on shape but also on the location and specificity of chemical bonds. In other words, what is involved is a stereochemical fit, and this can be represented only figuratively as a purely geometric phenomenon.

One more statement can be made about the inheritance of shape in viruses. When all the shape-specifying information is contained in one protein and therefore in one gene, the assembly is called a morphopoiesis of the first order. When additional information is contributed by other genes, the morphopoiesis is said to be of a higher order, the order of morphopoiesis equaling the number of implicated, independent "bits" of information.

Most viruses that infect animals are

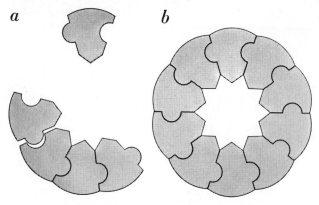

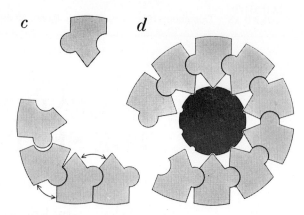

a   *b*   *c*   *d*

IDENTICAL SUBUNITS that have stringent fit (*a*) can assemble only into a specific ring (*b*); they are fully shape-specifying. Subunits with less stringent fit (*c*), however, assemble into a somewhat flexible chain that can assume many shapes unless there is a scaffold of some kind, such as a morphopoietic core (*d*). Once the ring has been shaped it should persist even if the core is removed.

not rod-shaped like the tobacco mosaic virus but nearly spherical. As long ago as 1956 F. H. C. Crick and James D. Watson suggested that small spherical viruses probably consisted of a number of identical protein subunits; they argued that this would represent the most efficient use of the genetic information in the small amount of nucleic acid inside the virus. Now, identical subunits bound together at specific sites must necessarily be arranged in a regular pattern that can be called a surface crystal. Analysis of spherical viruses by X-ray diffraction indicated that their surface crystal had a cubic symmetry—that is, a symmetry along three mutually perpendicular axes—and were therefore regular polyhedrons of a certain class. As the spherical viruses have been subjected to further X-ray analysis, to electron microscopy and to chemical study, it has become clear they are composed of subunits assembled into a capsid, or shell, that usually has the shape of an icosahedron: a polyhedron with 20 faces (each an equilateral triangle), 30 edges and 12 vertexes [see "The Structure of Viruses," by R. W. Horne; SCIENTIFIC AMERICAN Offprint 147]. D. L. D. Caspar of the Children's Cancer Research Foundation in Boston and Aaron Klug of the University of Cambridge have concluded after exhaustive investigation that there are compelling reasons, having to do not only with geometry but also with bonding properties and energy content, why icosahedral forms are the most likely.

How might an icosahedral surface crystal be formed from an array of asymmetric shape-specifying subunits? Consider a hexagonal lattice of arbitrary shapes in which groups of six shapes (hexamers) and three shapes (trimers) can be discerned [see top illustration on page 2302]. If a 60-degree sector of the pattern is removed, the edges can be rejoined, forming a cone. The lost segment is not missed; the shapes still fit one another exactly as before, but at the vertex of the cone a hexamer has been replaced by a group of five shapes (a pentamer). If 12 adjacent hexamers are taken as centers for the removal of 60-degree sectors, the result is the smallest icosahedron that can be built from this lattice [see illustration on page 2303]. It has 12 vertexes, each the center of a pentamer, and therefore has 60 identical subunits. The subunits of this minimal icosahedron are in perfect symmetry: each is in an "equivalent location," and when the shell is rotated any subunit can lie directly above another one. Clearly such a capsid could result from the assembly of 60 subunits that have stringent stereochemical fit. Thus an icosahedron can, at least in principle, be the result of first-order morphopoiesis: the subunits can be imagined to have complete shape-specificity.

This does not hold, however, for shells with more than 60 subunits. Caspar and Klug showed that larger shells are not perfectly symmetrical and that their subunits are only in "quasi-equivalent" locations. Quasi-equivalence makes possible the assembly of many more than 60 subunits into somewhat distorted shells that have icosahedral symmetry. In such cases there are variations of as much as 5 degrees in the angles of the bonds between subunits, the surface crystal has a variable curvature and the shell is somewhat flexible. This reduced stringency of fit represents a reduced content of information. Whether or not the information remains sufficient for first-order morphopoiesis is still not known. One has the feeling, however, that these large shells are not stable configurations until they have been completed. Caspar

compares them to an arch, which requires some kind of scaffolding until the keystone has been fitted.

To proceed to more complex shapes, let us consider a capsid that does not have cubic symmetry—that is not, so to speak, the same shape in all directions. In our laboratory we have been studying the bacteriophage called T4, which infects the colon bacillus. One of the more complex viral structures, the T4 particle consists of a polyhedral head and a tail assembly with many different components [see bottom illustration on pages 2302 and 2303]. We have been concerned primarily with the morphopoiesis of the head. Recent investi-

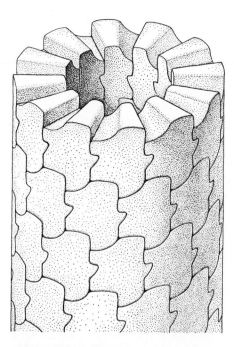

STRINGENT SUBUNITS assemble to make cylindrical and spherical shells. A cylindrical rod (*left*) is built from a translational

gations by M. F. Moody of the California Institute of Technology and in our laboratory indicate that the design of the head capsid can be represented by a folded hexagonal lattice; it is therefore closely related to the surface lattices of icosahedral shells. Whereas the icosahedron has axes of fivefold, threefold and twofold symmetry, however, the T4 capsid has only fivefold and twofold symmetry.

The shape of the T4 head capsid might be called a prolate icosahedron. It consists of the two pyramids of an icosahedron (each having a vertex with five facets) separated by two "equatorial bands" cut from an icosahedron. If the assembly of such a shape begins with a pyramid and proceeds to the addition of one equatorial band, something must influence the subunits to form a second band or they will close the shell into the usual kind of icosahedron. Some morphopoietic factor must exist that chooses one vertex to become the top of a pyramid and then enforces the building of two equatorial bands instead of only one. It must be a "long range" factor that is somehow able to relate two geometrically defined sites that are rather far apart.

What kind of factor it is we do not know. Two hypotheses have been formulated. The first supposes that the factor is contained in the virus shell—that it is a chemically distinct minor component of the capsid. The second supposes that

the factor acts on the growing capsid from the inside or the outside, somewhat like a scaffold.

There are observations and experiments that tend to support both hypotheses. Several investigators have established that the capsid of viruses in the group called the adenoviruses contains more than one protein; they have shown that different subunits react differently to an antiserum. In other viruses, including the T4 virus, the presence of two or more types of subunit has been demonstrated by the fact that subunits move at different speeds in an electric field, so that either their volume or their electric charge (or both) must be different. In none of these cases, however, has a morphopoietic role been demonstrated for the minor components; it is possible that they have another function.

The favored version of the second hypothesis—the scaffold hypothesis—envisions a morphopoietic core: a geometric body consisting of a minimum number of subunits that is built first and on which the capsid subunits grope their way into position before being linked together. The proper shape is thus forced on the capsid by the core, which stays inside the capsid, intermixed with the nucleic acid. Some time ago it was found that proteins are present inside the T4 head; these may be core proteins.

The genetics of the T4 virus has been thoroughly investigated, and more than 70 different genes for various char-

acteristics of the virus have been mapped [see "The Genetics of a Bacterial Virus," by R. S. Edgar and R. H. Epstein; SCIENTIFIC AMERICAN Offprint 1004]. The products of at least seven of these genes have been found to be essential for the assembly of a complete, stable virus head. If a mutation occurs in one of the genes and its product is therefore imperfect or missing, no normal head capsids are produced [see top illustration on page 2305].

Gene No. 23 is responsible for the major subunit of the capsid, which accounts for about 80 percent of the protein of the complete virus particle. A morphopoietic function has been established for two other genes: No. 66 and No. 20. Gene No. 66 directs the synthesis of an "elongation factor," without which normal prolate virus heads are not produced. Instead abnormal short heads are made; these particles contain about 20 percent less deoxyribonucleic acid (DNA) than normal virus particles and are therefore not active. Gene No. 20 apparently produces a "rounding up factor" that closes off the icosahedral shape. When it is missing or ineffective, long tubular heads that we call polyheads are made, as if the elongating factor were running wild.

Four more genes are known to be essential for the formation of stable head capsids. Two of them, No. 22 and No. 24, have yet to be identified with any

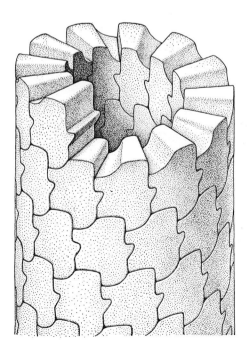

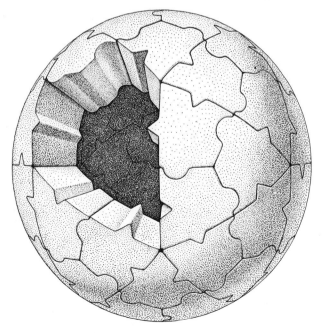

lattice, or a net of subunits arrayed side by side. Very slightly different subunits form a lattice that folds into a helical rod (*center*). A different kind of lattice, a hexagonal net with rotational symmetry, is the source of the sphere (*right*). It has 60 identical subunits arranged in pentamers, or groups of five. Five of these subunits have been removed in the drawing to show the structure.

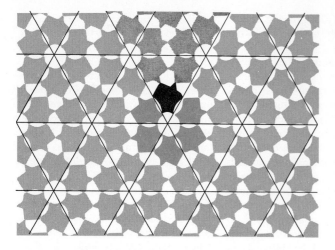

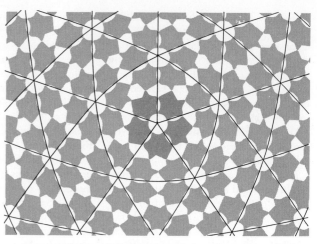

VIRUS SHELL can be visualized as being folded from a hexagonal lattice of asymmetric shapes (*left*) in which groups of six shapes (hexamers) can be distinguished (*dark shapes*). If a 60-degree sector is removed from such a lattice, the edges can be rejoined without disturbing the fit of the shapes; a cone is formed and a hexamer is replaced by a pentamer. This illustration is based on a pattern devised by D. L. D. Caspar of the Children's Cancer Research Foundation and Aaron Klug of the University of Cambridge.

specific function. The absence of gene No. 21 induces the formation of abnormal heads that apparently contain no DNA or only very small amounts of it. Gene No. 31 contributes a "solubility factor," without which the major protein derived from gene No. 23 aggregates into lumps instead of staying in solution and is therefore not available for the assembly of the capsid. Two of my students have demonstrated the action of gene No. 31 both in the test tube and in living cells of the bacterium infected by the T4 virus. If one applies the product of this gene to disrupted cells that contain lumps of the major virus protein, the lumps disappear. This test-tube result is confirmed with a particular mutant virus in which the product of gene No. 31 is inactive when it is formed at a high temperature but is activated as the temperature is lowered. When cells infected with this mutant are incubated at a high temperature, the lumps are produced; as soon as the temperature is lowered the lumps disappear and the redissolved product of gene No. 23 becomes available for virus assembly.

The fact that the same major subunit can be assembled into at least three morphologically distinct particles—the normal head, the short head and the polyhead—shows that the subunit derived from gene No. 23 is not fully shape-specifying. In an effort to understand how the head genes work we have concentrated on the polyhead, which appears to be a very simple variant. First we undertook to find out what order of

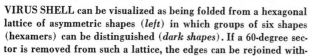

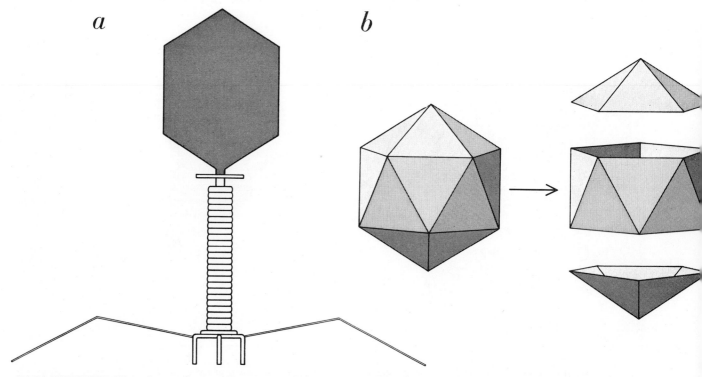

T4 BACTERIOPHAGE is shown schematically (*a*) as its form has been deduced from micrographs such as the one at the top of page 2304. It now seems the head capsid is a kind of prolate icosahedron. It is as if two pyramidal vertexes of an icosahedron

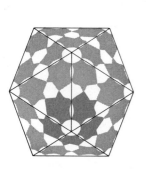

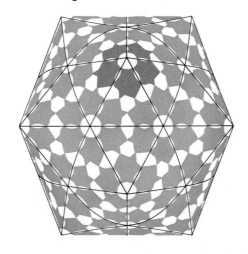

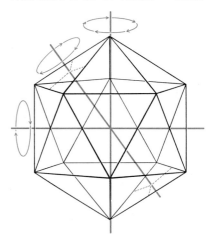

ICOSAHEDRON, a polyhedron with 20 faces and 12 vertexes, is built from the hexagonal lattice (*top of opposite page*). If each hexamer is converted into a pentamer, the result is the smallest virus shell for this lattice, a regular icosahedron with 60 subunits (*left*). The next larger shell for this lattice has 20 hexamers in addition to the pentamers, or 180 subunits (*center*). Like the shell at the left, it has icosahedral symmetry (*right*), that is, it has three kinds of axes of symmetry (*color*): fivefold, threefold and twofold.

morphopoiesis its assembly represents. To do so we made double mutants: viruses in which the functions of two head genes were blocked by mutations. In each case one mutation was in gene No. 20 (the polyhead gene) and the other in one of the other known head genes [*see bottom illustration on page 2305*]. The results indicate that polyheads are not formed without the active products of at least three genes: No. 23, No. 66 and No. 31. Since No. 31 produces a solubility factor, it is unlikely to contribute morphopoietic information. The other two, however, are certainly morphopoietic. We can say, then, that the morphopoiesis of polyheads is probably of the second order, with two independent functions carried out by the major protein of gene No. 23 and by the elongating factor of gene No. 66. This comparatively low order of morphopoiesis of the polyheads means that we can hope soon to know in detail just what the factors do; then it should be possible to isolate and purify them, learn their chemistry and eventually attempt to assemble polyheads in the test tube.

It is already clear that the shape-specifying information cannot be very stringent. This is indicated by the wide variability in the diameter of the polyheads and by the fact that various degrees of pitch can be imparted to the folded hexagonal lattice of subunits that forms a polyhead cylinder. The pitch can be measured because the polyheads in a sample prepared for electron microscopy are flattened and two layers of

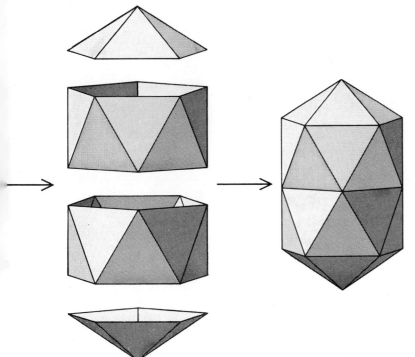

c

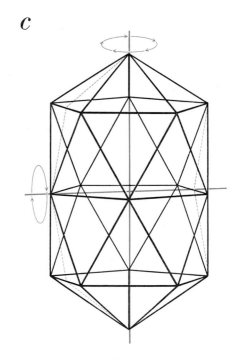

were separated by two 10-faceted "equatorial bands" instead of by the usual one band (*four drawings at "b"*). Whereas the icosahedron has three classes of symmetry, however, the prolate bacteriophage capsid has only two classes: fivefold and twofold (*c*).

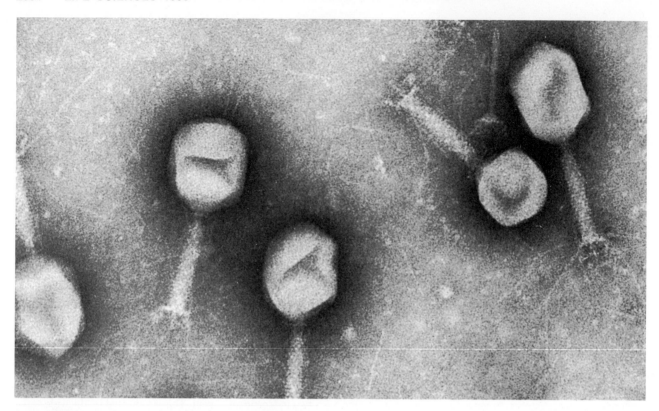

T4 BACTERIAL VIRUS, or bacteriophage, is complex in form: a polyhedral head with an elaborate tail assembly. The head capsid, or shell, is an assembly of protein subunits. It may be shaped by a morphopoietic, or form-making, core on which subunits are laid down. Such a scaffolding is presumably defined by morphopoietic genes. When the virus is mutant in one of these genes, No. 66, a short-headed variant is made (*second from right*). For this negative-contrast electron micrograph made by E. Boy de la Tour at Kansas State University the viruses were embedded in phosphotungstate, an electron-dense material. Viruses are enlarged 260,000 diameters.

"POLYHEADS," produced when virus is mutant in gene No. 20, are tubular assemblies of protein subunits. Unlike normal heads, they contain no deoxyribonucleic acid (DNA), but they are not always empty. This micrograph made by R. Favre and Boy de la Tour at the University of Geneva shows some full portions; they are not as flat as empty portions and are therefore surrounded by more dark phosphotungstate. The material inside them may be what is left of morphopoietic cores. Polyheads are enlarged 260,000 diameters.

HEAD GENES

20	21	22	23	66	24	31	RESULT
+	+	+	+	+	+	+	NORMAL HEADS
0	0	0	0	−	0	0	SHORT HEADS
−	−	−	+	+	−	+	POLYHEADS
0	−	0	0	0	0	0	"21 PARTICLES"
−	0	0	+	0	0	−	"LUMPS"
0	0	−	0	0	0	0	NO VISIBLE PROTEIN
0	0	0	−	0	0	0	NO VISIBLE PROTEIN
0	0	0	0	0	−	0	NO VISIBLE PROTEIN

FUNCTIONS of the seven head genes are illustrated. The table shows that for a given stage of synthesis to occur (*right*) certain genes must contribute their product effectively (+) and others must be nonproducing (−). In many cases the need for a gene product is not established (0). The table is based on investigations made by Sydney Brenner and his colleagues at the University of Cambridge and by the author's colleagues Boy de la Tour, Favre, F. Eiserling, R. S. Epstein, P. Geiduschek, G. Kellenberger and J. Sechaud.

hexagonal lattice are superposed. The moiré pattern this creates can be analyzed for information about the arrangement and orientation of the subunits.

The fact that the polyhead lattice is hexagonal tells us something else. A cylinder can practically build itself from a "translational" lattice in which the subunits are arrayed side by side. To fold a hexagonal net into a cylinder, however, is to subject it to a certain amount of stress and deformation. This is why it is unlikely that polyhead assembly would be a first-order morphopoiesis. Such reasoning provides theoretical support for the experimental results based on genetics.

As for the mode of action of the morphopoietic factors, our evidence is not yet conclusive. We do have some evidence against the idea that such factors are elements of the capsid itself. We isolated and purified normal and abnormal capsids and broke them down into subunits by treating the preparations with acetic acid or other agents. Then we analyzed the proteins by the technique of electrophoresis and established that the normal capsid contains two minor components in addition to the major component produced by gene No. 23. We were unable, however, to identify either of these minor proteins as the product of any known head gene. It therefore seems certain that the two known morphopoietic factors, the products of genes No. 66 and No. 20 that respectively govern elongation and rounding-up, are not present in the capsid.

The other possibility is that they are elements of a core that guides the assembly of subunits. We are far from proving this hypothesis, but the evidence for it is highly suggestive. Our electron micrographs indicate that all heads, normal and abnormal, do contain a core, whether or not they contain DNA. This is sometimes difficult to perceive, because cores that are not associated with DNA are severely affected by the process of fixation and staining for electron microscopy. For example, when polyheads are examined outside the bacterial cell (that is, after the cell in which they grew has burst and dissolved), most of them appear to be empty. When bacterial cells containing polyheads are fixed with great care and embedded in other material so that thin sections of them can be cut, the micrographs show that the polyheads have something inside them. The contents of the polyheads vary in appearance according to the method of fixation, but the polyheads in cells prepared in just the right way do show a definite architecture [*see top illustration on next page*]. This high degree of order indicates that what we are seeing is not just coagulated cell sap but a specialized structure.

Similar structures are visible in the particles produced when the product of gene No. 21 is nonfunctional [*see bottom illustration on next page*]. These particles are smaller than normal virus heads and contain no DNA or only a very small amount of it. They have a similar prolate shape, however, and each of them has a well-organized core.

One other point is pertinent in this connection. In the past the fact that virus preparations always contain some empty particles has led some observers to conclude that capsids can be built without the help of a core. The existence of empty shells does demonstrate that cap-

MUTANT GENES	POLYHEADS PRODUCED (MICRONS PER BACTERIUM)
20	30–100
20, 21	26
20, 22	24
20, 23	NONE
20, 66	VERY FEW, MALFORMED
20, 24	20
20, 31	NONE

DOUBLE-MUTANT experiment showed which genes must contribute their product to form polyheads. When only gene No. 20 was mutated, 30 to 100 microns of polyhead were formed per bacterium. Polyheads were formed in spite of double mutants except in the cases of genes No. 23, 66 and 31, so clearly those three genes are needed to make polyheads.

sids can remain stable without the permanent aid of a scaffolding device, but it does not rule out the need for such a device during the process of assembly. The emptying of a capsid is an experimental artifact that occurs frequently and is hard to avoid. The presence of empty viruses in electron micrographs therefore has no weight in any argument about the possibility that capsids can be built without a core.

To sum up, the larger a virus capsid is and the more elaborate its shape is, the more independent bits of information are required to prescribe the shape. Only the simplest virus shells can be the result of a single bit of information contained in subunits of a single type. For more complex shells such as the capsid of the T4 virus more information is necessary, and that information is stored in morphopoietic genes. In the T4 virus the functions of three such genes are known. Gene No. 23 is responsible for the major protein subunit, No. 66 for elongation and No. 20 for closing the prolate icosahedron. Although the pathways by which this information is expressed have yet to be defined, the idea of a structural scaffolding is supported by the observation of organized cores inside virus head structures. At this point we have a good idea of what problems remain to be solved and how to attack them.

The mechanism of shape-making in virus capsids is probably common to all structures made up of protein molecules. What we learn should therefore apply to such protein structures as the whiplike flagella and cilia possessed by many cells. The next important problem in this area is to understand the assembly and functioning of biological membrane, the principal structural element of cells and many of their components. Membranes consist of a double sheet of lipids, or fatty molecules, layered with one or two sheets of protein. If these proteins exist in lattice structures, whatever we learn about capsids will be applicable to membranes. Knowledge of the genetic control of shape in protein structures will not be enough, however, to explain the origin of shape in higher organisms. In multicellular systems cells differentiate into specialized groups. The shape of such an organism depends on the differential growth of specialized cells, and that growth is regulated in part by the interaction of cells. For such regulation one must look to more complex mechanisms, including genes that control the activity of other genes.

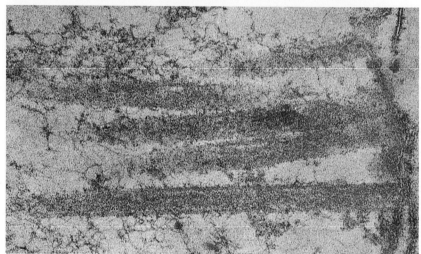

CORE MATERIAL is difficult to observe in polyheads. Bacteria were infected with T4 mutant in gene No. 20, then fixed and embedded with various techniques. With good preservation the content is seen to fill the polyheads homogeneously (*top*). In the best micrographs the content is seen to have fine structure (*bottom*), implying that it represents a specialized structure. The micrographs were made by Boy de la Tour; enlargement is 130,000 diameters.

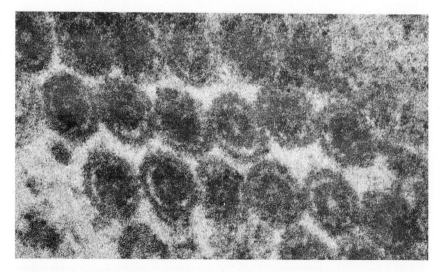

ORGANIZED CORES are also visible in the headlike bodies called "21 particles" that are synthesized by viruses mutant in gene No. 21. The particles in this micrograph made by Boy de la Tour, enlarged 280,000 diameters, are in a bacterium infected by such a mutant.

The Author

EDOUARD KELLENBERGER is a professor at the University of Geneva, where he directs both the Biophysical Laboratory of the Institute for Experimental Physics and the Center for Electron Microscopy. A native of Berne, Kellenberger interrupted his studies at polytechnical school in Zurich in 1939 to serve in the Swiss army during World War II. After the war he became a student at the University of Geneva, where he did research on electron optics and was instrumental in the formation of the Biophysics Laboratory and the Institute for Molecular Biology. He received his Ph.D. in biophysics from Geneva in 1953. Kellenberger is currently on leave and is serving as Invited Distinguished Regents' Professor at Kansas State University.

Bibliography

ASSEMBLY AND STABILITY OF THE TOBACCO MOSAIC VIRUS PARTICLE. D. L. D. Caspar in *Advances in Protein Chemistry: Vol. XVIII*, edited by C. B. Anfinsen, Jr., M. L. Anson and John T. Edsall. Academic Press, 1963.

CONTROL MECHANISMS IN BACTERIOPHAGE MORPHOPOIESIS. E. Kellenberger in *Principles of Biomolecular Organization*, edited by G. E. W. Wolstenholme and Maeve O'Connor. J. & A. Churchill Ltd., 1966.

PHYSICAL PRINCIPLES IN THE CONSTRUCTION OF REGULAR VIRUSES. D. L. D. Caspar and A. Klug in *Cold Spring Harbor Symposia on Quantitative Biology: Vol. XXVII*. Cold Spring Harbor Laboratory of Quantitative Biology, 1962.

PHYSIOLOGICAL STUDIES OF CONDITIONAL LETHAL MUTANTS OF BACTERIOPHAGE T4D. R. H. Epstein, A. Bolle, C. M. Steinberg, E. Kellenberger, E. Boy de la Tour, R. Chevalley, R. S. Edgar, M. Susman, G. H. Denhardt and A. Lielausis in *Cold Spring Harbor Symposia on Quantitative Biology: Vol. XXVIII*. Cold Spring Harbor Laboratory of Quantitative Biology, 1963.

SCIENTIFIC
AMERICAN   December 1966, Vol. 215, No. 6, pp. 106-116

OFFPRINT 1059

NUMERICAL TAXONOMY

by Robert R. Sokal

The computer has made it possible to consider large numbers of characteristics in classifying many phenomena, notably living organisms, fossil organisms and even imaginary organisms.

Classification is one of the fundamental concerns of science. Facts and objects must be arranged in an orderly fashion before their unifying principles can be discovered and used as the basis for prediction. Many phenomena occur in such variety and profusion that unless some system is created among them they would be unlikely to provide any useful information. Chemical compounds (particularly organic ones), groups of stars and the two million or so species of living organisms that inhabit the earth are examples of such phenomena.

The development of high-speed electronic computers has had a profound impact on the methods of classification in many scientific fields. The rapidity of the computer's operation has made it possible for the first time to consider large numbers of characteristics in classifying many phenomena. The writing of computer programs for such work has led to a renewed interest in the principles of classification, reviving such old questions as: What makes one classification better than another? What is a "natural" classification? What is similarity, and can it be quantified? The inquiry has progressed furthest in the field of taxonomy, or biological classification. The methods of numerical taxonomy (as this new field has come to be called), the conceptual revolution it has wrought, the nature of the controversy surrounding it, some future prospects for the field and its relevance to problems of classification in other sciences will be discussed in this article.

Many of the new procedures of numerical taxonomy and their theoretical justification have been the subject of intense disagreement between numerical taxonomists and supporters of traditional taxonomic practices and principles. Controversy, of course, is nothing new in science. Time and again the introduction of a new concept or the development of a new technique has aroused the passions of scientists representing conflicting points of view. Although debate about numerical taxonomy has not been as acrimonious as some debates in the history of science, it has certainly been spirited and continues undiminished. At recent biological conferences the symposiums on numerical taxonomy have been unusually well attended, often by people only remotely interested in the field who have heard that "a

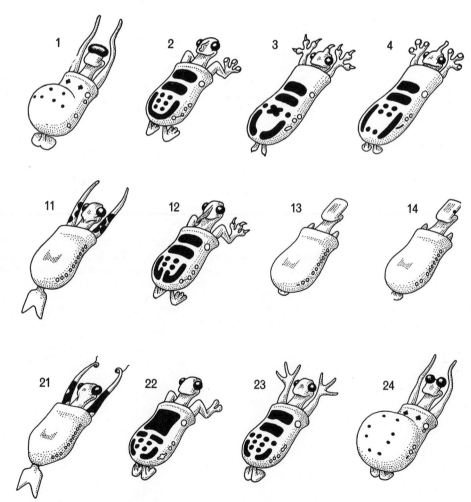

IMAGINARY ANIMALS, called Caminalcules after their creator, Joseph H. Camin of the University of Kansas, are used in experiments on the principles and practices of tax-

good fight" was about to take place in that session. What is all the shooting about?

In the early days of modern science, and for special purposes even today, classifications were based on a single property or characteristic, the choice of which might be quite arbitrary. Metals are divided into conductors and non-conductors, other substances into those that are soluble in water and those that are not; organisms are divided into unicellular ones and multicellular ones. Some of these classifications are arbitrary in the sense that there is a continuum of properties—as in the case of solubility, for which the line between soluble substances and insoluble ones is not distinct. In contrast one can almost always say whether an organism is unicellular or multicellular, so that with properties such as these the decisions can be quite clear-cut. Classifications based on one or only a few characters are generally called "monothetic," which means that all the objects allocated to one class must share the character or characters under consideration. Thus the members of the class of "soluble substances" must in fact be soluble.

Classifications based on many characters, on the other hand, are called "polythetic." They do not require any one character or property to be universal for a class. Thus there are birds that lack wings, vertebrates that lack red blood and mammals that do not bear their young. In such cases a given "taxon," or class, is established because it contains a substantial portion of the characters employed in the classification. Assignment to the taxon is not on the basis of a single property but on the aggregate of properties, and any pair of members of the class will not necessarily share every character.

It is obviously much more complicated to establish classifications based on many characters than it is to establish classifications based on only one character. The human mind finds it difficult to tabulate and process large numbers of characters without favoring one aspect or another. The comparative subjectivity of traditional approaches and the inability of taxonomists to communicate to one another the nature of their procedures have contributed to making taxonomy more of an art than a science.

The arrival of the computer has reversed this trend, and a new field with many possibilities for objective and explicit classification has opened up. Computer techniques have indeed been a principal force behind the gradual adoption of an operational approach in taxonomy; in order to use such techniques, classificatory procedures must be outlined in such a form that any scientist or a properly programmed computer can carry out the indicated operations and, given the same input data, arrive at the same results. This would preclude the often arbitrary decisions of conventional taxonomists, epitomized by the statement that "a species is whatever a competent taxonomist decides to call a species."

Before proceeding further I should remove a possible source of confusion.

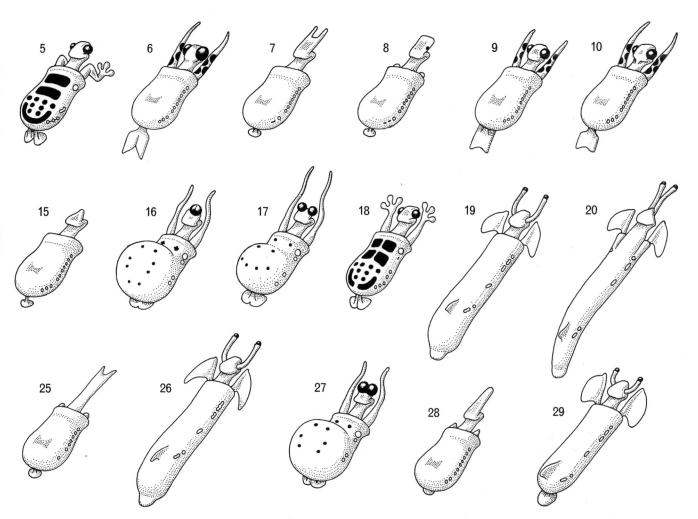

onomy, or biological classification. The 29 "recent" species of the organisms, depicted on these two pages, were generated by Camin according to rules known so far only to him. The drawings are based on Camin's originals, with slight modifications in perspective.

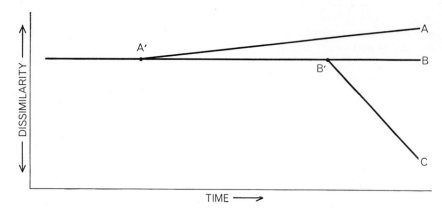

TAXONOMIC RELATIONSHIPS can be viewed from three distinct aspects. "Phenetically" (based on overall similarity among the objects to be classified) organism *B* is more closely related to organism *A* than it is to organism *C*, even though *C* evolved much later than *A* as a branch of stem *B*. "Cladistically" (based on common lines of descent) organisms *B* and *C* are closer to each other than either is to *A*, since they have an ancestor (*B′*) in common before either has a common ancestor (*A′*) with *A*. "Chronistically" (based on time) *A*, *B* and *C* are closer to one another than any of them is to *B′*, since they occupy same time horizon.

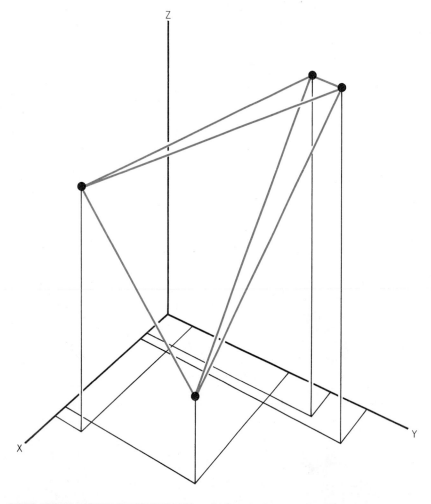

SIMILARITY CAN BE REPRESENTED as the distance between the objects to be classified (called operational taxonomic units, or OTU's for short) in a multidimensional space. In this example the similarity between all possible pairs taken from four objects is estimated on the basis of three characters, which are represented by the three coordinates axes *X*, *Y* and *Z*. The OTU's (*black balls*) are then plotted into this three-dimensional space according to their state, or value, for the three characters. Similar objects are plotted much closer to one another than dissimilar ones. In any real case there will, of course, be more than three characters and a multidimensional space—called a "hyperspace"—would be necessary.

This is the difference between the terms "classification" and "identification." When a set of unordered objects has been grouped on the basis of like properties, biologists call this "classification." Once a classification has been established the allocation of additional unidentified objects to the correct class is generally known as "identification." Thus a person using a key to the known wild flowers of Yellowstone National Park "identifies" a given specimen as a goldenrod. Some mathematicians and philosophers would also call this second process classification, but I shall strictly distinguish between the two. Here I am principally concerned with classification in the biologist's sense.

The purpose of taxonomy is to group the objects to be classified into "natural" taxa. Naturalness has been variously defined, but underlying the several definitions is the common idea that members of a natural taxon are mutually more highly related to one another than they are to nonmembers. This leads us to try to define what we mean by "taxonomic relationship." Conventional taxonomists wish to equate taxonomic relationships with evolutionary relationships, but numerical taxonomists have pointed out that taxonomic relations are actually of three kinds. "Phenetic" relationships are those based on overall similarity among the objects to be classified. "Cladistic" relationships are based on common lines of descent. Although close cladistic relationship generally implies close phenetic similarity, it is not always the case. Differences in evolutionary rates may give rise to lineages that diverged long ago but appear more similar than a subsequently diverged pair of stems, one or both of which has undergone rapid evolution [*see top illustration at left*]. The third kind of taxonomic relationship is the "chronistic," or temporal, relation among various evolutionary branches. Cladistic relationships for most organisms are known scantily, if at all, and are generally inferred from phenetic evidence. The "phylogenetic" classifications of conventional taxonomy are usually based on an undefined mixture of phenetic and cladistic relationships, and often merely represent an overall similarity among the classified organisms disguised in evolutionary terminology.

In view of these considerations numerical taxonomists propose to base classifications entirely on resemblance, defining natural classifications as those yielding taxa whose members are in some sense more similar to one another than they are to members of other taxa. It follows from this concept of naturalness, which is based on the ideas of J. S. L. Gilmour, a botanist at the University of Cambridge, that a natural taxon will be most predictive. If a classification is based on many correlated characters, predictions about the states of other characters in various groupings of the classification should be more successful than if the taxonomy were based on few characters. Furthermore, it is likely that a classification based on a great variety of characters will be of general utility to biology as a whole, whereas a classification resting on only a few characters is less likely to be generally useful, except for the special purposes relevant to the chosen characters. Thus a classification of animals into "swamp dwellers" and "animals not living in swamps" may be very useful for a study of the ecology of swamps but not for general zoology.

Overall phenetic similarity is based on all available characters without any differential weighting of some characters over others. A substantial part of the controversy about numerical taxonomy has centered on this point. Conventional taxonomists usually employ only a few characters in classification and weight these in terms of their presumed evolutionary importance. Numerical taxonomists contend that evolutionary importance is undefinable and generally unknown and that no consistent scheme for weighting characters before undertaking a classification has yet been proposed. To weight characters on the basis of their ability to distinguish groups in a classification, as is frequently advocated, is a logical fallacy. Since the purpose of employing the characters is to establish a classification, one cannot first assume what these classes are and then use them to measure the diagnostic weight of a character.

The nature of similarity is, of course, a fundamental problem of taxonomy, whatever one's theoretical approach. This ancient philosophical problem has recently become acute in a variety of fields because of the introduction of automata for classification and identification. What is the meaning of the statement "A is similar to B"? Only when qualified to the effect that "A is similar to B in such and such a respect" has this statement any meaning. It is one of the underlying assumptions

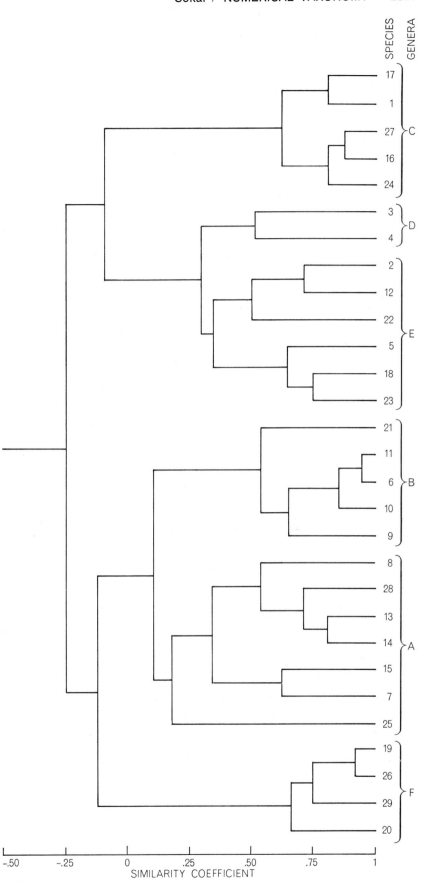

PHENOGRAM is a convenient two-dimensional representation of the results of a numerical classification, in this case the results of classifying the 29 recent species of Caminalcules depicted on pages 2308 and 2309. The species are indicated by the numbers at the tips of the branches. Phenograms tend to distort the original multidimensional relationships.

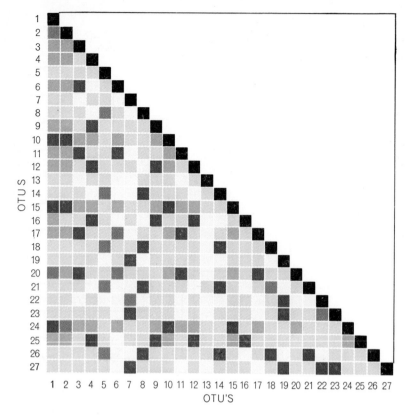

OTU'S

OTU'S

DISSIMILARITY (PHENETIC DISTANCE)

| 0 | .09–.48 | .49–88 | .89–1.28 | 1.29–1.68 | 1.69–2.08 |

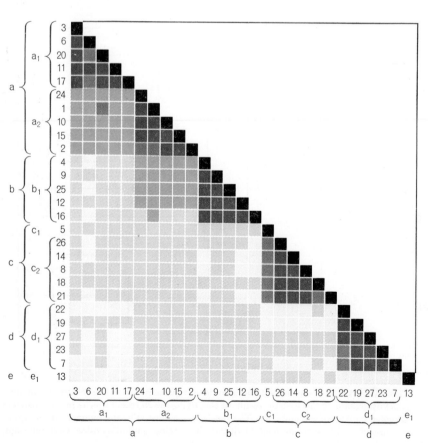

of numerical taxonomy that quantification of degrees of similarity is possible. The establishment of comparative similarities—for example "*A* is more similar to *B* than it is to *C*"—is fundamental to any attempt at clustering objects into homogeneous groups.

Similarity can be established only on the basis of homologous, or corresponding, characters. Hence it is not possible to compare the forelimbs of vertebrates without prior agreement on what to call a forelimb in each of the vertebrates to be compared, and on the correspondences between constituent parts of the appendages. Homology, as interpreted by numerical taxonomists, is the existing overall similarity in structure rather than similarity due to common ancestry, although this may often be the underlying cause. To describe such essential similarity one needs to base it on numerous "unit characters" of the structures to be compared. Numerical taxonomists regard unit characters as those that cannot be subdivided into logically or empirically independent characters. This is a complex subject, however, since the same set of biological characters can be described in innumerable slightly varying ways. One would not wish to use all these descriptions, yet how can one avoid redundancy by choosing the best ones?

Another problem is how many characters to choose for describing phenetic similarities. Is there an asymptotic similarity among organisms that is approached as more and more characters are measured, or will each additional set of characters contribute a new dimension to similarity, making the taxonomic structure of a group inherently unstable? All the evidence on this complicated question is not yet in. It might be assumed that if one knew the genetic fine structure of organisms, one could then develop an overall measure of similarity among organisms based on similarity of genetic structure.

SIMILARITY MATRIXES have been shaded to show the degree of similarity between pairs of 27 OTU's (in this case individuals from seven species of nematode worms). The darker the squares, the greater the similarity. The matrix at top has the OTU's arranged according to an arbitrary sequence of code numbers. The matrix at bottom has been rearranged to yield clusters of similar OTU's. The dark triangles along the diagonal indicate species; larger, less dark triangles represent genera. OTU 13 is not closely related to any of the other OTU's (*see illustration on opposite page*).

Yet even this would present complications, since the genetic code as it is now understood is in the nature of a program, certain portions of which come into play at different times during the development of an organism. Similarity in the programs might not reflect similarity in the products, and it is by no means certain whether genes or their effects should form the basis of a classification.

Moreover, since we do not as yet have measures of similarity between different genetic codes (except for certain limited instances), we are forced to resort to the morphological and physiological characters employed in conventional taxonomy. Recently we have found that although different types of characters in a taxonomic study may be correlated, this correlation is not sufficiently strong for a classification based on one set of characters (for example external characters) to agree fully with a classification based on a second set (for example internal characters). Thus a taxonomy of males may differ somewhat from one of females, and a classification of skeletal parts may not agree entirely with one based on soft parts. This is a necessary consequence of phenetic classification, and in order to obtain valid measures of overall similarity one has to use as many and as varied sets of characters as possible.

If classifications are to be established on overall similarity, numerical taxonomy is required to put the procedures on an operational and quantitative basis. Some of the procedures of numerical taxonomy were developed as early as the beginning of this century, but before the introduction of digital computers they never caught on, presumably because of the insuperable computational difficulties. The philosophical origins of the present development in taxonomy derive from the work of Michel Adanson, an 18th-century French botanist, who first rejected a priori assumptions on the importance of different characters and proposed basing natural taxa on his essentially phenetic concept of "affinity."

The recent development of numerical taxonomy starts with the almost simultaneous publication in 1957 of papers advocating this method by Peter H. A. Sneath, a British microbiologist, and by Charles D. Michener and myself, both entomologists at the University of Kansas. Two further independent studies by workers at the University of Ox-

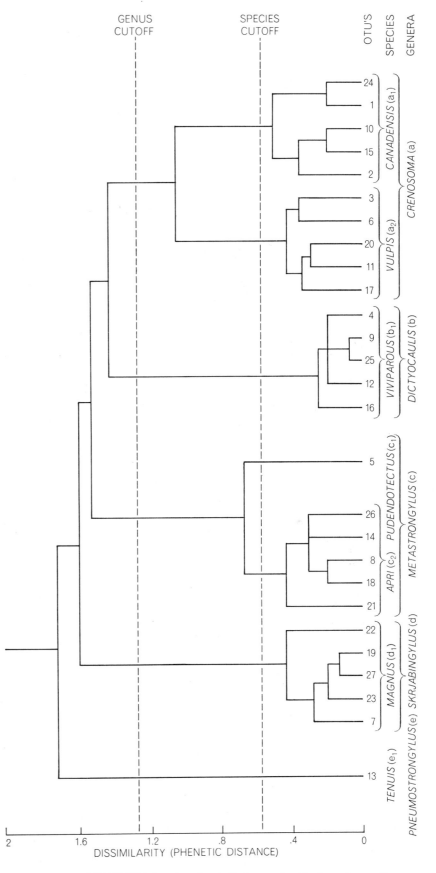

NEMATODE PHENOGRAM is based on the similarity matrix at bottom of opposite page. The brackets and lettering correspond to similar brackets and lettering in the similarity matrix. Broken vertical lines are "cutoff lines" for recognizing species and genera, which are indicated by their full names at right. Code numbers for OTU's are at tips of branches. Rearrangement of first two species has no effect on the taxonomic relationship illustrated.

ford and at the New York Botanical Garden followed in 1958 and 1960 respectively. Since that time the literature and the number of workers in the field have grown rapidly. At last count there were at least 200 published papers on numerical taxonomy, with more than 60 papers applying numerical taxonomy to diverse groups of organisms.

How does one produce a classification by numerical taxonomy? The objects to be classified are called "operational taxonomic units," or OTU's for short. They may be individuals as such, individuals representing species or higher-ranking taxa such as genera or families of plants or animals, or statistical abstractions of the higher-ranking taxonomic groups.

Classifications by numerical taxonomy are based on many numerically

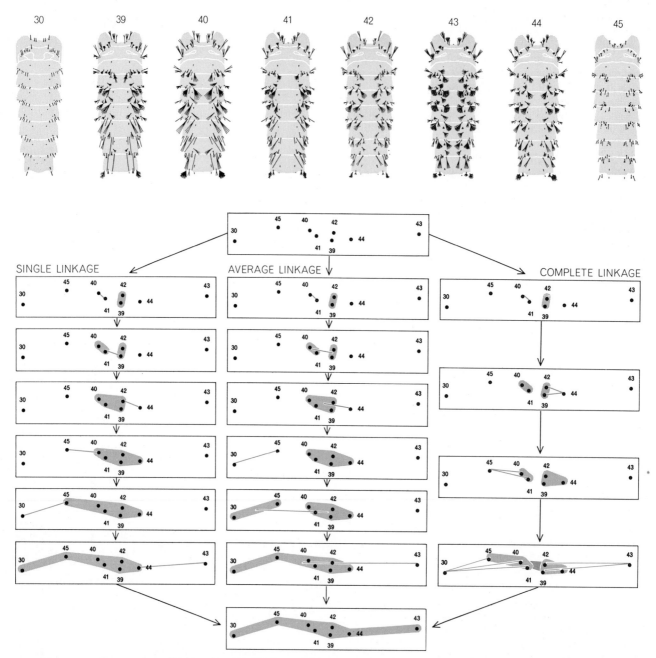

DIFFERENT CLUSTERING TECHNIQUES yield different classifications of the same taxonomic units. The numbered black dots represent eight species of mosquitoes described by pupal characteristics only (*drawings at top*). Species 30 belongs to the genus *Mansonia*; the others are species of *Anopheles*. For convenience of representation, distances among OTU's are shown in two-dimensional space only. Linkages between OTU's and clusters and between pairs of clusters are shown by solid-colored lines, previously established clusters by light-colored shading of the area occupied by the clustered OTU's. As clustering proceeds step by step the criteria for joining become less stringent; in other words, the distances between prospective joiners and established clusters increase. The single-linkage method (*left*) starts with the shortest distance between any pair of OTU's and takes up the other distances in order of magnitude. In average linkage (*center*) an OTU will join a cluster if the average distance between it and the "center of gravity" of the cluster is less than for any other such distance in the study. In complete linkage (*right*) joining takes place only when the relationships between a candidate for joining and established members of the clusters are all at the minimum criterion for a given clustering cycle. Although the initial clustering step is the same for all three methods and the final cluster, including all the OTU's, must necessarily also be the same, the intermediate clustering steps are obviously quite different at roughly equivalent stages. The results depicted here will not necessarily agree with comparable studies that include additional closely related OTU's.

recorded characters. These may be measurements that are appropriately represented numerically, or they may be coded in such a way that the differences between them are proportional to their dissimilarity. For example, a character called "hairiness of leaf" might be coded as follows: hairless, 0; sparsely haired, 1; regularly haired, 2; densely haired, 3. By this coding system we imply that the dissimilarity between densely haired and hairless is approximately three times the dissimilarity between sparsely haired and hairless. In some fields, such as microbiology, characters are almost always expressed by only two states corresponding to the presence (1) or the absence (0) of a given character, for example an enzyme.

All the characters and the taxonomic units to be classified are arranged in a data matrix, and the similarities between all possible pairs of OTU's are then computed based on all the characters. We shall not concern ourselves here with the variety of mathematical coefficients that have been devised to represent similarity between objects. One way of representing similarity (actually dissimilarity) is the distance between OTU's in a multidimensional space. Suppose the similarity between all possible pairs taken from four objects is to be estimated on the basis of three characters. We can visualize these characters as representing three coordinate axes [*see bottom illustration on page 2310*]. Each OTU is plotted into this three-dimensional space according to its state, or value, for the three characters. Those objects that are very similar will be plotted close to each other; dissimilar ones will be considerably farther apart. The computation of such straight-line distances is quite simple. In any real case there will, of course, be more than three characters and a multidimensional space would be necessary. Although it is not possible to represent such a "hyperspace" pictorially, the computation of distances within it is still quite simple. Thus we can view the objects to be classified as clusters of points in multidimensional space.

The similarities between pairs of OTU's are evaluated by a computer and printed out in a "similarity matrix," which shows the similarity value of each OTU with respect to every other one. Rather than give such a numerical table here, I have illustrated it graphically on page 2312, indicating magnitude of the similarity coefficient by depth of shading. Unless the OTU's to

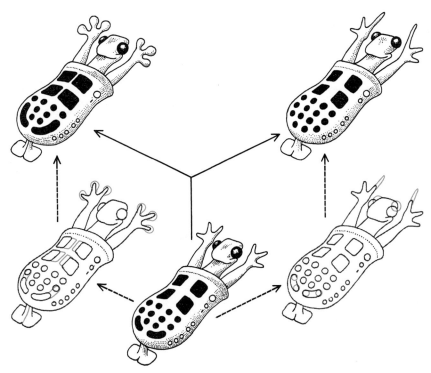

GENETIC CONTINUITY was accomplished in the generation of the Caminalcules by tracing the drawing of the primitive species (*bottom*) from sheet to sheet, making possible the preservation of all characters except for the desired morphological modifications (*color*).

be classified have been ordered previously, the pattern of shading in the similarity matrix is likely to be complex. We can attempt, however, to alter the arrangement of the OTU's in such a way that the dark-shaded areas (high-similarity values) will condense in triangular groups along the diagonal of the table. This procedure will yield a rough classification of these OTU's into groups.

For more precise classifications a variety of numerical clustering procedures have been developed, and these procedures are routinely carried out on the computer after the similarity matrix has been calculated. There is no generally accepted clustering method. Different methods will yield different results, depending on the underlying "similarity structure" of the objects to be clustered [*see illustration on opposite page*]. Attempts are being made currently to define an "optimal" classification mathematically so that the results of a numerical classification can be evaluated by this criterion.

The results of a numerical classification are usually represented by means of a "phenogram." These treelike diagrams indicate the similarity between OTU's or stems bearing more than one OTU along one axis. Because phenograms collapse multidimensional relationships into two dimensions, there is appreciable distortion of the original

relationships as shown in the similarity matrix. Estimates of the degree of distortion in a given phenogram are made routinely in numerical taxonomic studies as a precaution. Representing phenetic relationships by three-dimensional models of OTU's avoids some of the distortions encountered in phenograms. Since such models cannot be circulated widely, the possibility of publishing computer-produced "stereograms"—two-dimensional projections of three-dimensional models—is currently being investigated.

Describing the similarities among organisms is only one aim of taxonomy. Another is to trace the evolutionary lineages that gave rise to the diversity of organic life that exists today. To reconstruct the taxonomic relationships and evolutionary trends among a group of organisms one would need to describe their phenetic relationships through all points in time. One would also have to describe the group's "cladistics," the branching sequences in the evolutionary trees. Finally, one must furnish a correct time scale to the evolutionary reconstruction. At the moment there is no known way—short of a multidimensional reconstruction, which is impossible of practical achievement—to incorporate these elements into a unified system without large distortion of the phenetic relationships.

Some substantial recent advances in

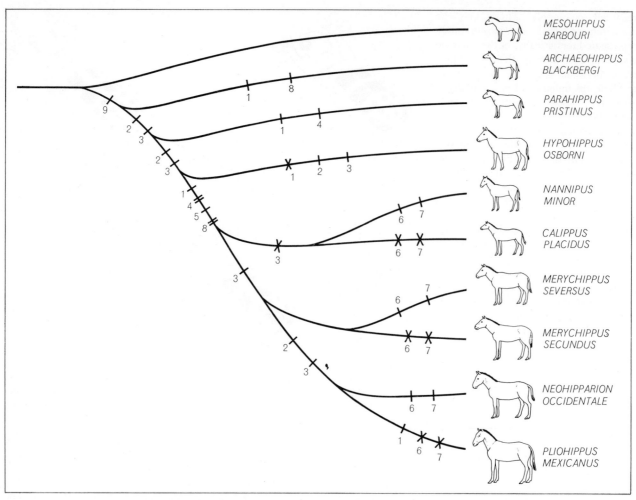

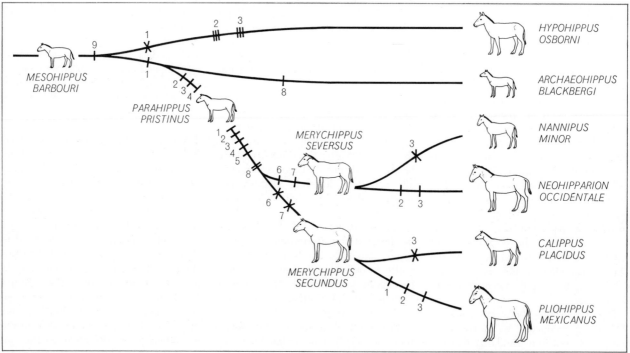

CLADOGRAMS, diagrams that delineate the branching sequences in an evolutionary tree, are shown here for a group of fossil horses. A computer program developed by Camin and the author constructs cladograms with the fewest number of evolutionary steps. The cladogram at top shows an early stage in the procedure; the one at bottom shows the most parsimonious solution, in which the 35 steps at top have been reduced to 31 steps. The cladogram at bottom corresponds to evolutionary branching sequence generally accepted by paleontologists. The evolutionary steps for various numbered skeletal and dental characters are marked on the branches. In the bidirectional evolution of a character one direction is shown by lines across branches, the other by X marks.

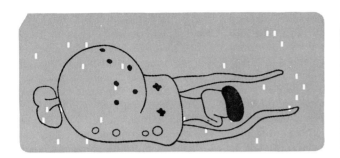

AUTOMATIC SCANNING of organisms for the purpose of establishing phenetic classifications was proved to be feasible in a recent experiment performed by F. James Rohlf and the author in which they successively placed 25 punch cards, each perforated with 25 randomly chosen holes, over drawings of a group of Caminalcules. One of the punch cards is shown at left superposed over a drawing of a Caminalcule belonging to species 1. In making the composite at right each of the 625 holes was scored 1 when a black line appeared through it and 0 when no black showed. (Actually fewer than 625 holes are visible here, since many holes on different cards coincided.) The illustrations of the organisms were compared on the basis of matching scores for corresponding masks and holes.

techniques for reconstructing cladistic sequences grew out of an experiment on the principles and practices of taxonomy carried out by a group of graduate students and faculty members at the University of Kansas. The study was based on a group of imaginary animals generated by Joseph H. Camin according to rules known so far only to him but believed to be consistent with what is generally known of evolutionary principles. Genetic continuity was accomplished by tracing the drawings of the animals from sheet to sheet, permitting the preservation of all characters except for the modifications that were desired. All 29 "recent" species of these "organisms," irreverently named Caminalcules by the graduate students, are shown on pages 2308 and 2309. Detailed studies of the assemblage of hypothetical animals by orthodox phylogenetic methodology by team members resulted in differing, but internally consistent, cladistic schemes, the choice among which was not easily apparent. Comparison by Camin of these various schemes with the "truth" led him to the observation that those trees that most closely resembled the true cladistic sequence invariably required for their construction the fewest number of postulated evolutionary steps for the characters studied.

Our experiments were based on three working assumptions: first, that character states could be numerically coded according to their presumed evolutionary trends; second, that evolution is irreversible, so that when a character evolves to state 2, it will not revert to state 1; third, that nature is fundamentally parsimonious, so that the diversity in character states within a given group was achieved at or close to the minimum number of evolutionary steps. From these assumptions Ca-

min and I developed a computational technique that constructs the most parsimonious cladistic tree, or cladogram, from an original data matrix. A computer program carries out these computations. The cladograms on the opposite page illustrate the type of change that is routinely carried out by the computer program. The cladograms estimate the branching sequences that occurred in the evolutionary history of a group of fossil horses. These methods have also given apparently meaningful results in studies of bees, vipers, certain plants, fossil protozoa and the structural rearrangements of chromosomes in blackflies and drosophila.

The computer program also evaluates the compatibility of each characteristic with all the other characters and weights it in terms of this criterion. It points out inconsistencies and has repeatedly discovered errors in coding, transcription or interpretation of the data.

A major impetus for the development and application of numerical taxonomy is the current introduction of automatic sensing and data-recording devices. The development of such instruments has proceeded very rapidly in recent years. Most prominent among the devices likely to be useful in taxonomy are optical scanners, which digitize drawings, photographs, microscope preparations and results of biochemical analysis. The veritable flood of information that will flow from these automatic sensors will require computer-based processing and classification, since the human mind is not able to digest these data by traditional means.

Recently F. James Rohlf and I have shown that data of this kind, collected in a quite unsophisticated manner, can be used to form adequate phe-

netic classifications. We employed the straightforward approach of recording agreement in visible structures over randomly selected minute areas of the images of pairs of organisms. Such a procedure would be feasible by means of optical scanners. Random masks, made from 25 punch cards each perforated with 25 randomly chosen holes, were placed over black-and-white drawings of two groups of "organisms." One group consisted of the 29 recent species of the Caminalcules; the second comprised published illustrations of the pupae of 32 species of mosquitoes. Each illustration was overlaid with all the masks, and each of the 625 holes was scored 1 when a black line appeared through it and 0 when no black showed [see illustration above]. Illustrations were compared on the basis of matching scores for corresponding masks and holes. A numerical classification of the images was surprisingly similar to studies by conventional taxonomy or by numerical taxonomy based on the detailed description of characters. Whenever phenetic taxonomies are acceptable, automatic scanning and classification may provide a rapid and reliable approach. Problems of the size and orientation of the organisms remain to be worked out, but they should not present insuperable technical difficulties. The implications of the success of this method are that experience and insight into the presumed biological and phylogenetic significance of characters may be less important for obtaining satisfactory classifications than had been generally supposed.

Thus there is every reason to believe that classifications from automatically obtained characters are possible. This finding will, of course, lead not only to automatic classification but also to automatic identification, which should be one of the more exciting prospects for research workers faced with routine identification problems.

Numerical taxonomists working in biological taxonomy are continually surprised and impressed by the applicability of their principles in numerous sciences and other fields of human activity. They marvel at the rapidity with which this knowledge is spreading throughout the biological, medical, geological and social sciences, as well as the humanities. Numerical taxonomy has been employed to classify soils and diseases, politicians and plant communities, archaeological artifacts and oil-bearing strata, socioeconomic neighborhoods and psychological types, languages and television programs—to name just some of the applications. Sneath has even used it to solve a jigsaw puzzle. This broad spectrum of applications for numerical taxonomy should not surprise us. After all, the precise categorization of human experience is one of the foundations for a scientific understanding of the universe. We should not, however, be overly impressed by the similarities in approach in these various sciences. There are appreciable differences in the principles of classification in diverse fields, and it is necessary to know when the problems of one discipline part company with those of another. Nonetheless, the common fund of basic ideas on similarity and classification is great enough to serve as the basis for a general science of taxonomy.

Biological taxonomy will be affected by the computer in many ways besides numerical taxonomy. Automatic data processing will revolutionize the storage and retrieval of taxonomic information for museums and catalogues. The approaches of numerical taxonomy have already done much to de-emphasize the often legalistic and sterile aspects of naming organisms. It is likely that developments in automatic data processing will rapidly relegate problems of nomenclature to the position of relative unimportance they merit. Some of the birth pangs of automation will be felt in taxonomy as in other fields, and traditionally-minded workers will presumably resist the changes. The controversy about numerical taxonomy will doubtless continue for some time to come until a new "synthetic" theory of taxonomy, accepting what is soundest from various schools, becomes established. The revolution the computer has wrought in taxonomy has only just begun.

The Author

ROBERT R. SOKAL is professor of statistical biology at the University of Kansas. Sokal was born in Vienna in 1926 but moved with his family to China at the beginning of World War II and received his high school and undergraduate education in Shanghai, where he obtained a B.S. in biology from St. John's University. He came to the U.S. in 1947 and acquired a Ph.D. in zoology at the University of Chicago in 1952. He has been a member of the Kansas faculty since 1951. Sokal is a National Institutes of Health career investigator. During 1959–1960 he was a National Science Foundation Senior Postdoctoral Fellow at University College London, and during 1963–1964 he was a Fulbright visiting professor at Hebrew University and Tel Aviv University in Israel. He is coauthor, with Peter H. A. Sneath, of *The Principles of Numerical Taxonomy*. Sokal wishes to acknowledge the assistance and constructive criticisms of Sneath, Joseph H. Camin, Charles D. Michener and F. James Rohlf in the preparation of this article.

Bibliography

A METHOD FOR DEDUCING BRANCHING SEQUENCES IN PHYLOGENY. Joseph H. Camin and Robert R. Sokal in *Evolution*, Vol. 19, No. 3, pages 311–326; September, 1965.

NUMERICAL PHENETICS AND TAXONOMIC THEORY. Ernst Mayr in *Systematic Zoology*, Vol. 14, No. 3, pages 237–243; September, 1965.

PRINCIPLES OF NUMERICAL TAXONOMY. Robert R. Sokal and Peter H. A. Sneath. W. H. Freeman and Company, 1963.

THE TWO TAXONOMIES: AREAS OF AGREEMENT AND OF CONFLICT. Robert R. Sokal and Joseph H. Camin in *Systematic Zoology*, Vol. 14, No. 3, pages 176–195; September, 1965.

SCIENTIFIC
AMERICAN January 1967, Vol. 216, No. 1, pp. 78-85   OFFPRINT 1060

RATS

by S. A. Barnett

These ubiquitous companions of man are detested as dangerous
pests, but they are worth studying for their own sake. Their social
behavior is subtly adapted to maintain the integrity of the group.

"The Common or Brown Rat is probably the most injurious and universal pest of the human race.... It does not appear to have a single redeeming feature." This forceful judgment, delivered by the English zoologists G. E. H. Barrett-Hamilton and M. A. C. Hinton half a century ago, reflects a widespread and partly justified horror of wild rats. Nevertheless, these animals are worth study for their own sake and not only as pests.

The species to which Barrett-Hamilton and Hinton referred is *Rattus norvegicus,* often called for no good reason the Norway rat. As a result of its emigrations during the past few centuries this animal is now present in most of the cold, temperate and subtropical regions of the world occupied by man; its range includes almost all of North America and much of Central and South America. In the Tropics, however, it is evidently at a disadvantage compared with other rats, notably *Rattus rattus,* commonly known as the black rat.

R. norvegicus is heavily built and often looks clumsy; it has small ears and a thick tail shorter than its head and body combined. A well-fed male may weigh a pound and attain a body length of nine inches. *R. rattus* is more delicately built and rarely reaches two-thirds of a pound. It has large ears and a long, slender tail [*see bottom illustration on next page*]. The two species cannot reliably be distinguished by color. *Norvegicus,* the "brown" rat, is sometimes black. *Rattus,* the "black" rat, has several color varieties. In warm countries, where it lives in the open, it is most often tawny; the black variety is common only where most of the rats live in buildings. Although *rattus* is more attractive in appearance than *norvegicus,* it is regarded with equal hostility by man, since it is commonly thought of as the principal carrier of plague.

Both species depend almost entirely on human communities for food and shelter, but they differ markedly in detail. *Rattus* thrives in a warm environment; it remains lively at temperatures that prostrate *norvegicus,* and in cold climates it lives only in buildings. *Norvegicus* is a burrowing animal and lives readily in hedgerows, earth banks, haystacks and the ground near sewers and streams. (It is a good swimmer.) *Rattus* is a climber. It has not been observed to burrow or swim; it can nest in trees. In ports such as London both species sometimes live in the same building—*norvegicus* in the basement and *rattus* in the attic. *Rattus* is often called the roof rat.

In temperate regions, including most of Europe, *rattus* is now found almost wholly in ports; in hot countries such as India the same is true of *norvegicus.* But *rattus* was widespread in Europe before *norvegicus* arrived there.

There are many tales, usually mythical, of large-scale movements by *norvegicus.* According to one that is often told, a massive invasion of Europe began in 1727; a German naturalist, Peter Simon Pallas, is said to have seen an army of these animals swimming the Volga at Astrakhan. But Pallas was not born until 1741, and the rats he described were crossing the Volga not toward Europe but in the opposite direction. At any rate, although rats sometimes emigrate in substantial numbers over short distances, the spread of *norvegicus* over Europe and other parts of the world must have been a fairly slow process.

It is commonly assumed that, when the two species meet, the larger *norvegicus* tears *rattus* to pieces, but this is unlikely. The only relevant experiment I know of was carried out in the winter of 1949–1950. My colleagues and I set up colonies of the two species in adjoining compartments of a converted stable near London. For the purposes of the experiment a door between the compartments was removed and a single source of food was put at the opening. Almost at once the largest *norvegicus* entered the other room and drove the *rattus* that lived in it from their nests. Thirteen of the *rattus* soon died, but six exceptionally belligerent individuals remained [*see illustration on page 2324*]. The deaths were not due to wounding, nor was there any evidence of starvation. As we shall see, the direct cause of death in such circumstances remains quite mysterious.

The rest of this account is devoted mainly to *norvegicus,* the "common" rat. What has made this species so successful in human environments? Among its assets are, first, its ability to live hugger-mugger in crowded underground colonies and, second, its readiness to eat anything man does.

Since rats are usually active only at night and live under cover, intimate knowledge of their social life depends on observing them in artificial colonies. From a single pair in a spacious cage or enclosure a large and thriving family can develop. How quickly a given population is attained can be calculated from the following approximations. A female rears six young per litter; the young are sexually mature after four months (later than laboratory rats); the gestation period is three weeks; a female can easily rear four litters in a year, even allowing for a period of infertility that may occur in winter.

Alternatively, a colony can be started with a group of young rats. They must be juveniles, because if adult males and

BROWN RAT, *Rattus norvegicus,* is the larger of the two species of rats that are most closely associated with man. A well-fed male may weigh one pound and attain a body length of nine inches; its ears are small and its thick tail is shorter than its body. The species varies in color: some individuals are black and the laboratory white rat is an albino variety. Brown rats are burrowers.

BLACK RAT, *Rattus rattus,* is the smaller species. It rarely weighs more than 11 ounces or exceeds seven inches in body length. Its ears are large and its tail is long and slender. Its color varies even more than the brown rat's; city-dwelling individuals are usually black but those that live in the open often have tawny coats. Unlike brown rats, black rats seek heights and even nest in trees.

females are put together the males come into conflict.

What happens if a strange rat is introduced into a peaceful family group? If the newcomer is a juvenile, it is ignored; if it is an adult female, it is ignored unless it is in estrus, when the males will attempt coitus (and probably succeed). If, however, it is an adult male, it is vigorously attacked. The attacks are not concerted; there is no "pack" behavior. Individual males act independently.

This intolerance of strangers is common among vertebrates. A region is defended, by a pair or by a larger group, against others of the same species. Among rats the defended region, or "territory," is held by a group in spite of the lack of cooperation among its members.

A prime effect of territorial behavior is to disperse the members of a population. Unfortunately we know little about the density of rat populations, although many guesses have been published. The most reliable census method is one devised by Dennis Chitty and Monica Shorten of the University of Oxford. Piles of wheat grain are put down at many points near the burrows of rats and on their runways, and the amount eaten is recorded. When daily consumption levels off, this quantity in grams is divided by 24 to give the minimum number of rats present. (The mean daily consumption of grain by the common rat is about 24 grams.)

Censuses by this method were taken in two English farming villages in 1948 and 1949. One village had 364 people, 55 cats, 25 dogs and at least 330 rats; the other had 266 people, 43 cats, 14 dogs and at least 180 rats. The rat populations—about as many rats as people— were probably unusually high. Good hygiene and efficient control by poison baiting could have kept numbers down.

Each village had about 15 distinct rat colonies, which were associated with sources of food such as farm buildings. The creation of a source of food, such as a new chicken run, quickly attracted rats where there had been none before. Rats are highly exploratory; hence they soon find new food supplies or other favorable features in their living area. The same kind of effect may be seen if a rat population is largely wiped out. The destruction by poisoning of most of the rats in a system of sewers, for instance, has often been followed by a rapid inflow of other rats, presumably from colonies in the surrounding earth or in the buildings above.

What controls the growth of a rat colony? When a few rats begin to breed in an area with plenty of food and cover, their rate of increase is slow at first, but it becomes rapid when there are plenty of fecund females; later it slows again. As density increases, several hostile forces can be expected to act progressively against still further increase. Predation by dogs, hawks and man may become more intense; nest sites for rearing young will be less easily found; infectious disease may increase. Any of these (or a shortage of food) could put a ceiling on further growth.

It is possible, however, that none will do so, and that social interactions will limit density before food and shelter fail, and before predators or parasites do more than kill the old and the weak. D. E. Davis, then at Johns Hopkins University, reduced a rat population by half by a strenuous trapping operation. The pregnancy rate of the survivors doubled in two months. Crowding evidently interferes with breeding, but we do not know just how. Females with litters may be pestered by males, although ordinarily a parturient female can drive away intruders from her nest merely by making sounds and perhaps a snapping movement of her head.

It is possible that the regulating process is far more complex, and involves several factors acting together. Hunger, for instance, increases aggressiveness in rats (as it does in man). Perhaps social interactions in a colony change when food becomes more difficult to get. If so, an increasing tendency among the colony members to attack other rats could reduce the fertility of the females and enhance centrifugal movement. The position of food and nests may also interact with territorial attacks. John B. Calhoun of the National Institute of Mental Health set up a large artificial colony of wild rats in Baltimore with a single, central source of food. Rats living at the periphery were at a considerable disadvantage, since they were subjected to attack by rats living in an inner circle nearer the food.

At the University of Glasgow we have made detailed studies of social behavior in colonies of wild rats. Rather surprisingly, if adult males were put together in a strange cage, they settled down without strife, grew well and survived (if left to do so) to old age. But if females were included, the result was a high death rate among the males; sometimes after a few weeks only one male remained, usually the largest. Yet the males did not fight for the females. Conflict flares when males are aroused by a female not yet in estrus and are frustrated in their attempts at coitus. Evidently sexual excitement without consummation lowers the threshold for territorial fighting among males. Recent experiments (as yet unpublished) have confirmed this. Resident males attack newcomers more vigorously if females are present than if they are absent.

Since male rats are combative animals, there must be something that makes them peaceable within the colony. Some species achieve this by a status system: each member of a herd or colony has a social status, or position in a peck order, that determines its behavior—dominant or submissive—toward other members. It is easy to assume that there is a regular "dominance hierarchy" among rats, but there is no good evidence for anything so elaborate. In artificial colonies all females are equal, but males of three types are observed.

The "alphas" move about without regard to other rats. Their movements are brisk; their skin is sleek; they grow well. There may be several alphas, in this sense, in one colony. "Betas" too look healthy and grow well, but they retreat at the approach of an alpha. The status of beta is reached (as in formal peck orders) through the experience of clashes; the beta has adapted itself to a "subordinate" role. Again, there may be several betas in a colony. Betas also behave subserviently toward strange males (which would ordinarily be attacked). They even greet strange males of a different species, R. rattus, in this way. Evidently the adoption of the beta status entails almost total inhibition of aggressive behavior.

The third kind of male is the "omega." It does not belong in a stable rat colony; this status soon ends in death. Most newcomers to an established colony rapidly fall into the omega position. Their fur is staring or bedraggled; they move about listlessly; they lose weight; they withdraw at the approach of another male. Perhaps in a large natural colony these distinctions would not be so clear. Omegas would hardly be found, but there might be "gammas," less flourishing than the sleek betas of laboratory experiments but not in a state of rapid decline.

None of this accounts for the difference between the pacific attitude toward fellow colony members and the attacks on strangers. Probably the distinction is made principally or wholly by odor. When strangers are present in

SUBMISSIVE POSTURE is assumed by a male brown rat (*left*) when confronted by another male. He lies on his side with eyes half-closed. This is one of several social signals that appear to prevent attack. Female rats sometimes adopt this submissive posture.

UNDERCRAWL is another action that a subordinate male (a "beta") may perform on meeting another male. Both black rats and brown rats have been observed acting in this way.

GROOMING is another social gesture that involves bodily contact both between male rats and between males and females. "Amicable" actions of this sort probably prevent attacks.

ONE-SIDED FIGHT takes place when a resident male (*right*) confronts a stranger. The stranger, shown in a defensive posture, may squeal or run away but does not fight. The resident may never draw blood, but a stranger that is persistently attacked dies in a few hours.

a colony, there is a marked increase in "recognition sniffing" among the residents. Evidently the members possess a specific scent that inhibits attack. Moreover, rats leave odor trails as they move about. The passage of rats over a white surface such as a whitewashed wall leaves a dark smear containing odorous secretions; these apparently attract other rats.

Other social signals that seem to inhibit aggression involve posture or bodily contact. A beta male, deficient in aggression, may greet another male with a "submissive" posture: he lies on his side with eyes half-closed. Or he may crawl under the newcomer, a quite specific act performed by *rattus* as well as by *norvegicus*. A third harmless and seemingly "amicable" act is grooming another rat. All of these acts can be seen among males of a stable colony, and the "submissive" posture is sometimes adopted by females also.

It is all too easy to guess at the function of these performances, but to interpret them with certainty is difficult. For instance, some people regard the grooming of one male by another as not amicable but as a muted form of aggression. This illustrates the hazardous subjectivity that is likely to influence our accounts of such behavior. What do we mean by "amicable behavior"? Crawling under another rat is a harmless action performed in situations in which conflict might occur; the word "amicable" is used in this article to name such behavior. These actions probably help to prevent attack by their effect on the animal to which they are directed (although this is not included in the definition). The extent to which they do have this effect is a matter for further experiment. Certainly some fierce males on their own ground are persistently belligerent toward strangers, whatever the latter do.

Although strangers are attacked, rats do not fight in the human sense: the attacked rat never retaliates. A typical assault begins when a large, ferocious male in his own territory approaches a strange male. His teeth chatter and his hair is raised; as he approaches he defecates and urinates. He now sniffs the intruder, turns his flank and adopts a highly characteristic "threat posture": the legs are extended, the back is arched and the rat moves around his opponent with mincing steps. Sometimes this formality is omitted; the resident leaps straight at the intruder with rapid movements of his forelimbs (which can be seen clearly only in slow-motion pictures). At the same time he may briefly nip a limb, an ear or the tail of the defender. After a few seconds of wild leaping the bout ends, but others follow rapidly.

At the end of a series of bouts the attacker withdraws for a time, but he is by no means exhausted. He can readily turn to another activity, such as coitus. His victim, on the other hand, is often left stretched out limply, breathing rapidly and irregularly.

Persistent persecution usually ends with the death of the victim in a few days. In an extreme case death has occurred in 90 minutes. The cause of these deaths is enigmatic. They often occur in the entire absence of wounding. (The bites are usually ineffectual, since a rat's hair and skin are thick.) No internal bleeding or other such pathological signs are found. The animals, initially healthy and vigorous, drop dead. To talk of "shock" is futile. "Vagal syncope" (a phrase hardly more precise than "heart failure") is little better. (The vagus is a nerve whose action slows the heartbeat.) It does, however, indicate where we should seek the source of disorder, namely in the brain.

Unfortunately we cannot yet describe what goes on in the nervous system of a rat under attack, but we know something of other changes. There are, for example, marked effects on the adrenals. During a brief, severe attack these glands greatly increase their output of hormones, and when a rat is persistently persecuted for days or weeks the adrenals enlarge. Increased activity and enlargement of the adrenals occur in a variety of adverse conditions, such as wounding, infection and exposure to cold. Adrenal hormones help an animal to resist stressful conditions. Their secretion is itself regulated by the nervous system. Hence in the adrenal changes of attacked rats we have a physiological effect of "social stress" that parallels what happens when the body is near the limits of endurance from other causes.

The existence of "betas" presents a further problem. They show that some males can withstand the stress of being attacked and can adapt themselves to it, but we do not know what enables a rat to become a beta. We do know that experience as an alpha does not armor a male against the ill effects of being attacked. A large, fierce, healthy male, accustomed to victory over newcomers in his own territory, succumbs when subjected to attack as an intruder in another's territory.

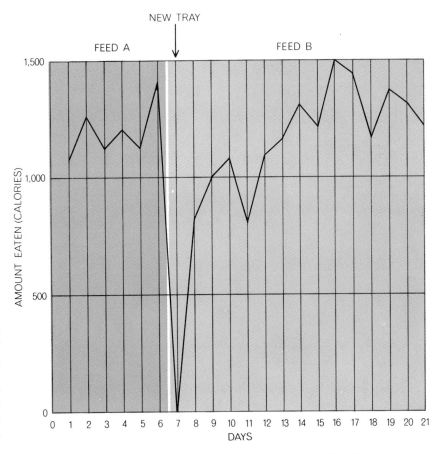

AVOIDANCE OF THE NEW is the normal behavior of wild rats in a familiar environment. Here a change from whole wheat to white flour as one item in the diet was sufficient to halt feeding. Such withdrawal from anything novel has a high survival value for the wild rat.

Nevertheless, it is doubtful that attack by a resident much smaller than the intruder would be severely traumatic. We have begun in Glasgow to study the effects of size systematically. The larger the intruder in relation to the attacker, the more time the attacker spends in the threat posture instead of in leaping and biting. This suggests that one function of the posture is to act as a harmless substitute for true attack. There is no clear evidence that it induces withdrawal in a newcomer. Perhaps its principal function is to limit conflict *within* colonies. Alphas in a stable group do posture at one another and then move away without further excitement, as if the impulse to fight had spent itself in harmless prancing.

The sexual, parental and filial behavior of rats, as well as their patterns of attack and submission, are regulated by signals typical of the species. When an adult male rat encounters a mature female, he approaches and sniffs, particularly at her genitalia. If she is not in estrus and he attempts coitus, she kicks him off with a thrust of a hind leg. If the female is receptive, she may herself approach the male and gently touch his flank with her nose. In all of this odors are evidently crucial signs of the physiological state of the performers.

Signals similarly guide a female with young. (The males have no parental role after insemination.) A pregnant female makes a nest of any material at hand. When the young are born, they are licked and assembled in a group in the nest. If the young are not licked, they do not develop the reflexes of elimination and soon die.

When the young fall or wander from the nest, they are retrieved. The young themselves make high-pitched squeaks when they need food or when they are cold. Charles Evans has recorded the noises of infant wild rats in our laboratory. They consist of a tone of about 3.1 kilocycles per second with a harmonic at 6.2 kilocycles; each squeak lasts about half a second and the squeaks are emitted at a high rate. They are readily localized by the female and no doubt guide her to strayed nestlings. A female employs several other senses in retrieving her young. Their appear-

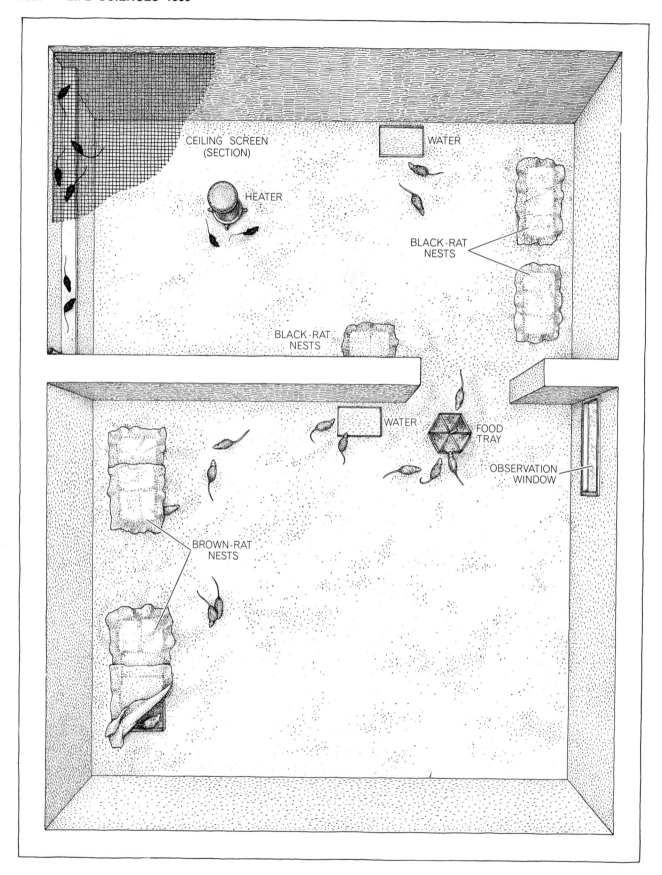

COMPETITION BETWEEN RAT SPECIES was induced experimentally by the author and his colleagues in 1949. They put colonies of brown and black rats in adjoining rooms and opened a connecting door when the brown colony totaled 29 and the black colony 19. A single feeding tray was placed by the open door. The largest of the brown rats almost immediately explored the black rats' nests (*top*). The black rats retreated to a high ledge (*top left*) or to the ceiling netting, which they left only to eat or drink. In a few days 13 of the black rats were dead, although none had been wounded. Only the six most "aggressive" of the black rats survived.

ance plays a part, including their size: larger nestlings are less reliably carried back to the nest than smaller ones. Their odor too is important. Experiment on laboratory rats has shown that no one of these features is indispensable.

The social behavior of even such simple mammals as rats clearly raises many questions. That it should do so sometimes surprises those who know only the laboratory varieties of rat. These useful creatures, a product of several decades of unnatural selection, have been much changed by domesticity. They are all members of the species *R. norvegicus,* as can easily be proved by crossing them with the wild form. Their tameness and high fertility as laboratory animals or as pets obviously set them apart from their wild cousins. They are also adapted to life in cages by having lost all the more violent forms of territorial behavior. "Attacks" on other rats mostly take the form of play, if they occur at all. The threat posture (and also amicable signals such as crawling under another rat) is usually absent. Accordingly a strange male can often be put in an occupied cage without harm.

Nevertheless, there remains much to be learned about wildness and tameness. Wild rats can be tamed if they are handled regularly from infancy. Conversely, laboratory rats left alone for long periods become fierce; this also happens if

they are allowed to run free. In Glasgow we have bred wild rats for 10 generations in the laboratory, and the later generations are less likely than their forebears to attack other rats. We do not know whether this is owing to selection of inherited differences or to the environment.

Laboratory rats have not only lost the capacity to give (and presumably to respond to) many social signals. They are also less resistant to cold than wild rats. Among other differences, they apparently lack the capacity to grow a thicker coat of hair in cold weather. Their adrenal glands are lighter than those of wild rats. Since the adrenals are particularly concerned with the immediate bodily response to stressful conditions, this appears to represent an inherited change allowed by the luxurious conditions of the laboratory.

In spite of the many differences between tame rats and wild ones, experiments on laboratory rats have given us much information about rats as animals that can survive in a natural environment. Concerning feeding behavior it is possible to combine information from the wild and the domestic forms. Wild or tame, they sample anything edible or potable they can reach. This insatiable "curiosity" and sampling would lead wild rats in man-made environments into danger but for an opposite kind of behavior. In a familiar environment any new food,

or any other new object, is initially avoided. If piles of poison bait or a number of bait boxes or traps are put in an area, the rats may completely disappear from their usual runways for a night or two. This is the main foundation of their reputation for cleverness. In human beings an automatic neophobia, or fear of anything new, is considered neurotic or stupid. For rats it has a high survival value. Probably it is strongly developed in them as a result of thousands of years of natural selection in human communities.

A further protection against man is provided by a simple learning process. A strange food, avoided at first, is later sampled in small amounts. If it is toxic, there is time for the ill effects of a small dose to develop. Feeding then ceases; when it is resumed, the rat refuses the bait (and anything that tastes like it) and may continue to do so for many months.

This "poison shyness" has an obverse characteristic in the ability to choose nutritionally favorable foods. "Dietary self-selection," first rigorously described some 30 years ago by L. J. Harris and his colleagues at the University of Cambridge, enables laboratory rats to select a mixture containing vitamin B_1 in preference to one without; rats can also adjust their intake of sodium chloride and other salts according to need. Since rats are omnivorous, in the wild state this ability no doubt helps them to achieve a balanced diet.

Avoiding dangerous foods and choosing nutritious ones depends on a kind of learning, or adapting behavior to experience. Work on the learning abilities, or intelligence, of rats has, however, been mainly directed toward the discovery of the "laws of learning" and their physiological basis; it has not been much motivated by interest in rats themselves. Nonetheless, the vast amount of work in this area has revealed something about rats as animals. Barrett-Hamilton and Hinton say they are "diabolically intelligent animals," but this notion is not borne out by their actual behavior. Laboratory rats readily learn to find their way to food or some other incentive through a system of branching passages—a maze. This ability is particularly appropriate in a burrowing animal, but it is probably widespread in the animal kingdom. The rats also display a more subtle form of learning that occurs in the *absence* of need: laboratory rats that have had the opportunity to wander about a maze when they were not hungry, and without finding food (or some other reward), can later learn, with a suitable incen-

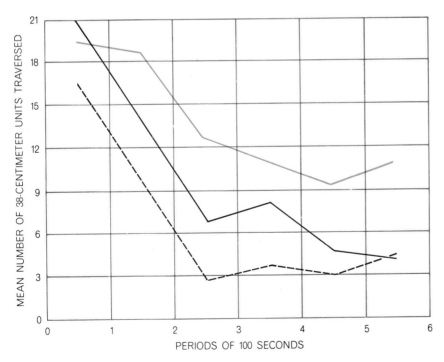

INTENSITY OF EXPLORATION by laboratory rats increases in response to greater environmental complexity. Rats put in a T-maze were more active (*colored line*) than rats put in an L-maze (*solid line*) and much more active than rats in an I-maze (*broken line*).

tive, to run through the maze correctly more quickly than rats that have never been in it. Like men, rats can pick up topographical information during casual exploration. The underlying process is called latent or exploratory learning. The cues employed may involve any of the senses; they may be the texture of a surface, the echo of footfalls, odors and even the slope of a passage.

Rats are adaptable in other ways. They use their forefeet when feeding and when building nests. They are manipulating animals and hence can readily learn to press a lever or pull a string for a reward. They have therefore been much used in the study of learning processes in problem boxes. They can also be induced to jump from a platform toward a door that falls open with the impact. The late K. S. Lashley of the Yerkes Laboratories for Primate Biology used an arrangement that had two doors marked with different patterns; rats could be trained to discriminate between these visual stimuli. Rats distinguish simple, bold patterns readily. Unlike monkeys, they cannot be trained to respond, say, to triangles in general—only to triangles of a fairly narrowly defined size, shape and orientation [see illustration at right].

Another intellectual limitation is revealed by the "oddity problem." A monkey, given three boxes, can easily learn always to open the one bearing a pattern *different* from that of the other two. Rats can do this, if at all, only with special preliminary training. A more general deficiency is social as well as intellectual. In spite of many legends, rats do not cooperate—to get food, for instance. They carry or drag food under cover, and a chunk of meat as heavy as a large rat may be dragged away by two or three rats at once, but the rats are as likely as not to be pulling in different directions.

The function of eating (as of sleeping) under cover is obvious. So, at first sight, is the hoarding of food in burrows. Yet much else may be carried away or piled in a corner by wild rats: coins, cakes of soap, small toys—anything that can be carried. This behavior, like miscellaneous gnawing, resembles play; it is performed in addition to activities such as feeding that are immediately essential for life. Indeed, one of the most conspicuous features of rat behavior is restlessness. The propensity for exploration is more easily studied in laboratory rats than in wild ones, since the tame rats are not neophobic. In the laboratory, exploration can be reduced to a

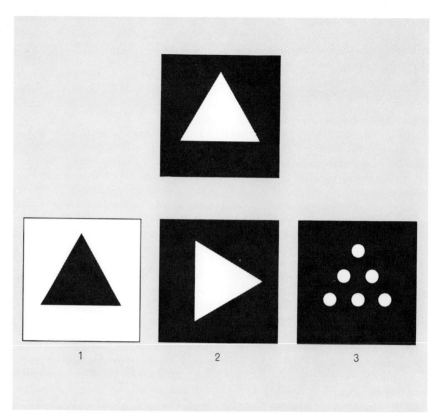

RAT REACTION to visual patterns shows little ability to recognize general likenesses. A rat trained to respond to the upright white triangle (*top*) makes only random responses when presented with any of the other three triangles (*bottom*). A similarly trained chimpanzee recognizes both solid triangles, and a two-year-old child recognizes all three.

minimum by putting a rat in (or on) a maze with a single "choice point": a T- or Y-shaped maze that allows a rat to turn either left or right. If the rat finds no reward in the first arm entered, it usually chooses the alternative arm on a second run; if there is again no reward, it continues to alternate thereafter.

What makes a rat behave in this way? Experiment has shown that novelty is the crucial feature: a rat usually chooses the less familiar kind of stimulation. Indeed, the opportunity to explore a complex area can be used instead of food or water as a reward to induce a rat to choose one passage rather than another. This well-developed neophilia has led some writers to use the term "curiosity drive" to refer to it; one might also say that rats often behave *as if* they wished to avoid boredom.

For wild rats the obvious function of exploratory behavior and food sampling, with the accompanying learning, is to keep them regularly informed on the amenities of their environment—food, water, shelter and other rats. Their neophobia prevents their "curiosity" from being lethal in man-made conditions.

Moreover, exploratory behavior (and probably play) also has an important role in the development of intelligence. D. O. Hebb of McGill University compared laboratory rats reared in the impoverished environment of a small cage with others that had spent their youth in larger enclosures containing diverse objects. The latter learned mazes more readily. Similarly, the learning of visual discriminations is aided by the rats' experience of a variety of visible patterns in early life.

This "learning to learn" is an immensely important feature of mammalian behavior. It is not confined to early life. A rat that has learned to solve one problem is usually quicker to solve a similar problem; for instance, the more experience it has in learning to find its way about, the more proficient it becomes at doing so (up to a point). This may involve unlearning some habits and replacing them with new ones. Rats, even if they are not diabolically clever, are in this respect also highly adaptable. These abilities have no doubt made possible the success of wild rats in the great variety of environments created by man, and have enabled rats to become the universal pest most people think they are.

The Author

S. A. BARNETT is a senior member of the department of zoology at the University of Glasgow. He took a first in zoology at the University of Oxford in 1937 and remained there doing research on chemical embryology. During and after World War II he did research for the British government on pest control and helped to fight plague in the Mediterranean region. He went to the University of Glasgow in 1951. His particular research interests are the physiology of social stress in wild rats and the physiology, behavior and genetics of breeding mice in an environment kept at −3 degrees centigrade. His book *Instinct and Intelligence* is scheduled for publication in the spring.

Bibliography

A History of British Mammals. Gerald E. H. Barrett-Hamilton. Gurney and Jackson, 1910.

The Rat: A Study in Behavior. S. A. Barnett. Aldine Publishing Company, 1963.

SPECIAL NOTE TO TEACHERS: Each article in this volume, plus more than 660 others, is available as a separate, self-bound SCIENTIFIC AMERICAN Offprint. Offprints may be ordered in any combination and in any quantity. Teachers who want to adopt articles for their courses, therefore, can ensure that each student has his own set. Students' sets are collated by the publisher before shipment.

SCIENTIFIC AMERICAN   February 1967, Vol. 216, No. 2, pp. 36-43   OFFPRINT **1061**

THE REPAIR OF DNA

by Philip C. Hanawalt and Robert H. Haynes

The two-strand molecule that incorporates the genetic information of the living cell is subject to damage. Experiments with bacteria reveal that the cell has a remarkable ability to repair such damage.

One of the most impressive achievements of modern industry is its ability to mass-produce units that are virtually identical. This ability is based not solely on the inherent precision of the production facilities. It also involves intensive application of quality-control procedures for the correction of manufacturing errors, since even the best assembly lines can introduce faulty parts at an unacceptable rate. In addition industry provides replacement parts for the repair of a product that is subsequently damaged by exposure to the hazards of its natural environment. Recent studies have demonstrated that living organisms employ analogous processes for repairing defective parts in their genetic material: deoxyribonucleic acid (DNA). This giant molecule must be replicated with extraordinary fidelity if the organism is to survive and make successful copies of itself. Thus the existence of quality-control mechanisms in living cells may account in large part for the fact that "like produces like" over many generations.

Until recently it had been thought that if the DNA in a living cell were damaged or altered, for example by ionizing radiation, the cell might give rise either to mutant "daughter" cells or to no daughter cells at all. Now it appears that many cells are equipped to deal with some of the most serious hazards the environment can present. In this article we shall describe the experimental results that have given rise to this important new concept.

The instructions for the production of new cells are encoded in the sequences of molecular subunits called bases that are strung together along a backbone of phosphate and sugar groups to form the chainlike molecules of DNA. A sequence of a few thousand bases constitutes a single gene, and each DNA molecule comprises several thousand genes. Before a cell can divide and give rise to two daughter cells, the DNA molecule (or molecules) in the parent cell must be duplicated so that each daughter cell can be supplied with a complete set of genes. On the basis of experiments made with the "chemostat"—a device for maintaining a constant number of bacteria in a steady state of growth—Aaron Novick and the late Leo Szilard estimated that bacterial genes may be duplicated as many as 100 million times before there is a 50 percent chance that even one gene will be altered. This is a remarkable record for any process, and it seems unlikely that it could be achieved without the help of an error-correcting mechanism.

The ability of cells to repair defects in their DNA may well have been a significant factor in biological evolution. On the one hand, repair would be advantageous in enabling a species to maintain its genetic stability in an environment that caused mutations at a high rate. On the other hand, without mutations there would be no evolution, mutations being the changes that allow variation among the individuals of a population. The individuals whose characteristics are best adapted to their environment will leave more offspring than those that are less well adapted. Presumably even the efficiency of genetic repair mechanisms may be subject to selection by evolution. If the repair mechanism were too efficient, it might reduce the natural mutation frequency to such a low level that a population could become trapped in an evolutionary dead end.

Although the error-correcting mechanism cannot yet be described in detail, one can see in the molecular architecture of DNA certain features that should facilitate both recognition of damage and repair of damage. The genetic material of all cells consists of two complementary strands of DNA linked side by side by hydrogen bonds to form a double helix [see illustration on page 2330]. Normally DNA contains four chemically distinct bases: two purines (adenine and guanine) and two pyrimidines (thymine and cytosine). The two strands of DNA are complementary because adenine in one strand is always hydrogen-bonded to thymine in the other, and guanine is similarly paired with cytosine [see lower illustration on page 2330]. The sequence of bases that constitute the code letters of the cell's genetic message is supplied in redundant form. Redundancy is a familiar stratagem to designers of error-detecting and error-correcting codes. If a portion of one strand of the DNA helix were damaged, the information in that portion could be retrieved from the complementary strand. That is, the cell could use the undamaged strand of DNA as a template for the reconstruction of a damaged segment in the complementary strand. Recent experimental evidence indicates that this is precisely what happens in many species of bacteria, particularly those that are known to be highly resistant to radiation.

The ability to recover from injury is a characteristic feature of living organisms. There is a fundamental difficulty, however, in detecting repair processes in bacteria. For example, when a population of bacteria is exposed to a dose of ultraviolet radiation or X rays, there is no way to determine in advance what proportion of the population will die. How can one tell whether the observed mortality accurately reflects all the damage sustained by the irradiated cells or whether some of the damaged cells have repaired themselves? Fortunately it is possible to turn the repair mechanism on or off at will.

A striking example can be found in the process called photoreactivation [*see bottom illustration on page 2332*]. Although hints of its existence can be traced to 1904, photoreactivation was not adequately appreciated until Albert Kelner rediscovered the effect in 1948 at the Carnegie Institution of Washington's Department of Genetics in Cold Spring Harbor, N.Y. Kelner was puzzled to find that the number of soil organisms (actinomycetes) that survived large doses of ultraviolet radiation could be increased by a factor of several hundred thousand if the irradiated bacteria were subsequently exposed to an intense source of visible light. He concluded that ultraviolet radiation had its principal effect on the nucleic acid of the cell, but he had no inkling what the effect was. In an article published before the genetic significance of DNA was generally appreciated, Kelner wrote: "Per-

haps the real stumbling block [to understanding photoreactivation] is that we do not yet understand at all well the biological role of that omnipresent and important substance—nucleic acid" [see "Revival by Light," by Albert Kelner; SCIENTIFIC AMERICAN, May, 1951].

It is now known that the germicidal action of ultraviolet radiation arises chiefly from the formation of two unwanted chemical bonds between pyrimidine bases that are adjacent to each other on one strand of the DNA molecule. Two molecules bonded in this way are called dimers; of the three possible types of pyrimidine dimer in DNA, the thymine dimer is the one that forms most readily [see upper illustration on page 2331]. It is thus not surprising that a given dose of ultraviolet radiation will create more dimers in DNA molecules that contain a high proportion of thymine bases than in DNA molecules with fewer such bases. Consequently bacteria whose DNA is rich in thymine tend to be more sensitive to ultraviolet

radiation than those whose DNA is not.

Richard B. Setlow, his wife Jane K. Setlow and their co-workers at the Oak Ridge National Laboratory have shown that pyrimidine dimers block normal replication of DNA and that bacteria with even a few such defects are unable to divide and form colonies [see "Ultraviolet Radiation and Nucleic Acid," by R. A. Deering; SCIENTIFIC AMERICAN Offprint 143]. In the normal replication of DNA each parental DNA strand serves as a template for the synthesis of a complementary daughter strand. This mode of replication is termed semiconservative because the parental strands separate in the course of DNA synthesis; each daughter cell receives a "hybrid" DNA molecule that consists of one parental strand and one newly synthesized complementary strand. The effect of a pyrimidine dimer on DNA replication may be analogous to the effect on a zipper of fusing two adjacent teeth.

Claud S. Rupert and his associates at

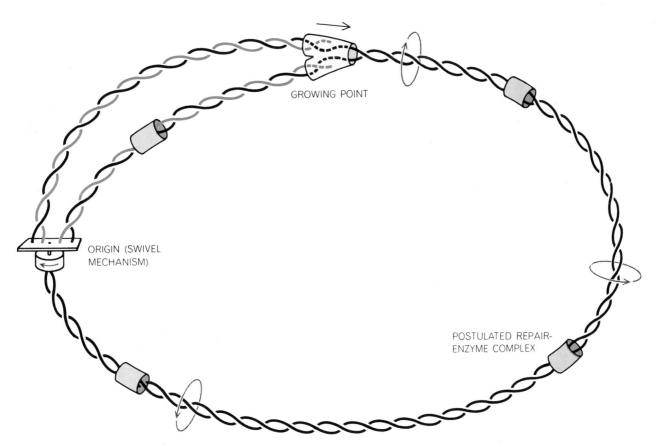

GROWING POINT

ORIGIN (SWIVEL MECHANISM)

POSTULATED REPAIR-ENZYME COMPLEX

REPLICATION OF BACTERIAL CHROMOSOME, a ring-shaped molecule of deoxyribonucleic acid (DNA), has now been shown to take two forms: normal replication and repair replication. In the former process the two strands that constitute the double helix of DNA are unwound and a daughter strand (*color*) is synthesized against each of them. In this way the genetic "message" is transmitted from generation to generation. The pairing of complementary subunits that underlies this process is illustrated on the next page. In repair replication, defects that arise in individual strands of DNA are removed and replaced by good segments. It is hypothesized that "repair complexes," composed of enzymes, are responsible for the quality control of the DNA structure. Although this diagram shows the swivel mechanism for unwinding the parent strands to be at the origin, it may in fact be located at the growing point.

Johns Hopkins University have shown that photoreactivation involves the action of an enzyme that is selectively bound to DNA that has been irradiated with ultraviolet. When this enzyme is activated by visible light (which simply serves as a source of energy), it cleaves the pyrimidine dimers, thereby restoring the two bases to their original form. Photoreactivation is thus a repair process that can be turned on or off merely by flicking a light switch.

Let us now consider another kind of repair mechanism in which light plays no role and that is therefore termed dark reactivation. This type of repair process can be turned off genetically, by finding mutant strains of bacteria that lack the repair capabilities of the original radiation-resistant strain. The "B/r" strain of the bacterium *Escherichia coli*,

first isolated in 1946 by Evelyn Witkin of Columbia University, is an example of a microorganism that is particularly resistant to radiation. The first radiation-sensitive mutants of this strain, known as B_{s-1}, were discovered in 1958 by Ruth Hill, also of Columbia.

Not long after the discovery of the B_{s-1} strain a number of people suggested that its sensitivity to radiation might be due to the malfunction of a particular enzyme system that enabled resistant bacteria such as B/r to repair DNA that had been damaged by radiation. This was a reasonable suggestion in view of the steadily accumulating evidence that DNA is the principal target for many kinds of radiobiological damage. Experiments conducted by Howard I. Adler at Oak Ridge and by Paul Howard-Flanders at Yale University lent further support to this hypothesis. It had been

known for some years that bacteria can exchange genes by direct transfer through a primitive form of sexual mating [see "Viruses and Genes," by Francois Jacob and Elie L. Wollman; SCIENTIFIC AMERICAN Offprint 89]. Howard-Flanders and his co-workers found bacteria of a certain radiation-resistant strain of *E. coli* (strain *K-12*) have at least three genes that can be transferred by bacterial mating to radiation-sensitive cells, thereby making them radiation-resistant. Since genes direct the synthesis of all enzymes in the living cell, these experiments supported the hypothesis that B_{s-1} and other radiation-sensitive bacteria lack one or more enzymes needed for the repair of radiation-damaged DNA.

The question now arises: Do the enzymes involved in dark reactivation operate in the same way as the enzyme that

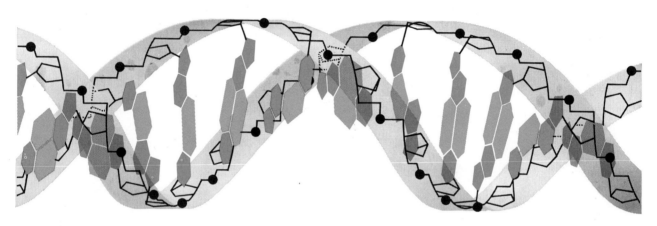

DNA MOLECULE is a double helix that carries the genetic message in redundant form. The backbone of each helix consists of repeating units of deoxyribose sugar (*pentagons*) and phosphate (*black dots*). The backbones are linked by hydrogen bonds between pairs of four kinds of base: adenine, guanine, thymine and cytosine. The bases are the "letters" in which the genetic message is written. Because adenine invariably pairs with thymine and guanine with cytosine, the two strands carry equivalent information.

DNA BASES are held together in pairs by hydrogen bonds. The cytosine-guanine pair (*left*) involve three hydrogen bonds, the thymine-adenine pair (*right*) two bonds. If the CH$_3$ group in thymine is replaced by an atom of bromine (*Br*), the resulting molecule is called 5-bromouracil. Thymine and 5-bromouracil are so similar that bacteria will incorporate either in synthesizing DNA. Because the bromine compound is so much heavier than thymine its presence can be detected by its effect on the weight of the DNA.

is known to split pyrimidine dimers in the photoreactivation process? Another possibility is that the resistant cells might somehow bypass the dimers during replication of DNA and leave them permanently present, although harmless, in their descendant molecules.

The actual mechanism is even more elegant than either of these possibilities; it exploits the redundancy inherent in the genetic message. The radiation-resistant strains of bacteria possess several enzymes that operate sequentially in removing the dimers and replacing the defective bases with the proper complements of the bases in the adjacent "good" strand. We shall recount the two key observations that substantiate this postulated repair scheme.

The excision of dimers was first demonstrated by Richard Setlow and William L. Carrier at Oak Ridge and was soon confirmed by Richard P. Boyce and Howard-Flanders at Yale. In their studies cultures of ultraviolet-resistant and ultraviolet-sensitive bacteria were grown separately in the presence of radioactive thymine, which was thereupon incorporated into the newly synthesized DNA. The cells were then exposed to ultraviolet radiation. After about 30 minutes they were broken open so that the fate of the labeled thymine could be traced. In the ultraviolet-sensitive strains all the thymine that had been incorporated into DNA was associated with the intact DNA molecules. Therefore any thymine dimers formed by ultraviolet radiation remained within the DNA. In the ultraviolet-resistant strains, however, dimers originally formed in the DNA were found to be associated with small molecular fragments consisting of no more than three bases each. (Thymine dimers can easily be distinguished from the individual bases or combinations of bases by paper chromatography, the technique by which substances are separated by their characteristic rate of travel along a piece of paper that has been wetted with a solvent.) These experiments provided strong evidence that dark repair of ultraviolet-damaged DNA does not involve the splitting of dimers in place, as it does in photoreactivation, but does depend on their actual removal from the DNA molecule.

Direct evidence for the repair step was not long in coming. At Stanford University one of us (Hanawalt), together with a graduate student, David Pettijohn, had been studying the replication of DNA after ultraviolet irradiation of a radiation-resistant strain of *E. coli*. In

EFFECT OF ULTRAVIOLET RADIATION on DNA is to fuse adjacent pyrimidine units: thymine or cytosine. The commonest linkage involves two units of thymine, which are coupled by the opening of double bonds. The resulting structure is known as a dimer.

EFFECT OF NITROGEN MUSTARD, a compound related to mustard gas, is to cross-link units of guanine within the DNA molecule. Unless repaired, the structural defects caused by nitrogen mustard and ultraviolet radiation can prevent the normal replication of DNA.

these experiments we used as a tracer a chemical analogue of thymine called 5-bromouracil. This compound is so similar to the natural base thymine that a bacterium cannot easily tell the two apart [*see right half of lower illustration on opposite page*]. When 5-bromouracil is substituted for thymine in the growth medium of certain strains of bacteria that are unable to synthesize thymine, it is incorporated into the newly replicated DNA. The fate of 5-bromouracil can be traced because the bromine atom in it is more than five times heavier than the methyl (CH_3) group in normal thymine that it replaces. Therefore DNA fragments containing 5-bromouracil are denser than normal fragments containing thymine. The density difference can be detected by density-gradient centrifugation, a technique introduced in 1957 by Matthew S. Meselson, Franklin W. Stahl and Jerome Vinograd at

the California Institute of Technology.

In density-gradient centrifugation DNA fragments are suspended in a solution of the heavy salt cesium chloride and are spun in a high-speed centrifuge for several days. When equilibrium is reached, the density of the solution varies from 1.5 grams per milliliter at the top of the tube to two grams per milliliter at the bottom. If normal DNA from *E. coli* is also present, it will eventually concentrate in a band corresponding to a density of 1.71 grams per milliliter. A DNA containing 5-bromouracil instead of thymine has a density of 1.8 and so will form a band closer to the bottom of the tube.

The entire genetic message of *E. coli* is contained in a single two-strand molecule of DNA whose length is nearly 1,000 times as long as the cell itself. This long molecule must be coiled up like a

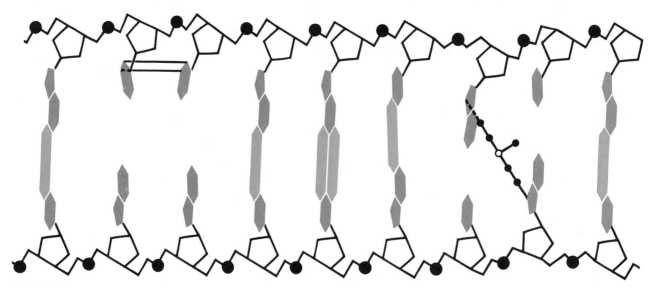

DEFECTS IN DNA probably distort the symmetry of its helical structure. To make the distortions more apparent this diagram shows the DNA in flattened form. A thymine dimer appears in the left half of the structure; a guanine-guanine cross-link is shown in the right half. The authors believe the repair complex recognizes the distortions rather than the actual defects in the bases.

skein of yarn to be accommodated within the cell [see "The Bacterial Chromosome," by John Cairns; SCIENTIFIC AMERICAN Offprint 1030]. Such a molecule is extremely sensitive to fluid shearing forces; in the course of being extracted from the cell it is usually broken into several hundred pieces.

If 5-bromouracil is added to a culture of growing bacteria for a few minutes (a small fraction of one generation), the DNA fragments isolated from the cells fall into several categories of differing density, each of which forms a distinct band in a cesium chloride density gradient. The lightest band will consist of unlabeled fragments: regions of the DNA molecule that were not replicated during the period when 5-bromouracil was present. A distinctly heavier band will contain fragments from regions that have undergone replication during the labeling period. This is the band containing hybrid DNA: molecules made up of one old strand containing thymine and one new strand containing 5-bromouracil in place of thymine. If synthesis proceeds until the chromosome has completed one cycle of replication and has started on the next cycle, some DNA fragments will have 5-bromouracil in both strands and therefore will form a band still heavier than the band containing the hybrid fragments. Finally, one fragment from each chromosome will include the "growing point" where the new strands are being synthesized on the pattern of the old ones, and thus will consist of a mixture of replicated and unreplicated DNA. This fragment, which is presumably shaped like a Y, will show up in the density gradient at a position

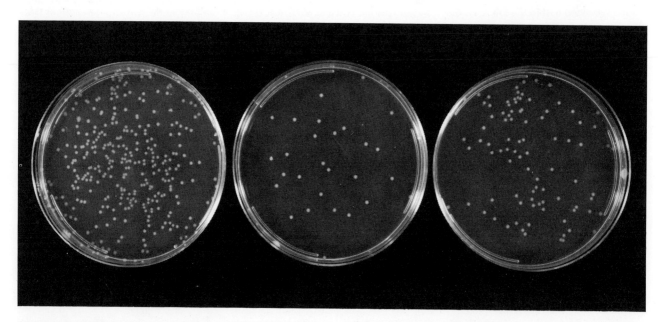

PHOTOREACTIVATION, a type of DNA repair process, is demonstrated in this photograph of three bacterial culture dishes. The dish at the left is a control: it contains 368 colonies of B/r strain of Escherichia coli. The middle dish contains bacteria exposed to ultraviolet radiation; only 35 cells have survived to form colonies. The bacteria in the dish at right were exposed to visible light following ultraviolet irradiation; it contains 93 colonies. Thus exposure to visible light increased the survival rate nearly threefold.

intermediate between the unlabeled DNA and the hybrid fragments containing 5-bromouracil.

When we used this technique to study DNA replication in bacteria exposed to ultraviolet radiation, we observed a pattern quite different from the one expected for normal replication. The DNA fragments containing the 5-bromouracil appeared in the gradient at the same position as normal fragments containing thymine! There could be no doubt of this because in these experiments we used 5-bromouracil labeled with tritium (the radioactive isotope of hydrogen) and thymine labeled with carbon 14 [*see illustration on next page*].

This pattern, which at first seems puzzling, is just the one to be expected if many thymine dimers—created at random throughout the DNA by ultraviolet radiation—had been excised and if 5-bromouracil had been substituted for thymine in the repaired regions. As a result many DNA fragments would contain 5-bromouracil, but no one fragment would contain enough 5-bromouracil to affect its density appreciably.

How can we be sure that the density distribution of 5-bromouracil observed in the foregoing experiment arises from "repair replication" rather than from normal replication? A variety of tests confirmed the repair interpretation. By using enzymes to break down the DNA molecule and separating the bases by paper chromatography we verified that the radioactive label was still in 5-bromouracil and had not been transferred to some other base. Various physical studies showed that the 5-bromouracil had been incorporated into extremely short segments that were distributed randomly throughout both DNA strands. This mode of DNA replication was not observed in the B_{s-1} strain of *E. coli*, the radiation-sensitive mutant that cannot excise pyrimidine dimers and therefore could not be expected to perform repair replication. Moreover, repair replication was not observed in the radiation-resistant bacteria in which visible light had triggered the splitting of pyrimidine dimers by photoreactivation; this indicates that repair replication is not necessary if the dimers are otherwise repaired *in situ*.

Finally it was shown that DNA repaired by dimer excision and strand reconstruction could ultimately replicate in the normal semiconservative fashion. This is rather compelling evidence for the idea that biologically functional DNA results from repair replication and that the process is not some aberrant

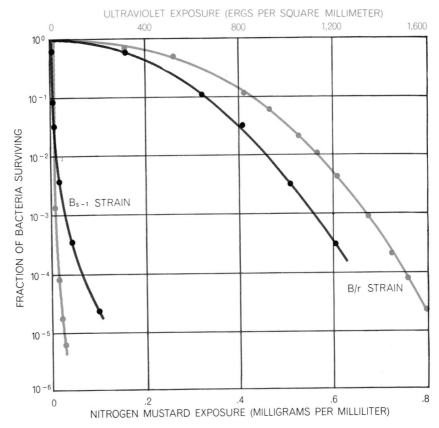

RESISTANCE TO LETHAL AGENTS is demonstrated by certain strains of *E. coli* but not by others. The *B/r* strain, for example, shows a high tolerance to doses of ultraviolet radiation (*colored curves*) and nitrogen mustard (*black curves*) that kill a large percentage of the sensitive B_{s-1} strain. This result suggests that the DNA repair mechanism of the *B/r* strain is effective in removing guanine-guanine cross-links produced by nitrogen mustard as well as in removing thymine dimers formed by exposure to ultraviolet radiation.

form of synthesis with no biological importance.

How can one visualize the detailed sequence of events that must be involved in this type of repair? Two models have been suggested, and the present experimental data seem to be equally compatible with each. The two models are distinguished colloquially by the terms "cut and patch" and "patch and cut" [*see illustrations on page 2335*]. The former refers to the model first proposed by Richard Setlow, Howard-Flanders and others. The latter refers to a model that took form during a discussion at a recent conference on DNA repair mechanisms held in Chicago.

The cut-and-patch scheme postulates an enzyme that excises a short, single-strand segment of the damaged DNA. The resulting gap is enlarged by further enzyme attack and then the missing bases are replaced by repair replication in the genetically correct sequence according to the rules that govern the pairing of bases.

In the patch-and-cut scheme the proc-

ess is assumed to be initiated by a single incision that cuts the strand of DNA near the defective bases. Repair replication begins immediately at this point and is accompanied by a "peeling back" of the defective strand as the new bases are inserted. This patch-and-cut scheme is attractive because it could conceivably be carried out by a single enzyme complex or particle that moves in one direction along the DNA molecule, repairing defects as it goes. Furthermore, it does not involve the introduction of long, vulnerable single-strand regions into the DNA molecule while the repair is taking place. Both models are undoubtedly oversimplifications of the actual molecular events inside the living cell, but they have great intuitive appeal and are helpful in planning further studies of the DNA repair process.

Repair replication would be of interest only to radiation specialists if it were not for the evidence that DNA structural defects other than pyrimidine dimers can be repaired and that similar repair

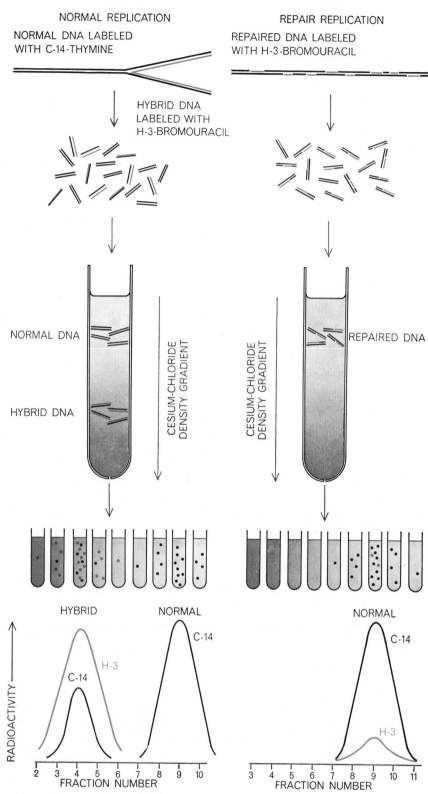

NORMAL REPLICATION

NORMAL DNA LABELED
WITH C-14-THYMINE

REPAIR REPLICATION

REPAIRED DNA LABELED
WITH H-3-BROMOURACIL

HYBRID DNA
LABELED WITH
H-3-BROMOURACIL

NORMAL DNA

HYBRID DNA

CESIUM-CHLORIDE
DENSITY GRADIENT

REPAIRED DNA

CESIUM-CHLORIDE
DENSITY GRADIENT

HYBRID   NORMAL

C-14

H-3

C-14

RADIOACTIVITY

2 3 4 5 6 7 8 9 10
FRACTION NUMBER

NORMAL

C-14

H-3

3 4 5 6 7 8 9 10 11
FRACTION NUMBER

TWO KINDS OF REPLICATION can be demonstrated by growing bacteria first in a culture containing thymine labeled with radioactive carbon 14 and then in a culture containing 5-bromouracil labeled with radioactive hydrogen 3. In normal replication (*left*), also known as semiconservative replication, daughter strands of "hybrid" DNA incorporate the 5-bromouracil (*color*). Because 5-bromouracil is much heavier than the thymine for which it substitutes, fragments of hybrid DNA form a separate heavier layer when they have been centrifuged and have reached equilibrium in a density gradient of cesium chloride. When the radioactivity in the various fractions is analyzed (*bottom left*), carbon 14 appears in two peaks but hydrogen 3 occurs in only one peak. If the experiment is repeated with DNA fragments that have undergone repair replication (*right*), they all appear to be of normal density. This implies that relatively little 5-bromouracil has been incorporated and also that the repaired segments are randomly scattered throughout the DNA molecule.

phenomena occur in organisms other than *E. coli*. We shall review some of the evidence indicating that repair replication is of general biological significance.

Just as strains of *E. coli* vary considerably in their sensitivity to ultraviolet radiation, so they vary considerably in their sensitivity to other mutagenic agents. One such agent is nitrogen mustard, so named because it is chemically related to the mustard gas used in World War I. It was the first chemical agent known to be capable of producing mutations and chromosome breaks in fruit flies and other organisms. Its biological action arises primarily from its ability to react with neighboring guanine bases in DNA, thereby producing guanine-guanine cross-links [*see lower illustration on page 2331*].

If one compares the survival curves of different strains of bacteria treated with nitrogen mustard with survival curves for bacteria subjected to ultraviolet radiation, one finds that the curves are almost identical [*see illustration on preceding page*]. This similarity led us to suggest that it is not the altered bases themselves that are "recognized" by the repair enzymes but rather the associated distortions, or kinks, that the alteration of the bases produces in the backbone of the DNA molecule. On this hypothesis one would predict that a wide variety of chemically different structural defects in DNA might be repaired by a common mechanism.

A substantial amount of biochemical evidence has now accumulated in support of this idea. We have established, for example, that repair replication of DNA takes place in *E. coli* that have been treated with nitrogen mustard. Others have found evidence that defects produced by agents as diverse as X rays, the chemical mutagen nitrosoguanidine and the antibiotic mitomycin *C* can all be repaired in radiation-resistant strains of *E. coli*. Walter Doerfler and David Hogness of Stanford have even found evidence that simple mispairing of bases between two strands of DNA can be corrected.

Finally, it now seems that certain steps in repair replication may also be involved in such phenomena as genetic recombination and the reading of the DNA code in preparation for protein synthesis. Evidence for these exciting possibilities has begun to appear in the work of Howard-Flanders, Meselson (who is now at Harvard University), Alvin J. Clark, of the University of California at Berkeley, Crellin Pauling of the University of California at Riverside and other investigators.

Repair replication has also been observed in a number of bacterial species other than *E. coli*. For example, Douglas Smith, a graduate student at Stanford, has demonstrated the repair of DNA in the pleuropneumonia-like organisms, which are probably the smallest living cells. These organisms, which are even smaller than some viruses, are thought to possess only the minimum number of structures needed for self-replication and independent existence [see "The Smallest Living Cells," by Harold J. Morowitz and Mark E. Tourtellotte; SCIENTIFIC AMERICAN Offprint 1005]. This suggests that repair replication may be a fundamental requirement for the evolution of free-living organisms.

In view of the impressive versatility of the repair replication process it is natural to ask if there is any type of DNA damage that cannot be mended by the cell. The evidence so far is limited and indirect, but William Rodger Inch, working at the Lawrence Radiation Laboratory of the University of California, has found that the *B/r* strain of *E. coli* is unable to repair all the damage caused when it is exposed to certain energetic beams of atomic nuclei produced by the heavy-ion linear accelerator (HILAC). Considering the extensive damage that must be done to cells by a beam of such intensely ionizing radiation, the result is not too surprising.

The discovery that cells have the facility to repair defects in DNA is a recent one. It is already apparent, however, that the process of repair replication could have broad significance for biology and medicine. Many questions remain to be investigated: What is the structure of the various repair enzymes? Are they organized into particulate units within the cell? What range of DNA defects can be recognized and repaired? Does DNA repair, as we now understand it, take place in the cells of mammals, or do even more complicated processes underlie the recovery phenomena that are observed after these higher types of cells are exposed to radiation? Might it be possible to increase the radiosensitivity of tumors by inhibiting the DNA repair mechanisms that may operate in cancer cells? If so, the idea could be of great practical value in the treatment of cancer.

These and many related questions are now being investigated in many laboratories around the world. Once again it has been demonstrated that the study of what may appear to be rather obscure properties of the simplest forms of life can yield rich dividends of much intellectual and practical value.

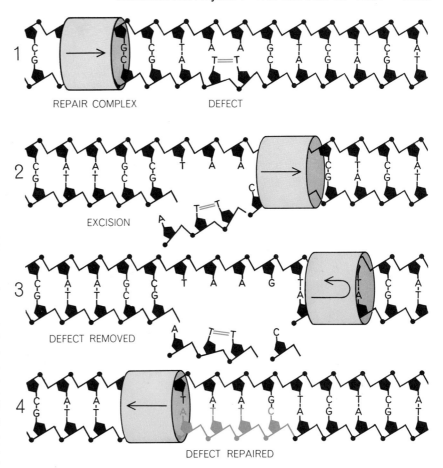

"CUT AND PATCH" repair mechanism was the first one proposed to explain how bacterial cells might remove thymine dimers (1) and similar defects from a DNA molecule. The hypothetical repair complex severs the defective strand (2) and removes the defective region (3). Retracing its path, it inserts new bases according to the rules of base pairing (4).

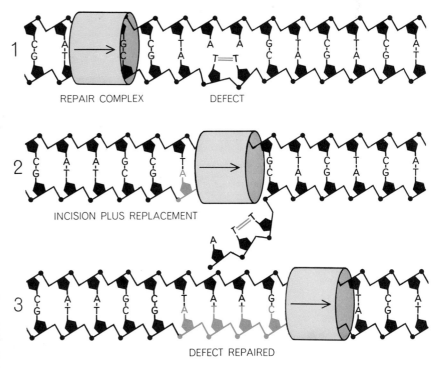

"PATCH AND CUT" mechanism has been proposed as an alternative to the cut-and-patch scheme. On the new model the repair complex inserts new bases as it removes defective ones.

The Authors

PHILIP C. HANAWALT and ROBERT H. HAYNES are respectively associate professor of biological sciences at Stanford University and associate professor of biophysics and medical physics at the University of California at Berkeley. Hanawalt majored in physics at Oberlin College, from which he was graduated in 1954, and did graduate work in physics and biophysics at Yale University, from which he received a Ph.D. in 1959. Haynes obtained a bachelor's degree in physics and a Ph.D. in biophysics from the University of Western Ontario. Haynes writes that he was "raised a true-blue Canadian Tory" but during a year as an exchange fellow in England "was subverted by the success of the British National Health Service and began drinking in workingmen's pubs." Looking back, he says, "it is clear that it was this experience that ensured I would later be on the side of the angels and the Free Speech Movement in Berkeley." Both Hanawalt and Haynes are teaching introductory courses in biology. Haynes writes: "Although I have always spent most of my time in research, I am convinced that recent events at Berkeley will accelerate the swing back to teaching in academia; and somewhat to my surprise I found teaching Biology 1 to be a rather exhilarating experience. In spite of my political stance at Berkeley, my interest in fine food and wine, poetry and ballet appears to be disconcertingly nonproletarian. However, it was in a scruffy Oxford pub that Hanawalt and I began our continuing collaboration."

Bibliography

THE DISAPPEARANCE OF THYMINE DIMERS FROM DNA: AN ERROR-CORRECTING MECHANISM. R. B. Setlow and W. L. Carrier in *Proceedings of the National Academy of Sciences*, Vol. 51, No. 2, pages 226–231; February, 1964.

EVIDENCE FOR REPAIR REPLICATION OF ULTRAVIOLET-DAMAGED DNA IN BACTERIA. David Pettijohn and Philip C. Hanawalt in *Journal of Molecular Biology*, Vol. 9, No. 2, pages 395–410; August, 1964.

A GENETIC LOCUS IN E. COLI K 12 THAT CONTROLS THE REACTIVATION OF UV-PHOTOPRODUCTS ASSOCIATED WITH THYMINE IN DNA. P. Howard-Flanders, Richard P. Boyce, Eva Simson and Lee Theriot in *Proceedings of the National Academy of Sciences*, Vol. 48, No. 12, pages 2109–2115; December 15, 1962.

STRUCTURAL DEFECTS IN DNA AND THEIR REPAIR IN MICROORGANISMS. Radiation Research, Supplement 6, edited by Robert H. Haynes, Sheldon Wolff and James E. Till. Academic Press, in press.

SCIENTIFIC
AMERICAN   August 1953, Vol. 189, No. 2, pp. 76-81   OFFPRINT 1062

THE GENETICS OF THE DUNKERS

by H. Bentley Glass

In the hands, ears and blood of the members of this
small religious sect a geneticist finds evidence for
an important force in human evolution: genetic drift.

THE DUNKERS, a small, sober religious sect that originally settled in eastern Pennsylvania, possess a characteristic of great interest to human geneticists. They are a group genetically isolated by strict marriage customs in the midst of a much larger community. Their beliefs have kept them distinct for more than two centuries. When Milton S. Sacks, director of the Baltimore Rh Typing Laboratory, and I were searching for a group in which to study how present blood-type and other hereditary differences arose in human populations, we turned to the Dunkers. Not only were they ideal for the study but also they opened up a larger area of inquiry. In them it is possible to perceive how racial differences which today distinguish millions of men first emerged and became set, so to speak, in small populations.

For 20 years anthropologists and geneticists have been increasingly aware of the importance in evolutionary processes of population size. In prehistoric times, when man was a hunter and gatherer, the world was sparsely inhabited. Hunting tribes are never large—1,000 people or so at most—and each tribe must range a rather large area to secure food and clothing. To keep this area inviolate and the tribe intact, primitive social customs include a simple avoidance of outsiders as well as active hostility, headhunting and cannibalism. Such customs tend to keep each tribe to itself and to make intermating between tribes quite rare. This was the period in human history when racial differences must have arisen and become set.

Such traits were probably established either by natural selection or by genetic drift, a term which may be explained as follows. In large populations chances in opposite directions tend to balance—e.g., boy babies would generally equal girls in number—and the frequency of any genetic trait is expected to repeat itself generation after generation. But in small groups chance fluctuates more around the expected norm. No single family, for instance, is certain to have an equal number of boys and girls, and a predictable number of families will have all one or the other. If, in a small population, the initial proportion of brown eyes and blue were equal, the following generation might by chance have 45 per cent brown eyes and 55 per cent blue. This variation would then be expected to repeat itself by genetic law. However, the next generation might again by chance return to the 50-50 ratio or might shift to 40 per cent brown and 60 blue. If the latter were to happen, the expectation for the next generation would again be shifted, and this cumulative change by pure chance is what is meant by genetic drift. The phenomenon might continue until the whole population was either blue or brown eyed. Which ever way it went, once it had gone all the way it could not easily drift back. At that point it would be fixed in character until some mutation of the gene for eye color occurred. The chance of this in a small population is low, because the probability that a single gene will mutate is generally only one in 100,000 or even one in a million.

The actual operations of genetic drift are hard to pin down at this late date. Some present-day primitive peoples have been observed to have sharp divergences of inherited traits. The Eskimos of Thule in northern Greenland, where we are building a big air base, have a much higher frequency of the gene for blood group O (83.7 per cent) and a lower frequency of the gene for blood group A (9 per cent) than other Eskimos. They live far to the north and rarely mingle with the more populous Eskimo communities of the south. The Thule tribe numbers only 57. While its differences are probably due to genetic drift, we cannot rule out the possibility that some pressure of natural selection has operated more rigorously on blood-group genes in the far north than in the milder south.

A parallel case occurs in the aborigines of South Australia, whose traits have been studied for more than a decade by Joseph B. Birdsell of the University of California at Los Angeles. Among the South Australian desert tribes is the Pitjandjara, whose frequency of the gene for blood group A exceeds 45 per cent. To the west is a tribe of the same stock but having a much lower frequency of the group A gene (27.7 per cent); to the east is an apparently unrelated tribe with a frequency of this gene still lower (20 to 25 per cent). All three tribes are much more nearly alike in frequency of genes for the blood group MN. This is a situation to be expected from genetic drift, for it is not likely that in small populations chance will act on unrelated genes in the same way. But here again it is impossible to prove that genetic drift is the real agent. Each tribe has its own slightly different territory, customs and way of life: who is to say that it is not natural selection in a particular environment which has favored the marked increase of blood-group A in the Pitjandjara?

To get at the elusive drift in the frequencies of alternative kinds of genes, a small community of known origin is required, existing as nearly inviolate as possible in a larger civilization. After some discussion, it became apparent to Sacks and me that these requirements might happily be met right here among various German religious sects which immigrated to the U. S. in the 18th and 19th centuries. Not only are many of these sects still held together by strict rules regarding marriage, but also we have precise knowledge of their racial origins. This gives a starting point for comparison, since the present genetic composition of their homeland is also known. Moreover, they are now isolated in a much larger population, which provides an even more important basis for comparison. If natural selection or intermarriage were to influence their gene frequencies, these frequencies would shift from those of the homeland toward those characteristic of the large surrounding population. But if any sharp divergencies showed up, they would be attributable not to natural selection but to genetic drift.

After some exploration, a Dunker community in Pennsylvania's Franklin

DUNKERS of the study described in this article live in Franklin County, Pa. Although they seldom marry outside the sect and their dress differs from that of their neighbors, their customs are not otherwise unusual.

GENETIC DRIFT is depicted by disembodied eyes. The group labeled 1 represents a small population in which 50 per cent of the people have brown eyes (*dark in drawing*) and 50 per cent have blue eyes (*light*). Group 2 shows a second generation in which 45 per cent of the people have brown eyes and 55 per cent have blue eyes. Group 3 indicates a third generation in which, if the proportion of brown eyes to blue did not return to that of the first generation, the percentages might be 40 for brown eyes and 60 for blue.

In all visible respects the Franklin County Dunkers live as their neighbors live. Most of them are farmers, though some have moved to the county's two medium-sized towns. They own cars and farm machinery; most have modest but comfortable frame houses; their food is typically American; the children attend public schools; medical care is good. Distinctions of dress are not conspicuous to the degree seen, for example, in the better-known Amish sect. Except for strict adherence to their religion, the Dunkers are typical rural and small-town Americans. In marriage pattern the community is not wholly self-contained. Over the last three generations about 13 per cent of their marriages were with members of other Old Order communities and about 24 per cent with converts, a factor taken into account in our study. Thus in each generation somewhat more than 12 per cent of the parents in the community came in from the general population. The equalizing force of this "gene flow" from outside would of course tend to make the Dunkers more like everyone else in hereditary makeup. The effects of genetic drift, if perceptible, would have to be large enough to overcome the equalizing tendency. Altogether the community now numbers 298 persons, or 350, if children who have left the church are included. For several generations the number of parents has been about 90. This, then, is exactly the type of small "isolate" in which the phenomenon of genetic drift might be expected to occur.

THE CHARACTERISTICS chosen for study in the Dunker group were limited to those in which inheritance is clearly established and in which alternative types are clear-cut, stable and, so far as is known, non-adaptive. The frequency records of these characteristics were available for both the West German and North American white populations, or at least the latter. Complete comparisons could be made for frequencies of the four ABO blood groups (O, A, B and AB) and the three MN types (M, MN and N). The Rh blood groups were almost as good. Although no Rh frequencies are available from West Germany, other European peoples have been studied, the English very extensively, and it is evident that all West Europeans are quite similar in this respect. Four other traits were examined in which the Dunkers could at least be compared with the surrounding American population. These were: (1) the presence or absence of hair on the middle segment of one or more fingers, known as "mid-digital hair"; (2) hitchhiker's thumb, technically called "distal hyperextensibility," the ability to bend the tip of the thumb back to form more than a 50-degree angle with the basal segment; (3) the nature of the ear lobes, which may be attached to the side of the

County was settled upon. No small part in influencing the choice was played by Charles Hess, a young medical student at the University of Maryland and a Dunker. He became interested in the project and gave invaluable help in collecting information and blood samples and in winning the cooperation of the Dunkers, without which the project could not have been carried out.

THE DUNKER sect, more formally known as the German Baptist Brethren, was founded in the province of Hesse in 1708, with a second center arising at Krefeld in the Rhineland. Between 1719 and 1729 some 20 families from the latter place and 30 from the former completely transplanted the sect to the New World, settling around Germantown, Pa. Over the next century the Dunkers doubled in number, and nearly all of them were descended from the original 50 families. To marry outside the church was a grave offense followed by either voluntary withdrawal or expulsion from the community. By 1882 the sect had grown to 58,000 and spread

to the Pacific Coast. Under this steady drain to the frontier the Pennsylvania groups remained fairly stationary in numbers. The Franklin County or Antietam Church community, the subject of this study, seems never to have grown larger than a few hundred persons up to 1882.

In that year a schism split the church and further contracted the size of this and other communities. For some time there had been trouble between those who wished to retain all the old tenets of the sect and those who wanted some relaxation of the more restrictive rules governing baptism, foot-washing, love feasts, head coverings for women, sober dress for men and the like. An open rupture finally separated the strict Old Order, as well as a Progressive group, from the main body, which went on to form the present-day Church of the Brethren. The Franklin County community studied by us remained in the Old Order, which from that day to this has numbered only about 3,000 people scattered in 55 communities over the country.

head or hang free; and (4) right- or left-handedness.

The findings were clear-cut. They show that in a majority of all these factors the Dunkers are neither like the West Germans nor like the Americans surrounding them, nor like anything in between. Instead, the frequencies of particular traits have deviated far to one extreme or the other. Whereas in the U. S. the frequency of blood group A is 40 per cent and in West Germany 45 per cent, among the Dunkers it has risen to nearly 60 per cent, instead of being intermediate as would be expected in the absence of genetic drift. On the other hand, frequencies of groups B and AB, which together amount to about 15 per cent in both major populations, have declined among the Dunkers to scarcely more than 5 per cent. These differences are statistically significant and unlike any ever found in a racial group of West European origin. One would have to go to the American Indians, Polynesians or Eskimos to find the like. The ancestry of all 12 persons with blood groups B and AB was checked to find out whether their B genes had been inherited from within the community. Only one had inherited this blood factor from a Dunker ancestor in the Franklin community; all the others had either been converts or married in from other Dunker groups. Evidently this gene was nearly extinct in the group before its recent reintroduction.

The three MN types showed even more unexpected trends. These have almost identical frequencies in West Germany and the U. S.: 30 per cent for type M, 50 for MN and 20 for N. In the Dunkers the MN percentage had diminished slightly, but frequencies for the other two types had deviated radically. M had jumped to 44.5 per cent and N had dropped to 13.5. One would have to go to the Near East or look in Finland, Russia or the Caucasus to find any whites with hereditary MN distributions like these. Only in the Rh blood groups do the Dunkers not differ greatly from their parent stock or adopted land. As against an average of close to 15 per cent for the Rh-negative type in both English and U. S. populations, the Dunkers show 11 per cent.

From the other traits in which comparisons were made almost equally striking conclusions can be drawn. Without going into details, the Dunkers had fewer persons with mid-digital hair or hitchhiker's thumb or an attached ear lobe than other U. S. communities. Only in right- and left-handedness, as in the Rh blood types, do the Dunkers agree well with the major populations used for comparison.

THERE SEEMS to be no explanation for these novel combinations of hereditary features except the supposition that genetic drift has been at work.

To clinch the matter, the Dunkers were divided into three age groups—3 to 27 years, 28 to 55 years and 56 years and older—roughly corresponding to three successive generations. When the ABO blood types were singled out, it was at once apparent that their frequencies were the same in all three generations. It follows that the unusual ABO distribution is of fairly long standing and antedates the birth of anyone still living. When the same analysis of MN blood types was made, however, a very different story emerged. In the oldest generation the M and N genes were exactly the same in frequency as in the surrounding population. In the second generation the frequency of M had risen to 66 per cent and N had dropped to 34. In the third generation this trend continued, M going to 74, N sinking to 26. While other genes remained unaltered in frequency, these genes were apparently caught in the act of drifting.

Let us consider the phenomenon a little more deeply. There can be no doubt from these instances that genetic drift does occur in small, reproductively isolated human groups in which the parents in any one generation number less than 100. Drift is probably somewhat effective, though slower, in populations two or three times that size. Such were the tribes of man before the dawn of agriculture. How inevitable it was, then, that numerous hereditary differences, perhaps of a quite noticeable but really unimportant kind, became established in different tribes. It is my opinion, no doubt open to dispute, that most inherited racial differences are of this kind and were not materially aided by natural selection.

Some traits, of course, must originally have been fixed by selection. Dark skin is probably a biological advantage in the

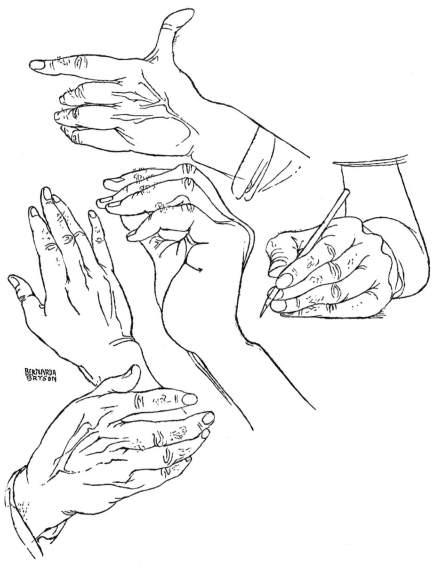

THREE OTHER CHARACTERISTICS were studied. One was "hitchhiker's thumb" (*hand at top*), the ability to bend the end of the thumb backward at an angle of more than 50 degrees. The second was "mid-digital hair" (*hands at lower left*), or hair on the middle segments of the fingers. The third was right-handedness v. left-handedness (*hand at right*).

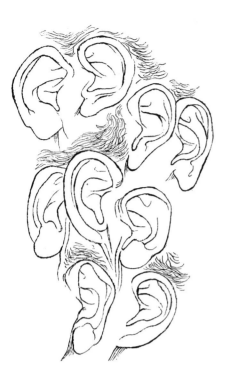

EAR LOBES either hang free or are attached to the head. Among Dunkers there are fewer attached lobes than among the U.S. population as a whole.

tropics, while pale skin may be an advantage in weaker northern light. The same may hold for kinky hair as against straight hair, for dark eyes as against light eyes, and the like. Many possibilities of this kind have been suggested in a recent book, *Races: A Study of the Problems of Race Formation in Man*, by Carleton S. Coon, Stanley M. Garn and Joseph B. Birdsell. I remain skeptical when I think of the prevailing hairlessness of man in many regions where more body hair would have helped to keep him warm. I am particularly skeptical of any selective advantage in blondness, "the most distinctive physical trait or group of traits shown by Europeans." It seems more likely that these traits confer no advantage to speak of, in Europe or elsewhere. I would add that if blonds had been eliminated by selection in other parts of the world, and if a blond type happened by genetic drift to become established in Europe, then it could have persisted and spread in large populations and given rise to the present racial distribution of the blond caucasoid or "Nordic" man.

THE STUDY of the Dunker community confirms the suspicion of many anthropologists that genetic drift is responsible for not a few racial characteristics. Further studies along these lines, together with studies of mortality and fertility in contrasted hereditary types, may in time tell us which racial traits were established because of selective advantage and which owe their presence solely to chance and genetic drift.

The Author

H. BENTLEY GLASS is professor of biology at The Johns Hopkins University, associate editor of *The Quarterly Review of Biology*, and, at the moment, acting chairman of the editorial board of the American Association for the Advancement of Science, responsible for the publication of *Science* and *The Scientific Monthly*. What with a weekly, a monthly and a quarterly magazine to worry about, he remarks, "life is full of deadlines." Glass was born in China in 1906 and had his pre-college education in mission schools there. He took his undergraduate work at Baylor University and his Ph.D. at the University of Texas.

Bibliography

GENETIC DRIFT IN A RELIGIOUS ISOLATE: AN ANALYSIS OF THE CAUSES OF VARIATION IN BLOOD GROUP AND OTHER GENE FREQUENCIES IN A SMALL POPULATION. Bentley Glass, Milton S. Sacks, Elsa F. Jahn and Charles Hess in *The American Naturalist*, Vol. 86, No. 828, pages 145-159; May-June, 1952.

RACES: A STUDY OF THE PROBLEMS OF RACE FORMATION IN MAN. Carleton S. Coon, Stanley M. Garn and Joseph B. Birdsell. Charles C. Thomas, 1950.

SCIENTIFIC
AMERICAN   October 1953, Vol. 189, No. 4, pp. 65-76   OFFPRINT 1063

HUMAN GROWTH

by George W. Gray

The complete physical, physiological and psychological histories of
160 boys and girls recorded by the Denver Child Research Council
are yielding a clear picture of how a normal individual grows up.

Among the 160 children of various ages whose development is being followed in the remarkable study of human growth by the Child Research Council in Denver, Col., is a boy whom we shall call Tommy Smith. In nursery school he was a top member of his class—a happy, normal, healthy, highly intelligent youngster. But as he approached the age of five, the records began to show a flattening of his growth curve: he lost weight and stopped gaining in height. The staff nutritionist, calling at his home for a check-up, found that the boy's appetite had fallen off sharply. He was not eating enough, particularly not enough milk, and the result was a shortage in his intake of proteins and minerals. Actually, the whole staff for some time had been noticing symptoms of retardation in this apparently healthy boy. The psychologists had reported that Tommy had regressed in mind as well as in body. His I.Q. rating had dropped. He seemed tense, anxious, uncertain. His inner strains were reflected in his responses to the Rorschach inkspot test, the thematic apperception test and other psychological techniques.

A clue to his trouble was disclosed by one of these techniques: doll play. Three dolls, representing a man, a woman and a small boy, were placed on the floor, together with an assortment of doll furniture and other household accessories. Tommy proceeded to "play house," and in his play he sent the mother doll off "to the office," put the father doll in the kitchen getting the next meal and wondered aloud whether the little boy doll would grow up into a man. Maybe, he speculated, the boy would become a woman and go off to the office "like mamma."

Here was the anxiety that underlay Tommy's loss of interest in food, his interrupted growth and his lapses in I.Q. It turned out that the doll drama re-

enacted his actual home situation. Tommy's mother had a job which kept her away from home from early morning until late afternoon. The father, whose business hours were not exacting, did many of the housekeeping chores, fed and dressed the boy and took him to and from school. Because the mother frequently came home exhausted, the father often put the child to bed. It was all very confusing to Tommy. He was at the stage in which a normal boy wants to identify himself with a male figure, but his family setup was such that he was not certain what the figure stood for—and anyway, he was not sure that he wanted to be that kind of man.

The Child Research Council is not a clinic: it does not treat diseases or disorders. But when symptoms come to light in the course of its research, it calls them to the attention of the parents and their family physician. In this case the

parents finally recognized that their son's disturbance stemmed from themselves, and they immediately made adjustments to correct the situation. The mother went on half time at her business and made it her main job to love and care for Tommy. The father relinquished many of his mothering services. Within a few months after this realignment of the parental roles, Tommy was a much happier and better adjusted boy. He was eating so voraciously that the family doctor had to advise cutting down on his carbohydrates; his height and weight resumed their growth, and again he stood head and shoulders above his classmates in intelligence tests.

"This is not an unusual case," says Alfred H. Washburn, director of the Child Research Council. "I'm quite sure that other people working in guidance centers with play techniques could tell similar stories. But the episode does illustrate

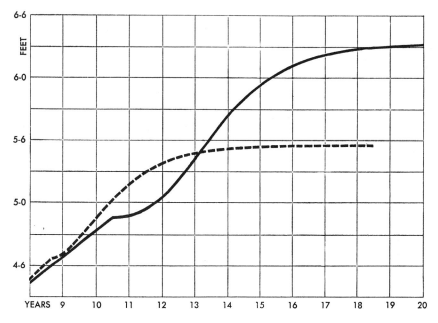

RATES OF GROWTH of a boy (solid line) and a girl (broken line) are contrasted by these curves. Girls enter and complete the adolescent phase of rapid growth earlier than boys.

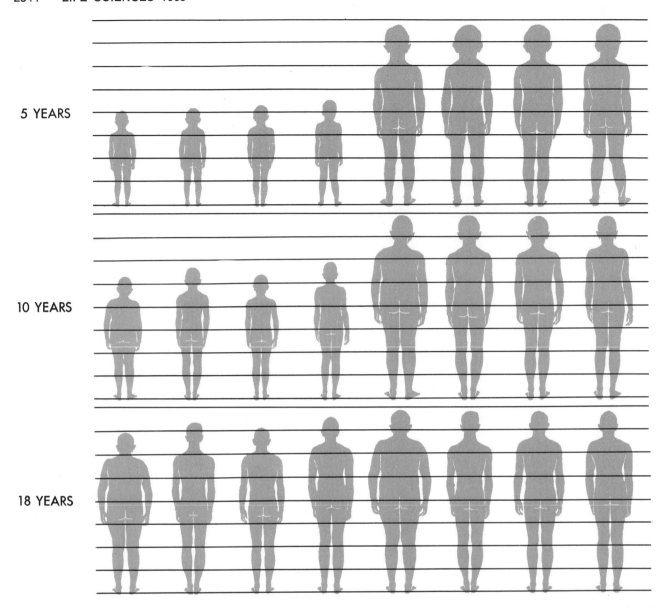

5 YEARS

10 YEARS

18 YEARS

CHANGES IN PROPORTIONS OF THE BODY that come with growth are illustrated by profiles of changing figures of four boys and four girls. The drawings are based upon photographic records kept by Child Research Council. In each panel, four figures are pic-

the three-fold nature of growth, and the interdependence of the growth factors. Human growth is a sensitively balanced complex of processes in which body structure, physiological function and emotion each plays its indispensable part—and a disturbance or deficiency of one factor can seriously affect the others. Here in Denver we are endeavoring to follow the course of each of these factors through the entire life spans of our children. We are keeping records of each individual from infancy into childhood and from childhood into adulthood. We intend to continue the study of each life until accident or old age eventually writes its finis."

Washburn, a tall, rangy man now in his late fifties, is a native of Boston who was graduated from Amherst College in

1916 and from the Harvard Medical School in 1921. Classmates recall that as a student he was not bashful about challenging medical dogma. During his internship something that he read in a book prompted Washburn to scribble this query in the margin: *Why hasn't medicine been more concerned with the problem of understanding the whole life cycle of a human being during healthy growth?*

Why not, indeed? There was a vast file of assorted information on the anatomy, physiology, psychology, behavior and diseases of the human system. There were multitudinous tomes on man-in-the-abstract. But never had a satisfactory study been made of the life cycle of even *one* human individual. "We know more about how a garden pea or a hog or a

laboratory rat grows and adapts to varying environmental conditions," reflected Washburn, "than we do about how a person grows up and becomes the kind of adult he is."

With such ideas stewing in his brain, the young medical graduate went West to start the private practice of pediatrics in Portland, Ore. While there he held an instructorship at the University of Oregon. The following year the University of California called him to Berkeley, and soon Washburn was the gadfly of its faculty with his persistent questions about the life cycle, about what is normal in human growth and about the importance of making a beginning toward a science of man.

Meanwhile an interest in these same questions was fermenting among physi-

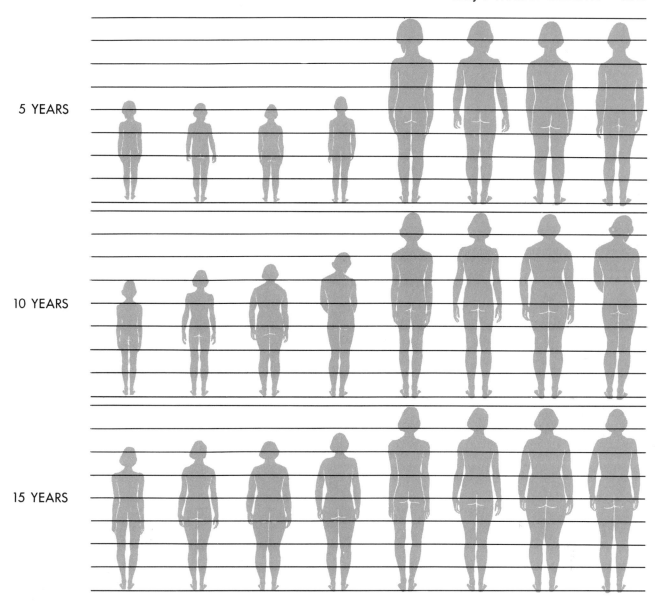

5 YEARS

10 YEARS

15 YEARS

tured at relative actual height at left and, at right, all of the figures are blown up to the same arbitrary height to bring out contrasts in proportion. Major change in both sexes is relative increase of height to breadth of body as long bones achieve growth.

cians and public-spirited citizens in Colorado. In the early 1920s a group in Denver had set up a project in preventive medicine to examine children periodically for early signs of tuberculosis and respiratory disease. But after five years of operation its financial support had failed, and the project would have lapsed but for the intervention of a few local physicians and scientists. They had caught the vision of a larger objective. Instead of limiting the examinations to tests for disease, they asked, why not consider the child as a whole, study each as an individual and follow his pattern of growth and adaptation continuously?

The proponents of this idea enlisted the interest of the president of the University of Colorado, and the project had a new birth. It was incorporated by the

State as the Child Research Council. The University of Colorado School of Medicine offered laboratory and administrative quarters in its building, and the Council agreed to make its findings available to the school. But a leader was needed, and at this stage the Council discovered Washburn, then an associate professor at California. It invited the transplanted New Englander to Denver, bombarded him with questions on his favorite theme, and hired him on the spot to become director of its research. That was in 1930. Washburn gathered an extraordinary team of investigators which has now been working together closely for more than two decades.

The oldest of the 160 persons whose life cycles are being followed by Dr. Washburn and his 26 associates is now

32 years of age, and the youngest was born last month. Occasionally the group loses a subject: a family moves to another city, a girl grows up and marries an outsider, a boy goes away to a distant job. But such losses are kept at a minimum by selecting the subjects from stable families. By adding three to five new babies annually, the Council has steadily increased its roster. The current enrollment is about as large as the present staff can keep track of, but the staff may eventually be increased to where it can enroll a maximum of 200 subjects.

"We have to realize that most of the children we are studying now will outlive every member of our present staff," Washburn observes. "Other investigators will complete the observations that we begin, and reap the harvest of what

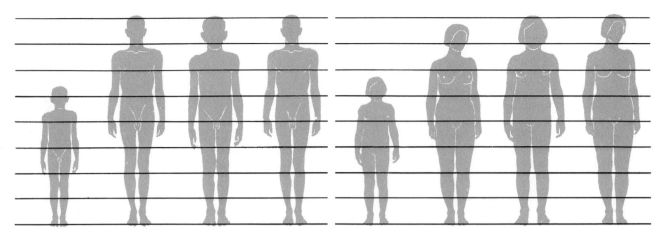

HOW BOY AND GIRL CHANGE in build between the age of five and completion of growth (boy at 18, girl at 15) is shown here.

In each panel the figures are paired at the same relative age. The figures at right in each panel are blown up to same height.

we have sown. All the more important, then, is our obligation to plan the program on an adequate scale, to start each study with a full realization of what it may mean for the future and to record the findings with thoroughness and a scrupulous care for accuracy and relevance.

"Our effort is based on the theory that the adult is what he is, and behaves as he does, as a result of his total transactions of living—and that means the sum of his experiences from conception on to his present age. We proceed on the hypothesis that this continual interplay between the individual and his environment is susceptible of observation, measurement and interpretation at three levels of organization—physical, physiological and psychological. Those three categories define our study: *physical* growth and adaptation as shown by structure, *physiological* growth and adaptation as shown by functioning, and *psychological* growth and adaptation as shown by mental ability, emotional attitudes, social behavior and other ingredients of personality.

"We have tackled this many-sided, long-range and difficult research on the assumption that, from learning how people succeed or fail in adjusting to their world, we can obtain information which will guide children toward becoming happier, healthier and more useful members of society."

Physical Growth

Photography is an indispensable tool for studying growth. With X-ray photography the Council measures the

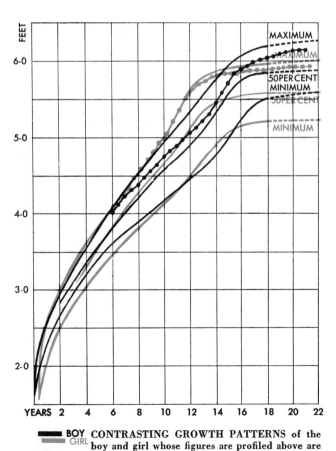

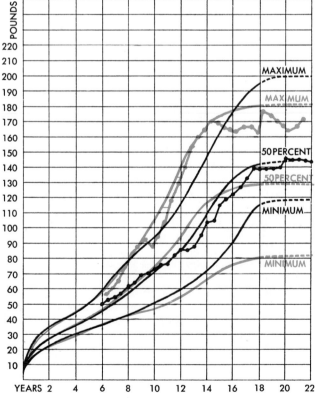

BOY **GIRL** CONTRASTING GROWTH PATTERNS of the boy and girl whose figures are profiled above are

shown in charts which compare the curves of these individuals (beaded lines) with maximum, minimum and median curves for

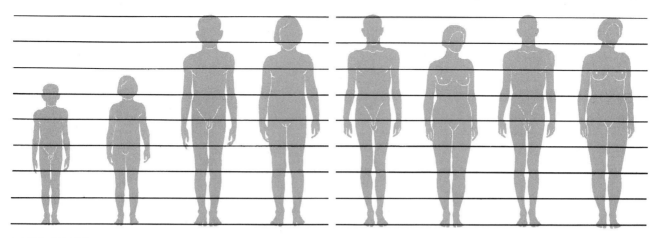

HOW BOY AND GIRL CONTRAST at the same stages of growth is shown in these two panels. In panel at left their figures are compared at the age of five; at right, at the completion of growth, with the figures blown up to same height at right in each panel.

growth of leg bones, arm bones, the head, chest, spine, heart, lungs, teeth and other internal organs and tissues; with direct photography it records the shape of bodily development. Nothing shows so plainly where and at what rate physical growth is taking place as a series of photographs of the same individual, taken at regular intervals over a period of years.

Edith Boyd, a pediatrician who specializes in anatomy, devised a simple technique which has enormously increased the value of the photographic

records. "I took an enlarger," explained Dr. Boyd, "and projected all the photographs of a subject at various ages to the same height; for example, using the height of the subject at his current age, say 16, the images of the child at one year, at five years, at 10 and at 12 were all blown up to this height. Then I could see at a glance what changes had taken place in his body form.

"One of the biggest differences among people is their distribution of mass— whether they are long-legged or short-legged, how wide they are for their

height, whether the hips or the shoulders are wider. In the series of pictures blown up to the same height, I found that I could measure how much of the child's mass was made up of his foot, how much of his leg, his thigh and so on up the body. I could follow and trace changes in the relative masses of these structural features. In a baby or small child, the shoulders may be wide compared to the hips; as a boy approaches school age, his shoulders and hips may come about even; as he goes into his puberty growth, his hips broaden out. While the boy's

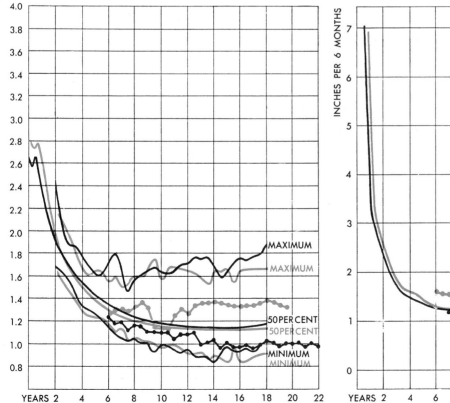

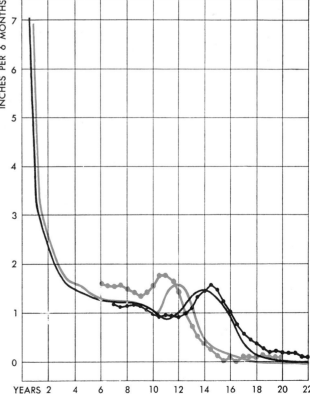

healthy children of the Denver group. Charts from left to right are height, weight, ratio of increase in height and weight, and rate of

growth. The girl is shown to be relatively heavy for her height, the boy relatively light. Girl's rate of growth peaks earlier than boy's.

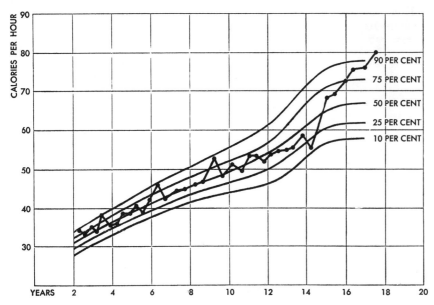

BASAL METABOLISM is a sensitive indicator of the demands of growth. X-ray pictures at the bottom of spread explain why this boy's metabolism ascends so sharply at 15 years.

hip mass is growing, the shoulder mass is standing still, so the ratio changes."

Dr. Boyd showed a series of photographs of a girl from infancy to her eleventh year. "Her shoulders will broaden, but her hips will grow still wider," she commented. "For a boy the probability is that as he grows into adolescence, his hips will not grow proportionately wider, but his shoulders will—and that, of course, is one of the major sex differences in physique.

"When a person reaches adulthood, growth is completed only in the sense that the body has reached its maximum stature. There will be further changes in the structure, but they will be more gradual, and a photograph every five years instead of every year should be sufficient. The oldest photograph in our present file was taken at age 28. I don't see why we shouldn't attempt to trace the structural changes of aging just as we trace the structural changes of growing up. Every period of life is significant in a life-cycle study. And so I hope my successor will follow these subjects through to the end."

Another pediatrician on the staff, Jean Deming, specializes in biometrics. Dr. Deming has subjected the growth data collected by Dr. Boyd to mathematical analysis and plotted the results in a curve for each individual. Actually two curves are necessary: one, known as the Rachel Jens curve, represents growth from birth to the beginning of adolescence; the other, an elongated S called the Gompertz curve, covers the period of adolescence. The Rachel Jens curve is fairly uniform for both boys and

girls. But the Gompertz curve of adolescent growth is markedly different for the two sexes. In girls, the curve begins to bend upward into the first arm of the S at an earlier age and at a more rapid rate of ascent than in boys. But while the typical boy's curve starts later, and turns upward more slowly, it keeps ascending long after the typical girl's curve has leveled off.

"Plotting the growth of children brings out at a glance facts which, though obvious and well known, are apt to be ignored until they are shown graphically," said Dr. Deming. "One of these differences is the earlier maturing of the girl. You can see it dramatized in these two curves," and she picked up a sheet comparing a boy's and a girl's growth in height. "Note how almost parallel the two curves are up to the start of the girl's adolescence, which in this case occurred at 8½ years. The boy's adolescent growth spurt did not begin until he was 10½, when the girl's height was far above his, and she kept above him until about 13. Thereafter the boy kept on growing at a rapid rate, while the girl leveled off.

"We are all familiar with the fact that in junior high school the typical girl is much larger and more grown up than the typical boy of the same age. She's not interested in dates with these small boys; she wants to go with older boys. It is interesting also to see how the curve follows the personality pattern. The growth curve of a feminine type of boy—with a soft rounded body and a greater interest in dolls than in baseball, for example—usually follows the typical girl's

pattern. Similarly girls of the tomboy type usually have a growth pattern conforming to that of boys."

Internal Structure

The staff member primarily responsible for measuring the growth of the internal structure of the body is Marian Maresh. She also is a pediatrician with a specialty: X-ray. Some of the most exciting discoveries of physical growth have come through roentgenology. Dr. Maresh works in close collaboration with Dr. Deming and Dr. Boyd in interpreting the X-ray pictures. The Council's collection of X-ray photographs of the chest is the largest on healthy children in the world.

"This collection of films," said Dr. Maresh, "has helped us to define the range of normality and to understand the variations that an individual child may have and still remain healthy. We had been taught in medical school that a child's chest film must look a certain way. Now we know that each child has his own standard and carries it through life, as far as we have gone. As he grows up, he may have a severe pneumonia or any of a number of other acute infections, but as soon as he has recovered, he will swing back to his own pattern of normality. He will not carry with him the so-called scars of repeated infections, unless he is chronically ill.

"As for sinuses, we have found that their appearance in a child has very little relation to his health. He may have small

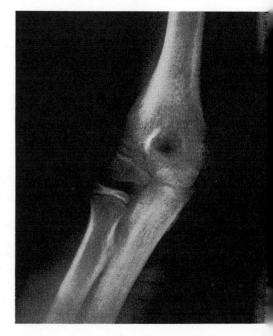

ELBOW JOINT is site of one of the principal milestones in the process of growth. This is the fusion of

sinuses or large sinuses, occasionally cloudy sinuses, and still be a healthy child. This, of course, is quite contrary to what one finds in grown-ups. An adult with a cloudy sinus is apt to be sick."

The Council's chest X-rays have shown that the range of variability in the size and shape of the normal heart is greater than anatomists had believed. "Heart size is related to body size," declared Dr. Maresh. "A child who has been growing fast and is overweight is going to have a large heart. A child of medium body build, whose height-weight relationship is about average, will usually have a heart of average size. He will seldom have a small heart such as we find in the thin child. When it comes to shape, the hearts of healthy children have differences so great that some of them suggest textbook pictures of congenital heart disease—and yet nothing is wrong. The shape of a child's heart is his own business. After he gets that shape, he is going to keep it, barring affliction with a serious disease."

The growth spurt that marks the entrance to adolescence is revealed with a wealth of minutiae by the X-ray photographs. Within a few months the bones, lungs, heart and other organs may grow at a speed double or even treble the previous rate. As the general growth of the body slows down after adolescence, the heart actually decreases in size. This is not strange when you remember that the heart is a muscle. Muscles grow with use and diminish as the use grows less—and the heart is no exception.

Every child is an individual. Each has a unique structural pattern, which may or may not conform to what has been regarded as normal. In her X-ray study of the growth of bones, for example, Dr. Maresh has found a wide variation in the age at which the junctions between the long bones mature. Most boys are born with no wrist bones, only a soft cartilage, and girls rarely have more than one bone in the wrist at birth. The cartilage progressively calcifies into eight small bones. The rate at which they form has been taken as an index to bone development. But the Denver records show that at the age of five a healthy child may have anywhere from two to seven bony centers in the wrist; only 20 per cent of the children have the number heretofore regarded as normal for that age.

"The bone studies are my absorbing interest just now," went on Dr. Maresh. "We X-ray the left arm and leg at two-month intervals during the first six months of life, at six-month intervals from then on through adolescence and yearly thereafter. So I build up a serial picture of the growth of the upper arm, lower arm, upper leg, lower leg, and the relation of each to the growth of the body as a whole. The major difference between boys and girls is in the relative length of the forearm, which is longer in boys. That partly explains why women can't wear men's coats. My shoulders are as broad as my husband's, but his coat sleeves come down to the middle of my hand. This is a sex difference I did not

expect to find. There is no difference between the male and female in the relative length of the upper arm bone or in the length of the legs in relation to body height.

Five of the children in the Denver study group are cousins; their five fathers are all brothers. These children present a wide range in size; one, a boy, is among the smallest for his age in the entire group, and another, a girl, is one of the largest girls of her age. Despite the size variation, all five children have the same structural pattern. Their pattern of relative bone length is somewhat unusual—yet it is the same for all. "We believe," remarked Dr. Maresh, "that eventually we're going to learn how people are put together, and where they inherit the bits that make up the differences. It seems clear that what a child inherits is not his body as a whole, but segments of it, or functions of it, or perhaps patterns of development."

Physiological Growth

As the body grows toward its adult form, new functions are developed and old ones are extended. The production of blood, the input of food, the output of energy, the reaction of nerve and muscle to stimuli—each plays a part in this business of growing up. And so the Child Research Council has a team of biochemists, nutritionists, hematologists and others who concentrate their talents on the physiological aspects of growth, under the general supervision of Robert

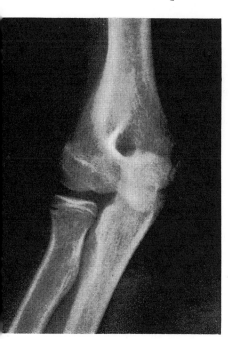
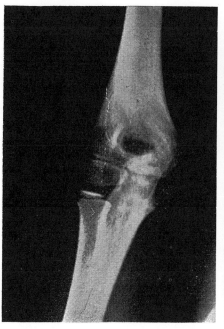
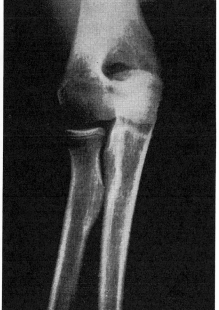

the little bony center at the end of the long bone in the upper arm with that bone. These

two pairs of pictures show a boy's elbow (left) and a girl's before and after fusion. The boy's metabolism (*see chart on opposite page*) showed steep increase when this fusion was occurring.

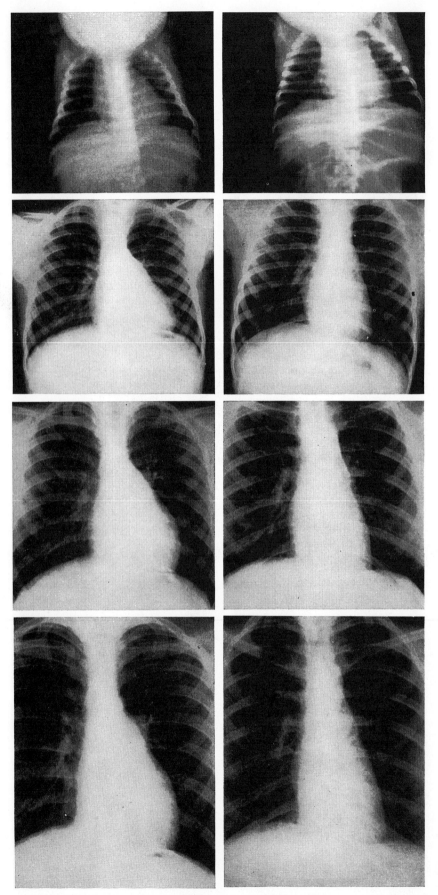

CHANGES IN HEART SIZE in response to the demands of growth found in this study have upset accepted notions of what "normal" heart size is in children. Here the heart of a boy (left) and a girl are shown at comparable stages of growth from infancy to adolescence.

McCammon, the assistant director of the council.

Fundamental to life is metabolism—the two-way process by which nutrients are built into new tissue and, inversely, broken down to release energy. Basal metabolism, the minimum expenditure of energy required by the body at rest, is a base-line for the study of all physiological phenomena. One of the first routines established by the Council was the periodic measurement of the basal metabolism of its children. As data from these studies accumulated, staff members were appalled to discover how little was available in the way of standards for comparison. Actually the Council's own measurements of metabolic rates, published in 1940, were the first reliable tables for the ages from infancy to adolescence. Today those rates recorded in Denver are the norms for medical practice in many parts of the world.

In the same way the Council instituted studies to determine the level of red cells, white cells and other cellular components of the blood at various stages of growth. A similar inquiry measured the proportions of albumin, globulins and other proteins in the blood. Many of these blood determinations have been widely accepted by pediatricians as the most comprehensive data on blood-cell and blood-protein levels in early life.

An infant's blood differs from that of older children in its proportions of both cells and proteins, and differs still more from that of adults. There are also striking sex differences. For example, girls tend to have fewer white cells than boys, but a larger proportion of their white cells are of the specialized infection-fighting kind known as lymphocytes. At certain age levels the girls have fewer red cells per unit of blood than the boys have. Carotene, a substance the body uses to make vitamin A, is found in greater abundance in infant girls than in infant boys. But when the children reach 12 or thereabouts, the situation reverses: then the boy's blood has the greater proportion of carotene. "This finding has fascinating implications," said Dr. Washburn, "for it indicates an inverse relationship between growth and a food factor. In infancy males tend to grow more rapidly than females, but at age 12 most girls are moving into their adolescent growth spurt, while the boys' growth is still on the slow side. And note that in each sex it is only at the period of accelerated growth that the carotene level falls to a low point. I don't know what it means yet, but here we have what seems to be a relationship between the intake of a food substance, the sex of the individual and the pattern of growth."

The record of each child's food intake begins even before the baby is born. In the third month of the mother's pregnancy, Virginia Beal, the nutritionist, visits the home, examines the menus and checks on the variety and quantities of food consumed. After the infant's arrival, these periodic check-ups record exactly what the child is eating. In several cases Miss Beal has been able to spot deficiencies and predict nutritional disorders.

"On one occasion," related Washburn, "Miss Beal came in and said: 'This baby is not getting enough protein, minerals or vitamin D—she's headed for rickets.' The other staff members were highly skeptical. We had never seen a case of rickets in our entire series of children and we couldn't believe that any nutritional measurement could be so accurate. But three months later Dr. Maresh brought me an X-ray film of that child, and there it unmistakably was in the photograph. The case was mild, to be sure, but the bone structure showed evidence of rickets."

The primary purpose of these nutritional studies is to see how the child's growth correlates with its food intake. "Quantitative, as well as qualitative, changes in the blood, bones and teeth have long been recognized as related to the composition of the diet," said Washburn. "But no one yet has done a good job of determining exactly how they are related. We have found evidence that the dietary standards recommended by the National Research Council may need correcting. Our data show that the NRC stated requirements for certain nutrients during the first five years of life are too high. Not even our healthiest children are living up to them. For certain other nutrients the NRC standards are probably too low. We have found that some of our children are getting more vitamins than they need or can use. In the case of vitamins A and D, an overdose can be damaging, and this whole field of accessory food factors needs appraising to determine how much of each vitamin is the optimum ration for a growing child."

It is fascinating to watch the correlations between physical and physiological growth. One of the milestones in physical growth is the joining of the first little bony center in the elbow with the long bone of the upper arm. While this fusion is taking place, the basal metabolic rate rapidly rises to a higher level. It is as though the two processes had to be synchronized as the body's whole system poises for the tremendous adolescent growth spurt.

Dr. McCammon and the group of biochemists and physiologists recently discovered a correlation between the levels of the blood proteins beta and gamma globulin and the development of lymph tissue in the body. When a child's blood contains high levels of these globulins, he is apt to have larger tonsils, larger adenoids and more lymph nodes of every kind. The observations suggest that such children are more resistant to colds and other respiratory diseases than children with a smaller endowment of globulins.

The protein content of the blood is related to the functioning of the heart. Over the years the Child Research Council has accumulated thousands of electrocardiograms of its children, and these are now in process of being analyzed. The results so far indicate that the difference in timing between the peaks and valleys of a child's electrically-recorded heart waves are correlated in some way with the levels of globulins and other plasma proteins in its blood.

"We might theorize," said Washburn, "that the same circumstance which leads the child to build up resistance to infections—namely, his stock of plasma proteins—is also concerned with keeping his heart functioning efficiently. This opens an interesting possibility. It suggests that here we may have a means of evaluating a child's ability to adapt to environmental handicaps."

Globulin relationships seem to pop up everywhere. Recently Washburn, in collaboration with the staff biochemist, Virginia Trevorrow, and the staff hematologist, Adula Meyers, completed a study of red cell sedimentation. Physicians have long used this test to diagnose certain diseases: they take a sample of blood from the patient and record the time it takes for the red cells to settle in a test tube. Fast sedimentation is taken to be a sign of an active infection, such as acute rheumatic fever or active tuberculosis. But Washburn and his associates have found that the blood of perfectly healthy children sometimes has a fast sedimentation rate, while that of rheumatic fever patients sometimes is slow. From many years of study they have concluded that there is no necessary relationship between an infection and the speed of sedimentation. They believe the sedimentation rate is influenced in part by the relative amount of certain proteins in the blood. And one of these proteins is gamma globulin! Some of the proteins are found in connection with infections,

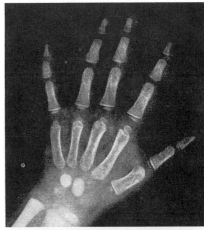

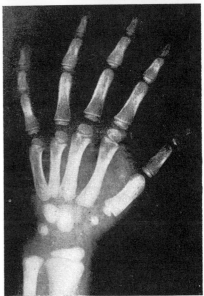

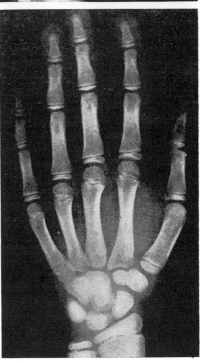

BONES OF WRIST are index of growth. Calcification of seven bones in child's wrist is shown at two, four and eight years.

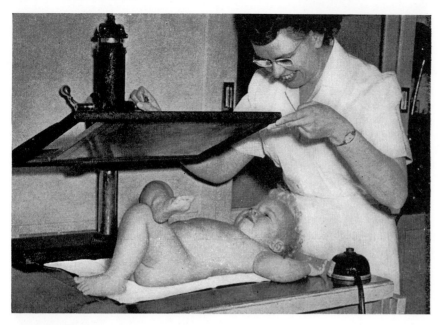

INFANT SUBJECT of study is here in midst of one of her first complete physical examinations at Denver Child Research Council which may record growth throughout her entire life.

others not; some increases in a protein represent good resistance, others not—and so the speed of sedimentation alone can no longer be accepted as a signal or measure of disease.

Psychological Growth

The Denver children vary widely in Intelligence Quotient. Moreover, the I.Q. is not constant; not only do individuals fluctuate but the group as a whole goes down at certain age levels. Studies conducted by Arnold Hilden indicate that a majority of the children are unable to function at their best in intelligence tests in the period from about age five to eight, and there is another dip at adolescence, when many youngsters fall back from 5 to 15 points.

There is a close correlation between a child's anxiety level and his performance in an intelligence test. It was found, for example, that a boy who suddenly dropped from a consistently high I.Q. to a low one was seething with resentment against his new step-mother—although she doted on him and never dreamed that the "honey-sweet" boy was other than an obedient, loving son. In instance after instance, when the I.Q. took a sudden tumble examination revealed that there was some home conflict or other development, real or imaginary, which was a source of emotional strain. It is significant that the drop in I.Q. between the fifth and eighth years coincides with the period when the child is preparing for or just entering school—a time of trial, uneasiness and uncertainty for most children. Similarly the slowing down at

adolescence synchronizes with a characteristically unsettled period in the teen-ager's emotional life.

Recognizing the critical role of the emotions, the Council gives particular attention to the dynamic aspects of psychology. John Benjamin, an M.D. who has had broad experience in psychiatry, is in charge of these studies. They begin before the child is born, when Dr. Benjamin or one of his associates calls at the home to get acquainted with the parents. This prenatal visit affords an opportunity to appraise the home, the attitude of the parents toward the expected baby and the emotional and cultural climate in which it will receive its first impressions of the world—the initial environmental stimuli to growth and adaptation.

The child's early impressions are important and at about six months they become enormously so. The second half of its first year is a period of acute sensitivity. Any attitude on the part of the mother that suggests withdrawal or denial of her love, any prolonged separation of the baby from the mother, any quarreling or other chronic conflicts in the home, can have serious repercussions. The anxieties which result from such situations can adversely affect the baby's intake of food, retard its growth and build up an emotional pattern which is reflected years later in its attitudes and behavior. Just how long the effect persists is not yet known, for the Council's studies of anxiety in infants extend back less than a decade. The Council has cases in which emotional traumas inflicted in the first year or two of life have shown specific outcroppings in the per-

sonalities of children four or five years later. Some of the resulting symptoms are enough to send the shivers down your back.

There are mothers to whom breast feeding is repugnant but who dutifully nurse their babies because they have been told, or have the impression, that it is best for the baby. No matter how conscientious such a mother may be, it is very difficult for her to give the breast feedings with the full sense of pleasure and satisfaction that the child craves. Actually a mother who feeds her infant from a bottle and at the same time lovingly cuddles it against her will do a better job of child raising. She will be rearing hers with much less of the uncertainty, doubt and anxiety that inevitably beset an infant whose mother dislikes the nursing process heartily and goes about it with a coldness and matter-of-factness that cannot be disguised.

The baby's reaction may express itself in the rejection of food or in bowel disturbances such as minor diarrhea and minor constipation. The Council psychologists have observed many cases in which an emotional upset was followed by disturbances in intake of food, in handling of food and in growth.

An experiment with animals made by a graduate student of the University of Colorado last year under Dr. Benjamin's supervision brings at least a suggestion of corroborative evidence. Twenty laboratory rats were divided into two groups. Each group was supplied with exactly the same kinds and amounts of food and was provided with the same living conditions. But the rats of one group were caressed and cuddled by the investigator, while the other group was treated coldly. "It sounds silly," said Washburn, "but the petted rats learned faster and grew faster." The experiment is now being repeated, with biochemical extensions, to find out if possible how the cuddled group could grow faster on the same food intake.

Besides the usual psychological and personality tests, the Council psychologists make use of many informal techniques to study their children from the second year on. These include doll play, free play, painting, drawing and clay modeling.

In free play all the toys are displayed, and the child is free to pick up anything and play with whatever strikes its fancy. Sometimes the child will take out the toys indiscriminately, scatter them around the room, and do nothing constructive. "This is harder to interpret than direct play," said Washburn, "but the child who merely throws things about is usually disturbed, though he doesn't know how to express his anxiety."

I was given an opportunity to listen in on a free play experience of a 4½-year-old boy observed by Katherine Tennes, one of the psychologists. The child ran quickly to the open cupboard of toys and took out two pistols. "I want a gun," he said. Handing a gun to Mrs. Tennes, he added: "Here's one for you." Then he said: "I'm Roy Rogers, and you're an Indian." He told her to sit in a chair, climbed to the top of the cupboard and shouted: "I'm going to shoot you!" After shooting, he remarked: "My father's name is Roy Rogers." Then, noticing a dish of candy on the cupboard, he asked: "Can I have a piece of candy?" When Mrs. Tennes nodded, he took a piece and ate it.

"Now that is a very simple episode," explained Mrs. Tennes, "but it conveyed a lot of meaning. This boy has aggressive feelings toward people, but he is usually quiet and polite. He expresses in play the feelings which in the ordinary circumstances of his life he is not permitted to show directly. He identified himself with Roy Rogers because Roy Rogers is someone who can't be hurt. The fact that he then called his father Roy Rogers showed that he has made a very positive identification with his father. That is one of the things we are interested in finding out about a child—whether he identifies more with his father or with his mother. It will make a difference in the smoothness of his adjustments as he grows up. The candy incident illustrated the usual polite, subdued behavior to which he returns when he is confronted with a reality situation."

Sometimes the free play becomes highly dramatic, and even violent, with the starkest sort of symbolism reminiscent of Freudian theory. What comes out in the play is checked by other procedures. In the finger painting, for example, an aggressive child will almost invariably select violent colors, such as red or purple, and lay them on in vertical strokes with broad lines, whereas one who is mild-mannered and placid usually paints with horizontal lines and soft colors.

These techniques are useful not only for unmasking the anxieties which are troubling the growing child, but also as instruments for testing, validating, and expanding personality theory. After all, the subject of the process of growing up is a person, and the final objective of all these studies—physical, physiological and psychological—is to understand how an infant person, starting at scratch, becomes the kind of adult that he does.

The Author

GEORGE W. GRAY was born in Texas and, at the University of Texas, began to prepare for a career in physiology. Within a year, however, he left the University because of illness. After his recovery he worked for the Houston *Post* and then went to Harvard University. He graduated in 1912 and joined the staff of the New York *World*. During the 1920s he turned freelance and began to concentrate on the natural sciences, contributing many articles to magazines, as well as writing a number of books. "The Great Ravelled Knot," won him the A.A.A.S.-George Westinghouse Science Writing Award for the best magazine article of the year 1948. For most of his career, Gray enjoyed a unique appointment on the staff of the Rockefeller Foundation, visiting the scientists and institutions supported by the Foundation and interpreting their work in reports for other members of the staff and the board of directors.

Bibliography

THE SIGNIFICANCE OF INDIVIDUAL VARIATIONS. Alfred H. Washburn in *Journal of Pediatrics*, Vol. 8, No. 1, pp. 31-37; January, 1936.

PEDIATRIC POTPOURRI. Alfred H. Washburn in *Pediatrics*, Vol. 8, No. 2, pp. 299-306; August, 1951.

NUTRITIONAL INTAKE OF CHILDREN. I. CALORIES, CARBOHYDRATE, FAT AND PROTEIN. Virginia A. Beal in *Journal of Nutrition*, Vol. 50, No. 2, pp. 223-234; June, 1953.

STANDARDS FOR THE BASAL METABOLISM OF CHILDREN FROM 2 TO 15 YEARS OF AGE INCLUSIVE. Robert C. Lewis, Anna Marie Duval and Alberta Iliff in *Journal of Pediatrics*, Vol. 23, No. 1, pp. 1-18; July, 1943.

SCIENTIFIC AMERICAN February 1955, Vol. 192, No. 2, pp. 84-91

OFFPRINT 1064

BONE

by Franklin C. McLean

The rigid framework of the body is a remarkably active and versatile tissue. Of current physiological interest is its dual function in maintaining the level of calcium in the blood.

Bone is a busy and in many ways quite amazing tissue. It houses the factory (the bone marrow) that produces most of the cells in the blood; it stores minerals and doles them out as needed to other parts of the body; it repairs itself after an injury; it grows, like any other living tissue, until the body reaches adulthood. Not the least of its wonderful properties is the fact that while it is growing and constantly building itself, it also serves as the rigid structural support for the body, like the steel framework of a building. Some years ago I was vividly reminded of this while the Grand Central Terminal in New York City was being rebuilt. During the whole reconstruction, which took several years, trains ran on schedule in and out of the station; the terminal functioned as usual. Just so, as the bones are being built, the body goes on with its normal daily activities.

The key to bone's unique manner of growth and to its outstanding quality—hardness—is its mineral building material, often called the "bone salt." For a century this mineral has been a subject of controversy and thorny investigation. It has now become possible at last to describe the nature of the mineral and its physiological functions in the body. The mineral is composed chiefly of calcium, phosphate and carbonate. Especially interesting is its calcium. The mechanism by which bone takes up, stores and releases calcium into the blood in measured amounts to keep the level constant forms a fascinating chapter in modern physiology which will be the subject of this article.

A bone grows by a continual process of tearing down and building up a little at a time. As it grows, it steadily becomes stronger. Its growth in thickness and growth in length go on by somewhat different methods. The body's long bones, for example, grow in thickness as follows: bone-destroying cells called osteo-clasts erode the inside of the bone, enlarging the marrow cavity, while bone-forming cells called osteoblasts at the same time build up the bone on the outside. Fractures of bone are repaired by much the same method: first a soft, fibrous scar, called a callus, provisionally joins the broken ends; then osteoblasts gradually replace this soft tissue with hard, new bone. Meanwhile osteoclasts trim off any fragments or jagged edges of bone that might interfere with function and any excess bone made during the rebuilding.

Growth in length takes place by a method more like the extension of a tunnel under a river than the rebuilding of the Grand Central Terminal. During the childhood period before it reaches full growth, every long bone is capped near each end by a disk of cartilage. One might think of the disk as corresponding to the chamber in which tunnel drillers work and which advances as they bore under the river. The disk grows in thickness away from the bone, and as it grows, bone-forming cells coming in from behind convert the rear part of the cartilage into bone—like men coming up with concrete to replace mud in the wake of the tunnelers. The cartilage disk is made up of columns of cells in a honeycomb-like structure [*see photograph at the top of the opposite page*], so that the advance of the bone is like myriads of parallel tunneling operations rather than a single one. Each operation removes a column of cartilage cells and deposits a hard mineral, comparable to concrete, in the tunnel walls. Eventually, as each long bone reaches its predetermined limit of growth, the cartilage stops growing and is completely replaced by bone.

Nature has designed the growth system and the structure of bone to give the

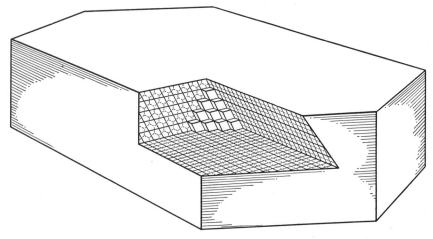

CRYSTAL of bone is hydroxyapatite. This model of a single crystal is cut to show the unit cells of its molecular structure. The model enlarges the crystal some five million times.

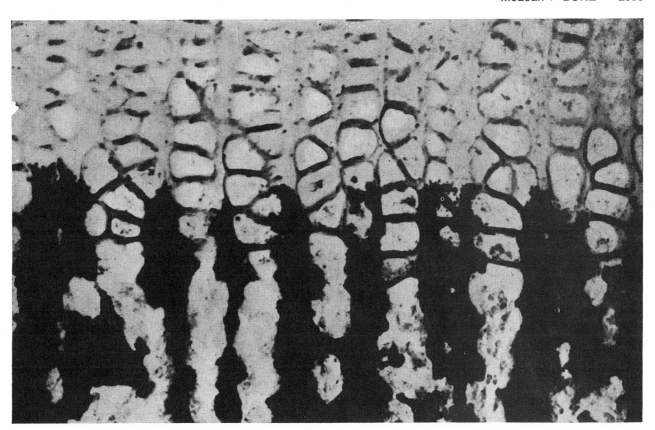

CARTILAGE DISK at the end of the leg bone of a puppy is shown in longitudinal section by this photomicrograph. The cartilage is the light material at the top. The dark material at the bottom is the bone, which tunnels into the cartilage during growth.

COLLAGEN FIBERS in a human leg bone are shown by this electron micrograph. Normally the fibers are obscured by crystals, but here they have been made visible by removing the calcium from the bone. The electron micrograph was made by R. A. Robinson.

greatest degree of support with minimum weight. The bones are hollow, in accord with the well-known engineering principle that a given weight of a rigid material is much stronger in the form of a tube than as a solid rod. But the space within the bones is not wasted; it is filled with the blood-forming bone marrow.

As we have noted, bone is built large-ly of a mineral, deposited in an organic matrix. The mineral includes not only calcium, phosphate and carbonate but also citrate, water and small amounts of other elements, especially sodium, magnesium, potassium, fluorine and chlorine. It resembles certain minerals widely distributed in rocks; indeed, it has the crystal structure of the apatite family of minerals. The most abundant mineral of this group in nature is fluorapatite.

The crystals of the bone mineral, as analyzed by X-ray diffraction studies, seem to have a chemical composition like that of fluorapatite, except for hydroxyl (OH) groups in place of the fluorine. The hydroxyapatite has the formula $3 \, Ca_3(PO_4)_2 \cdot Ca(OH)_2$. This accounts for the calcium and phosphate, but where are the carbonate and citrate, the other chief constituents of bone mineral?

The location of these substances has been one of the chief sources of controversy. It used to be thought that the bone mineral was a single compound, joined molecule to molecule continuously throughout the bone. There is now, however, abundant evidence that the mineral is discontinuous and inhomogeneous in structure. It may be compared to a wall of bricks and mortar. The bricks are the crystals of hydroxyapatite; the mortar is largely made up of carbonate and citrate ions, both of which are too large to be admitted to the crystals of hydroxyapatite. Included in the mortar are other ions found in bone —chiefly sodium and magnesium, as well as a fraction of the calcium. Running through it also are the fibers of the organic matrix, made up of a protein known as collagen. And the remaining space in the mortar is filled with a semiliquid substance which transports materials to the bone mineral from the circulating blood and *vice versa*. A tracer dye or radioactive material introduced into the blood stream soon reaches much of the bone mineral through this fluid medium.

The two fractions of the mineral—the crystals and the intercrystalline portion —have markedly different physical and chemical properties. The crystals are relatively stable in structure and resist solution in aqueous fluids, but are subject to rapid ion exchange reactions at their surfaces. They are extremely small: in a single gram there are so many crystals that their surface areas are reported to add up to more than 100 square meters. Calculations from these figures lead to the rather startling conclusion that the total surface area of the crystals of bone salt in the skeleton of a 154-pound man exceeds 100 acres!

The intercrystalline fraction, estimated to make up about 4 per cent of the mineral by weight, is much more soluble than the crystals, and its metallic elements, notably calcium, are easily returned to the circulating blood by simple solution.

More than 99 per cent of the calcium of the body is in the bones. But

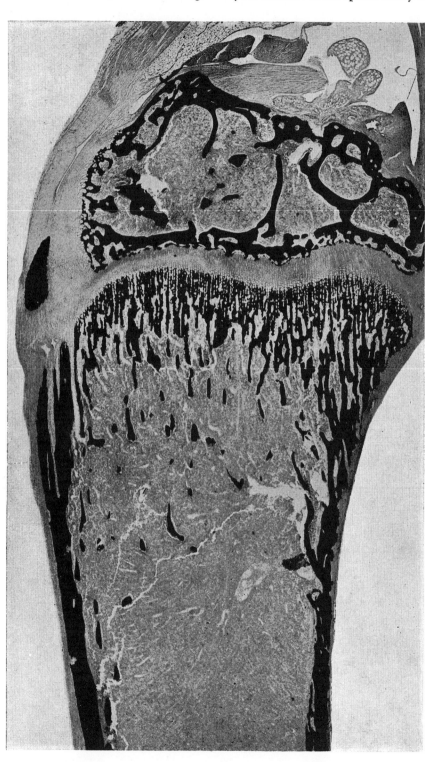

GROSS ANATOMY is shown by this longitudinal section of the upper end of a leg bone of a rat. The gray band running from left to right above the center of the picture is the cartilage disk. The black material is the stained bone, which here again may be seen tunneling into the cartilage. The gray material running down the center of the bone is marrow.

calcium is also important to the body in other respects. It is necessary for the clotting of blood, for the beating of the heart, for the contraction of the skeletal muscles and for the normal functioning of the nervous system. To insure that these functions are carried out continuously in an optimum manner, the concentration of calcium in the blood plasma must be maintained at an approximately constant level. This is accomplished by a self-regulating mechanism which draws on the large reserve of calcium in the bones.

Everyone is familiar with the fact that warm-blooded animals have a thermostatically controlled mechanism which automatically keeps the body temperature relatively constant in spite of large fluctuations in the temperature of the external environment. In recent years such self-regulating processes have acquired the name "feedback." The condition that is being regulated is itself the stimulus activating the regulatory mechanism; information about the output is fed back to an earlier stage of the process so as to influence its action and thereby control the output. The role of feedback in the regulation of the calcium-ion concentration in the blood plasma is only now beginning to be understood in all its implications. The regulating system is rather complex, and can be best understood in terms of a mechanism made up of two parts.

I am writing this in a large room in a Vermont house during a cold spell. At one end of the room is a fireplace, which supplies a fairly constant amount of heat to the room, but only as long as I keep it supplied with fuel; it has no self-regulatory mechanism. At the other end of the room is a gas-fired floor furnace, controlled by a thermostat. Whenever the temperature of the room drops below a certain level, the thermostat feeds this information back to the furnace and heat is supplied by automatic control. Thus the room is heated from two separate sources, one of which is automatic and the other not.

Similarly bone furnishes calcium to the blood plasma in two ways, one of which is not regulated physiologically. Like the fireplace that delivers a constant amount of heat to my room, the labile part of the bone's mineral structure—the intercrystalline fraction—yields up a considerable and constant supply of calcium to the blood. It does so by simple solution, and this traffic between the bones and blood depends only on chemical dynamics. The exchange goes on with extraordinary rapidity; under certain conditions as much as 100 per

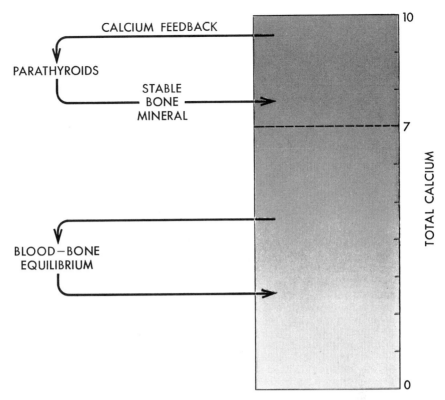

FEEDBACK MECHANISM regulating the level of calcium in the blood is illustrated in this diagram. The normal concentration of calcium in the blood plasma is 10 milligrams per 100 cubic centimeters. Seven milligrams of this is supplied by the fraction of bone mineral between the bone crystals. When the level falls below 10 milligrams, the parathyroid glands secrete a hormone which promotes the release of calcium from the stable crystalline reserve.

cent of the calcium in the plasma may be replaced every minute. This exchange alone can keep the level of calcium in the plasma at 70 per cent of the normal calcium content—the normal level being about 10 milligrams per 100 cubic centimeters.

The rest of the calcium is supplied, in just the amount needed to maintain the normal level, by means of a feedback mechanism involving the parathyroid glands—four tiny bodies embedded in the thyroid. When the level of calcium ions in the plasma falls below normal, the parathyroid glands increase their secretion of hormones. The hormones, in turn, promote the dissolution of components of bone. Thus they are able to wrest calcium from the stable crystals, as well as from the labile fraction of the bone mineral. Like the thermostat in my Vermont house, which is able to call on an independent source of fuel, the parathyroid hormone has access to a source of calcium not readily soluble in an aqueous medium.

It is probable, although this is still somewhat controversial, that the parathyroid hormone exerts its influence by controlling the activity of the bone-destroying cells, the osteoclasts. How these

cells dissolve bone is not understood. One current hypothesis is that they may remove calcium from the bone mineral by forming a chelating agent—the recently discovered type of compound that has the ability to grasp metallic ions and take them out of a substance in which they are strongly bound [see "Chelation," by Harold F. Walton; SCIENTIFIC AMERICAN, June, 1953]. The prototype of these agents, commercially named Versene, has a much greater affinity for calcium than does the bone mineral itself; a Versene solution readily dissolves calcium out of the bone crystals. There is no positive evidence that osteoclasts actually produce a chelating agent. But it may well be that the body does form such an agent to dissolve the crystals of the bone mineral.

This brief article has touched on only a few highlights of the current research on the physiology of bone. The subject is now beginning to come into its own, and it is opening up fresh perspectives which suggest interesting new investigations and should lead to a better understanding and more effective treatment of bone disorders.

The Author

FRANKLIN C. McLEAN is emeritus professor of pathological physiology at the University of Chicago. He was born in Maroa, Ill., in 1888, went to the University of Chicago and took his M.D. at Rush Medical College in 1910. His career has been varied: he was a professor of medicine at Peiping Union Medical College in China, a lieutenant colonel in the Chemical Warfare Service and has written 148 research papers on various subjects. In the foreword to his forthcoming book, *Bone,* he notes that his interest in calcium goes back 20 years to researches with A. Baird Hastings, now at the Harvard Medical School, on calcium in the blood. "Following this, I began an exploration of the blood-bone relationship, and shortly thereafter, in collaboration with William Bloom, this led to a conscious effort to bridge some of the gaps between the chemical and morphological approaches to an understanding of bone. Our interests then broadened, until it became apparent that we were concerned with every aspect of the physiology and biochemistry of bone." McLean has given much of his spare time to helping Negroes to enter medicine, especially through the National Medical Fellowships, Inc., of which he is secretary-treasurer. In 1953 the Chicago Commission on Human Relations cited him as having "given 25 years of devoted effort to improving medical care for Negroes, breaking down barriers to their training in medical colleges and advancing them in the medical profession."

Bibliography

Bone: An Introduction to the Physiology of Skeletal Tissue. Franklin C. McLean and Marshall R. Urist. The University of Chicago Press, 1955.

A Textbook of Histology. Alexander A. Maximow and William Bloom. W. B. Saunders Company, 1952.

SPECIAL NOTE TO TEACHERS: Each article in this volume, plus more than 660 others, is available as a separate, self-bound SCIENTIFIC AMERICAN Offprint. Offprints may be ordered in any combination and in any quantity. Teachers who want to adopt articles for their courses, therefore, can ensure that each student has his own set. Students' sets are collated by the publisher before shipment.

SCIENTIFIC AMERICAN   August 1956, Vol. 195, No. 2, pp. 87-94   OFFPRINT 1065

SICKLE CELLS AND EVOLUTION

by Anthony C. Allison

Why has the hereditary trait in which the red blood cells are sickle-shaped persisted for so many generations? The surprising answer is that under some conditions it is actually beneficial.

Persevering study of small and seemingly insignificant phenomena sometimes yields surprising harvests of understanding. This article is an account of what has been learned from an oddly shaped red blood cell.

Forty-six years ago a Chicago physician named James B. Herrick, examining a Negro boy with a mysterious disease, found that many of his red blood cells were distorted into a crescent or sickle shape. After Herrick's report, doctors soon recognized many other cases of the same disease. They learned that it was hereditary and common in Negroes [see "Sickle-Cell Anemia," by George W. Gray; SCIENTIFIC AMERICAN, August, 1951]. The curious trait of the sickled blood cells gradually attracted the in-

terest of physiologists, biochemists, physical chemists, geneticists, anthropologists and others. And their varied investigations of this quirk of nature led to enlightenment on many unexpected subjects: the behavior of the blood's hemoglobin, inherited resistance to disease, the movements of populations over the world and the nature of some of the agencies that influence human evolution.

Let us review first what has been learned about the sickle cell phenomenon itself. As every student of biology knows, the principal active molecule in the red blood cells is hemoglobin, which serves as the carrier of oxygen. It appears that an unusual form of hemoglobin, pro-

duced under the influence of an abnormal gene, is responsible for the sickling of red cells. This hemoglobin molecule differs only slightly from the normal variety, and when there is an ample supply of oxygen it behaves normally: *i.e.*, it takes on oxygen and preserves its usual form in the red cells. But when the sickle cell hemoglobin (known as hemoglobin S)-loses oxygen, as in the capillaries where oxygen is delivered to the tissues, it becomes susceptible to a peculiar kind of reaction. It can attach itself to other hemoglobin S molecules, and they form long rods, which in turn attract one another and line up in parallel. These formations are rigid enough to distort the red cells from their normal disk shape into the shape

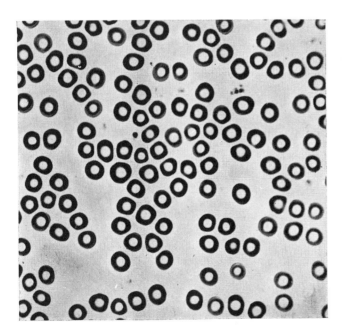

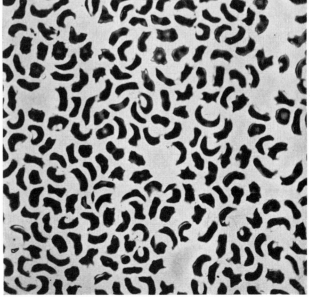

RED BLOOD CELLS of an individual with sickle cell trait, *i.e.*, a sickle cell gene from only one parent, are examined under the microscope. At the left are oxygenated red cells; they are disk-shaped. At the right are the same cells deoxygenated; they are sickle-shaped.

of a sickle [*see photomicrographs on page 2359*]. The sickled cells may clog blood vessels; and they are soon destroyed by the body, so that the patient becomes anemic. The destruction of the hemoglobin converts it into bilirubin—the yellow pigment responsible for the jaundiced appearance often characteristic of anemic patients.

Most sufferers from sickle cell anemia die in childhood. Those who survive have a chronic disease punctuated by painful crises when blood supply is cut off from various body organs. There is no effective treatment for the disease.

From the first, a great deal of interest focused on the genetic aspects of this peculiarity. It was soon found that some Negroes carried a sickling tendency without showing symptoms of the disease. This was eventually discovered to mean that the carrier inherits the sickle cell gene from only one parent. A child who receives sickle cell genes from both parents produces only hemoglobin S and therefore is prone to sickling and anemia. On the other hand, in a person who has a normal hemoglobin gene from one parent and a hemoglobin S from the other sickling is much less likely; such persons, known as carriers of the "sickle cell trait," become ill only under exceptional conditions—for example, at high altitudes, when their blood does not receive enough oxygen.

The sickle cell trait is, of course, much more common than the disease. Among Negroes in the U. S. some 9 per cent carry the trait, but less than one fourth of 1 per cent show sickle cell anemia. In some Negro tribes in Africa the trait is present in as much as 40 per cent of the population, while 4 per cent have sickle cell genes from both parents and are subject to the disease.

The high incidence of the sickle cell gene in these tribes raised a most interesting question. Why does the harmful gene persist? A child who inherits two sickle cell genes (*i.e.*, is homozygous for this gene) has only about one fifth as much chance as other children of surviving to reproductive age. Because of this mortality, about 16 per cent of the sickle cell genes must be removed from the population in every generation. And yet the general level remains high without any sign of declining. What can be the explanation? Carriers of the sickle cell trait do not produce more children than those who lack it, and natural mutation could not possibly replace the lost sickle cell genes at any such rate.

The laws of evolution suggested a possible answer. Carriers of the sickle cell trait (a sickle cell gene from one parent and a normal one from the other) might have some advantage in survival over those who lacked the trait. If people with the trait had a lower mortality rate, counterbalancing the high mortality of sufferers from sickle cell anemia, then the frequency of sickle cell genes in the population would remain at a constant level.

What advantage could the sickle cell trait confer? Perhaps it protected its carriers against some other fatal disease—say malaria. The writer looked into the situation in malarious areas of Africa and found that children with the sickle cell trait were indeed relatively resistant to malarial infection. In some places they had as much as a 25 per cent better chance of survival than children without the trait. Children in most of Central Africa are exposed to malaria nearly all year round and have repeated infections during their early years. If they survive; they build up a considerable immunity to the disease. In some unknown way the sickle cell trait apparently protects young children against the malaria parasite during the dangerous years until they acquire an immunity to malaria.

On the African continent the sickle cell gene has a high frequency among people along the central belt, near the Equator, where malaria is common and is transmitted by mosquitoes through most

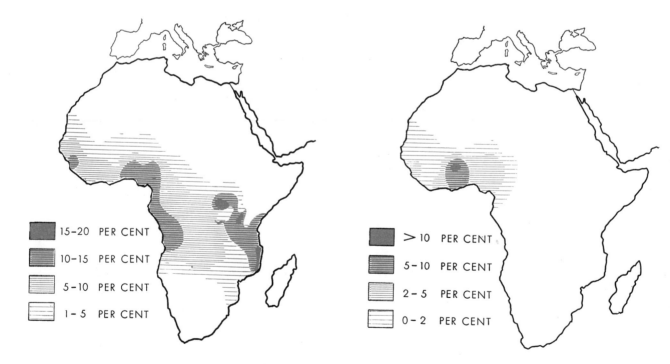

FREQUENCY OF THE SICKLE CELL GENE is plotted in per cent on the map of Africa. High frequencies are confined to a broad belt in which malignant tertian malaria is an important cause of death.

FREQUENCY OF THE HEMOGLOBIN C GENE is similarly plotted. Unlike the sickle cell gene, which has a widespread distribution, this gene is confined to a single focus in West Africa.

15-20 PER CENT
10-15 PER CENT
5-10 PER CENT
1-5 PER CENT

> 10 PER CENT
5-10 PER CENT
2-5 PER CENT
0-2 PER CENT

of the year. North and south of this belt, where malaria is less common and usually of the benign variety, the sickle cell gene is rare or absent. Moreover, even within the central belt, tribes in nonmalarious areas have few sickle cell genes.

Extension of the studies showed that similar situations exist in other areas of the world. In malarious parts of southern Italy and Sicily, Greece, Turkey and India, the sickle cell trait occurs in up to 30 per cent of the population. There is no reason to suppose that the peoples of all these areas have transmitted the gene to one another during recent times. The sickle cell gene may have originated independently in the several populations or may trace back to a few such genes passed along among them a thousand years ago. The high frequency of the gene in these populations today can be attributed mainly to the selective effect of malaria.

On the other hand, we should expect that when a population moves from a malarious region to one free of this disease, the frequency of the sickle cell gene will fall. The Negro population of the U. S. exemplifies such a development. When Negro slaves were first brought to North America from West Africa some 250 to 300 years ago, the frequency of the sickle cell trait among them was probably not less than 22 per cent. By mixed mating with Indian and white people this figure was probably reduced to about 15 per cent. In the absence of any appreciable mortality from malaria, the loss of sickle cell genes through deaths from anemia in 12 generations should have reduced the frequency of the sickle cell trait in the Negro population to about 9 per cent. This is, in fact, precisely the frequency found today.

Thus the Negroes of the U. S. show a clear case of evolutionary change. Within the space of a few hundred years this population, because of its transfer from Africa to North America, has undergone a definite alteration in genetic structure. This indicates how rapidly human evolution can take place under favorable circumstances.

Since the discovery of sickle cell hemoglobin (hemoglobin S), many other abnormal types of human hemoglobin have been found. (They are usually distinguished by electrophoresis, a separation method which depends on differences in the amount of the negative charge on the molecule.) One of the most

HEMOGLOBIN MOLECULES are represented as ellipsoids in these drawings. At the top are normal hemoglobin molecules, which are arranged almost at random in the red blood cell. Second and third from the top are sickle cell hemoglobin molecules, which form long helixes when they lose oxygen. Fourth is an aggregate of normal (*white*) and sickle cell molecules (*black*), in which every fourth molecule of the helix is normal. Fifth is an aggregate of hemoglobin C (*gray*) and sickle cell molecules; every other molecule is hemoglobin C.

common of these other varieties is called hemoglobin C. It, too, causes anemia in persons who have inherited the hemoglobin C gene from both parents. Moreover, the combination of hemoglobin S and hemoglobin C (one inherited from each parent) likewise leads to anemia. These two hemoglobins combine to form the rodlike structures that cause sickling of the red blood cells [see drawings on page 2361].

The hemoglobin C gene is largely confined to West Africa, notably among people in the northern section of the Gold Coast, where the frequency of the trait runs as high as 27 per cent. Whether

hemoglobin C, like hemoglobin S, protects against malaria is not known. But the C gene must give some advantage, else it would not persist. Obviously inheritance of both C and S is a disadvantage, since it leads to anemia. As a consequence we should expect to find that where the C gene is present, the spread of the S gene is retarded. This does seem to be the case: in the northern Gold Coast the frequency of the S gene goes no higher than 5 per cent.

Another gene producing abnormal hemoglobin, known as the thalassemia gene, is common in Greece, Italy, Cyprus, Turkey and Thailand. The trait

is most prevalent in certain areas (e.g., lowlands of Sardinia) where malaria used to be serious, but there have not yet been any direct observations as to whether its carriers are resistant to malaria. The trait almost certainly has some compensating advantage, for it persists in spite of the fact that even persons who have inherited the gene from only one parent have a tendency to anemia. The same is probably true of another deviant gene, known as the hemoglobin E gene, which is common in Thailand, Burma and among some populations in Ceylon and Indonesia.

By now the identified hemoglobin types form a considerable alphabet: besides S, C, thalassemia and E there are D, G, H, I, J, K and M. But the latter are relatively rare, from which it can be inferred that they provide little or no advantage.

For anyone interested in population genetics and human evolution, the sickle cell story presents a remarkably clear demonstration of some of the principles at play. It affords, for one thing, a simple illustration of the principle of hybrid vigor. Hybrid vigor has been investigated by many breeding experiments with fruit flies and plants, but in most cases the crossbreeding involves so many genes that it is impossible to say what gene combinations are responsible for the advantages of the hybrid. Here we can see a human cross involving only a single gene, and we can give a convincing explanation of just how the hybridization provides an advantage. In a population exposed to malaria the heterozygote (hybrid) possessing one normal hemoglobin gene and one sickle cell hemoglobin gene has an advantage over either homozygote (two normal genes or two sickle cell genes). And this selective advantage, as we can observe, maintains a high frequency of a gene which is deleterious in double dose but advantageous in single dose.

Secondly, we see a simple example of inherited resistance to disease. Resistance to infection (to say nothing of disorders such as cancer or heart disease) is generally complex and unexplainable, but in this case it is possible to identify a single gene (the sickle cell gene) which controls resistance to a specific disease (malaria). It is an unusually di-

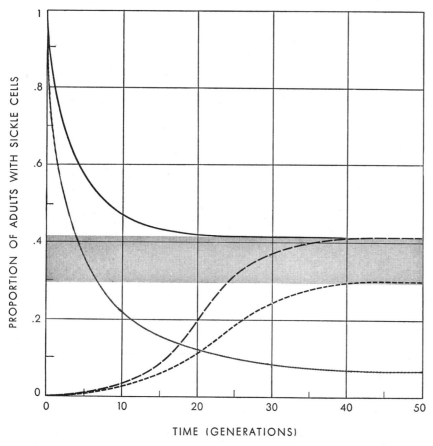

RATE OF CHANGE IN FREQUENCY of adults with sickle cells under different conditions is shown in this chart. The horizontal gray band represents the equilibrium frequency in a region where individuals with the sickle cell trait have an evolutionary advantage of about 25 per cent over individuals without the sickle cell trait. If a population of individuals with a low sickle cell frequency enters the region, the frequency will increase to an equilibrium value (long dashes). If hemoglobin C is already established in the same population, the frequency will increase to a lower value (short dashes). If a population of individuals with a high sickle cell frequency enters the region, the frequency will decrease (solid line). If this population enters a nonmalarious region, the frequency will fall to a low value (gray line).

rect manifestation of the fact, now universally recognized but difficult to demonstrate, that inheritance plays a large role in controlling susceptibility or resistance to disease.

Thirdly, the sickle cell situation shows that mutation is not an unmixed bane to the human species. Most mutations are certainly disadvantageous, for our genetic constitution is so carefully balanced that any change is likely to be for the worse. To adapt an aphorism, all is best in this best of all possible bodies. Nonetheless, the sickle cell mutation, which at first sight looks altogether harmful, turns out to be a definite advantage in a malarious environment. Similarly other mutant genes that are bad in one situation may prove beneficial in another. Variability and mutation permit the human species, like other organisms, to adapt rapidly to new situations.

Finally, the sickle cell findings offer a cheering thought on the genetic future of civilized man. Eugenists often express alarm about the fact that civilized societies, through medical protection of the ill and weak, are accumulating harmful genes: *e.g.*, those responsible for diabetes and other hereditary diseases. The sickle cell history brings out the other side of the story: improving standards of hygiene may also *eliminate* harmful genes—not only the sickle cell but also others of which we are not yet aware.

PHENOTYPE	GENOTYPE	ELECTROPHORETIC PATTERN	HEMOGLOBIN TYPES
NORMAL	Hb^A -- Hb^A		A
SICKLE CELL TRAIT	Hb^S -- Hb^A		SA
SICKLE CELL ANEMIA	Hb^S -- Hb^S		SS
HEMOGLOBIN C SICKLE CELL ANEMIA	Hb^C -- Hb^S		CS
HEMOGLOBIN C DISEASE	Hb^C -- Hb^C		CC

HEMOGLOBIN SPECIMENS from various individuals are analyzed by electrophoresis. The phenotype is the outward expression of the genotype, which refers to the hereditary make-up of the individual. The H-shaped symbols in the genotype column are schematic representations of sections of human chromosomes, one from each parent. The horizontal line of the H represents a gene for hemoglobin type. Hb^A is normal hemoglobin; Hb^S, sickle cell hemoglobin; Hb^C, hemoglobin C. This kind of electrophoretic pattern is made on a strip of wet paper between a positive and a negative electrode. The specimen of hemoglobin is placed on the line at the left side of each strip. In this experiment hemoglobin A migrates faster toward the positive electrode than sickle cell hemoglobin, which migrates faster than hemoglobin C. Thus the pattern for individuals with two types of hemoglobin is double.

The Author

ANTHONY C. ALLISON is a postgraduate fellow at the University of Oxford, where he is engaged in research on cell metabolism in the Medical Research Council Laboratories, directed by the famous biochemist H. A. Krebs. Allison was stimulation I was looking for. It took me four years to realize the significance of the fact that the amount of information we can remember is not an invariant measure of our mnemonic capacity. At about the time the light broke I became involved in the work of the Lincoln Laboratory and had to postpone further development of this line of thought until I returned to Harvard last year. The present article, therefore, is the result of eight years' wondering in the bewilderness. And as careful readers are sure to detect, I'm not home yet."

Bibliography

SICKLE-CELL ANEMIA. George W. Gray in *Scientific American*, Vol. 185, No. 2, pages 56-59; August, 1951.

PROTECTION AFFORDED BY SICKLE-CELL TRAITS AGAINST SUBTERTIAN MALARIAL INFECTION. A. C. Allison in *British Medical Journal*, Vol. 1, pages 290-301; February, 1954.

SCIENTIFIC AMERICAN March 1967, Vol. 216, No. 3, pp. 24-31

OFFPRINT **1066**

TOXIC SUBSTANCES
AND ECOLOGICAL CYCLES

by George M. Woodwell

Radioactive elements or pesticides such as DDT that are released in the environment may enter meteorological and biological cycles that distribute them and can concentrate them to dangerous levels.

The vastness of the earth has fostered a tradition of unconcern about the release of toxic wastes into the environment. Billowing clouds of smoke are diluted to apparent nothingness; discarded chemicals are flushed away in rivers; insecticides "disappear" after they have done their job; even the massive quantities of radioactive debris of nuclear explosions are diluted in the apparently infinite volume of the environment. Such pollutants are indeed diluted to traces—to levels infinitesimal by ordinary standards, measured as parts per billion or less in air, soil and water. Some pollutants do disappear; they are immobilized or decay to harmless substances. Others last, sometimes in toxic form, for long periods. We have learned in recent years that dilution of persistent pollutants even to trace levels detectable only by refined techniques is no guarantee of safety. Nature has ways of concentrating substances that are frequently surprising and occasionally disastrous.

We have had dramatic examples of one of the hazards in the dense smogs that blanket our cities with increasing frequency. What is less widely realized is that there are global, long-term ecological processes that concentrate toxic substances, sometimes hundreds of thousands of times above levels in the environment. These processes include not only patterns of air and water circulation but also a complex series of biological mechanisms. Over the past decade detailed studies of the distribution of both radioactive debris and pesticides have revealed patterns that have surprised even biologists long familiar with the unpredictability of nature.

Major contributions to knowledge of these patterns have come from studies of radioactive fallout. The incident that triggered worldwide interest in large-scale radioactive pollution was the hydrogen-bomb test at Bikini in 1954 known as "Project Bravo." This was the test that inadvertently dropped radioactive fallout on several Pacific islands and on the Japanese fishing vessel *Lucky Dragon*. Several thousand square miles of the Pacific were contaminated with fallout radiation that would have been lethal to man. Japanese and U.S. oceanographic vessels surveying the region found that the radioactive debris had been spread by wind and water, and, more disturbing, it was being passed rapidly along food chains from small plants to small marine organisms that ate them to larger animals (including the tuna, a staple of the Japanese diet).

The U.S. Atomic Energy Commission and agencies of other nations, particularly Britain and the U.S.S.R., mounted a large international research program, costing many millions of dollars, to learn the details of the movement of such debris over the earth and to explore its hazards. Although these studies have been focused primarily on radioactive materials, they have produced a great deal of basic information about pollutants in general. The radioactive substances serve as tracers to show the transport and concentration of materials by wind and water and the biological mechanisms that are characteristic of natural communities.

One series of investigations traced the worldwide movement of particles in the air. The tracer in this case was strontium 90, a fission product released into the earth's atmosphere in large quantities by nuclear-bomb tests. Two reports in 1962 —one by S. Laurence Kulp and Arthur R. Schulert of Columbia University and the other by a United Nations committee— furnished a detailed picture of the travels of strontium 90. The isotope was concentrated on the ground between the latitudes of 30 and 60 degrees in both hemispheres, but concentrations were five to 10 times greater in the Northern Hemisphere, where most of the bomb tests were conducted.

It is apparently in the middle latitudes

FOREST COMMUNITY is an integrated array of plants and animals that accumulates and reuses nutrients in stable cycles, as indicated schematically in black. DDT participates in parallel cycles (*color*). The author measured DDT residues in a New Brunswick forest in which four pounds per acre of DDT had been applied over seven years. (Studies have shown about half of this landed in the forest, the remainder dispersing in the atmosphere.) Three years after the spraying, residues of DDT were as shown (in pounds per acre).

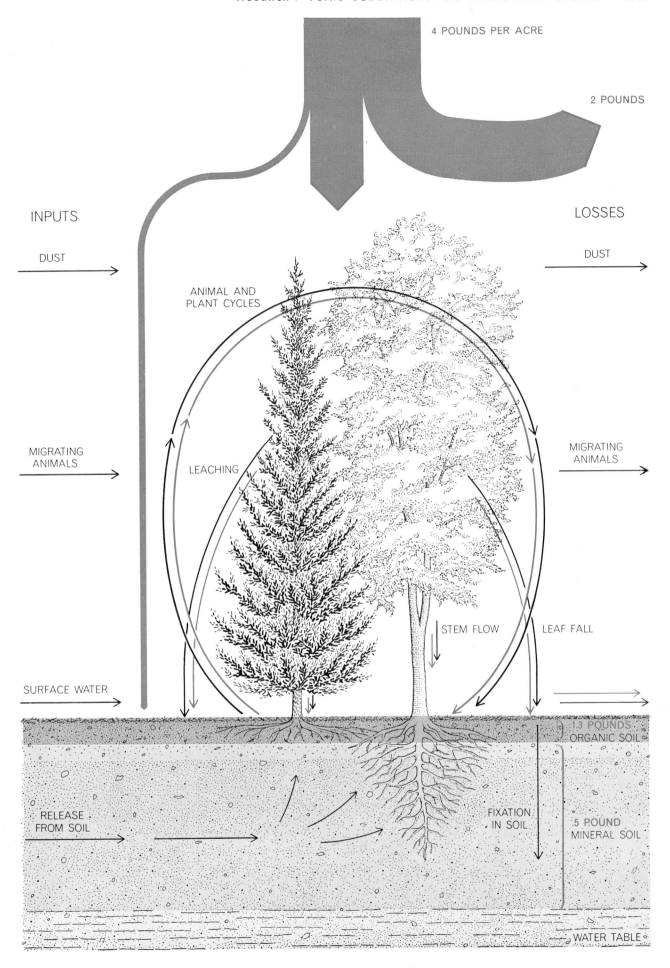

4 POUNDS PER ACRE

2 POUNDS

INPUTS

LOSSES

DUST

DUST

ANIMAL AND
PLANT CYCLES

MIGRATING
ANIMALS

LEACHING

MIGRATING
ANIMALS

STEM FLOW

LEAF FALL

SURFACE WATER

1.3 POUNDS
ORGANIC SOIL

RELEASE
FROM SOIL

FIXATION
IN SOIL

.5 POUND
MINERAL SOIL

WATER TABLE

that exchanges occur between the air of upper elevations (the stratosphere) and that of lower elevations (the troposphere). The larger tests have injected debris into the stratosphere; there it remains for relatively long periods, being carried back into the troposphere and to the ground in the middle latitudes in late winter or spring. The mean "half-time" of the particles' residence in the stratosphere (that is, the time for half of a given injection to fall out) is from three months to five years, depending on many factors, including the height of the injection, the size of the particles, the latitude of injection and the time of year. Debris injected into the troposphere has a mean half-time of residence ranging from a few days to about a month. Once airborne, the particles may travel rapidly and far. The time for one circuit around the earth in the middle latitudes varies from 25 days to less than 15. (Following two recent bomb tests in China fallout was detected at the Brookhaven National Laboratory on Long Island respectively nine and 14 days after the tests.)

Numerous studies have shown further that precipitation (rain and snowfall) plays an important role in determining where fallout will be deposited. Lyle T. Alexander of the Soil Conservation Service and Edward P. Hardy, Jr., of the AEC found in an extensive study in Clallam County, Washington, that the amount of fallout was directly proportional to the total annual rainfall.

It is reasonable to assume that the findings about the movement and fallout of radioactive debris also apply to other particles of similar size in the air. This conclusion is supported by a recent report by Donald F. Gatz and A. Nelson Dingle of the University of Michigan, who showed that the concentration of pollen in precipitation follows the same pattern as that of radioactive fallout. This observation is particularly meaningful because pollen is not injected into the troposphere by a nuclear explosion; it is picked up in air currents from plants close to the ground. There is little question that dust and other particles, including small crystals of pesticides, also follow these patterns.

From these and other studies it is clear that various substances released into the air are carried widely around the world and may be deposited in concentrated form far from the original source. Similarly, most bodies of water—especially the oceans—have surface currents that may move materials five to 10 miles a day. Much higher rates, of course, are found in such major oceanic currents as

the Gulf Stream. These currents are one more physical mechanism that can distribute pollutants widely over the earth.

The research programs of the AEC and other organizations have explored not only the pathways of air and water transport but also the pathways along which pollutants are distributed in plant and animal communities. In this connection we must examine what we mean by a "community."

Biologists define communities broadly to include all species, not just man. A natural community is an aggregation of a great many different kinds of organisms, all mutually interdependent. The basic conditions for the integration of a community are determined by physical characteristics of the environment such as climate and soil. Thus a sand dune supports one kind of community, a freshwater lake another, a high mountain still another. Within each type of environment there develops a complex of organisms that in the course of evolution becomes a balanced, self-sustaining biological system.

Such a system has a structure of interrelations that endows the entire community with a predictable developmental pattern, called "succession," that leads toward stability and enables the community to make the best use of its physical environment. This entails the development of cycles through which the community as a whole shares certain resources, such as mineral nutrients and energy. For example, there are a number of different inputs of nutrient elements into such a system. The principal input is from the decay of primary minerals in the soil. There are also certain losses, mainly through the leaching of substances into the underlying water table. Ecologists view the cycles in the system as mechanisms that have evolved to conserve the elements essential for the survival of the organisms making up the community.

One of the most important of these cycles is the movement of nutrients and energy from one organism to another along the pathways that are sometimes called food chains. Such chains start with plants, which use the sun's energy to synthesize organic matter; animals eat the plants; other animals eat these herbivores, and carnivores in turn may constitute additional levels feeding on the herbivores and on one another. If the lower orders in the chain are to survive and endure, there must be a feedback of nutrients. This is provided by decay organisms (mainly microorganisms) that break down organic debris

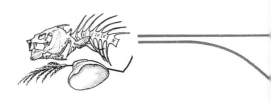

ORGANIC DEBRIS
MARSH **13 POUNDS PER ACRE**
BOTTOM **.3 POUND PER ACRE**

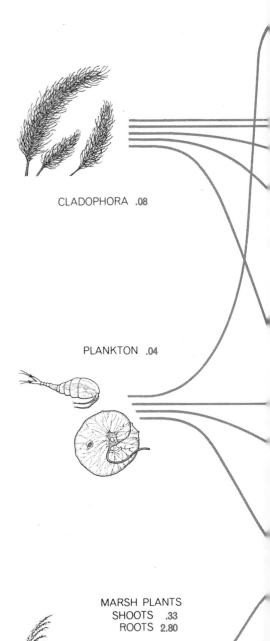

CLADOPHORA .08

PLANKTON .04

MARSH PLANTS
SHOOTS .33
ROOTS 2.80

FOOD WEB is a complex network through which energy passes from plants to herbivores and on to carnivores within a biologi-

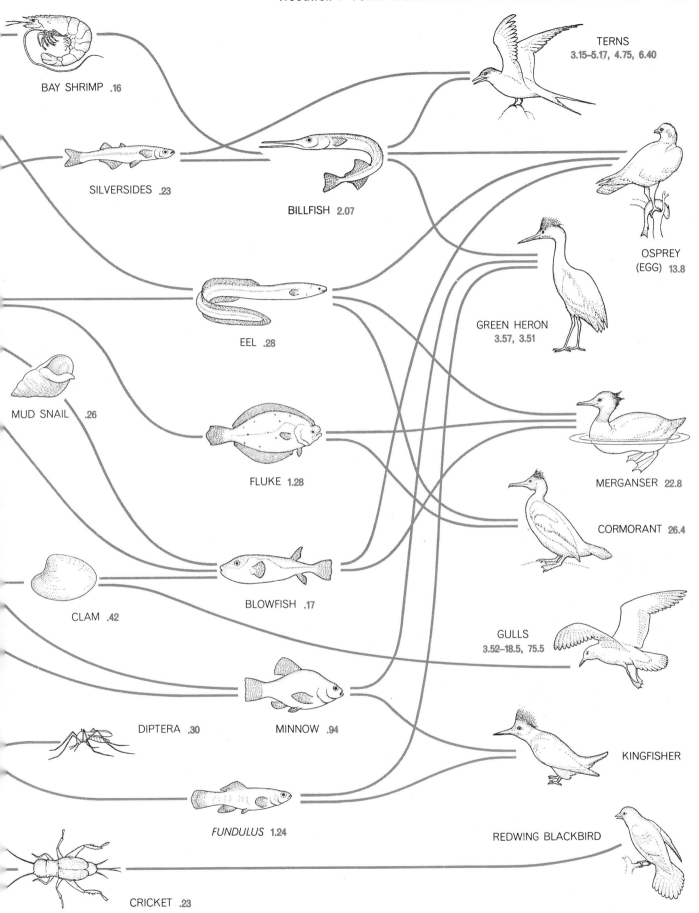

BAY SHRIMP .16

TERNS
3.15–5.17, 4.75, 6.40

SILVERSIDES .23

BILLFISH 2.07

OSPREY
(EGG) 13.8

EEL .28

GREEN HERON
3.57, 3.51

MUD SNAIL .26

FLUKE 1.28

MERGANSER 22.8

CORMORANT 26.4

CLAM .42

BLOWFISH .17

GULLS
3.52–18.5, 75.5

DIPTERA .30   MINNOW .94

KINGFISHER

FUNDULUS 1.24

REDWING BLACKBIRD

CRICKET .23

cal community. This web showing some of the plants and animals in a Long Island estuary and along the nearby shore was developed by Dennis Puleston of the Brookhaven National Laboratory. Numbers indicate residues of DDT and its derivatives (in parts per million, wet weight, whole-body basis) found in the course of a study made by the author with Charles F. Wurster, Jr., and Peter A. Isaacson.

into the substances used by plants. It is also obvious that the community will not survive if essential links in the chain are eliminated; therefore the preying of one level on another must be limited.

Ecologists estimate that such a food chain allows the transmission of roughly 10 percent of the energy entering one level to the next level above it, that is, each level can pass on 10 percent of the energy it receives from below without suffering a loss of population that would imperil its survival. The simplest version of a system of this kind takes the form of a pyramid, each successively higher population receiving about a tenth of the energy received at the level below it.

Actually nature seldom builds communities with so simple a structure. Almost invariably the energy is not passed along in a neatly ordered chain but is spread about to a great variety of organisms through a sprawling, complex web of pathways [see illustration on preceding two pages]. The more mature the community, the more diverse its makeup and the more complicated its web. In a natural ecosystem the network may consist of thousands of pathways.

This complexity is one of the principal factors we must consider in investigating how toxic substances may be distributed and concentrated in living communities. Other important basic factors lie in the nature of the metabolic process. For example, of the energy a population of organisms receives as food, usually less than 50 percent goes into the construction of new tissue, the rest being spent for respiration. This circumstance acts as a concentrating mechanism: a substance not involved in respiration and not excreted efficiently may be concentrated in the tissues twofold or more when passed from one population to another.

Let us consider three types of pathway for toxic substances that involve man as the ultimate consumer. The three examples, based on studies of radioactive substances, illustrate the complexity and variety of pollution problems.

The first and simplest case is that of strontium 90. Similar to calcium in chemical behavior, this element is concentrated in bone. It is a long-lived radioactive isotope and is a hazard because its energetic beta radiation can damage the mechanisms involved in the manufacture of blood cells in the bone marrow. In the long run the irradiation may produce certain types of cancer. The route of strontium 90 from air to man is rather direct: we ingest it in leafy vegetables, which absorbed it from the soil or received it as fallout from the air, or in milk and other dairy products from cows that have fed on contaminated vegetation. Fortunately strontium is not usually concentrated in man's food by an extensive food chain. Since it lodges chiefly in bone, it is not concentrated in passing from animal to animal in the same ways other radioactive substances may be (unless the predator eats bones!).

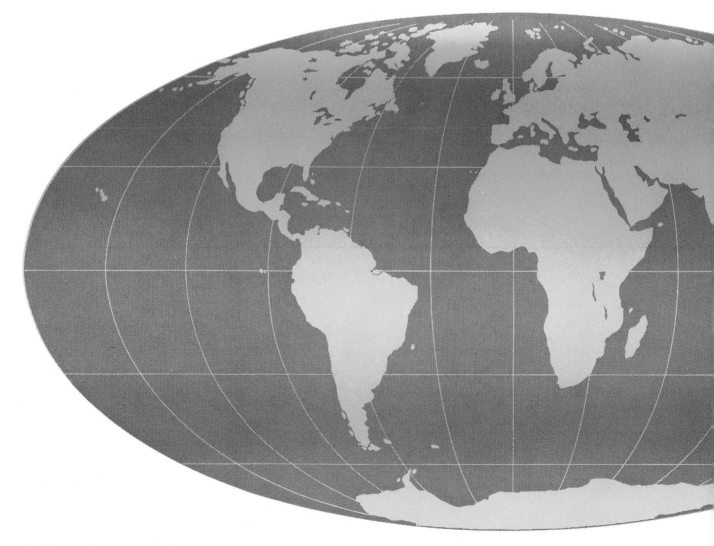

FALLOUT is distributed around the earth by meteorological processes. Deposits of strontium 90, for instance, are concentrated between 30 and 60 degrees north, as shown by depth of color on the map and by the curve (right). Points on the chart represent individual samples. The data are from a study made in 1963 and 1964 by Robert J. List and colleagues in several U.S. agencies. Such

Quite different is the case of the radioactive isotope cesium 137. This isotope, also a fission product, has a long-lived radioactivity (its half-life is about 30 years) and emits penetrating gamma rays. Because it behaves chemically like potassium, an essential constituent of all cells, it becomes widely distributed once it enters the body. Consequently it is passed along to meat-eating animals, and under certain circumstances it can accumulate in a chain of carnivores.

A study in Alaska by Wayne C. Hanson, H. E. Palmer and B. I. Griffin of the AEC's Pacific-Northwest Laboratory showed that the concentration factor for cesium 137 may be two or three for one step in a food chain. The first link of the chain in this case was lichens growing in the Alaskan forest and tundra. The lichens collected cesium 137 from fallout in rain. Certain caribou in Alaska live mainly on lichens during the winter, and caribou meat in turn is the principal diet of Eskimos in the same areas. The inves-

tigators found that caribou had accumulated about 15 micromicrocuries of cesium radioactivity per gram of tissue in their bodies. The Eskimos who fed on these caribou had a concentration twice as high (about 30 micromicrocuries per gram of tissue) after eating many pounds of caribou meat in the course of a season. Wolves and foxes that ate caribou sometimes contained three times the concentration in the flesh of the caribou. It is easy to see that in a longer chain, involving not just two animals but several, the concentration of a substance that was not excreted or metabolized could be increased to high levels.

A third case is that of iodine 131, another gamma ray emitter. Again the chain to man is short and simple: The contaminant (from fallout) comes to man mainly through cows' milk, and thus the chain involves only grass, cattle, milk and man. The danger of iodine 131 lies in the fact that iodine is concentrated in the thyroid gland. Although iodine

131 is short-lived (its half-life is only about eight days), its quick and localized concentration in the thyroid can cause damage. For instance, a research team from the Brookhaven National Laboratory headed by Robert Conard has discovered that children on Rongelap Atoll who were exposed to fallout from the 1954 bomb test later developed thyroid nodules.

The investigations of the iodine 131 hazard yielded two lessons that have an important bearing on the problem of pesticides and other toxic substances released in the environment. In the first place we have had a demonstration that the hazard of the toxic substance itself often tends to be underestimated. This was shown to be true of the exposure of the thyroid to radiation. Thyroid tumors were found in children who had been treated years before for enlarged thymus glands with doses of X rays that had been considered safe. As a result of this discovery and studies of the effects of iodine 131, the Federal Radiation Council in 1961 issued a new guide reducing the permissible limit of exposure to ionizing radiation to less than a tenth of what had previously been accepted. Not the least significant aspect of this lesson is the fact that the toxic effects of such a hazard may not appear until long after the exposure; on Rongelap Atoll 10 years passed before the thyroid abnormalities showed up in the children who had been exposed.

The second lesson is that, even when the pathways are well understood, it is almost impossible to predict just where toxic substances released into the environment will reach dangerous levels. Even in the case of the simple pathway followed by iodine 131 the eventual destination of the substance and its effects on people are complicated by a great many variables: the area of the cow's pasture (the smaller the area, the less fallout the cow will pick up); the amount and timing of rains on the pasture (which on the one hand may bring down fallout but on the other may wash it off the forage); the extent to which the cow is given stored, uncontaminated feed; the amount of iodine the cow secretes in its milk; the amount of milk in the diet of the individual consumer, and so on.

If it is difficult to estimate the nature and extent of the hazards from radioactive fallout, which have been investigated in great detail for more than a decade by an international research program, it must be said that we are in a poor position indeed to estimate the hazards from pesticides. So far the

studies have not been made for pesticides but it appears that DDT may also be carried in air and deposited in precipitation.

STRONTIUM 90 (MILLICURIES PER SQUARE MILE)

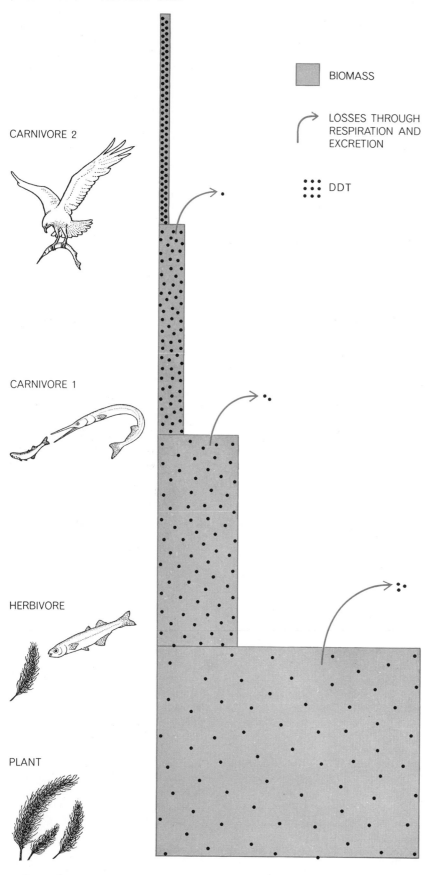

BIOMASS

LOSSES THROUGH RESPIRATION AND EXCRETION

DDT

CARNIVORE 2

CARNIVORE 1

HERBIVORE

PLANT

CONCENTRATION of DDT residues being passed along a simple food chain is indicated schematically in this diagram. As "biomass," or living material, is transferred from one link to another along such a chain, usually more than half of it is consumed in respiration or is excreted (arrows); the remainder forms new biomass. The losses of DDT residues along the chain, on the other hand, are small in proportion to the amount that is transferred from one link to the next. For this reason high concentrations occur in the carnivores.

amount of research effort given to the ecological effects of these poisons has been comparatively small, although it is increasing rapidly. Much has been learned, however, about the movement and distribution of pesticides in the environment, thanks in part to the clues supplied by the studies of radioactive fallout.

Our chief tool in the pesticide inquiry is DDT. There are many reasons for focusing on DDT: it is long-lasting, it is now comparatively easy to detect, it is by far the most widely used pesticide and it is toxic to a broad spectrum of animals, including man. Introduced only a quarter-century ago and spectacularly successful during World War II in controlling body lice and therefore typhus, DDT quickly became a universal weapon in agriculture and in public health campaigns against disease-carriers. Not surprisingly, by this time DDT has thoroughly permeated our environment. It is found in the air of cities, in wildlife all over North America and in remote corners of the earth, even in Adélie penguins and skua gulls (both carnivores) in the Antarctic. It is also found the world over in the fatty tissue of man. It is fair to say that there are probably few populations in the world that are not contaminated to some extent with DDT.

We now have a considerable amount of evidence that DDT is spread over the earth by wind and water in much the same patterns as radioactive fallout. This seems to be true in spite of the fact that DDT is not injected high into the atmosphere by an explosion. When DDT is sprayed in the air, some fraction of it is picked up by air currents as pollen is, circulated through the lower troposphere and deposited on the ground by rainfall. I found in tests in Maine and New Brunswick, where DDT has been sprayed from airplanes to control the spruce budworm in forests, that even in the open, away from trees, about 50 percent of the DDT does not fall to the ground. Instead it is probably dispersed as small crystals in the air. This is true even on days when the air is still and when the low-flying planes release the spray only 50 to 100 feet above treetop level. Other mechanisms besides air movement can carry DDT for great distances around the world. Migrating fish and birds can transport it thousands of miles. So also do oceanic currents. DDT has only a low solubility in water (the upper limit is about one part per billion), but as algae and other organisms in the water absorb the substance in fats, where it is highly soluble, they make room for more DDT to be dissolved into the water. Accordingly water that never contains more than a trace of DDT can continuously transfer it from deposits on the bottom to organisms.

DDT is an extremely stable compound that breaks down very slowly in the environment. Hence with repeated spraying the residues in the soil or water basins accumulate. Working with Frederic T. Martin of the University of Maine, I found that in a New Brunswick forest where spraying had been discontinued in 1958 the DDT content of the soil increased from half a pound per acre to 1.8 pounds per acre in the three years between 1958 and 1961. Apparently the DDT residues were carried to the ground very slowly on foliage and decayed very little. The conclusion is that DDT has a long half-life in the trees and soil of a forest, certainly in the range of tens of years.

Doubtless there are many places in the world where reservoirs of DDT are accumulating. With my colleagues Charles F. Wurster, Jr., and Peter A. Isaacson of the State University of New York at Stony Brook, I recently sampled a marsh along the south shore of Long Island that had been sprayed with DDT for 20 years to control mosquitoes. We found that the DDT residues in the upper layer of mud in this marsh ranged up to 32 pounds per acre!

We learned further that plant and animal life in the area constituted a chain that concentrated the DDT in spectacular fashion. At the lowest level the plankton in the water contained .04 part per million of DDT; minnows contained one part per million, and a carnivorous scavenging bird (a ring-billed gull) contained about 75 parts per million in its tissues (on a whole-body, wet-weight basis). Some of the carnivorous animals in this community had concentrated DDT by a factor of more than 1,000 over the organisms at the base of the ladder.

A further tenfold increase in the concentrations along this food web would in all likelihood result in the death of many of the organisms in it. It would then be impossible to discover why they had disappeared. The damage from DDT concentration is particularly serious in the higher carnivores. The mere fact that conspicuous mortality is not observed is no assurance of safety. Comparatively low concentrations may inhibit reproduction and thus cause the species to fade away.

That DDT is a serious ecological hazard was recognized from the beginning of its use. In 1946 Clarence Cottam and

LOCATION	ORGANISM	TISSUE	CONCENTRATION (PARTS PER MILLION)
U.S. (AVERAGE)	MAN	FAT	11
ALASKA (ESKIMO)			2.8
ENGLAND			2.2
WEST GERMANY			2.3
FRANCE			5.2
CANADA			5.3
HUNGARY			12.4
ISRAEL			19.2
INDIA			12.8–31.0
U.S. CALIFORNIA	PLANKTON		5.3
CALIFORNIA	BASS	EDIBLE FLESH	4–138
CALIFORNIA	GREBES	VISCERAL FAT	UP TO 1,600
MONTANA	ROBIN	WHOLE BODY	6.8–13.9
WISCONSIN	CRUSTACEA		.41
WISCONSIN	CHUB	WHOLE BODY	4.52
WISCONSIN	GULL	BRAIN	20.8
MISSOURI	BALD EAGLE	EGGS	1.1–5.6
CONNECTICUT	OSPREY	EGGS	6.5
FLORIDA	DOLPHIN	BLUBBER	ABOUT 220
CANADA	WOODCOCK	WHOLE BODY	1.7
ANTARCTICA	PENGUIN	FAT	.015–.18
ANTARCTICA	SEAL	FAT	.042–.12
SCOTLAND	EAGLE	EGGS	1.18
NEW ZEALAND	TROUT	WHOLE BODY	.6–.8

DDT RESIDUES, which include the derivatives DDD and DDE as well as DDT itself, have apparently entered most food webs. These data were selected from hundreds of reports that show DDT has a worldwide distribution, with the highest concentrations in carnivorous birds.

Elmer Higgins of the U.S. Fish and Wildlife Service warned in the *Journal of Economic Entomology* that the pesticide was a potential menace to mammals, birds, fishes and other wildlife and that special care should be taken to avoid its application to streams, lakes and coastal bays because of the sensitivity of fishes and crabs. Because of the wide distribution of DDT the effects of the substance on a species of animal can be more damaging than hunting or the elimination of a habitat (through an operation such as dredging marshes). DDT affects the entire species rather than a single population and may well wipe out the species by eliminating reproduction.

Within the past five years, with the development of improved techniques for detecting the presence of pesticide residues in animals and the environment, ecologists have been able to measure the extent of the hazards presented by DDT and other persistent general poisons. The picture that is emerging is not a comforting one. Pesticide residues have now accumulated to levels that are catastrophic for certain animal populations, particularly carnivorous birds. Furthermore, it has been clear for many years that because of their shotgun effect these weapons not only attack the pests but also destroy predators and competitors that normally tend to limit proliferation of the pests. Under exposure to pesti-

cides the pests tend to develop new strains that are resistant to the chemicals. The result is an escalating chemical warfare that is self-defeating and has secondary effects whose costs are only beginning to be measured. One of the costs is wildlife, notably carnivorous and scavenging birds such as hawks and eagles. There are others: destruction of food webs aggravates pollution problems, particularly in bodies of water that receive mineral nutrients in sewage or in water draining from heavily fertilized agricultural lands. The plant populations, no longer consumed by animals, fall to the bottom to decay anaerobically, producing hydrogen sulfide and other noxious gases, further degrading the environment.

The accumulation of persistent toxic substances in the ecological cycles of the earth is a problem to which mankind will have to pay increasing attention. It affects many elements of society, not only in the necessity for concern about the disposal of wastes but also in the need for a revolution in pest control. We must learn to use pesticides that have a short half-life in the environment—better yet, to use pest-control techniques that do not require applications of general poisons. What has been learned about the dangers in polluting ecological cycles is ample proof that there is no longer safety in the vastness of the earth.

The Author

GEORGE M. WOODWELL is an ecologist at the Brookhaven National Laboratory. His original field of study was botany; he received an undergraduate degree in that subject at Dartmouth College in 1950 and master's and doctor's degrees from Duke University in 1956 and 1958 respectively. From 1957 to 1962, when he joined the Brookhaven staff, he taught at the University of Maine. He notes that his article "in no way reflects an official attitude of the U.S. Atomic Energy Commission or Brookhaven National Laboratory."

Bibliography

ENVIRONMENTAL RADIOACTIVITY. Merril Eisenbud. McGraw-Hill Book Company, Inc., 1963.

PESTICIDES AND THE LIVING LANDSCAPE. Robert L. Rudd. University of Wisconsin Press, 1964.

REPORT OF THE UNITED NATIONS SCIENTIFIC COMMITTEE ON THE EFFECTS OF ATOMIC RADIATION. Official Records of the General Assembly, 13th Session, Supplement No. 17, 1958; 17th Session, Supplement No. 16, 1962; 19th Session, Supplement No. 14, 1964.

SCIENTIFIC
AMERICAN March 1967, Vol. 216, No. 3, pp. 32-37   OFFPRINT 1067

THE HEART'S PACEMAKER

by E. F. Adolph

A group of specialized cells regulates the fundamental rhythm
of an animal's heart. The pacemaker also limits the heart's
range of responses to the influences of nerves and hormones.

The heart of a mouse at rest beats about 500 times a minute; in contrast, the elephant's basal heart rate is only 35 beats a minute. In the mouse's lifetime of one to two years its heart totals as many beats as the elephant's does in 25 to 50 years. What governs an animal's heart rate? Obviously it is regulated in part from outside the heart in response to the demands of exercise or stress. But the heart itself has its own pacemaker, regulating its fundamental rhythm and setting limits on its range of rates. Recent experimental investigations in various animals, including observation of the beginnings of the heartbeat in the embryo, have done much to illuminate the operation and regulation of the pacemaker.

The embryonic heart starts beating at a certain age that is characteristic for each animal. In the chick, for instance, the first beats arise at about the 30th hour of the embryo's life [see illustration, pages 2374 and 2375]. Rhythmic contractions of the heart muscle begin in the right ventricle. A number of hours later the right atrium, or auricle, which meanwhile has taken shape behind the ventricle, also starts to beat. Its beat is faster and it sets the pace, the ventricular cells falling in step with its timing. Finally the venous sinus, which eventually sets apart a group of cells known as the sinoatrial node, develops to the rear of the right atrium, and this structure, beating still faster, takes over the pacemaking function. The sinoatrial node remains the basic pacemaker throughout the animal's life. Other regions of the heart muscle contract rhythmically according to its lead, but most of them lose the capacity to initiate beats of their own accord.

It is an interesting fact that the various muscle cells of the embryo heart differ in their intrinsic beating tempo, yet all are coordinated by the pacemaker. In the tubular heart of a salamander embryo, for example, W. M. Copenhaver of the Columbia University College of Physicians and Surgeons showed by cutting across the heart at various levels that at least eight different intrinsic beating rates can be detected along the length of the heart, each successive region rearward toward the sinus having a faster intrinsic rate. Indeed, when the cells of any embryo heart are separated from one another (by the use of the enzyme trypsin to break down the cement that holds them together), it is found that each cell beats with its own rhythm, depending mainly on the region of the heart from which it came. When, on the other hand, individual cells or fragments of heart tissue are brought together in intimate contact, they synchronize their contractions. Invariably the cell that has the fastest beat takes over the pacemaking. There are indications, however, that the pace is not entirely set by a single cell; the other cells seem to have some influence, and the actual beating rate possibly results from a consensus.

The sinoatrial pacemaker as a whole, consisting of hundreds or thousands of cells, has an intrinsic regulation. Whether in the embryo or maintained in an unchanging chemical medium at a constant temperature, it will beat at a constant rate hour after hour. A disturbance such as deprivation of oxygen can slow the rate, but as soon as normal conditions are restored the pacemaker resumes its basal rhythm. In each species of animal the pacemaker has a certain characteristic rate; for each species there is a "set point"—a standard rate—to which the heart adheres except during disturbing circumstances.

Copenhaver performed experiments with salamander embryos that dramatically tested the autonomy of the pacemaker. Using two different species—the tiger salamander and the spotted salamander—he transplanted the heart from one species to the other before the heart had begun to beat. Which beat would the transplanted heart take up, the donor animal's or the host's? In every case it beat at its own rate, not at that of the host, although in some cases it was pumping the host's blood, and it maintained its own beating pattern throughout the animal's life. The tiger salamander's heart normally beats more rapidly than the spotted salamander's during the first days of life and then slows to less than the spotted salamander's rate; it still showed the same pattern when it was transplanted into a spotted salamander, whether it was grafted in place of the animal's heart or was implanted in the abdomen or tail as a second heart.

The heart of any animal changes its rate with age, usually increasing in rate as the embryo grows and decreasing in later life. In Copenhaver's experiments the transplanted heart, whether it had belonged originally to a tiger salamander or to a spotted salamander, followed its own typical pattern of tempo changes with age. In short, the pacemaker of a given species is endowed not with a particular pace but with a whole program of paces that will develop during its lifetime. This program obviously is implanted in the future pacemaker tissue during the early development of the embryo, when the heart tissue is differentiating. Experiments in the culture of potential heart tissues have shown that such is indeed the case.

How does the pacemaker work? On this central question there are, unfor-

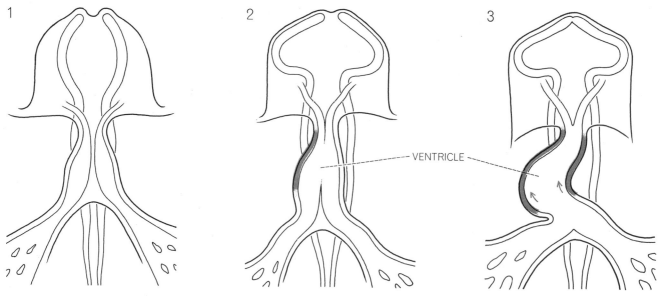

PACEMAKING CHANGES in an embryonic chicken heart are depicted in color; arrows show the direction of impulse conduction.

At 27 hours (1) beating has not begun. The first contractions arise (2) in the ventricle. Gradually they originate farther to the rear,

tunately, very few clues so far. The pacemaking cells look distinctly different from other cells. Under the microscope we can see that the cells in the sinoatrial node are more widely separated from one another and have less contractile structure than the cells in other heart tissues. Electrical exploration of the pacemaking cells reveals another distinctive feature [*see upper illustration on page 2378*]. By inserting a microelectrode in an individual cell one finds that during the diastolic, or passive, phase of the beat cycle the inside of the cell loses its negativity gradually until it reaches a transition point, after which it completes its depolarization rapidly (and actually becomes positive for an instant). This pattern of gradual depolarization is peculiar to pacemaker cells.

One is tempted to compare these cells to an electric condenser, which discharges periodically after accumulating charge gradually. The condenser model does not, however, quite fit the process of the cell. Indeed, no model yet suggested has given us much enlightenment on how the pacemaker translates metabolic energy into its rhythmic beat, how it synchronizes the discharges of its many

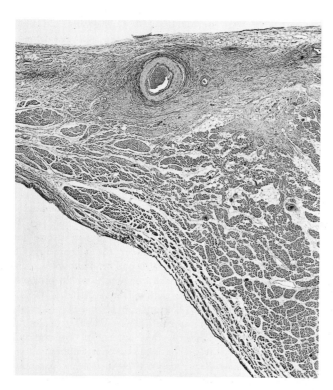

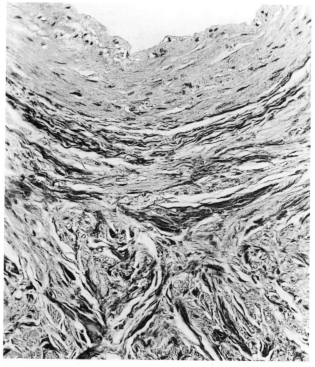

HUMAN PACEMAKER appears in photomicrographs of two thin slices of heart. At left, in an enlargement of 12 diameters, the sinus node is the dense tissue organized around an artery. At right, in an

enlargement of 260 diameters, the internal structure of the node is evident. The darker tissue is the framework of collagen. Within this frame bundles of sinus-node fibers interweave in all directions.

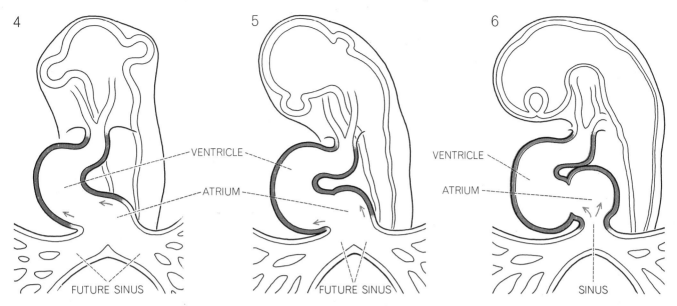

reaching the atrium (5) and finally the sinus (6). Drawings, which slowly turn the embryo from a frontal view at 1 to a view of the left side at 6, were adapted from *Early Embryology of the Chick*, by Bradley M. Patten, published by the McGraw-Hill Book Company.

cells or how it changes the tempo of its beat as it ages.

Perhaps some enlightenment will come from studies of the pacemakers of invertebrate animals. In the lobster, for instance, the heartbeat is activated by a small group of nerve cells outside the heart. Donald M. Maynard of the University of Michigan studied a species of lobster in which the pacemaker consists of nine nerve cells—four small and five large. He found that any one of the small cells triggers a burst of impulses from all nine, and repetitive bursts from the group are responsible for the rhythmic beats of the heart. How are the discharges from the four small nerve cells regulated? If the interactions of these cells could be unraveled, one might find a clue to the coordinated action of the thousands of cells that constitute the pacemaker in the heart of a vertebrate.

We may well ask: Of what use are the vertebrate pacemaker's thousands of cells? It has been suggested that perhaps only a few of them are pacemaking at any given time and the rest act as reserves. In that case, however, what would prevent one uncontrolled cell from starting a beat of its own? A single cell that began to beat at a pace twice that of the others could throw the entire system into confusion. A more plausible hypothesis is that all the pacemaker cells are under mutual control. So far, however, only feeble evidence of communication among the pacemaker cells has been discovered.

Notwithstanding the lack of information about how natural pacemakers operate, artificial pacemakers have been devised, and they are serving today to keep alive many people with damaged hearts. The best solution to their problem would be the implantation of living pacemaker tissue from a human donor or an animal one. In the embryo of a salamander such a transplant takes beautifully, and the implanted tissue can drive the host's heart quite satisfactorily. Unfortunately in mammals implanted tissue does not wed itself to the heart but simply forms a scar. The only available artificial pacemaker for human use, therefore, is a mechanical one. It consists of a device that produces rhythmic electrical discharges, and wires from this device feed the discharges to the excitable tissues of the heart. The artificial pacemaker can maintain a steady heartbeat; it does not, however, respond to bodily needs that call for a speedup of the beat.

What are the extrinsic, or external, mechanisms that affect the natural pacemaker of the heart, and how do they act? In our laboratory at the University of Rochester School of Medicine and Dentistry we have explored these questions, along with those concerning the intrinsic beat itself, by studying the development of the heart's behavior in animals from the early fetal stage to adulthood.

In the fetus of a rat the heart begins to beat in the 10th day of life. At that stage the heart is still free of any stimulation from nerves, and about the only factors that can change its intrinsic beat are temperature, oxygen and blood supply. From day to day during the growth of the fetus the rate of the intrinsic beat increases. The pacemaker remains relatively insensitive to extrinsic influences, even after nerves grow into the heart on the 16th day, and the insensitivity continues until near birth (on the 22nd day).

By adulthood an animal's heartbeat has become subject to strong influences from the parasympathetic and sympathetic nervous systems. Several investigators, including Raymond C. Truex and David M. Long, then at Hahnemann Medical College, have measured the extent of these influences in the dog. The heart rate of a dog at rest is about 90 beats a minute. If the animal is given a dose of atropine, which blocks parasympathetic nerve impulses from reaching the heart, its rate jumps to 250 beats a minute. Evidently, then, under normal circumstances a flow of impulses from the parasympathetic nerves acts as a restraining influence on the heart rate. On the other hand, the sympathetic nerves have a prodding effect. If these nerves are cut so that no impulses reach the heart, the heartbeats slow to 65 a minute. In short, the sympathetic system acts as an accelerator and the parasympathetic system as a brake, and under normal conditions the two systems counteract each other. When the nerve supply to the heart is completely cut (blocking both systems), the dog's heart beats about 110 times a minute. Perhaps in an adult dog this is the intrinsic rate of the pacemaker itself.

What the experiments show in general is that a continuous interplay normally goes on among the pacemaker and the two nervous systems controlling the heart, whose sources are centered

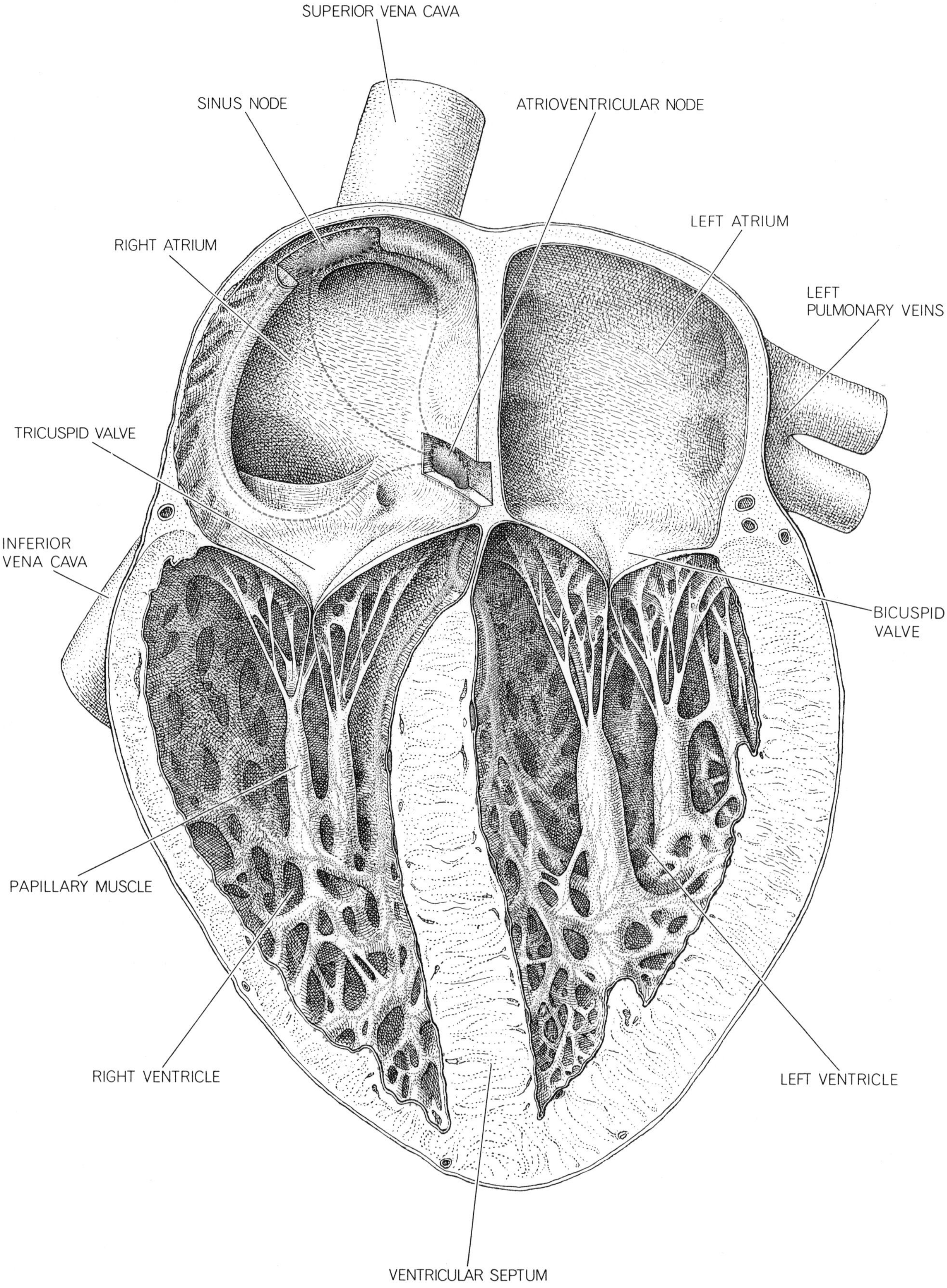

SUPERIOR VENA CAVA

SINUS NODE

ATRIOVENTRICULAR NODE

RIGHT ATRIUM

LEFT ATRIUM

LEFT PULMONARY VEINS

TRICUSPID VALVE

INFERIOR VENA CAVA

BICUSPID VALVE

PAPILLARY MUSCLE

RIGHT VENTRICLE

LEFT VENTRICLE

VENTRICULAR SEPTUM

CUTAWAY VIEW of the human heart, showing the rear portion, depicts the pacemaker and the path of its impulses in color. The pacemaker is the structure near the top of the heart; it is variously called the sinus node and the sinoatrial node. Impulses from the pacemaker spread along the paths indicated by the broken lines to the atrioventricular node, from which they are transmitted to the ventricles. Pacemaker cells differ from both nerve cells and muscle cells; they are usually described as modified muscle cells.

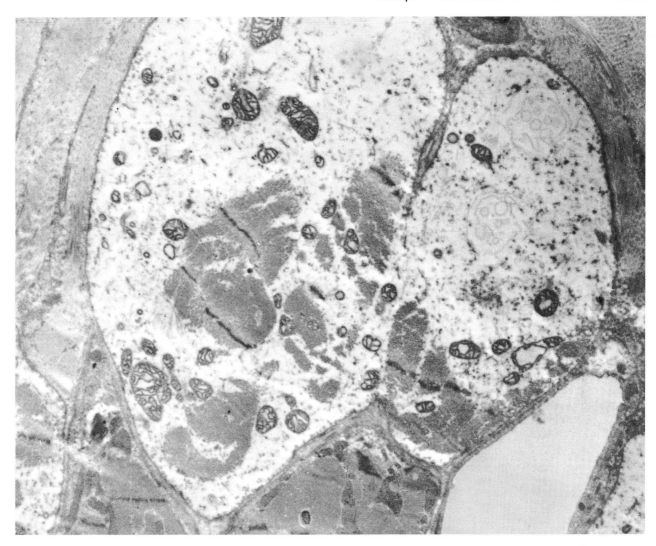

PACEMAKER CELLS appear at an enlargement of 18,000 diameters in this electron micrograph by Thomas N. James of the Henry Ford Hospital in Detroit. The cells, which are the lighter structures, are from the heart of a dog. The darker cells are working myocardial cells, which are not involved in pacemaking. The featureless area at bottom right is one of the capillaries of the heart.

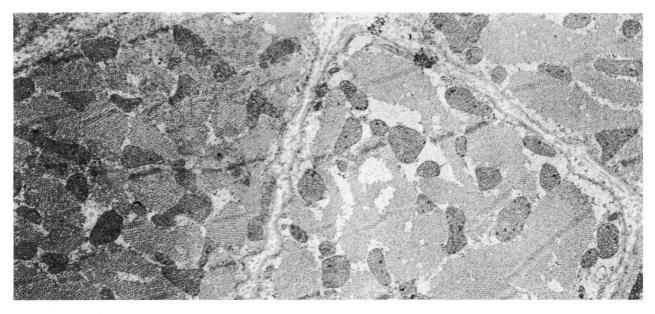

MYOCARDIAL CELLS, which have a muscular function in the heartbeat, differ in structure from pacemaker cells. The latter predominate only in the sinus node. Electron micrograph by James shows parts of three dog myocardial cells enlarged 18,000 diameters.

in the medulla oblongata of the brainstem. The pacemaker's pace is modified by rhythmic impulses from these nervous systems, and they in turn are guided by activities of the body that call for an increase or a decrease in the pumping action of the heart. Both types of nervous mechanism, however, and hormonal controls as well, work only within fixed limits, which depend on the animal's age and size. In a puppy, for example, the sympathetic nerves exert a much stronger effect on the pacemaker than the parasympathetic nerves do, whereas in the adult dog the reverse is true. Similarly, the pacemaker and the nervous controls combine to give the mouse a more rapid basal beat than the elephant, and an elephant's heart can never beat as fast as that of a mouse.

Precisely what is the ceiling for an animal's heart rate? We investigated the question in the rat by applying rhythmic electric shocks to drive the heart to its maximal capacity. The rats were anesthetized and the driving electric impulses were delivered through fine wire electrodes inserted in the chest. We found that in the fetus the heart's maximal rate was about 350 beats a minute; in a newborn rat, about 450 beats a minute, and in an adult rat, some 750 beats a minute. At these high rates the heart was very inefficient: it pumped little blood because it had no time to fill before each contraction. We can deduce that the limit of tempo set up in the pacemaker may serve as a protective mechanism; if the pacemaker drove the heart too fast, it might produce the uncoordinated, disorderly type of contraction known as fibrillation.

We found further that the hormones isopropyl noradrenalin and thyroxin, whose ability to speed up the heart has long been well known, raised the rats' heart rates to high levels but not to the limits of the heart's capacity. In each case the rate of the rat's heartbeat under maximal prodding rose with age until the animal reached the age of 10 days, after which it leveled off [see lower illustration at right].

The normal heart rate at rest, on the other hand, presents a different picture as the animal ages. Instead of leveling off at the age of 10 days it continues to rise. This rise is attributed mainly to the influence of the maturing nervous system rather than to change in the intrinsic tempo of the pacemaker itself. It was found that administration of a drug that blocks the prodding action of the sympathetic impulses almost eliminated the

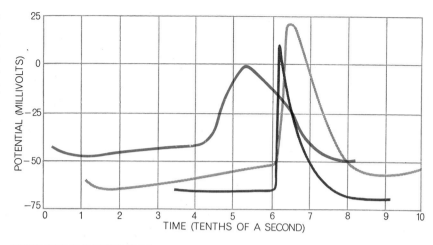

ELECTRICAL POTENTIALS in one pacemaker cell (*color*) and two nonpacemaker cells of a rabbit heart were measured by intracellular electrodes. Only cells capable of pacemaking show the gradual changes of polarization indicated by the colored curve for a single beat.

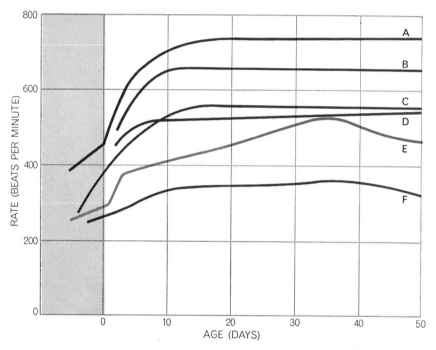

VARIATIONS IN RATE of rats' hearts under different conditions are shown for ages beginning four days before birth and ending at maturity. The colored curve represents the normal rate after birth. Other curves are: *A*, maximal rate when the heart is driven by electric shocks; *B*, rate after administration of stimulating hormones thyroxin and isopropyl noradrenalin; *C*, rate under latter hormone alone; *D*, rate under thyroxin alone, and *F*, rate after administration of the drug propranolol, which blocks accelerating nerve impulses.

heart rate increase with age. Our experiments show that the sympathetic nerves begin to affect the heart rate in rats a day or two before birth, whereas the parasympathetic system does not begin to act on the heart until about 16 days after birth. Thereafter the rate is under the control of the two systems acting competitively, with the sympathetic system apparently exerting slightly more influence than the parasympathetic.

To sum up, it appears that when the heart of the embryo begins to beat, it

functions as an independent organ, driven only by its own inherent pacemaker. As it grows older it becomes receptive to one extrinsic influence after another and through them becomes the servant of many organs and activities of the body. In the adult animal it is capable of a wide range of responses to the body's needs. The full development of its responses and regulation does not come until long after birth, but we can see the beginnings of the arrangements even before the animal is born.

The Author

E. F. ADOLPH is emeritus professor of physiology at the University of Rochester. He was graduated from Harvard College in 1916, obtained a Ph.D. from Harvard in 1920 and taught zoology at the University of Pittsburgh before going to the School of Medicine and Dentistry at the University of Rochester in 1925 as assistant professor of physiology. He has been interested in a number of regulatory processes in physiology, particularly the beginnings of such processes in the individual. In 1953 he was president of the American Physiological Society. Although he retired in 1960, he continues to work regularly in his laboratory at the university.

Bibliography

ACTIVITY IN A CRUSTACEAN GANGLION, II: PATTERN AND INTERACTION IN BURST FORMATION. Donald M. Maynard in *The Biological Bulletin,* Vol. 109, No. 3, pages 420–436; December, 1955.

CAPACITIES FOR REGULATION OF HEART RATE IN FETAL, INFANT, AND ADULT RATS. E. F. Adolph in *American Journal of Physiology,* Vol. 209, No. 6, pages 1095–1105; December, 1965.

HEART, BLOODVESSELS, BLOOD AND ENTODERMAL DERIVATIVES. W. M. Copenhaver in *Analysis of Development,* edited by Benjamin H. Willier, Paul A. Weiss and Viktor Hamburger. W. B. Saunders Company, 1955.

RANGES OF HEART RATES AND THEIR REGULATION AT VARIOUS AGES (RAT). E. F. Adolph in *American Journal of Physiology,* Vol. 212, No. 3, pages 595–602; March, 1967.

SOME OBSERVATIONS ON THE GROWTH AND FUNCTION OF HETEROPLASTIC HEART GRAFTS. W. M. Copenhaver in *Journal of Experimental Zoology,* Vol. 82, No. 2, pages 239–271; November 5, 1939.

SCIENTIFIC
AMERICAN February 1967, Vol. 216, No. 2, pp. 27-35

OFFPRINT 1068

ORTHODOX AND UNORTHODOX METHODS OF MEETING WORLD FOOD NEEDS

by N. W. Pirie

The orthodox methods must be pressed, but it seems they cannot solve the problem without the aid of the unorthodox ones. And the adoption of unorthodox methods calls for basic changes in cultural attitudes.

The world has been familiar with famine throughout recorded history. Until the present century some people have been hungry all the time and all the people have been hungry some of the time. Now a few industrialized countries have managed, by a mixture of luck, skill and cunning, to break loose from the traditional pattern and establish systems in which most of the population can expect to go through life without knowing hunger. Instead their food problems are overnutrition (about which much is now being written) and malnutrition. Malnutrition appears when the food eaten is supplying enough energy, or even too much, but is deficient in some components of a satisfactory diet. Its presence continually and on a large scale is a technical triumph of which primitive man was incapable because he lacked the skill to process the food he gathered in a manner that would remove some of the essential components but leave it palatable and pleasing in appearance. Furthermore, until the development of agriculture few foods contained the excess carbohydrate that characterizes much of the world's food today. The right policy in technically skilled countries, however, is not to try to "go back to nature" and eat crude foods. Processing does good as well as harm. What we now need is

widespread knowledge of the principles of nutrition and enough good sense to use our technical skill prudently.

It is salutary to remember how recently this pattern was established. There was some hunger in Britain 50 years ago and much hunger 50 years before that. Still earlier many settlements in now well-fed regions of Australia and the U.S. had to be abandoned because of starvation. It is said that scurvy killed about 10,000 "forty-niners," and California was the scene of some of the classic descriptions of the disease. One has to learn how to live and farm in each new region; it cannot be assumed that methods that are successful in one country will work elsewhere. It is therefore probable that methods will be found for making the currently ill-fed regions productive and self-sufficient. The search for them should be started immediately and should be conducted without too much regard for traditional methods and preconceptions.

The problem can be simply stated: How can human affairs be managed so that the whole world can enjoy the degree of freedom from hunger that the industrialized countries now have?

It is well known that in many parts of the world not only is there a food shortage but also the population is in-

creasing rapidly. Some of the reasons for this situation are fairly easy to establish. When the conditions of life change slowly, compensating changes can keep pace with them. In Europe during the 16th century half of the children probably never reached the age of five. There are no general statistics for this period, but in the 17th century 22 out of the 32 British royal children (from James I to Anne) died before they were 21, and it is unlikely that the poor fared better than royalty. The establishment of our present standards of infant mortality had little to do with medical knowledge. Until this century the farther away one could keep from doctors, except for the treatment of physical injury, the better. It was increasing technical skill in bringing in clean water and getting rid of sewage that made communities healthy, and this skill was applied by people who had never heard of germs or, like Florence Nightingale, disbelieved what they were told. But the change came slowly enough for families to adjust the birthrate to suit the new conditions. Moreover, there was incompletely filled land to be used. What René Dubos calls the "population avalanche" is on us because it is now possible to undertake public health measures on a larger scale and finish them quicker than heretofore.

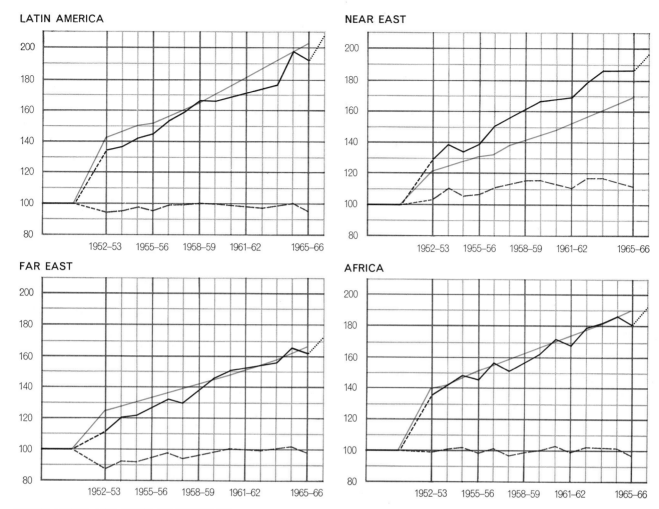

POPULATION AND FOOD PRODUCTION are compared for four developing regions in these charts prepared by the Food and Agriculture Organization of the United Nations. The colored curve is population; the solid black curve, food production; the broken gray curve, food production per caput. The figures for population are in millions; those for food production are given according to an index of 100 for the prewar average. The food production figures for 1965–1966 (July 15, 1965, to July 15, 1966) show the effects of adverse weather in many parts of the world. In that period world food production per caput fell 2 percent. The dots at end of food production curve show increase required to regain per caput level of 1964–1965. Mainland China is not represented in Far East figures.

Once the principles are understood the hygiene of an area can be improved quickly by a few people, and the population as a whole gets the advantage of improved health without having to take any very active steps to achieve it. Even where methods for improving conventional agriculture are known their application is of necessity slower, because it depends on a change in the outlook of most of the people in a farming community rather than in the outlook of the few who control water and sewage. Furthermore, fecundity is potentially unlimited but food production is not. Clearly, therefore, the "avalanche" will have to be stopped. It is important to remember, however, that it cannot be stopped in any noncoercive way without the cooperation of the people; that means more education, which means more hygiene and so, at least for a time, a still greater increase in the population. The

first result of an effective campaign for contraception will be an increase in population rather than a diminution. More effort should be put into the encouragement of contraception. And more research is needed on improved methods, leading to the ideal: that people should have to do something positive to reverse a normal state of infertility, so that no conception would be inadvertent. This, however, is a complement to, and not a substitute for, work on the production of more food. Strained as existing supplies are, it seems inevitable that they will be strained still further during the next half-century. After that the entire world may have established the population equilibrium that now exists in some industrialized countries.

The normal humane reaction in the presence of misery is pity, and this reaction is followed, where appropriate,

by charity. Hence the immense effort that is now being put into shipping the food surpluses, accumulated in some parts of the world, to areas of need. This is commendable and spiritually satisfying to the donor, but for two reasons it has little effect on the real problem. The amount of surplus food is not large enough to make much of a dent in the world's present need. The surplus could be increased, but the logistic problem of shipping still greater quantities of food would be formidable. The more serious objection to charity, except during temporary periods of crisis, is that it discourages the recipient. A century ago the philanthropist Edward Denison remarked: "Every shilling I give away does fourpence worth of good by keeping the recipients' miserable bodies alive and eighteenpence worth of harm by helping to destroy their miserable souls." Nearly 1,000 years ago Maimonides categorized the forms of charity and concluded that the most commendable form was to act in such a way that charity would become unnecessary.

Trade is the obvious alternative to charity. Unfortunately the developing countries are in a poor bargaining position. Since 1957 the prices paid for their primary products declined so much that the industrialized countries made a saving of $7,000 million and an extra profit of $3,000 million because of the increased cost of manufactured goods. The developing countries thus lost $10,000 million—about the same as the total "aid" they received from commercial, private and international sources. (The figures are from the *Financial Times* of London for July 19, 1965.) With the market rigged against them in this way it is not likely that they will soon be able to buy their food as countries such as Britain do. At present the industrialized countries are exporting about 30 million tons of grain a year, largely against credit. It is unlikely that this state of affairs can last; half of the world cannot permanently feed the other half.

The idea that the developing parts of the world should be fed by either charity or trade depends on the assumption that they are in some way unsuited for adequate food production. This idea is baseless. Once the methods have been devised, food can be produced in most places where there is sunlight and water; for political stability food must be produced where the mouths are. Any country dependent on imports for its main foodstuffs is to some extent controlled by others.

The problem can be more narrowly stated: How to produce enough food in the more populous parts of the world?

Food production can and will be increased in many orthodox ways. There is still some uncultivated but cultivable land, irrigation and drainage can be improved and extended, fertilizers can be used on a much greater scale and the general level of farming technique can be improved. If all the farmers in a region were as skilled as the best 10 percent of them, there would probably be enough food for everyone today. These improvements could be achieved by vigorous government action and without further research.

In the Temperate Zone plant breeders have greatly increased cereal yields during the past 20 years, and these improved varieties could be used more widely. There have been no comparable developments with food crops in the Tropical Zone, but there is no reason

to think that progress there could not be equally spectacular. This research should not be limited to cereals. In many parts of the wet Tropics yams (*Dioscoria* and *Colocasia*) are staple foods but the varieties used contain little protein. There is, however, some evidence that the protein content of yams varies; a New Guinea variety called Wundunggul contains 2.5 percent nitrogen. If this nitrogen is all in protein, the yam contains 15 percent protein and is worthy of serious study.

It is generally agreed that pests and

diseases rob us of as much as a third of our crops. When the improvements outlined above have been made, the proportional loss as well as the absolute one could become greater, since well-nourished crops, growing uniformly in large fields, are particularly susceptible. The cost of treatment may be only a tenth of the value of the crop saved; the methods are well publicized by firms making pesticides. There is no need to labor this aspect of the problem here. More attention should, however, be given to losses during storage; the need for

SYNTHETIC FOOD is represented by Incaparina, made of maize, sorghum and cottonseed by the Quaker Oats Company. The product has been skillfully promoted by Quaker Oats in Central America. The Spanish words at the top of this 500-gram package mean: "For 25 glasses or portions." Those below "Incaparina" mean: "It is very nourishing and costs little."

satisfactory storage techniques for use in primitive conditions is especially acute. So much mystical nonsense has been written by believers in the merits of "natural" foods that most scientists show understandable impatience at the idea that pesticide residues may be harmful to the ultimate consumer of the protected crop. Furthermore, a food shortage may well do more harm to a community than sensibly applied pesticides can do. There is, nevertheless, great scope here for research on improved techniques.

There are such good prospects that productivity can be increased by each, or even all, of these methods if they are assiduously developed that it seems to many experts that there is no immediate need for any more radical approach to the problem of world feeding. This is the attitude of the United Nations Food and Agriculture Organization (F.A.O.). One cannot praise too highly its work in compiling statistics and persistently calling attention to the need for agricultural improvements. On the other hand, while recognizing that the F.A.O. is not a research organization, one can deplore its equally persistent tendency to denigrate every unorthodox approach to the problem. History may partly excuse this attitude. Ever since the time of Malthus prophets have been making our flesh creep with warnings of impending famine. Conditions have remained much the same—or have improved. These prophecies remain unfulfilled because 400 years of explora-

tion enabled new land to be cultivated, 200 years of biological research laid the foundation for scientific agriculture, and 50 years of rational chemistry made it possible to produce fertilizers by fixing the nitrogen of the air. The cautious prophet should therefore not say that hunger is inevitable but that it is probable unless the relevant research is done on an adequate scale. The time to do it is now, before the need has become more acute.

The main product of agriculture is carbohydrate. The foods that make up the world's diet—the cereals, potatoes, yams, cassava and so on—are from 1 to 12 percent protein on the basis of dry weight. An adult man needs 14 percent protein in his food; children and pregnant or lactating women need from 16 to 20 percent. However great an increase there may be in the consumption of conventional bulk foods, there will be a protein deficit. Moreover, it will be exacerbated if food is made palatable by the addition of fats and sugar, which give energy but contain no protein. Too much stress cannot be laid on the fact that the percentage of protein in a diet is the vital thing; increased consumption of low-protein food makes the consumer fat but as malnourished as before.

Recognition of the importance of protein sources, and their deficiency in most of the world's diet, has come slowly. It is nonetheless gathering momentum. Fifteen years ago little attention was paid to protein sources by international agencies and gatherings such as the International Nutrition Congress. Now protein

is one of the main themes. Audiences at these gatherings are a step ahead of the management. At the International Congress of Food Science and Technology last year, for example, the session "Novel Protein Sources" proved more popular than those who had allocated the rooms had foreseen; that session was more uncomfortably overcrowded than any other. The remainder of this article will be exclusively concerned with protein. All the components of a diet are needed, but the need for protein will be the most difficult to meet.

Animal products—meat, milk, cheese, eggs, fish—are widely esteemed and are used as protein concentrates to improve diets that are otherwise mainly carbohydrate. About a third of the world's cattle population is in Africa and India; most of these animals are relatively unproductive and are maintained largely for reasons of prestige and religion. It is easy to sidestep the main problem and argue that the protein shortage in these countries could be ameliorated, even if it could not be abolished, if herds were culled and the remainder made fully productive. The more thoughtful Africans and Indians realize this, and the situation will doubtless change. But every community tends to devote an amount of effort to nonproductive activity that seems to outsiders unreasonable. In the Middle Ages cathedrals were built by people who lived in hovels, and we now spend more on space research than on research in agriculture and medicine. Change is inevitable, and contemporary forms of religious observance and prestige are certain to be modified; the transition will not be hastened by nagging from outside.

According to most forecasters, the need to grow crops on land now used to maintain animals will lead to a decline in meat consumption in industrial countries, and the essential disappearance of meat is sometimes predicted. Although the decline is probable, the disappearance is not. There is much land that is suitable for grazing but not for tillage. Furthermore, there will always be a great deal of plant residue that (perhaps after supplementation with urea) can be more conveniently used as animal feed than in any other way. It is by no means certain, however, that we will always use the ideal herbivore. There is good reason to think that several species of now wild herbivore, running together, give a greater return of human food in many areas of tropical bush or savanna than domesticated species [see "Wildlife Hus-

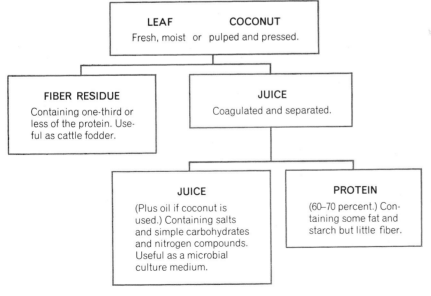

LEAVES AND COCONUT are a source of protein if fiber and juice are removed from them. This chart shows the steps of the process and also indicates the uses of by-products.

bandry in Africa," by F. Fraser Darling; SCIENTIFIC AMERICAN, November, 1960]. In addition, wild herbivores generally yield more protein per pound "on the hoof" than domestic species. These are matters that are being investigated by the International Biological Program. Even better results may be achieved after a few years of skilled breeding. Ruminants such as the antelope and the water buffalo are not the only species worthy of attention, and land is not the only site available for grazing. The capybara, a large rodent, is well adapted to South America and is palatable. Water weeds, and plants growing in swamps and on lake margins, contribute hardly anything to human nutrition. They could be collected and fed to land animals, but it would seem to be more efficient to domesticate the *Sirenia* (the freshwater manatee and the marine dugong) and use them as sources of meat. These herbivores are wholly aquatic and so, unlike semiaquatic species such as tapirs and hippopotamuses, do not compete for food with more familiar animals.

It is usual in articles such as this one to stress the importance of fish. This is admirable, but stress should not be allowed to drift into obsession. The more cautious forecasters estimate that the fish catch could be increased only two- or threefold without depleting stocks. Moreover, much of the world's population lives far from large bodies of water, and since fishing has an accident rate twice as high as coal mining it is likely to remain a relatively unattractive occupation. In the past decade the wet weight of fish caught annually increased from 29 million tons to 52 million, but the proportion used as human food decreased from 83 percent to 63. The remainder was used as fodder, mainly in the already well-fed countries. When still more fish are caught, the temptation to use a still larger proportion as fodder will be greater because much of the extra catch will consist of unfamiliar species. By grinding and solvent extraction these unfamiliar fishes can be turned into an edible product containing 80 percent protein. This process has suffered from every form of misfortune: the use of unsuitable solvents, commercial overstatement, excessive hygienic caution and political intrigue. It is nevertheless sound in principle and will do much to increase the amount of food protein made on an industrial scale and distributed through international channels.

One also hears of "fish farming." Activity that could properly be given this

MANATEE, an aquatic mammal, is an example of an unorthodox source of meat. It can also control aquatic weeds, which it eats. An adult manatee is between nine and 15 feet long.

CAPYBARA, a large rodent that lives in South America, has also been suggested as a source of meat. Like the manatee, it feeds on aquatic weeds. An adult is about four feet long.

ELAND, a large African antelope, is an accepted meat animal. Its importance as a food source is that it is adapted to grazing on marginal lands that are not suited to agriculture.

title is possible in lagoons but unlikely in the oceans because fish move too freely, and fertilizer, intended to encourage the growth of their food, spreads too easily into the useless unlit depths. With mollusks and crustaceans, farming becomes much more promising and deserves more scientific attention than it gets. Food for such marine invertebrates does not seem to be the limiting factor; many of them can use the world's largest biological resource, the million million tons of organic matter in suspension in the sea. Sedentary mollusks are limited by predators and attachment sites. The predators could be controlled and the sites, with modern materials, could be increased.

Animals that live on something that we could not use as food—forage growing in rough country, straws and other residues, phytoplankton and other forms of marine organic matter—cannot properly be said to have a "conversion efficiency." We either use an animal converter or these materials are wasted. Efficiency has a real meaning when we consider animals that live either on crops that people could eat or on crops grown on land that could have grown food. The inefficiency of animal conversion, expressed as pounds of protein the animal must eat to make a pound of protein in the animal product that people eat, is much greater than is generally realized. This unawareness probably arises from the tendency among animal feeders to present their results as the ratio of the dry food eaten to the wet weight (includ-

ing all inedible parts) of the carcass produced. Furthermore, the figures generally relate only to one phase of the animal's life, without allowance for unproductive periods. It is unlikely that the true efficiency of protein conversion is often greater than one pound of food protein for every seven pounds of fodder protein; it is generally less. Although animal products are highly esteemed in most countries, their production is an extravagance when it depends on land or fodder that could have been used to feed people. The extravagance may be tolerated in well-fed countries but not in those that are short of food.

As I have indicated, the world's main food crops need to be supplemented with protein. Peas and beans, which are 25 to 40 percent protein, are traditionally used. Green vegetables and immature flowers are gaining recognition. They can yield 400 pounds of edible protein per acre in a three-to-four-month growing period, but because they contain fiber and other indigestible components a person cannot get more than two or three grams of protein from them in a day. This amount, however, is much more than is normally consumed, and such plants offer a rewarding field for research. The varieties cultivated in industrialized countries are often ill-adapted to other climatic conditions. The work of vegetable improvement that was done in Europe in the 18th and 19th centuries should now be replicated in the wet Tropics. Biochemical control would

be needed to ensure that what is being produced is not only nontoxic but also nutritionally valuable. This would be an excellent project for the International Biological Program; the raw materials have worldwide distribution and the need is also worldwide.

The residue that is left when oil is expressed from soya, groundnut, cottonseed and sunflower is now for the most part used as animal feed or fertilizer or is simply discarded. It contains about 20 million tons of protein, that is, twice the world's present estimated deficit. Because its potential value is not yet widely realized, most of this material is at present so contaminated, or damaged by overheating during the expressing of the oil, that it is useless as a source of human food. But methods are being devised, notably in the Indian state of Mysore and in Guatemala, for processing the oilseeds more carefully in order to produce an acceptable food containing 40 to 50 percent protein. The avoidance of damage during processing is not the only problem that arises with oilseeds; each species contains, or may contain, harmful components, for example gossypol in cottonseed, enzyme inhibitors in soya and aflatoxin in peanuts. Gossypol can be extracted or low-gossypol strains of cotton can be used (it is said, however, that these are particularly attractive to insect pests); enzyme inhibitors can be destroyed, and the infestation that produces aflatoxin can be prevented by proper harvesting and storage. The alternative of extracting a purified protein concentrate from the residues is often advocated. This approach seems mistaken; it increases the cost of the protein fivefold. In addition, the process is in the main simply the removal of starch or some other digestible carbohydrate, and carbohydrate has to be added to the protein concentrate again during cooking.

The residue left after expressing oil from an oilseed can be used because it contains little fiber. Coconuts and the leaves from many species of plants are also potential protein sources, but they contain so much fiber that it is essential to separate the protein if more than two or three grams is being eaten each day. The process of separation, although simple, is still in its infancy, and many improvements remain to be made. Units for effecting it are working in Mysore, at the Rothamsted Experimental Station and elsewhere. In wet tropical regions the conventional seed-bearing plants often do not ripen, but coconuts thrive and leaves grow exuberantly. It is in these

TANKS ARE FILLED WITH LITTLE FISH from a truck (*left*) at a fish meal plant in the Peruvian port of Callao. The fish are anchovetas, a variety of anchovy. By grinding and solvent extraction they are converted into a product that contains 80 percent protein.

BAGS OF FISH MEAL are piled in the yard of the same plant. Fish meal is currently used primarily as a supplement to feed for domestic animals. In 1965 Peru harvested 7.46 million metric tons of fish, a catch that makes it the world's leading fishing nation.

regions that protein separation has its greatest potentiality.

The protein sources discussed in the last two paragraphs would be opened up by handling conventional agricultural products in unusual ways. Attention is also being given to completely novel forms of production based on photosynthesis by unicellular algae and other microorganisms. The early work was uncritical and, considering the small increases in the rate of fixation of carbon dioxide given by these methods compared with conventional agriculture, the necessary expenditure on equipment was out of proportion. It is an illusion to think that algae have any special photosynthetic capacity. Their merit is that it is much easier to spread an algal suspension, rather than a set of slowly expanding seedlings, uniformly over a sunlit surface so as to make optimal use of the light. Recently more realistic methods, using open tanks and the roofs of greenhouses in which other plants can be grown during the winter, have been tried in Japan and Czechoslovakia. The product resembles leaf protein in many ways but contains more indigestible matter because the algal cell walls are not removed; it may prove possible either to separate the protein from the cell walls or to digest the walls with enzymes.

All the processes discussed so far depend on what might be called current photosynthesis. Microorganisms that do not themselves photosynthesize can produce foodstuffs from the products of photosynthesis in the immediate past

(straw, sawdust or the by-product liquor from leaf-protein production) or in the remote past (petroleum, coal or methane). The former substrates would have to be collected over a wide area, whereas the latter are concentrated in a few places and so lend themselves to convenient large-scale industrial processing. At first sight this seems advantageous, and in fact it would be so were we merely concerned with increasing the amount of food in the world. That will be the problem later; now the important thing is, as I have said, to make food where the mouths are, and elaborate and sophisticated techniques are not well adapted to this end. The most valuable aspect of the research now being done in many countries on microbial growth on fossil substrates such as petroleum is that it will familiarize people with the idea of microbial food and so will hasten its acceptance when it is produced from local materials.

Finally, there is synthetic food. Plants make fats and carbohydrates so economically that it is unlikely synthesis could be cheaper. Many of the abundant plant proteins do not have an amino acid composition ideally suited to human needs. These proteins are sometimes complementary, so that the deficiencies of each can be made good by judicious mixing. When this is not possible, the deficient amino acids can be synthesized or made by fermentation and then added to the food. Production of amino acids for this purpose will probably be possible only in industrialized countries; their use may therefore seem to violate the principle

that food must be where the mouths are. The quantities needed, however, are small. It is obviously better to upgrade an abundant local protein by adding .5 percent of methionine to it rather than import a whole protein to make up this one deficiency.

The food that is now needed or that will soon be needed in the underprivileged parts of the world might be supplied by charity, by the extension of existing methods of agriculture or by novel processes. I have argued that the first cannot be satisfactory and that it would be dangerous to assume that the second will suffice. Without wishing in any way to minimize the importance of what is being done in these two directions, it seems necessary to take novelties seriously. By definition a novelty is novel. That is to say, it may have an unfamiliar appearance, texture or flavor. In commenting on any of the proposals made—the use of strange animals, oilseed residues or leaf and microbial protein—it is irrelevant to say that they are unfamiliar. If the world is to be properly fed, products such as these will probably have to be used. Our problem is to make them acceptable.

Socrates, when one of his companions said he had learned little by foreign travel, replied: "That is not surprising. You were accompanied by yourself." Similarly, food technologists, accustomed to the dietary prejudices of Europe and the U.S., are apt to project their prejudices onto other communities. They have two opposite obsessions: to fabricate a "chewy" texture in their product and to produce a bland stable powder with an indefinite shelf life. Neither quality is universal in the familiar foods of most of the world. The former may have merits, although these probably do not outweigh the extra difficulties involved. It is odd that, at a time when people in industrialized countries are beginning to revolt against uniform and prepacked foods, we should be bent on foisting the latter quality off on others. Instead, novelties should be introduced into regions where they will most smoothly conform with local culinary habits. Novel forms of fish and mollusks are probably well adapted to Southeast Asia, where fermented fish is popular. Leaf, oilseed or microbial protein would fit smoothly into a culture accustomed to porridge, gruel and curry. It is important to remember the irrational diversity of our tastes. Even in Europe and the U.S. a flavor and appearance unacceptable in an egg is acceptable in cheese, a smell unacceptable in chicken is acceptable in pheasant or partridge, and a flavor unacceptable in wine is acceptable in grapefruit juice. These things are a matter of habit, and habits, although they will not change in a day or even a month, can readily be changed by suitable example and persuasion. The essential first step is to find out what is meant by the word "suitable."

Enough experience is now accumulating for us to define the parameters of success. The four most important are:

First, research on the novelty should be done privately and completely, so that when popularization starts there can be no rationally based doubts about the merits of the product.

Second, the novelty should manifestly be eaten by the innovators themselves. It is folly to ask people to practice what we only preach—we must practice it ourselves.

Third, example is the main factor leading to a change in habits; it is therefore essential to get the support of influential local people—from film stars to political leaders. Care should be taken that the first users are not underprivileged groups (prisoners, refugees and so on), because the stigma will not easily be removed.

Last, an adequate and regular supply of the product should be assured before there is any publicity, because it is hard to reawaken interest that has waned because the product is not obtainable.

All these proposals, except that of the simplest form of agricultural extension, call for research. It is worth considering who should do it and what form opposition is likely to take. Opposition to innovation is an interesting and underinvestigated part of psychopathology. It takes three main forms: total, quasi-logical and "instant."

Total opposition is the denial of the problem. Even today there are those who, in the course of condemning some specific proposal, sometimes deny that a protein shortage exists or is impending. This is a point that should be settled at the very beginning: "Do we have a problem or not?" Fortunately for research, and for humanity, the international agencies are in agreement that we do.

Quasi-logical opposition comes from economists. They may accept the problem but argue that some proposed solutions will be too expensive. There are two relevant questions: "Compared with what?" and "How do you know when it has not been tried?" When there are several equally feasible methods for getting the extra food that is needed in a region, a comparison of their probable costs is obviously worthwhile. But when all costs are, for various reasons, unknown, the exercise becomes futile because assumptions play a larger part in it than rigid economic argument, and scientists are better qualified than economists to make the assumptions; they know more of the facts, are aware of more possibilities and are less subject to romantic illusion.

"Instant opposition" arises because innovators are apt to irritate right-minded people, and enthusiasm invites skepticism. The innovator must therefore expect to run into trouble. When someone made the old comment that genius was an infinite capacity for taking trouble,

MUSSELS ARE GROWN in this floating "park" in Vigo Bay on the northwestern coast of Spain. Suspended from each of the large anchored raftlike structures are ropes on which the mussels are seeded and grow to maturity (*see photograph on following page*).

Samuel Butler replied: "It isn't. It is an infinite capacity for getting into trouble and for staying in trouble for as long as the genius lasts." In an attenuated form the principle applies even when genius is not involved. There are many different ways of getting into trouble, and it is as naïve and illogical to assume that an idea must be correct because it is meeting opposition as it is to take "instant opposition" seriously.

The governments of countries with a food shortage know that, for a decade at least, more people will be better fed if money is spent on importing food rather than on setting up a research project on means to make more food from local products for local consumption. The more farsighted statesmen realize that ultimately the research will have to be done, but it is hard to resist political pressure, and resistance is hampered by the high cost of primitive agriculture. In a market in New Guinea local sweet potatoes cost three times as much per calorie as imported wheat, and fresh fish cost twice as much per gram of protein as canned fish. So poor countries are hardly likely to mount research projects.

At the other extreme are the giants of private enterprise. They already do very well selling soft drinks and patent foods in underdeveloped countries, and their skill in creating a market, regardless of the real merits of their product, is unrivaled. Thus baby foods, which few experts regard as superior to mother's milk, were used in Uganda by 42 percent of the families in 1959, whereas only 14 percent had used them in 1950. Undoubtedly there are efficient firms that operate with strict integrity, and a few of them have ventured into the production of low-cost protein-rich foods. After the necessary research and preliminary publicity had been done with money from international sources, the Quaker Oats Company has done a masterly job in making, distributing and popularizing Incaparina (maize, sorghum and cottonseed) in Central America. And skilled advertising increased the sales of Pronutro (soya, peanuts and fish) tenfold in two years. Other attempts have failed because the possible profit, when one is selling to poor people without misleading them with meretricious advertising, is too small to cover the costs of the preliminary educational campaign. That, as I have suggested, can be managed only with the cooperation of governments and the local leaders of opinion.

Large-scale private enterprise will probably not find this activity lucrative,

and from some points of view the methods of production that would be used may not be desirable. Already more than a third of the world's city population (12 percent of the total population) live in shantytowns on the fringes of cities, and rural depopulation is accelerating. This, together with transport difficulties, makes it at least arguable that research attention should be focused on simple techniques adapted for use in a large village or small town, rather than on fully industrialized techniques. The latter have their place, but they should not become our exclusive concern.

If neither the governments of needy countries nor private enterprise is likely to undertake the necessary research and development, it remains for the governments of industrialized countries, the international agencies and the foundations. So far these groups have been reluctant to admit that any radical changes in research policy will be needed, but times are changing. The novelties are now at least mentioned by the F.A.O. even if only to be gently damned with a few misstatements. On the Barnum principle, "I don't care what people say about me so long as they talk about me," this is a step forward. The governments of wealthy countries supply most of the support for the international agencies, they support other forms of aid, and much knowledge that is of use in poorer countries is an international by-product of their more parochial research. They may feel that they are already doing their share. Our best hope must therefore lie with the foundations. Several institutes of food technology are needed to undertake fundamental and applied research on the production of food from local products for local consumption. At least one of the institutes should be in the wet Tropics and all should give particular attention to protein sources. Using locally available material, each institute should study all the types of raw material discussed here. This will ensure that similar criteria are applied to all of them and that the assessment of their merits is made objectively and is not colored by interinstitutional rivalry. These institutes should also be responsible for work on the presentation and popularization of the products made. It may be that an extension of normal agriculture will meet the world's food needs for a few more years, but ultimately more radical research will be needed. It would be prudent to start it before the need is even more pressing than it is at present.

ROPE COVERED WITH MUSSELS is lifted from the water after mussels are mature.

The Author

N. W. PIRIE is head of the department of biochemistry at the Rothamsted Experimental Station in England. A Fellow of the Royal Society, he has interested himself not only in biochemical matters but also in social issues. Among the former are the separation and the properties of several plant viruses; factors controlling the infectability of plants by viruses, and the preparation of edible proteins from leaves. Pirie writes: "That is recounted in 100-plus papers. Another 100-plus deal in a general way with fractionation of macromolecules and the criteria of purity; classification of viruses and similar entities; contraception and the population problem; protein sources and other aspects of world food supplies, and strictures on government policies on such issues as air raid precautions, nuclear weapon testing and the planning of scientific research." Pirie was graduated from the University of Cambridge and served in the biochemical laboratory there from 1929 to 1940, when he went to the Rothamsted Station.

Bibliography

THE STATE OF FOOD AND AGRICULTURE 1966. Food and Agriculture Organization of the United Nations. Rome, 1966.

SCIENTIFIC AMERICAN   April 1967, Vol. 216, No. 4, pp. 28-37   OFFPRINT 1069

THE INDUCTION OF CANCER BY VIRUSES

by Renato Dulbecco

Normal cells cultured in glassware can be transformed into cancer cells by several viruses. Such "model" systems are studied to find how the virus, with fewer than 10 genes, can produce the change.

Cancer, one of the major problems of modern medicine, is also a fascinating biological problem. In biological terms it is the manifestation of changes in one of the more general properties of the cells of higher organisms: their ability to adjust their growth rate to the architectural requirements of the organism. To learn more about cancer is therefore to learn more about this basic control mechanism. Over the past decade dramatic advances in our knowledge of cancer have resulted from the use of viruses to elicit the disease in simple model systems. A certain understanding of the molecular aspects of cancer has been attained, and the foundation has been laid for rapid progress in the foreseeable future.

A cancer arises from a single cell that undergoes permanent hereditary changes and consequently multiplies, giving rise to billions of similarly altered cells. The development of the cancer may require other conditions, such as failure of the immunological defenses of the organism. The fundamental event, however, is the alteration of that one initial cell.

There are two main changes in a cancer cell. One change can be defined as being of a regulatory nature. The multiplication of the cells of an animal is carefully regulated; multiplication takes place only when it is required, for example by the healing of a wound. The cancer cell, on the other hand, escapes the regulatory mechanisms of the body and is continuously in a multiplication cycle.

The other change of the cancer cell concerns its relations with neighboring cells in the body. Normal cells are confined to certain tissues, according to rules on which the body's overall architecture depends. The cancer cell is not confined to its original tissue but invades other tissues, where it proliferates.

The basic biological problem of cancer is to identify the molecular changes that occur in the initial cancer cell and determine what causes the changes. The particular site in the cell affected by the changes can be approximately inferred from the nature of the changes themselves. For example, a change in the regulation of cell growth and multiplication must arise from a change in the regulation of a basic process in the cell, such as the synthesis of the genetic material deoxyribonucleic acid (DNA). The alterations in relations with neighboring cells are likely to flow from changes in the outside surface of the cell, which normally recognizes and responds to its immediate environment.

Experimental work directed toward the solution of this central problem makes use of cancers induced artificially rather than cancers that occur spontaneously. Spontaneous cancers are not suitable for experiments because by definition their occurrence cannot be controlled; moreover, when a spontaneous cancer becomes observable, its cells have often undergone numerous changes in addition to the initial one. In recent years model systems for studying cancers have been developed by taking advantage of the fact that animal cells can easily be grown in vitro—in test tubes or boxes of glass or plastic filled with a suitable liquid medium. This is the technique of tissue culture.

Since the use of tissue culture has many obvious experimental advantages, methods for the induction of cancer in vitro have been developed. The most successful and most widely employed systems use viruses as the cancer-inducing agent. In these systems the initial cellular changes take place under con-trolled conditions and can be followed closely by using an array of technical tools: genetic, biochemical, physical and immunological.

It may seem strange that viruses, which are chemically complex structures, would be preferable for experimental work to simple cancer-inducing chemicals, of which many are available. The fact is that the action of cancer-inducing chemicals is difficult to elucidate; they have complex chemical effects on a large number of cell constituents. Furthermore, even if one were to make the simple and reasonable assumption that chemicals cause cancer by inducing mutations in the genetic material of the cells, the problem would remain enormously difficult. It would still be almost impossible to know which genes are affected, owing to the large number of genes in which the cancer-causing mu-

NORMAL AND TRANSFORMED cells are shown on the opposite page in three stages of density, or growth, increasing to the right in each row. Normal cells (A, C) tend to adhere to one another and form either a pattern of bundles (A) or a mosaic-like arrangement referred to as pavement (C). Cells that have been transformed by viruses (B, D, E) generally overlap one another and form irregular patterns. The cellular bodies are dark gray and contain a lighter round or oval nucleus in which two or more dark nuclei are embedded. Two of the cultures (A, B) are a strain of hamster cells identified as "BHK." The other three cultures are "3T3" cells derived from a mouse. Two of the cultures (B, E) have been transformed by polyoma virus; one (D) has been transformed by simian virus 40, also known as SV 40. The cells were photographed in the living state by the author, using a phase-contrast microscope, at the Salk Institute for Biological Studies.

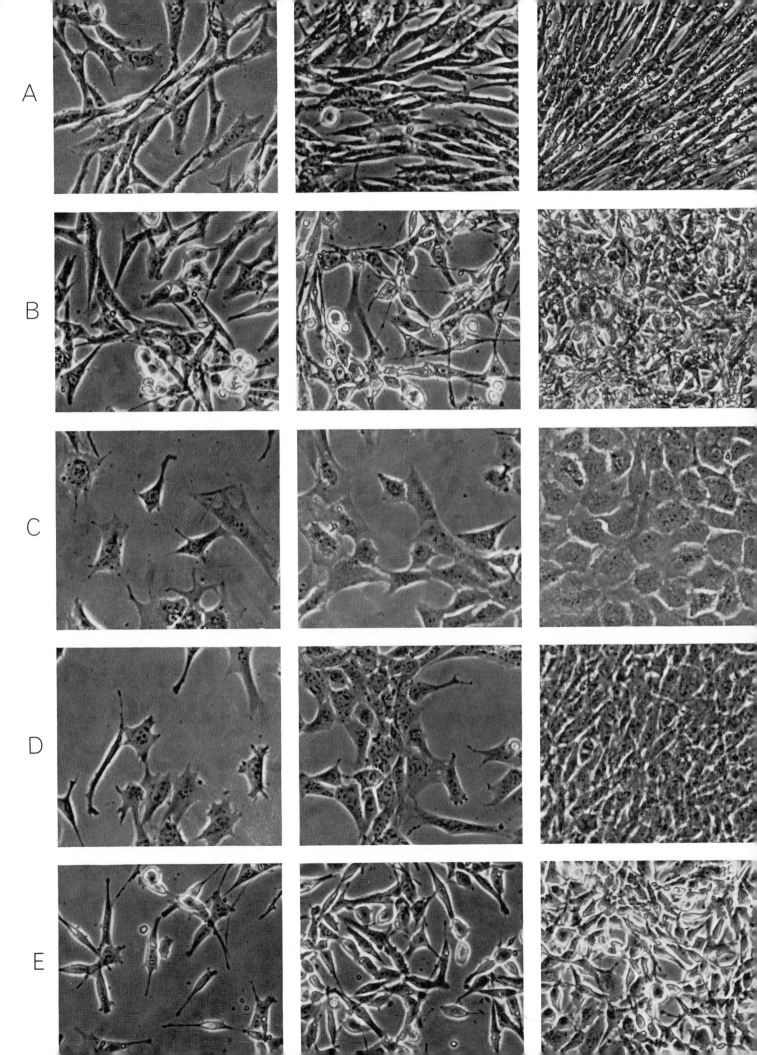

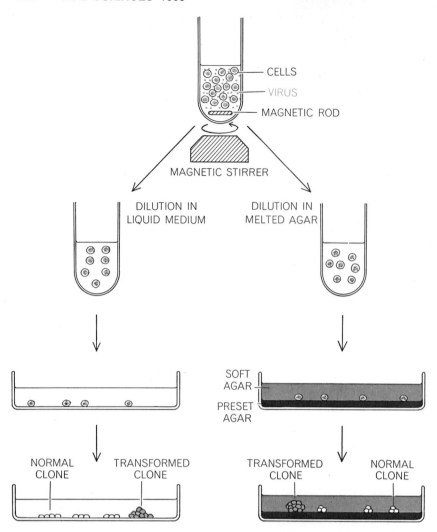

CELLS
VIRUS
MAGNETIC ROD

MAGNETIC STIRRER

DILUTION IN
LIQUID MEDIUM

DILUTION IN
MELTED AGAR

SOFT
AGAR
PRESET
AGAR

NORMAL
CLONE

TRANSFORMED
CLONE

TRANSFORMED
CLONE

NORMAL
CLONE

TRANSFORMATION EXPERIMENT produces cell colonies that differ in appearance, depending on the nature of the culture medium. BHK (hamster) cells are first incubated with polyoma virus for about an hour at 37 degrees centigrade, being stirred constantly. During this time viral particles enter the cells. The infected cells are then diluted either in a liquid medium or in melted agar and transferred to culture dishes. In the agar system the melted agar is poured on a layer of preset agar. The dishes are incubated at 37 degrees C. Cell colonies in the liquid medium develop in contact with the bottom of the container, whereas those in agar form spherical colonies above the preset agar layer. The results of using the two kinds of media are shown in the photographs on the opposite page.

tation could occur. It is estimated that there are millions of genes in an animal cell, and the function of most of them is unknown. With viruses the situation can be much simpler. As I shall show, cancer is induced by the genes of the virus, which, like the genes of animal cells, are embodied in the structure of DNA. Since the number of viral genes is small (probably fewer than 10 in the system discussed in this article), it should be possible to identify those responsible for cancer induction and to discover how they function in the infected cells. The problem can thus be reduced from one of cellular genetics to one of viral genetics. The reduction is of several orders of magnitude.

A number of different viruses have the ability to change normal cells into cancer cells in vitro. In our work at the Salk Institute for Biological Studies we employ two small, DNA-containing viruses called the polyoma virus and simian virus 40 (SV 40), both of which induce cancer when they are inoculated into newborn rodents, particularly hamsters, rats and, in the case of the polyoma virus, mice. Together these viruses are referred to as the small papovaviruses.

In tissue-culture studies two types of host cell are employed with each virus. In one cell type—the "productive" host cell—the virus causes what is known as a productive infection: the virus multiplies unchecked within the cell and finally kills it. In another type of cell— the "transformable" host cell—the virus

causes little or no productive infection but induces changes similar to those in cancer cells. This effect of infection is called transformation rather than cancer induction because operationally it is recognized from the altered morphology of the cells in vitro rather than from the production of cancer in an animal.

In the experimental work it is convenient to employ as host cells, particularly for transformation studies, permanent lines of cellular descent, known as clonal lines, that are derived from a single cell and are therefore uniform in composition. By using these clonal lines the changes caused by the virus can be studied without interference from other forms of cellular variation; one simply compares the transformed cells with their normal counterparts. Two lines that are widely employed are the "BHK" line, which was obtained from a hamster by Ian A. Macpherson and Michael G. P. Stoker of the Institute of Virology of the University of Glasgow, and the "3T3" line, which was obtained from a mouse by George J. Todaro and Howard Green of the New York University School of Medicine. BHK cells are particularly suitable for transformation by the polyoma virus; 3T3 cells are readily transformed by SV 40 and less easily by the polyoma virus.

In a typical transformation experiment a suspension of cells in a suitable liquid medium is mixed with the virus [see illustration at left]. The cells are incubated at 37 degrees centigrade for an hour; they are stirred constantly to prevent them from settling and clumping together. A sample of the cells is then distributed in a number of sterile dishes of glass or plastic that contain a suitable nutrient medium. The dishes are incubated at 37 degrees C. for a period ranging from one to three weeks. The cells placed in the dishes settle and adhere to the bottom. There they divide, each cell giving rise to a colony [see illustration at left on opposite page]. If the number of cells is sufficiently small, the colonies remain distinct from one another and are recognizable to the unaided eye after about 10 days' incubation; they can be studied sooner with a low-power microscope. When the colonies are fully developed, they are usually fixed and stained. Colonies of normal and transformed cells can be recognized on the basis of morphological characters I shall describe. By picking a colony of transformed cells and reseeding its cells in a fresh culture, clonal lines of transformed cells can be easily prepared. The transformation of BHK cells can also be studied by a selective method that involves suspending the cells in melted agar, which then sets. Transformed cells give rise to spherical colonies, visible to the unaided eye, whereas normal cells grow little or not at all [see illustration at right below].

Colonies of transformed cells, and cultures derived from such colonies, differ morphologically from their normal counterparts in two obvious ways; these differences show that changes have occurred in the regulatory properties of the cells and also in the way they relate to their neighbors. The transformed cultures are thicker because they continue to grow rapidly, whereas normal cultures slow down or stop; in addition the transformed cells are not regularly oriented with respect to each other because they fail to respond to cell-to-cell contact. The altered response to contacts can be best appreciated in time-lapse motion pictures of living cultures.

In sparse BHK cultures the cells move around actively; if a cell meets another cell in its path, it usually stops moving and slowly arranges itself in contact with and parallel to the other cell. In this way a characteristic pattern of parallel lines and whorls is generated, since the cells do not climb over each other. In a culture of a derivative of the BHK line transformed by polyoma virus the same active movement of the cells is observed. When a cell meets another in its path, however, it continues to move, climbing over the other. In this way the arrangement of the cells becomes chaotic, without any discernible pattern [see illustration on page 2391].

These alterations of the transformed cells indicate their intimate relatedness to cancer cells. The relatedness is shown in a more dramatic way by the ability of the transformed cells to grow into a cancer when injected, in sufficient number, into a live host that does not present an insurmountable immunological barrier to their survival. For example, BHK cells, which were originally obtained from a hamster, can be transplanted into hamsters; similarly, cells of inbred strains of mice can easily be transplanted into mice of the same strain. The injection of roughly a million transformed cells into a hamster or mouse will be followed by the development of a walnut-sized tumor at the site of inoculation in about three weeks. Untransformed cells, on the other hand, fail to produce tumors.

A crucial finding is that the transformation of healthy cells is attributable to the genes present in the viral DNA that penetrates the cells at infection. The viral genes are the units of information that determine the consequences of infection. Each viral particle contains a long, threadlike molecule of DNA wrapped in a protein coat. Each of these molecules is made up of two strands twisted around each other. Attached to the molecular backbone of each strand is the sequence of nitrogenous bases that contains the genetic information of the virus in coded form. There are four kinds of base, and the DNA molecule of a papovavirus has some 5,000 bases on each strand. Each species of virus has a unique sequence of bases in its DNA; all members of a species have the same base sequence, except for isolated differences caused by mutations.

The double-strand molecule of DNA is so constructed that a given base in one strand always pairs with a particular base in the other strand; these two associated bases are called complementary. Thus the two DNA strands are also complementary in base sequence. Complementary bases form bonds with each other; the bonds hold the two strands firmly together. The two strands fall apart if a solution of DNA is heated to a fairly high temperature, a process

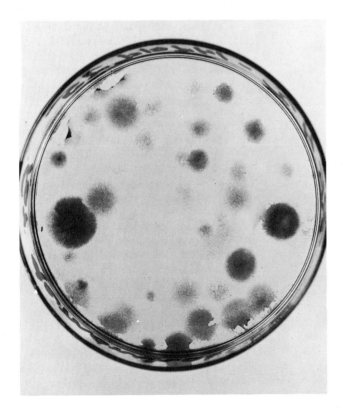
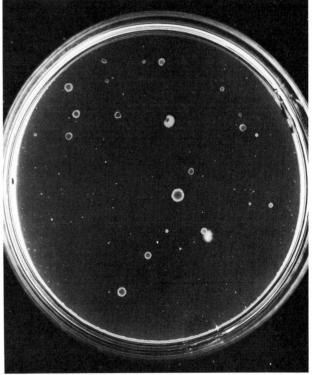

TWO KINDS OF CELL COLONY are depicted in these photographs made in the author's laboratory. Colonies formed by 3T3 (mouse) cells exposed to SV 40 particles grow on the bottom of a plastic dish under a liquid nutrient medium (left). The two large, dark colonies on opposite sides of the culture dish consist of transformed cells. The other colonies are made up of normal cells. Colonies formed by BHK (hamster) cells exposed to polyoma virus are suspended in agar (right). Transformed cells create large spherical colonies, which appear as white disks with gray centers. Colonies of normal cells are small or invisible.

called denaturation. If the heated solution is then slowly cooled, a process called annealing, the complementary strands unite again and form double-strand molecules identical with the original ones.

When suitable cells are exposed to a virus, a large number of viral particles are taken up into the cells in many small vesicles, or sacs, which then accumulate around the nucleus of the cell. Most of the viral particles remain inert, but the protein coat of some is removed and their naked DNA enters the inner compartments of the cell, ultimately reaching the nucleus. Evidence that cell transformation is caused by the viral DNA, and by the genes it carries, is supplied by two experimental results.

The first result is that cell transformation can be produced by purified viral DNA, obtained by removing the protein coat from viral particles; this was first shown by G. P. Di Mayorca and his colleagues at the Sloan-Kettering Institute. The extraction of the DNA is usually accomplished by shaking the virus in concentrated phenol. In contrast, the empty viral coats do not cause transformation. These DNA-less particles are available for experimentation because they are synthesized in productively infected cells together with the regular DNA-containing particles. The empty coats have a lower density than the complete viral particles; hence the two can be separated if they are spun at high speed in a heavy salt solution, the technique known as density-gradient centrifugation.

A more sophisticated experiment performed at the University of Glasgow also rules out the possibility that the transforming activity resides in contaminant molecules present in the extracted DNA. The basis for this experiment is the shape of the DNA molecules of papovaviruses. The ends of each molecule are joined together to form a ring. When the double-strand filaments that consti-

tute these ring molecules are in solution, they form densely packed supercoils. If one of the strands should suffer a single break, the supercoil disappears and the molecule becomes a stretched ring. Supercoiled molecules, because of their compactness, settle faster than stretching-ring molecules when they are centrifuged. Thus the two molecular types can be separated in two distinct bands.

By this technique polyoma virus DNA containing both molecular types can be separated into fractions, each of which contains just one type. Examination of the biological properties of these fractions shows that the transforming efficiency is strictly limited to the two bands of the viral DNA. Similarly, only the material in the two bands will give rise to productive infection. This result, among others, rules out the possibility that transformation is due to fragments of cellular DNA, which are known to be present in some particles of polyoma virus and therefore contaminate the preparations of viral DNA. The contaminant molecules have a very different distribution in the gradient.

The second result demonstrates directly that the function of a viral gene is required for transformation, by showing that a mutation in the viral genetic material can abolish the ability of the virus to transform. This important finding was made by Mike Fried of the California Institute of Technology, who studied a temperature-sensitive mutant line of polyoma virus called Ts-a. The virus of this line behaves like normal virus in cells at 31 degrees C., causing either transformation or productive infection, depending on the cells it infects. At 39 degrees C., however, the effect of the mutation is manifest, and the virus is unable to cause either transformation or infection; it is simply inactive [see top illustration on opposite page].

We can now inquire whether the viral gene functions needed to effect transformation are transient or continuous. In other words, do the genes act only once and produce a permanent transformation of the cell line or must they act continuously to keep the cell and its descendants transformed?

A result pertinent to this question is that the transformed cells contain functional viral genes many cell generations after transformation has occurred, although they never contain, or spontaneously produce, infectious virus. The presence of viral genes has been demonstrated particularly well by T. L. Benjamin at Cal Tech, who has shown that the transformed cells contain virus-specific

PRODUCTIVE
INFECTION

TRANSFORMATION

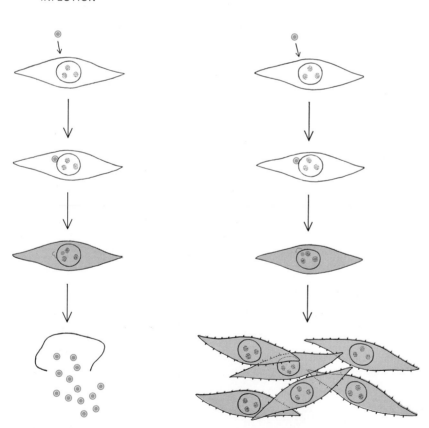

VIRAL INVASION OF CELLS can have two different results. One result is "productive infection" (*left*), in which viral particles (*color*) mobilize the machinery of the cell for making new viral particles, complete with protein coats. The cell eventually dies, releasing the particles. The other result is transformation (*right*), in which the virus alters the cell so that it reproduces without restraint and does not respond to the presence of neighboring cells. Viral particles cannot be found in the transformed cells. The tint of color in these cells indicates the presence of new functions induced by the genes of the virus. The change in the cell membrane (*lower right*) denotes the presence of a virus-specific antigen.

ribonucleic acid (RNA). To make the significance of this finding clear it should be mentioned that the instructions contained in the base sequence of the DNA in cells or viruses are executed by first making a strand of RNA with a base sequence complementary to that of one of the DNA strands. This RNA, called messenger RNA, carries the information of the gene to the cellular sites where the proteins specified by the genetic information are synthesized. Each gene gives rise to its own specific messenger RNA. If one could show that viral messenger RNA were present in transformed cells, one would have evidence not only that the cells contain viral genes but also that these genes are active. The viral RNA molecules can be recognized among those extracted from transformed cells, which are mostly cellular RNA, by adding to the mixture of RNA molecules heat-denatured, single-strand viral DNA. When the mixture of RNA and DNA is annealed, only the viral molecules of RNA enter into double-strand molecules with the viral DNA. The reaction is extremely sensitive and specific.

It is likely, therefore, that the viral genes persisting in the transformed cells are instrumental in maintaining the transformed state of the cells. This idea is supported by the observation that the form of the transformed cells is controlled by the transforming virus. This is seen clearly in cells of the line 3T3, which can be transformed by either SV 40 or polyoma virus. The transformed cells, although descended from the same clonal cell line, are strikingly different [see illustration on page 2391]. Similar differences are observed in other cell types transformed by the two viruses. Since the cells were identical before infection, the differences that accompany transformation by two different viruses can be most simply explained as the result of the continuing function of the different viral genes in the same type of cell. In fact, it is difficult to think of a satisfactory alternative hypothesis.

It must be clear, however, that there is no conclusive evidence for this continuing role of the viral genes. It is therefore impossible to exclude an entirely different interpretation of the observation. One can argue, for example, that the persistence of the viral genes is irrelevant for transformation, and that the genes remain in the cells as an accidental result of the previous exposure of the cells, or of their ancestors, to the virus. Indeed, under many other circumstances viruses are often found in association with cells without noticeably affecting them. A conclusive clarification of the

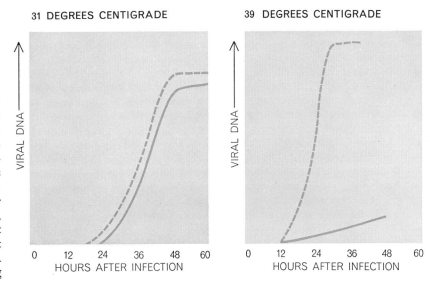

TEMPERATURE-DEPENDENT STRAINS OF POLYOMA VIRUS act normally at a temperature of 31 degrees C. (left) but exhibit mutated behavior at 39 degrees C. (right). The solid curves show the amount of viral deoxyribonucleic acid (DNA) synthesized in productive host cells containing the mutant virus. Broken curves show the viral DNA output in cells containing "wild type" (ordinary) polyoma virus. The mutant virus is called Ts-a.

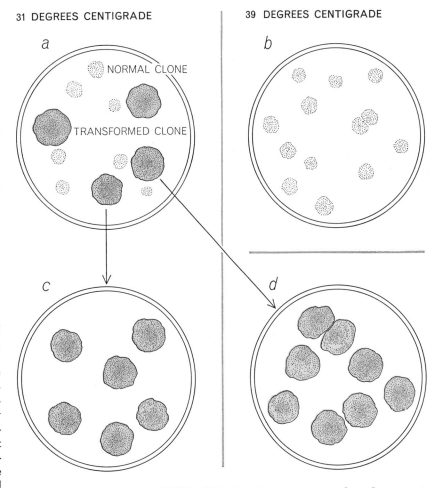

TRANSIENT ROLE OF TS-A GENE, which gives rise to temperature-dependent mutants of polyoma virus, can be demonstrated by raising the temperature of experimental cultures after the cells have been transformed by the virus. The mutant virus is able to transform cells at low temperature (a) but not at high temperature (b). Transformed cell colonies, or clones, remain transformed, as expected, at low temperature (c), but they also remain transformed when the temperature is raised (d). This experiment provides evidence that the Ts-a gene is needed for the initial transformation of the cell but is not needed thereafter.

role of the persisting viral genes is being sought by using temperature-dependent viral mutants analogous to the Ts-a mutant I have mentioned. A virus bearing a temperature-dependent mutation in a gene whose function is required for maintaining the cells in the transformed state would cause transformation at low temperature. The cells, however, would revert to normality if the ambient temperature were raised. A small-scale search for mutants with these properties has already been carried out in our laboratory but without success; a large-scale search is being planned in several laboratories.

It should be remarked that no protein of the outer coat of the viral particles is ever found in the transformed cells. Thus the gene responsible for the coat protein is always nonfunctional. This could be either because the transformed cells have an incomplete set of viral genes and the coat gene is absent or because some genes remain "silent." The silence of these genes in turn could be attributed to failure either of transcription of the DNA of the gene into messenger RNA or of translation of the messenger RNA into protein. If failure of transcription were the mechanism, transformed cells would be similar to lysogenic bacteria. Such bacteria have a complete set of genes of a bacteriophage (a virus that infects bacteria), but most of the viral genes are not transcribed into RNA. No other significant similarities exist, however, between ordinary lysogenic bacteria and transformed cells; therefore it is more likely that the coat gene is either absent or, if it is present, produces messenger RNA that is not translated into coat protein. Whatever the mechanism, the lack of expression of the coat-protein gene, and probably of other genes as well, is essential for the survival of the transformed cells, since it prevents productive infection that would otherwise kill the cells.

So far we have considered the genes of the virus in abstract terms. Let us now consider them in concrete ones by asking how many genes each viral DNA molecule possesses and what their functions are. The function of a viral gene is the specification, through its particular messenger RNA, of a polypeptide chain, which by folding generates a protein subunit; the subunits associate to form

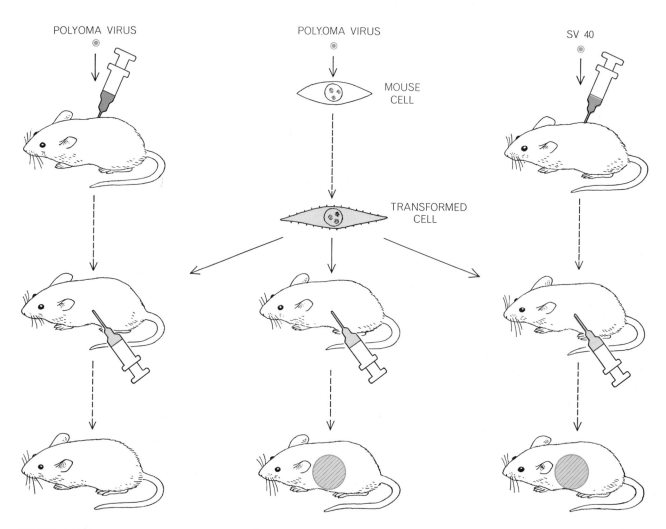

IMMUNIZATION EXPERIMENT shows that an animal will not develop a tumor after receiving a massive injection of transformed cells if it has previously received a mild inoculation of the virus used to transform the cells. Thus the animal at left, which has been immunized by an injection of polyoma virus, does not develop a tumor when injected with cells transformed by polyoma virus. The animal in the middle, not so immunized, develops a tumor following the injection of polyoma-transformed cells. The animal at right, which has received an injection of a different virus, SV 40, is not immunized against cells transformed by polyoma virus, hence it too develops a tumor. It would not develop a tumor, however, if injected with cells transformed by SV 40. Cells transformed by either polyoma virus or SV 40 contain a new antigen in their surface that makes them foreign to the animal strain from which they derive and therefore subject to its immunological defenses. These defenses can be mobilized by direct injection of the virus.

a functional viral protein. The final product can be an enzyme or a regulator molecule that can control the function of other genes (viral or cellular), or it can be a structural protein such as the coat protein of the viral particles.

As I have said, each strand of the DNA of the small papovaviruses contains about 5,000 bases. Three bases are required to specify one amino acid, or one building block, in a polypeptide chain; therefore 5,000 bases can specify some 1,700 amino acids. It can be calculated from the total molecular weight of the coat protein of the viral particles and from the number of subunits it has that between a third and a fourth of the genetic information of the virus is tied up in specifying the coat protein. This genetic information is irrelevant for transformation, because no coat protein is made in the transformed cells. What remains, therefore, is enough genetic information to specify about 1,200 amino acids, which can constitute from four to eight small protein molecules, depending on their size. This is the maximum number of viral genetic functions that can be involved in the transformation of a host cell.

In order to discover these viral genetic functions the properties of normal cells have been carefully compared with the properties of cells that have been either transformed or productively infected. Characteristics present in the infected cultures can be considered to result, directly or indirectly, from the action of viral genes. We shall call these new characteristics "new functions." In this way six new functions have been discovered in the infected cells, in addition to the specification of the viral coat protein [see illustration, page 2399]. Some of the new functions can be recognized biochemically; others can be shown by immunological tests to act as new cellular antigens.

The genetic studies with the papovaviruses have not gone far enough to reveal whether each of the new functions indeed represents the function of a separate viral gene, or whether all the gene functions have been identified. On the basis of the possible number of genes and the number of new functions it is likely that most, if not all, of the gene functions have been detected. At present the new functions are being attributed to the genes, and a large-scale effort is being made to produce temperature-sensitive mutants that will affect each of the genes separately. By studying the effect of such mutations on transformation it will

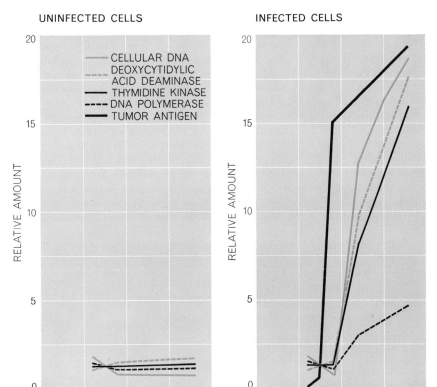

ACTIVATION OF DNA SYNTHESIS, along with activation of enzymes needed for its production, is a major consequence of viral infection of animal cells. Resting, uninfected cells make little DNA or enzymes associated with its synthesis (left). The values plotted are for kidney cells of an African monkey. When the cells are infected with SV 40, the output of DNA and associated enzymes rises steeply (right). Before these cellular syntheses are activated a new virus-specific protein, the "T antigen," whose role is unknown, appears.

be possible to establish the role of each gene in an unambiguous way.

For the moment we must limit ourselves to examining the various new functions and making educated guesses about their possible role in transformation. If transformation is continuously maintained by the function of viral genes, two new functions are particularly suspect as agents of transformation. One function involves a virus-specific antigen present on the surface of transformed cells; the other is the activation of the synthesis of cellular DNA and of cellular enzymes required for the manufacture of DNA by productively infected cells.

The induction of a virus-specific antigen on the cell surface was detected independently by Hans Olof Sjögren of the Royal Caroline Institute in Stockholm and by Karl Habel of the National Institutes of Health. They have shown that if an animal is inoculated with a mild dose of SV 40 or polyoma virus, it will develop an immune response that will enable it to reject cells transformed by the virus. Whereas the cells grow to form a tumor in the untreated animals, they

are immunologically rejected by and form no tumor in the immunized animals [see illustration on opposite page]. Rejection occurs only if the animals were immunized by the same virus used for transforming the cells. For instance, immunity against cells transformed by polyoma virus is induced by polyoma virus but not by SV 40, and vice versa. This shows that the antigen is virus-specific. The antigenic change is an indication of structural changes in the cellular surface, which may be responsible for the altered relations of transformed cells and their neighbors.

The activation of cellular syntheses, discovered independently in several laboratories, can be demonstrated in crowded cultures. If the cells in the culture are uninfected, they tend to remain in a resting stage. In these cells the synthesis of DNA, and of enzymes whose operation is required for DNA synthesis (such as deoxycytidylic acid deaminase, DNA polymerase and thymidine kinase), proceeds at a much lower rate than it does in growing cells. After infection by a small papovavirus a burst of new synthesis of both DNA and enzymes occurs; a viral function thus activates a group of cellular genes that were previously inactive [see illustration on preceding page]. If the infection of the cells is productive, the activation of cellular syntheses occurs before the cells are killed. The activating viral function must act centrally, presumably at the level of transcription or translation of cellular genes that receive regulatory signals from the periphery of the cell; the signals themselves should be unchanged, since the cell's environment, in which the signals originate, is not changed. If the viral gene

responsible for the activating function persists and operates in the transformed cells, it will make the cells insensitive to regulation of growth. Direct evidence for the operation of this mechanism in the transformed cells, however, has not yet been obtained.

A third viral function may be connected with such activation. This is the synthesis of a protein detected as a virus-specific antigen and called the T antigen (for tumor antigen). This antigen, discovered by Robert J. Huebner and his colleagues at the National Institute of Allergy and Infectious Diseases, differs

in immunological specificity from either the protein of the viral coat or the transplantation antigen [see lower illustration on this page]. The T antigen is present in the nucleus of both productively infected and transformed cells. In productive infection the T antigen appears before the induction of the cellular syntheses begins, and before the viral DNA replicates. Therefore the T antigen may represent a protein with a control function; for instance, it may be the agent that activates the cellular syntheses. For this assumption also direct evidence is lacking.

A fourth viral function relevant to transformation is the function of the gene bearing the Ts-a mutation, which we can call the Ts-a gene. The reader will recall that a virus line carrying this mutation transforms cells at low temperature but not at high temperature. Cells transformed at low temperature, however, remain transformed when they are subjected to the higher temperature, in spite of the inactivation of the gene [see bottom illustration, page 2395]. Thus the function of the Ts-a gene is only transiently required for transformation. In order to evaluate the significance of this result we must also recall that in productive infection the function of the Ts-a gene is required for the synthesis of the viral DNA. Therefore the transient requirement of this function in transformation may simply mean that the viral DNA must replicate before transformation takes place. If so, the Ts-a gene is not directly involved in transformation.

Another interpretation is possible. The function of the Ts-a gene is likely to be the specification of an enzyme involved in the replication of the viral DNA, for example a DNA polymerase, or a nuclease able to break the viral DNA at specific points, or even an enzyme with both properties. The action of a specific nuclease seems to be required for the replication of the viral DNA because the viral DNA molecules are in the form of closed rings. A nuclease, in breaking one of the strands, could provide a swivel around which the remainder of the molecule could rotate freely, allowing the two strands to unwind. The enzyme, although required for the replication of the viral DNA, may also affect the cellular DNA, for instance by causing breaks and consequently mutations. Such breaks have been observed in the DNA of cells that have been either productively infected or transformed by papovaviruses. If the Ts-a gene indeed acts on the DNA of the host cell, it could play a direct role in the transformation of the cell. Its actions would appear to

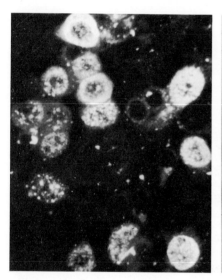
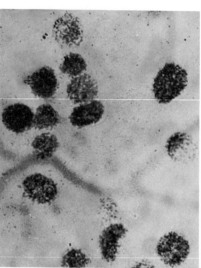

SITE OF VIRAL-COAT PROTEIN SYNTHESIS in infected cells is found to coincide with the site of DNA synthesis. A culture of mouse kidney cells was exposed to radioactive thymidine (needed in DNA synthesis) some 20 hours after infection with polyoma virus. Six hours later the culture was fixed and stained with antibodies coupled to a fluorescent dye that are specific for the coat protein of the virus. When the culture was photographed in ultraviolet light (left), the brilliant fluorescence of the bound antibodies showed that some of the cell nuclei were rich in coat protein. Then the culture was coated with a photographic film to disclose where beta rays emitted by the radioactive thymidine would expose grains of silver. The result (right) shows that the nuclei rich in coat protein were the same ones that had accumulated thymidine and were thus the site of DNA synthesis.

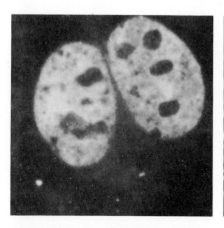
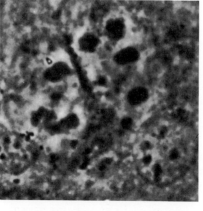

LOCATION OF T ANTIGEN in mouse cells transformed by SV 40 can be established by staining the cells with fluorescent antibodies that are specific for the T antigen (left). The same cells were also photographed in the phase-contrast microscope to show details of cell structure (right). It can be seen that the fluorescent antibodies nearly fill two large nuclei.

be transient, however, since mutations in the cellular DNA would not be undone if the Ts-a gene were subsequently inactivated by raising the temperature of the system. A more definite interpretation of the Ts-a results must await the completion of the biochemical and genetic studies now in progress in several laboratories.

The last two of the six new viral functions observed in infected cells are not sufficiently well known to permit evaluation of their possible roles in cell transformation. One of these two functions is the induction of a thymidine kinase enzyme that is different from the enzyme of the same type normally made by the host cell. Thymidine kinase participates at an early stage in a synthetic pathway leading to the production of a building block required in DNA synthesis. There are reasons to believe, however, that the thymidine kinase induced by the virus may have a general regulatory effect in activating the DNA-synthesizing machinery of the cell after infection. One reason is that the viral thymidine kinase has not been found in transformed cells. Since this enzyme is induced by many viruses containing DNA, whether or not they cause transformation, its induction by the papovaviruses may be connected exclusively with productive infection.

The last new function is one observed so far only with SV 40. After cells have been productively infected with this virus they are changed in some way so that they become productive hosts for a completely different kind of virus, an adenovirus, even though they are normally not a suitable host for such viruses. Little is known about the biochemical steps involved.

The central mechanism of cell transformation and cancer induction would appear to be contained within the half-dozen viral functions I have discussed, perhaps together with a few others as yet unknown. Thus the problem is narrowly restricted. It is likely that the dubious points still remaining will be resolved in the near future, since the dramatic advances of the past several years have set the stage for rapid further progress.

This article should not be concluded without an attempt's being made to answer a question that will undoubtedly have arisen in the minds of many readers: Why are viruses able to induce cancer at all? For the two viruses discussed in this article, at least, it seems likely that the viral functions that are probably responsible for cell transformation have been selected by evolutionary processes

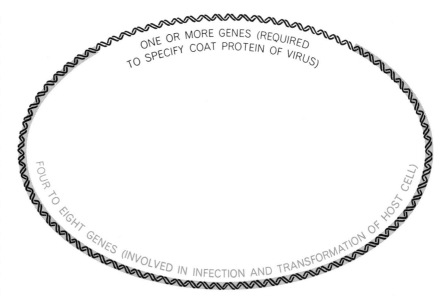

SEVEN FUNCTIONS IDENTIFIED WITH VIRUS ACTIVITY

1. Specification of antigen found on surface of transformed cells.

2. Specification of factor that activates synthesis of cellular DNA.

3. Specification of antigen (T antigen) found in nuclei of infected and transformed cells.

4. Specification of enzyme involved in initial replication of viral DNA. (Attributed to the Ts-a gene.)

5. (Facilitation of cell infection by other viruses.)

6. (Induction of thymidine kinase enzyme.)

7. (Specification of coat protein of virus.)

SEVEN VIRAL FUNCTIONS have been identified in the infection and transformation of cells. The DNA present in the polyoma virus and SV 40 takes the form of a single ring-shaped molecule consisting of two helically intertwined strands (*top*). Each strand contains some 5,000 molecular subunits called bases that embody the genetic information of the virus in coded form. These bases, in groups of three, specify the amino acids that link together to form protein molecules. Thus 5,000 bases can specify some 1,700 amino acids, or enough to construct some six to 12 proteins. By definition it takes one gene to specify one protein. It is estimated that a third to a fourth of the bases in the viral DNA are needed to specify the protein in the coat of the virus. The remaining bases, enough for four to eight genes, specify the proteins involved in infection and transformation. Little is yet known about the fifth function in this list of seven. Functions 6 and 7 are not involved in cell transformation.

to further the multiplication of the virus. Because the virus is small and cannot contain much genetic information it must exploit the synthetic mechanisms of the cell, including a large number of cellular enzymes, to achieve its own replication. Furthermore, in the animal hosts in which these viruses normally multiply, most cells that can undergo productive infection are in a resting stage and have their DNA-synthesizing machinery turned off. Thus the evolution of a viral function capable of switching on this machinery is obviously quite advantageous to the virus. This function must be very similar to the function of the cellular gene that regulates cellular DNA synthesis (and overall growth) in the absence of viral infection. The functions of the viral gene and of the cellular

gene, however, must differ in one point, again for selective reasons: the cellular function must be subject to control by external signals, whereas the viral function must not be. The virus-induced alteration of the cellular surface seems also to be connected, in a way not yet understood, with viral multiplication, since in many viral infections viral proteins appear on the surface of cells.

The cancer-producing action of the papovaviruses can therefore be considered a by-product of viral functions developed for the requirements of viral multiplication. These viral functions lead to cancer development because they are similar to cellular functions that control cell multiplication, but they somehow escape the regulatory mechanisms that normally operate within the cell.

The Author

RENATO DULBECCO is resident fellow at the Salk Institute for Biological Studies. Born in Italy, he took a medical degree at the University of Torino in 1936 and remained there as a teacher and researcher until 1947. Moving to the U.S. in that year, he was at Indiana University for two years and at the California Institute of Technology for 14, including nine years as professor of biology. Dulbecco joined the Salk Institute in 1963 but spent the academic year 1963–1964 as Royal Society Visiting Professor at the University of Glasgow. Since 1964 he has served as a trustee of the Salk Institute while continuing his research activities there.

Bibliography

CELL TRANSFORMATION BY DIFFERENT FORMS OF POLYOMA VIRUS DNA. Lionel Crawford, Renato Dulbecco, Mike Fried, Luc Montagnier and Michael Stoker in *Proceedings of the National Academy of Sciences*, Vol. 52, No. 1, pages 148–152; July, 1964.

IMMUNOLOGICAL DETERMINANTS OF POLYOMA VIRUS ONCOGENESIS. Karl Habel in *The Journal of Experimental Medicine*, Vol. 115, No. 1, pages 181–193; January 1, 1962.

STUDIES ON SPECIFIC TRANSPLANTATION RESISTANCE TO POLYOMA-VIRUS-INDUCED TUMORS, I: TRANSPLANTATION RESISTANCE INDUCED BY POLYOMA VIRUS INFECTION. Hans Olof Sjögren in *Journal of the National Cancer Institute*, Vol. 32, No. 2, pages 361–393; February, 1964.

TRANSFORMATION OF CELLS IN VITRO BY DNA-CONTAINING VIRUSES. Renato Dulbecco in *The Journal of the American Medical Association*, Vol. 190, No. 8, pages 721–726; November 23, 1964.

TRANSFORMATION OF PROPERTIES OF AN ESTABLISHED CELL LINE BY SV 40 AND POLYOMA VIRUS. George J. Todaro, Howard Green and Burton D. Goldberg in *Proceedings of the National Academy of Sciences*, Vol. 51, No. 1, pages 66–73; January, 1964.

VIRUS-CELL INTERACTION WITH A TUMOR-PRODUCING VIRUS. Marguerite Vogt and Renato Dulbecco in *Proceedings of the National Academy of Sciences*, Vol. 46, No. 3, pages 365–370; March 15, 1960.

SCIENTIFIC
AMERICAN April 1967, Vol. 216, No. 4, pp. 56-66   OFFPRINT 1070

THE ANTIQUITY OF HUMAN WALKING

by John Napier

Man's unique striding gait may be the most significant ability that
sets him apart from his ancestors. A big-toe bone found in Tanzania
is evidence that this ability dates back more than a million years.

WALKING CYCLE extends from the heel strike of one leg to the
next heel strike by the same leg. In the photograph, made by Gjon
Mili in the course of a study aimed at improvement of artificial legs
that he conducted for the U.S. Army, multiple exposures trace the
progress of the right leg in the course of two strides. The ribbons
of light allow analysis of the movement (see illustration below).

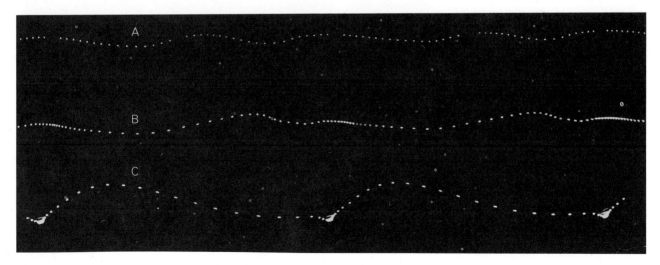

SINE CURVE described by the hip of a walking man was recorded
on film by means of the experimental system illustrated above. An
interrupter blade, passing in front of the camera lens at constant
speed, broke the light from lamps attached to the walker into the
three rows of dots. The speed of hip (a), knee (b) or ankle (c)
during the stride is determined by measuring between the dots.

Human walking is a unique activity during which the body, step by step, teeters on the edge of catastrophe. The fact that man has used this form of locomotion for more than a million years has only recently been demonstrated by fossil evidence. The antiquity of this human trait is particularly noteworthy because walking with a striding gait is probably the most significant of the many evolved capacities that separate men from more primitive hominids. The fossil evidence—the terminal bone of a right big toe discovered in 1961 in Olduvai Gorge in Tanzania—sets up a new signpost that not only clarifies the course of human evolution but also helps to guide those who speculate on the forces that converted predominantly quadrupedal animals into habitual bipeds.

Man's bipedal mode of walking seems potentially catastrophic because only the rhythmic forward movement of first one leg and then the other keeps him from falling flat on his face. Consider the sequence of events whenever a man sets out in pursuit of his center of gravity. A stride begins when the muscles of the calf relax and the walker's body sways forward (gravity supplying the energy needed to overcome the body's inertia). The sway places the center of body weight in front of the supporting pedestal normally formed by the two feet. As a result one or the other of the walker's legs must swing forward so that when his foot makes contact with the ground, the area of the supporting pedestal has been widened and the center of body weight once again rests safely within it. The pelvis plays an important role in this action: its degree of rotation determines the distance the swinging leg can move forward, and its muscles help to keep the body balanced while the leg is swinging.

At this point the "stance" leg—the leg still to the rear of the body's center of gravity—provides the propulsive force that drives the body forward. The walker applies this force by using muscular energy, pushing against the ground first with the ball of his foot and then with his big toe. The action constitutes the "push-off," which terminates the stance phase of the walking cycle. Once the stance foot leaves the ground, the walker's leg enters the starting, or "swing," phase of the cycle. As the leg swings forward it is able to clear the ground because it is bent at the hip, knee and ankle. This high-stepping action substantially reduces the leg's moment of inertia. Before making contact with the

ground and ending the swing phase the leg straightens at the knee but remains bent at the ankle. As a result it is the heel that strikes the ground first. The "heel strike" concludes the swing phase; as the body continues to move forward the leg once again enters the stance phase, during which the point of contact between foot and ground moves progressively nearer the toes. At the extreme end of the stance phase, as before, all the walker's propulsive thrust is delivered by the robust terminal bone of his big toe.

A complete walking cycle is considered to extend from the heel strike of one leg to the next heel strike of the same leg; it consists of the stance phase followed by the swing phase. The relative duration of the two phases depends on the cadence or speed of the walk. During normal walking the stance phase constitutes about 60 percent of the cycle and the swing phase 40 percent. Although the action of only one leg has been described in this account, the opposite leg obviously moves in a reciprocal fashion; when one leg is moving in the swing phase, the other leg is in its stance phase and keeps the body poised. Actually during normal walking the two phases overlap, so that both feet are on the ground at the same time for about 25 percent of the cycle. As walking speed increases, this period of double leg-support shortens.

Anyone who has watched other people walking and reflected a little on the process has noticed that the human stride

demands both an up-and-down and a side-to-side displacement of the body. When two people walk side by side but out of step, the alternate bobbing of their heads makes it evident that the bodies undergo a vertical displacement with each stride. When two people walk in step but with opposite feet leading, they will sway first toward each other and then away in an equally graphic demonstration of the lateral displacement at each stride. When both displacements are plotted sequentially, a pair of low-amplitude sinusoidal curves appear, one in the vertical plane and the other in the horizontal [see illustrations on page 2401]. General observations of this kind were reduced to precise measurements during World War II when a group at the University of California at Berkeley led by H. D. Eberhart conducted a fundamental investigation of human walking in connection with requirements for the design of artificial legs. Eberhart and his colleagues found that a number of functional determinants interacted to move the human body's center of gravity through space with a minimum expenditure of energy. In all they isolated six major elements related to hip, knee and foot movement that, working together, reduced both the amplitude of the two sine curves and the abruptness with which vertical and lateral changes in direction took place. If any one of these six elements was disturbed, an irregularity was injected into the normally smooth, undulating flow of walking, thereby producing a limp. What is more important,

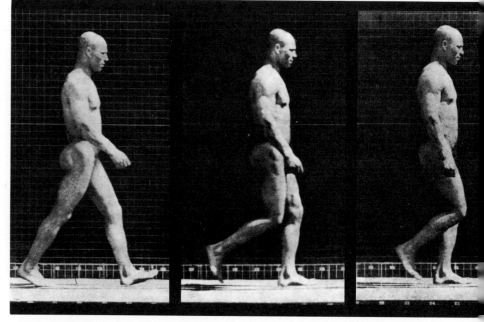

WALKING MAN, photographed by Eadweard Muybridge in 1884 during his studies of human and animal motion, exhibits the characteristic striding gait of the modern human.

the irregularity brought about a measurable increase in the body's energy output during each step.

The Evidence of the Bones

What I have described in general and Eberhart's group studied in detail is the form of walking known as striding. It is characterized by the heel strike at the start of the stance phase and the push-off at its conclusion. Not all human walking is striding; when a man moves about slowly or walks on a slippery surface, he may take short steps in which both push-off and heel strike are absent. The foot is simply lifted from the ground at the end of the stance phase and set down flat at the end of the swing phase. The stride, however, is the essence of human bipedalism and the criterion by which the evolutionary status of a hominid walker must be judged. This being the case, it is illuminating to consider how the act of striding leaves its distinctive marks on the bones of the strider.

To take the pelvis first, there is a well-known clinical manifestation called Trendelenburg's sign that is regarded as evidence of hip disease in children. When a normal child stands on one leg, two muscles connecting that leg and the pelvis—the gluteus medius and the gluteus minimus—contract; this contraction, pulling on the pelvis, tilts it and holds it poised over the stance leg. When the hip is diseased, this mechanism fails to operate and the child shows a positive Trendelenburg's sign: the body tends to fall toward the unsupported side.

The same mechanism operates in walking, although not to the same degree. During the stance phase of the walking cycle, the same two gluteal muscles on the stance side brace the pelvis by cantilever action. Although actual tilting toward the stance side does not occur in normal walking, the action of the muscles in stabilizing the walker's hip is an essential component of the striding gait. Without this action the stride would become a slow, ungainly shuffle.

At the same time that the pelvis is stabilized in relation to the stance leg it also rotates to the unsupported side. This rotation, although small, has the effect of increasing the length of the stride. A familiar feature of the way women walk arises from this bit of anatomical mechanics. The difference in the proportions of the male and the female pelvis has the effect of slightly diminishing the range through which the female hip can move forward and back. Thus for a given length of stride women are obliged to rotate the pelvis through a greater angle than men do. This secondary sexual characteristic has not lacked exploitation; at least in our culture female pelvic rotation has considerable erotogenic significance. What is more to the point in terms of human evolution is that both the rotation and the balancing of the pelvis leave unmistakable signs on the pelvic bone and on the femur: the leg bone that is joined to it. It is by a study of such signs that the walking capability of a fossil hominid can be judged.

Similar considerations apply to the foot. One way the role of the foot in walking can be studied is to record the vertical forces acting on each part of the foot while it is in contact with the ground during the stance phase of the walking cycle. Many devices have been built for this purpose; one of them is the plastic pedograph. When the subject walks across the surface of the pedograph, a motion-picture camera simultaneously records the exact position of the foot in profile and the pattern of pressures on the surface. Pedograph analyses show that the initial contact between the striding leg and the ground is the heel strike. Because the foot is normally turned out slightly at the end of the swing phase of the walking cycle, the outer side of the back of the heel takes the brunt of the initial contact [*see illustration on next page*]. The outer side of the foot continues to support most of the pressure of the stance until a point about three-fifths of the way along the sole is reached. The weight of the body is then transferred to the ball of the foot and then to the big toe. In the penultimate stage of push-off the brunt of the pressure is under the toes, particularly the big toe. Finally, at the end of the stance phase, only the big toe is involved; it progressively loses contact with the ground and the final push-off is applied through its broad terminal bone.

The use of pedographs and similar apparatus provides precise evidence about the function of the foot in walking, but every physician knows that much the

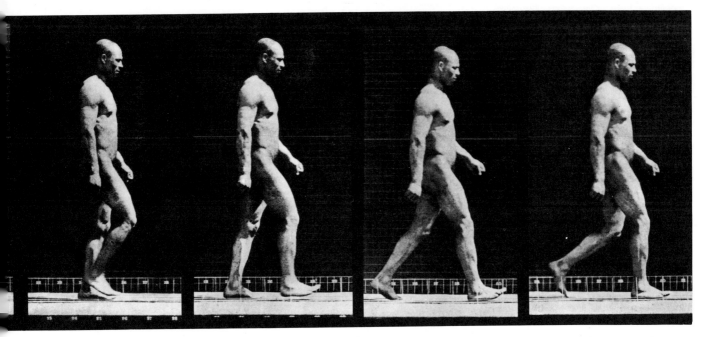

The free foot strikes the ground heel first and the body's weight is gradually transferred from heel to ball of foot as the opposite leg lifts and swings forward. Finally the heel of the stance foot rises and the leg's last contact with the ground is made with the big toe.

same information is recorded on the soles of everyone's shoes. Assuming that the shoes fit, their pattern of wear is a true record of the individual's habitual gait. The wear pattern will reveal a limp that one man is trying to hide, or unmask one that another man is trying to feign, perhaps to provide evidence for an insurance claim. In any case, just as the form of the pelvis and the femur can disclose the presence or absence of a striding gait, so can the form of the foot bones, particularly the form and proportions of the big-toe bones.

The Origins of Primate Bipedalism

Almost all primates can stand on their hind limbs, and many occasionally walk in this way. But our primate relatives are all, in a manner of speaking, amateurs; only man has taken up the business of bipedalism intensively. This raises two major questions. First, how did the basic postural adaptations that permit walking—occasional or habitual—arise among the primates? Second, what advantages did habitual bipedalism bestow on early man?

With regard to the first question, I have been concerned for some time with the anatomical proportions of all primates, not only man and the apes but also the monkeys and lower primate forms. Such consideration makes it possible to place the primates in natural groups according to their mode of locomotion. Not long ago I suggested a new group, and it is the only one that will concern us here. The group comprises primates with very long hind limbs and very short forelimbs. At about the same time my colleague Alan C. Walker, now at Makerere University College in Uganda, had begun a special study of the locomotion of living and fossil lemurs. Lemurs are among the most primitive offshoots of the basic primate stock. Early in Walker's studies he was struck by the frequency with which a posture best described as "vertical clinging" appeared in the day-to-day behavior of living lemurs. All the animals whose propensity for vertical clinging had been observed by Walker showed the same proportions—that is, long hind limbs and short forelimbs—I had proposed as forming a distinct locomotor group.

When Walker and I compared notes, we decided to define a hitherto unrecognized locomotor category among the primates that we named "vertical clinging and leaping," a term that includes both the animal's typical resting posture and the essential leaping component

in its locomotion. Since proposing this category a most interesting and important extension of the hypothesis has become apparent to us. Some of the earliest primate fossils known, preserved in sediments laid down during Eocene times and therefore as much as 50 million years old, are represented not only by skulls and jaws but also by a few limb bones. In their proportions and details most of these limb bones show the same characteristics that are displayed by the living members of our vertical-clinging-and-leaping group today. Not long ago Elwyn L. Simons of Yale University presented a reconstruction of the lemur-like North American Eocene primate *Smilodectes* walking along a tree branch in a quadrupedal position [see "The Early Relatives of Man," by Elwyn L. Simons; SCIENTIFIC AMERICAN Offprint 622]. Walker and I prefer to see *Smilodectes* portrayed in the vertical clinging posture its anatomy unequivocally indicates. The fossil evidence, as far as it goes, suggests to us that vertical clinging and leaping was a major primate locomotor adaptation that took place some 50 million years ago. It may even have been the initial dynamic adaptation to tree life from which the subsequent locomotor patterns of all the living pri-

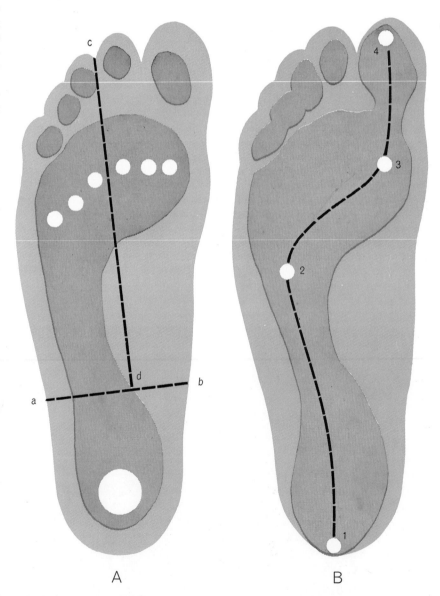

A   B

DISTRIBUTION OF WEIGHT in the human foot alters radically as action takes the place of rest. When motionless (*A*), the foot divides its static load (half of the body's total weight) between its heel and its ball along the axis *a–b*. The load on the ball of the foot is further divided equally on each side of the axis *c–d*. When striding (*B*), the load (all of the body's weight during part of each stride) is distributed dynamically from the first point of contact (*1, heel strike*) in a smooth flow via the first and fifth metatarsal bones (*2, 3*) that ends with a propulsive thrust (*4, push-off*) delivered by the terminal bone of the big toe.

mates, including man, have stemmed.

Walker and I are not alone in this view. In 1962 W. L. Straus, Jr., of Johns Hopkins University declared: "It can safely be assumed that primates early developed the mechanisms permitting maintenance of the trunk in the upright position.... Indeed, this tendency toward truncal erectness can be regarded as an essentially basic primate character." The central adaptations for erectness of the body, which have been retained in the majority of living primates, seem to have provided the necessary anatomical basis for the occasional bipedal behavior exhibited by today's monkeys and apes.

What we are concerned with here is the transition from a distant, hypothetical vertical-clinging ancestor to modern, bipedal man. The transition was almost

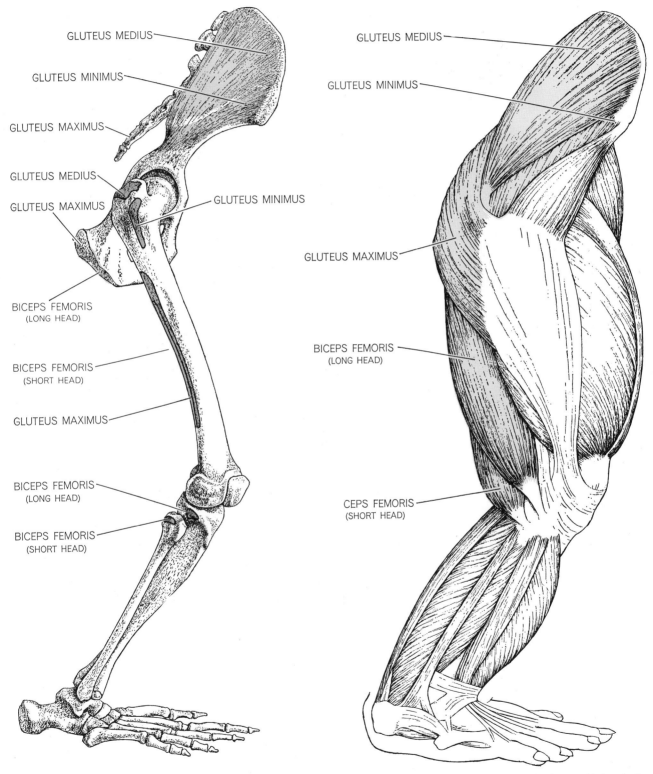

QUADRUPEDAL POSTURE needs two sets of muscles to act as the principal extensors of the hip. These are the gluteal group (the gluteus medius and minimus in particular), which connects the pelvis to the upper part of the femur, and the hamstring group. which connects the femur and the lower leg bones. Of these only the biceps femoris is shown in the gorilla musculature at right. The skeletal regions to which these muscles attach are shown in color at left. In most primates the gluteus maximus is quite small.

certainly marked by an intermediate quadrupedal stage. Possibly such Miocene fossil forms as *Proconsul,* a chimpanzee-like early primate from East Africa, represent such a stage. The structural adaptations necessary to convert a quadrupedal ape into a bipedal hominid are centered on the pelvis, the femur, the foot and the musculature associated with these bones. Among the nonhuman primates living today the pelvis and femur are adapted for four-footed walking; the functional relations between hipbones and thigh muscles are such that, when the animal attempts to assume a bipedal stance, the hip joint is subjected to a stress and the hip must be bent. To compensate for the resulting forward shift of the center of gravity, the knees must also be bent. In order to alter a bent-hip, bent-knee gait into

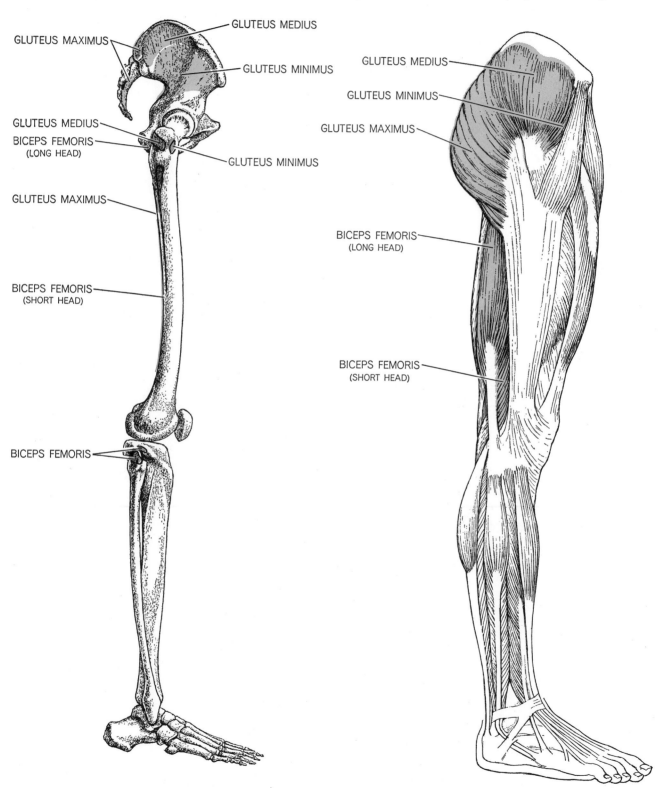

BIPEDAL POSTURE brings a reversal in the roles played by the same pelvic and femoral muscles. Gluteus medius and gluteus minimus have changed from extensors to abductors and the function of extending the trunk, required when a biped runs or climbs, has been assumed by the gluteus maximus. The hamstring muscles, in turn, now act mainly as stabilizers and extensors of the hip. At right are the muscles as they appear in man; the skeletal regions to which their upper and lower ends attach are shown in color at left.

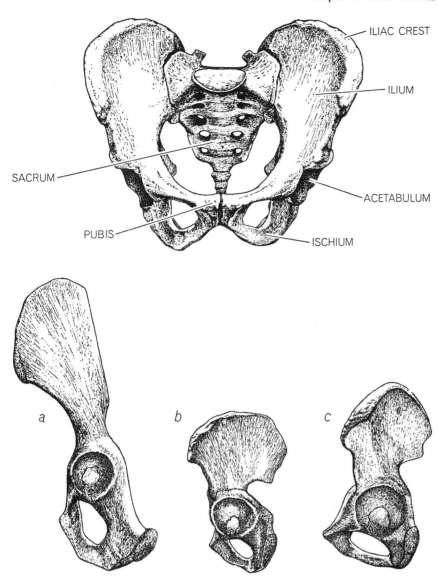

COMPONENTS OF THE PELVIS are identified at top; the bones are those of the human pelvis. Below, ilium and ischium of a gorilla (*a*), of *Australopithecus* (*b*) and of modern man (*c*) are seen from the side (the front is to the left in each instance). The ischium of *Australopithecus* is longer than man's; this almost certainly kept the early hominid from striding in the manner of *Homo sapiens*. Instead the gait was probably a kind of jog trot.

prisingly unimportant role in man's ability to stand, or even to walk on a level surface. In standing, for example, the principal stabilizing and extending agents are the muscles of the hamstring group. In walking on the level the gluteus maximus is so little involved that even when it is paralyzed a man's stride is virtually unimpaired. The gluteus maximus comes into its own in man when power is needed to give the hip joint more play for such activities as running, walking up a steep slope or climbing stairs [*see illustration, page 2409*]. Its chief function in these circumstances is to correct any tendency for the human trunk to jackknife on the legs.

Because the gluteus maximus has such a specialized role I believe, in contrast to Washburn's view, that it did not assume its present form until late in the evolution of the striding gait. Rather than being the initial adaptation, this muscle's enlargement and present function appear to me far more likely to have been one of the ultimate refinements of human walking. I am in agreement with Washburn, however, when he states that changes in the ilium, or upper pelvis, would have preceded changes in the ischium, or lower pelvis [see "Tools and Human Evolution," by Sherwood L. Washburn; SCIENTIFIC AMERICAN Offprint 601]. The primary adaptation would probably have involved a forward curvature of the vertebral column in the lumbar region. Accompanying this change would have been a broadening and a forward rotation of the iliac portions of the pelvis. Together these early adaptations provide the structural basis for improving the posture of the trunk.

Assuming that we have now given at least a tentative answer to the question of how man's bipedal posture evolved, there remains to be answered the question of why. What were the advantages of habitual bipedalism? Noting the comparative energy demands of various gaits, Washburn points out that human walking is primarily an adaptation for covering long distances economically. To go a long way with a minimum of effort is an asset to a hunter; it seems plausible that evolutionary selection for hunting behavior in man was responsible for the rapid development of striding anatomy. Gordon W. Hewes of the University of Colorado suggests a possible incentive that, acting as an agent of natural selection, could have prompted the quadrupedal ancestors of man to adopt a two-footed gait. In Hewes's view the principal advantage of bipedalism over quadrupedalism would be the free-

man's erect, striding walk, a number of anatomical changes must occur. These include an elongation of the hind limbs with respect to the forelimbs, a shortening and broadening of the pelvis, adjustments of the musculature of the hip (in order to stabilize the trunk during the act of walking upright), a straightening of both hip and knee and considerable reshaping of the foot.

Which of these changes can be considered to be primary and which secondary is still a matter that needs elucidation. Sherwood L. Washburn of the University of California at Berkeley has expressed the view that the change from four-footed to two-footed posture was initiated by a modification in the form and function of the gluteus maximus, a thigh muscle that is powerfully

developed in man but weakly developed in monkeys and apes [*see illustrations on preceding two pages*]. In a quadrupedal primate the principal extensors of the trunk are the "hamstring" muscles and the two upper-leg muscles I have already mentioned: the gluteus medius and gluteus minimus. In man these two muscles bear a different relation to the pelvis, in terms of both position and function. In technical terms they have become abductor muscles of the trunk rather than extensor muscles of the leg. It is this that enables them to play a critical part in stabilizing the pelvis in the course of striding. In man the extensor function of these two gluteal muscles has been taken over by a third, the gluteus maximus. This muscle, insignificant in other primates, plays a sur-

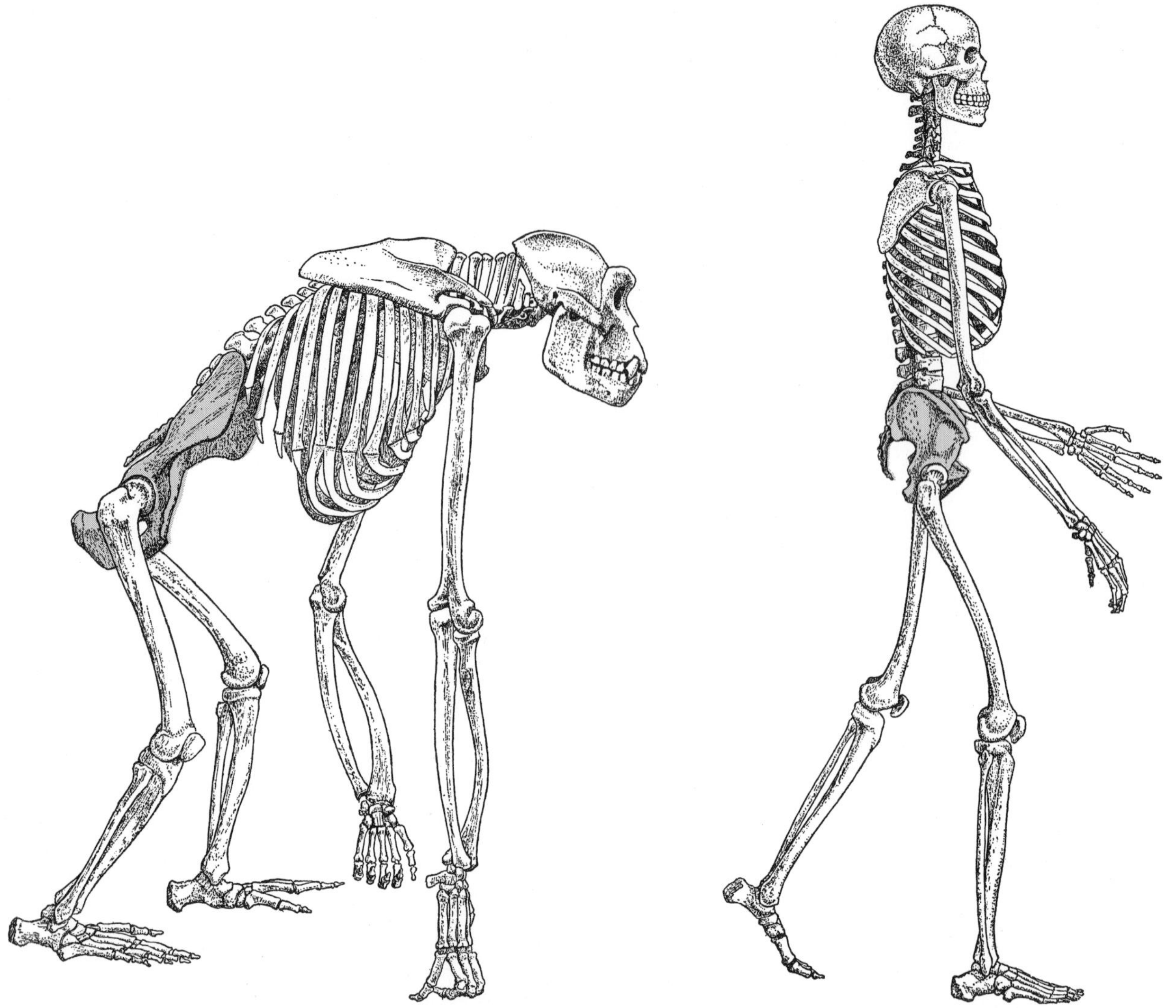

SHAPE AND ORIENTATION of the pelvis in the gorilla and in man reflect the postural differences between quadrupedal and bipedal locomotion. The ischium in the gorilla is long, the ilium extends to the side and the whole pelvis is tilted toward the horizontal (*see illustration on preceding page*). In man the ischium is much shorter, the broad ilium extends forward and the pelvis is vertical.

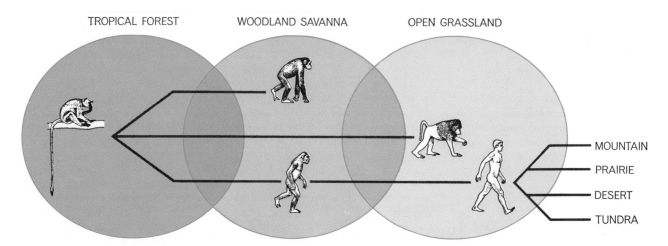

TROPICAL FOREST   WOODLAND SAVANNA   OPEN GRASSLAND

MOUNTAIN
PRAIRIE
DESERT
TUNDRA

ECOLOGICAL PATHWAY to man's eventual mastery of all environments begins (*left*) with a quadrupedal primate ancestor living in tropical forest more than 20 million years ago. During Miocene times mountain-building produced new environments. One, a transition zone between forest and grassland, has been exploited by three groups of primates. Some, for example the chimpanzees, have only recently entered this woodland savanna. Both the newly bipedal hominids and some ground-living quadrupedal monkeys, however, moved beyond the transition zone into open grassland. The quadrupeds, for example the baboons, remained there. On the other hand, the forces of natural selection in the new setting favored the bipedal hominid hunters' adaptation of the striding gait typical of man. Once this adaptation developed, man went on to conquer most of the earth's environments.

ing of the hands, so that food could be carried readily from one place to another for later consumption. To assess the significance of such factors as survival mechanisms it behooves us to review briefly the ecological situation in which our prehuman ancestors found themselves in Miocene times, between 15 and 25 million years ago.

The Miocene Environment

During the Miocene epoch the worldwide mountain-building activity of middle Tertiary times was in full swing. Many parts of the earth, including the region of East Africa where primates of the genus *Proconsul* were living, were being faulted and uplifted to form such mountain zones as the Alps, the Himalayas, the Andes and the Rockies. Massive faulting in Africa gave rise to one of the earth's major geological features: the Rift Valley, which extends 5,000 miles from Tanzania across East Africa to Israel and the Dead Sea. A string of lakes lies along the floor of the Rift Valley like giant stepping-stones. On their shores in Miocene times lived a fantastically rich fauna, inhabitants of the forest and of a new ecological niche—the grassy savanna.

These grasslands of the Miocene were the domain of new forms of vegetation that in many parts of the world had taken the place of rain forest, the dominant form of vegetation in the Eocene and the Oligocene. The savanna offered new evolutionary opportunities to a variety of mammals, including the expanding population of primates in the rapidly shrinking forest. A few primates—the ancestors of man and probably also the ancestors of the living baboons—evidently reacted to the challenge of the new environment.

The savanna, however, was no Eldorado. The problems facing the early hominids in the open grassland were immense. The forest foods to which they were accustomed were hard to come by; the danger of attack by predators was immeasurably increased. If, on top of everything else, the ancestral hominids of Miocene times were in the process of converting from quadrupedalism to bipedalism, it is difficult to conceive of any advantage in bipedalism that could have compensated for the added hazards of life in the open grassland. Consideration of the drawbacks of savanna living has led me to a conclusion contrary to the one generally accepted: I doubt that the advent of bipedalism took place in this environment. An environment neglected by scholars but one far better suited for the origin of man is the woodland-savanna, which is neither high forest nor open grassland. Today this halfway-house niche is occupied by many primates, for example the vervet monkey and some chimpanzees. It has enough trees to provide forest foods and ready escape from predators. At the same time its open grassy spaces are arenas in which new locomotor adaptations can be practiced and new foods can be sampled. In short, the woodland-savanna provides an ideal nursery for evolving hominids, combining the challenge and incentive of the open grassland with much of the security of the forest. It was probably in this transitional environment that man's ancestors learned to walk on two legs. In all likelihood, however, they only learned to stride when they later moved into the open savanna.

Moving forward many millions of years from Miocene to Pleistocene times, we come to man's most immediate hominid precursor: *Australopithecus*. A large consortium of authorities agrees that the shape of the pelvis in *Australopithecus* fossils indicates that these hominids were habitually bipedal, although not to the degree of perfection exhibited by modern man. A few anatomists, fighting a rearguard action, contend that on the contrary the pelvis of *Australopithecus*

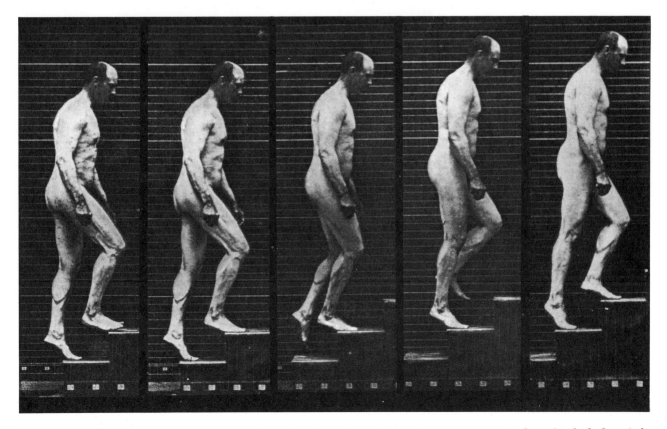

STAIR-CLIMBING, like running, is a movement that brings the human gluteus maximus into play. Acting as an extensor of the trunk, the muscle counteracts any tendency for the body to jackknife over the legs. Photographs are from Muybridge's collection.

shows that these hominids were predominantly quadrupedal. I belong to the first school but, as I have been at some pains to emphasize in the past, the kind of upright walking practiced by *Australopithecus* should not be equated with man's heel-and-toe, striding gait.

From Bipedalist to Strider

The stride, although it was not necessarily habitual among the earliest true men, is nevertheless the quintessence of the human locomotor achievement. Among other things, striding involves extension of the leg to a position behind the vertical axis of the spinal column. The degree of extension needed can only be achieved if the ischium of the pelvis is short. But the ischium of *Australopithecus* is long, almost as long as the ischium of an ape [see illustration on page 2407]. Moreover, it was shown that in man the gluteus medius and the gluteus minimus are prime movers in stabilizing the pelvis during each stride; in *Australopithecus* this stabilizing mechanism is imperfectly evolved. The combination of both deficiencies almost entirely precludes the possibility that these hominids possessed a striding gait. For *Australopithecus* walking was something of a jog trot. These hominids must have covered the ground with quick, rather short steps, with their knees and hips slightly bent; the prolonged stance phase of the fully human gait must surely have been absent.

Compared with man's stride, therefore, the gait of *Australopithecus* is physiologically inefficient. It calls for a disproportionately high output of energy; indeed, *Australopithecus* probably found long-distance bipedal travel impossible. A natural question arises in this connection. Could the greater energy requirement have led these early representatives of the human family to alter their diet in the direction of an increased reliance on high-energy foodstuffs, such as the flesh of other animals?

The pelvis of *Australopithecus* bears evidence that this hominid walker could scarcely have been a strider. Let us now turn to the foot of what many of us believe is a more advanced hominid. In 1960 L. S. B. Leakey and his wife Mary unearthed most of the bones of this foot in the lower strata at Olduvai Gorge known collectively as Bed I, which are about 1.75 million years old. The bones formed part of a fossil assemblage that has been designated by the Leakeys, by Philip Tobias of the University of the Witwatersrand and by me as possibly the earliest-known species of man: *Homo*

habilis. The foot was complete except for the back of the heel and the terminal bones of the toes; its surviving components were assembled and studied by me and Michael Day, one of my colleagues at the Unit of Primatology and Human Evolution of the Royal Free Hospital School of Medicine in London. On the basis of functional analysis the resem-

blance to the foot of modern man is close, although differing in a few minor particulars. Perhaps the most significant point of resemblance is that the stout basal bone of the big toe lies alongside the other toes [see upper illustration on next page]. This is an essentially human characteristic; in apes and monkeys the big toe is not exceptionally robust and

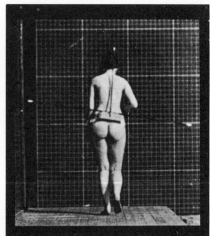
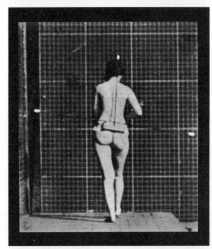
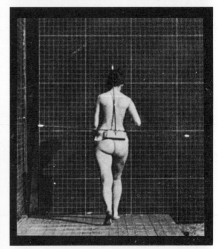

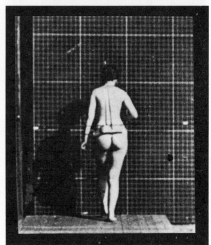

PELVIC ROTATION of the human female is exaggerated compared with that of a male taking a stride of equal length because the two sexes differ in pelvic anatomy. Muybridge noted the phenomenon, using a pole with whitened ends to record the pelvic oscillations.

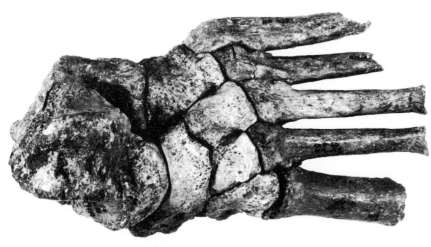

PRIMITIVE FOOT, complete except for the back of the heel and the tips of the toes, was unearthed from the lower level at Olduvai Gorge in Tanzania. Attributed to a very early hominid, *Homo habilis*, by its discoverer, L. S. B. Leakey, it is about 1.75 million years old. Its appearance suggests that the possessor was a habitual biped. Absence of the terminal bones of the toes, however, leaves open the question of whether the possessor walked with a stride.

BIG-TOE BONE, also discovered at Olduvai Gorge, is considerably younger than the foot bones in the top illustration but still probably more than a million years old. It is the toe's terminal bone (*bottom view at left, top view at right*) and bore the thrust of its possessor's push-off with each swing of the right leg. The tilting and twisting of the head of the bone in relation to the shaft is unequivocal evidence that its possessor walked with a modern stride.

diverges widely from the other toes. The foot bones, therefore, give evidence that this early hominid species was habitually bipedal. In the absence of the terminal bones of the toes, however, there was no certainty that *Homo habilis* walked with a striding gait.

Then in 1961, in a somewhat higher stratum at Olduvai Gorge (and thus in a slightly younger geological formation), a single bone came to light in an area otherwise barren of human bones. This fossil is the big-toe bone I mentioned at the beginning of this article [*see lower illustration above*]. Its head is both tilted and twisted with respect to its shaft, characteristics that are found only in modern man and that can with assurance be correlated with a striding gait. Day has recently completed a dimensional analysis of the bone, using a multivariate statistical technique. He is able to show that the fossil is unquestionably human in form.

There is no evidence to link the big-toe bone specifically to either of the two recognized hominids whose fossil remains have been recovered from Bed I at Olduvai: *Homo habilis* and *Zinjanthropus boisei*. Thus the owner of the toe remains unknown, at least for the present. Nonetheless, one thing is made certain by the discovery. We now know that in East Africa more than a million years ago there existed a creature whose mode of locomotion was essentially human.

The Author

JOHN NAPIER is reader in anatomy at the Royal Free Hospital School of Medicine of the University of London and director of the school's Unit of Primate Biology and Human Evolution. Son of a former professor of tropical medicine at the University of Calcutta, Napier was educated in England, receiving a medical degree from St. Bartholomew's Hospital in London. In 1963 he obtained a D.Sc. from the University of London. Napier's principal interests are teaching and research in primate biology. With his wife he is about to publish a textbook on the primates. Napier has appeared on numerous television programs dealing with primates and human evolution.

Bibliography

THE APE-MEN. Robert Broom in *Scientific American;* November, 1949.

THE FOOT AND THE SHOE. J. R. Napier in *Physiotherapy*, Vol. 43, No. 3, pages 65–74; March, 1957.

A HOMINID TOE BONE FROM BED 1, OLDUVAI GORGE, TANZANIA. M. H. Day and J. R. Napier in *Nature*, Vol. 211, No. 5052, pages 929–930; August 27, 1966.

SCIENTIFIC
AMERICAN April 1967, Vol. 216, No. 4, pp. 96-104   OFFPRINT 1071

THE EVOLUTION OF BEE LANGUAGE

by Harald Esch

Different species of bees communicate in different ways. When primitive bees are compared with more advanced ones, it seems that communication by sound preceded communication by dancing.

There can be no doubt that many members of the animal kingdom "talk" to their own kind, but it is a curious fact that of all the communicating animals the only one whose language man has been able to translate in much detail is the bee. We owe this breakthrough into animal language to the sharp observation and dedicated curiosity of the Austrian zoologist Karl von Frisch. Studying color vision in bees many years ago, von Frisch placed a color-marked dish of sugar sirup near a beehive. He noted that once a bee discovered this rich deposit of food many other bees from the same hive promptly began to visit it. Clearly the discoverer must have informed its hivemates. How had it told them? Von Frisch investigated the matter by a series of ingenious experiments. He set out sugar dishes at various locations, sometimes miles away from the hive, and observed the behavior of the discoverers of these food sources when they returned to the hive. He found that the scouts "spoke" to the hive by means of a dance that told the direction and distance of the food dish.

After pursuing these experiments for many years alone von Frisch began to publish summaries of his findings in the late 1940's, and they piqued the interest of eminent scientists [see "The Language of the Bees," by August Krogh;

SCIENTIFIC AMERICAN Offprint 21]. Captivated by the explicitness of the bees' systematic language, many investigators (linguists as well as biologists) have been drawn to the study. It offers leads concerning not only the mysteries of animal communication but also the origin and evolution of language itself.

Intensive investigations over the past two decades have shown that the language of the bees is more complex than was first supposed. Its "vocabulary" includes sounds and scents as well as the movements of the dances. By examining these elements and studying bees of various species we are now beginning to develop some conception of how the bee language probably evolved. Let us review the investigations and see where they have led.

Von Frisch, who started his observations on the honeybee, discovered that when the food site was at an appreciable distance from the hive, the returning forager used a "wagging" dance to give the location to its hivemates. The dancer, wagging its abdomen, performs a short, straight run in a certain direction, then runs back in a semicircle to the starting point and makes the straight run again in the same direction, and it repeats this performance again and again, sometimes as many as 200 times. Von Frisch learned that the direction of the straight run shows the direction of the food site. The direction is related to the position of the sun in the sky. When the dance is performed within the hive, the dancer makes its runs on the vertical combs. A run straight upward means that the direction of the food site is toward the sun; straight downward, away from the sun; any other direction is indicated by angling the run from the vertical line.

How does the dancer indicate the distance to the food site? Von Frisch deduced that this information resided in the tempo of the dance: the number of runs per minute [see "Dialects in the Language of the Bees," by Karl von Frisch; SCIENTIFIC AMERICAN Offprint 130]. The slower the tempo, the greater the distance. Von Frisch's measurements showed a correlation between the distance and the dance tempo. For example, when the food dish was 1,000 feet from the hive, the forager bee performed the wagging dance at the rate of 30 runs per minute; when the dish was 2,000 feet away, the dancer's rate was 22 runs per minute.

Still, there were several puzzling questions. In the total darkness of the hive how could the bees observe and interpret the dance? Furthermore, how could one be sure that the supposed relation between the dance tempo and the distance was actually meaningful to the bees? A human observer with a stopwatch could plot and translate this information, but what reason was there to believe the bees possessed the same ability? Indeed, it turned out on further investigation that at least half a dozen other elements in the dancing bee's ritual could be correlated similarly with the distance to the food site.

In the summer of 1955 I took a job in the bee research laboratory at the University of Bonn (during a vacation from the study of physics), and I was introduced into the fascinating world of bee language by Wolfgang Steche, a former student of von Frisch's. Prompted by questions Steche raised about the bees' method of giving distance information, I undertook some new experiments. Perhaps the distance information lay in the wagging part of the dance

BEES OF TWO SPECIES visit a feeding station set up by the author during his investigation of bee communication. The big bee is *Apis mellifera*, the common honeybee. The small ones are *Trigona varia*, one of the six stingless Brazilian species chosen for study. Painted "petals" provide visual cues that help the bees to find the station; red paint contains a reflector of ultraviolet so that the bees, blind to red, can see it.

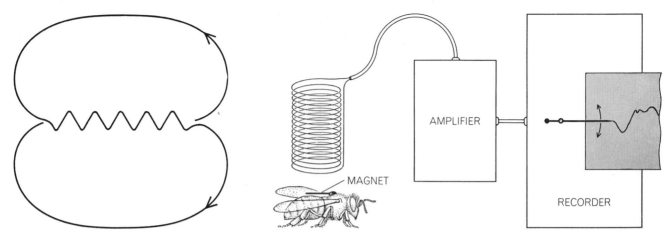

HONEYBEE'S DANCE (*figure-eight pattern at left*) was recorded by means of a magnet attached to the bee. The wagging movements produced voltage changes in a sensing coil. These changes, after amplification, were reproduced on an oscillograph (*right*), reveal-

rather than in the tempo of the entire dance. This hypothesis promised to be difficult to investigate, because the bee's wagging movements are so rapid that they are barely detectable by the unaided eye. I was able to bring them within the scope of measurement, however, by attaching a tiny magnet to the bee's abdomen and holding a coil over the bee during its dance; the motions of the magnet produced fluctuations of electric voltage in the coil, and these fluctuations, recorded with an oscillograph, gave a detailed account of the wagging movements [*see illustration at top of these two pages*].

The oscillograms showed that the wagging of the dancing bee generally has a constant frequency of about 15 wags per second. The duration of the wagging during a run varies, however.

It turned out that the wagging time, or the total number of wags in a run, was correlated with the distance to the food site: the greater the distance, the more wagging movements per run. Further analysis of the oscillograms, however, introduced confusion into the picture. The length of the time interval between the successive wagging runs (or, as we might say, the nonwagging time) also was closely correlated with the distance to the food site! Which, then, was the actual cue, the wagging time or the nonwagging time?

I became so intrigued with the problem that in 1960 I joined von Frisch in his laboratory, and this time we set up a more elaborate experiment. I built an artificial bee that performed a wagging dance like a live bee. My dummy's dance was controlled by tape recordings of the

dances of the real bees, and apparently it mimicked their dances faithfully [*see illustration at bottom of these two pages*]. The bees in a hive followed my dummy's dance and showed great interest in it. Nevertheless, it did not move them to go forth into the field to look for the food source. Evidently some crucial feature of the bee language was missing in the dummy.

I reexamined the tape recordings of the live bees' dance closely and found that during their wagging the bees produced some kind of vibration at a frequency of about 250 cycles per second—a vibration my dummy could not match. This frequency is in the range of the sound spectrum. I therefore placed a microphone in the hive to catch any sounds the dancing bees might be emitting. Sure enough, the microphone re-

ANIMATED DUMMY (*center of photograph at left*), made of wood but identical in odor with the hive's inhabitants, was driven by a motor (*far right*) in mimicry of a returned forager's actions (*bee in motion in second photograph*). The honeybees clustered

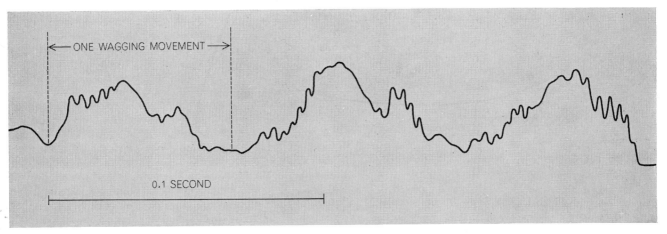

ONE WAGGING MOVEMENT

0.1 SECOND

ing motions too rapid for the unaided eye to detect. On the oscillograph tracing the .07-second distance from trough to trough is the duration of one wag; the briefer, low-amplitude oscillations imposed on the wag curve record the noises made by the bee's wings.

vealed that during its wagging a bee gave forth strong sound signals, generated by vibrations of its wings. The period of sound emission coincided exactly with the duration of the wagging run. Since the length of a bee's wagging run had already been found to be closely correlated with the distance to the food site it had visited, we now had to consider the possibility that the bees used sound as the cue to distance. In other words, the language of the bees might be based not only on kinetics but also on phonetics!

At about the same time that I came on these findings Adrian M. Wenner of the University of California at Santa Barbara, working independently, also discovered the audible "talk" of bees [see "Sound Communication in Honey-bees," by Adrian M. Wenner; SCIENTIFIC AMERICAN Offprint 181]. That sounds constitute part of the language of the bees seems quite plausible. The bee, as everyone knows, is by nature a noisy animal. Its use of sound for communication would help to explain the ability of the bees to receive the messages of foragers in the dark of the hive. Moreover, linguists have pointed out that it would be strange indeed if a language as well developed as that of the honeybee were entirely devoid of sound elements or vocalization.

Nevertheless, some investigators are unwilling to accept the idea of bee "speech," on the ground that there is no evidence bees can hear sounds. It must be said that definitive proof of specific hearing ability has not been established. There is plenty of indirect evidence, however, that bees do perceive and respond to sound.

By the use of electrophysiological methods Hans Joachim Autrum of Germany showed many years ago that a bee can detect sound through its legs. Bees standing on a vibrating surface were able to sense very slight vibrations with an amplitude as small as 13 millimicrons. In effect the surface on which the bee stands serves as an "eardrum." However, skepticism about the hearing ability of bees, or at least their ability to interpret sounds, arose from the fact that attempts to elicit meaningful responses to sounds in bees were invariably unsuccessful. It was found that bees could not be guided to a feeding place by sound cues alone. I made a similar finding with some recent experiments of my own. At the entrance to a hive I

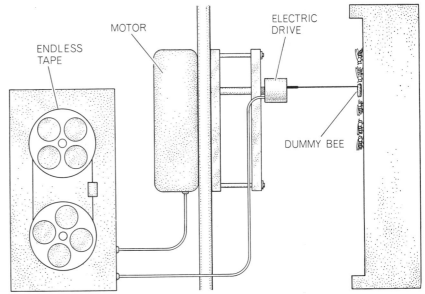

ENDLESS TAPE

MOTOR

ELECTRIC DRIVE

DUMMY BEE

around both the dummy and the genuine forager, stimulated by their dancing. No bees, however, left the hive to search for food proclaimed by the dummy's dance. The author concluded that bee communication involves more than the wagging dance alone.

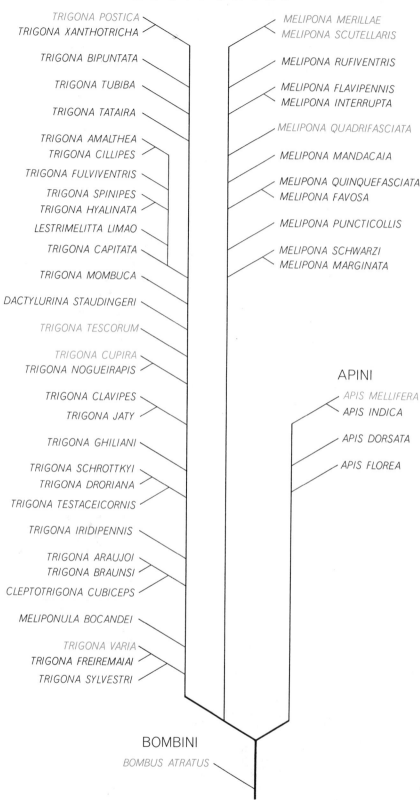

THREE TRIBES of social bees within the family Apidae are arrayed according to their social complexity. Lowest on the tree, the bumblebee *Bombus*, lacks communication of any kind. The social behavior of various genera in the tribe Meliponini shows increasing complexity. Some bees of the genus *Trigona*, for example, have foragers that make scent trails and alert the hive after finding food. Foragers of the genus *Melipona* vary their sound signals to indicate the distance from the hive to the food source. Most advanced are honeybees of the genus *Apis*. They dance to announce both the distance and the direction of a food source. Species whose names appear in color were studied by the author.

built three runways leading to three feeding dishes. I would place food in one of the three dishes and then cause the runway to that station to vibrate, as a cue to the location of the food. Even after extensive periods of training the bees did not learn to use the vibration as a significant signal (although tests beforehand had shown that they could perceive the vibration). The bees never solved the "maze" but continued to visit all three dishes at random, ignoring the vibration cue. A visual cue, however, proved quite effective. When I put a blue mark on the runway to the food, it took the bees only three or four trials to discover that the marking meant food, and thereafter they invariably chose the correct runway.

Almost by accident I happened on observations of another kind that revealed that, although sounds or similar vibrations per se may not be meaningful stimuli for the bees, the sounds associated with the wagging dance certainly play a crucially significant role in communication. I noticed that often a returning forager performed its wagging dance in the hive silently; for some unknown reason these dancers failed or were unable to produce any sound, although in all other respects their dance followed the normal pattern. What particularly interested me was that in every such case, although the bees in the hive followed the dance, not a single bee went to the feeding station the dancer had discovered! I observed more than 15,000 of these silent dances, and all of them uniformly failed to guide bees to the food site.

Surely, then, sound must be an important part of the bee language. With that fact reasonably well established, we are in a position to make some plausible conjectures about the evolution of the language.

Some time ago a former student of von Frisch's, Martin Lindauer, working with Warwick E. Kerr in Kerr's laboratory in Rio Claro in Brazil, began to investigate the communication system of a family of tropical bees known as stingless bees, of which there are about 200 species in Brazil. These insects, distant relatives of the honeybee, do not dance; they communicate with their fellows primarily by means of sound. A forager returning to the hive buzzes to its hive-mates with its vibrating wings, gives them samples of the food it has collected and by the scent clinging to its body lets them know the odor of the food source. The excited bees soon set off to seek it.

I had the opportunity of working with Kerr's group in Rio Claro in 1964, and we analyzed recordings of the sounds made by foraging stingless bees. The analysis showed that some of these bees (of the genus *Melipona*) use a kind of Morse code to indicate the distance to the food site: a series of short dashes (sounds of short duration) to show that the site is nearby, a series of longer-drawn-out sounds to indicate longer distances. The length of each single sound signal, like the length of the honeybee's wagging run and its accompanying sound, corresponds to the relative distance to the site. The stingless bees' sound language enables hive members to find food sites as much as several hundred yards away from the hive.

How do the recruited bees learn the direction of the site? This, we found, is a rather primitive and complex process. The forager, followed by the recruited group, starts off in the general direction of the site and for the first 20 to 30 yards flies an erratic, zigzag course. The leader then goes into straight flight and leaves the followers behind. They return to the hive and wait near the entrance for the forager to return. When it does, it passes around new samples of the food and again takes off for the site with the group following for a short distance. After several repetitions of this partway guidance, some members of the group, as if they have suddenly understood the message concerning direction, take off and make their own way to the food site.

From these clues and certain other

FIVE BEE SPECIES studied by the author not only differed in modes of communication but also made different kinds of nests. The bumblebee (*d*) and *Trigona viria* (*b*) both construct horizontal nests with individual "pots" where food or eggs are stored. *Trigona postica* (*a*) and *Melipona quadrifasciata* (*c*) also build horizontal nests and store their food in pots but raise their broods in cells like the honeybees. The European honeybee (*e*) and its dwarf relative *Apis florea* (*f*) store both food and brood in vertical cell arrays.

known facts about the behavior of insects we can begin to draw a hypothesis about the origins and evolution of the bee language. In the first place, the rhythmic noisemaking and dancing activities of the foragers on their return to the hive have well-known antecedents in primitive insect behavior. A moth alighting from a flight rocks back and forth rhythmically on its feet for a time, and the duration of this rocking tends to be related to the length of the flight it has just completed. In the moth the rhythmic aftermath seems to answer some basic physiological need; it takes place even when the head and much of the upper body is cut away. We can surmise that in the highly social bee this inherent behavior, potentially so useful for conveying information about the preceding flight, could easily have evolved into the distance-indicating code of the bee language.

The indication of direction also has precedents in insect evolution. At the most primitive, straightforward level an insect forager personally leads the group to the food. An ant scout, for instance, escorts its fellows to a food source it has found, following a trail of scent spots it

has laid down on its way back to the colony. Lindauer and Kerr discovered the same behavior in a primitive species of stingless bee (*Trigona postica*). The forager of this species, in its flight back to the hive, stops every two or three yards to mark a stone, a tree or a bush with a strong scent that it secretes from its mandibular glands. When it reaches the hive, it runs noisily about in great excitement, bumps its hivemates, passes out samples of the food and finally, when it has collected a group of followers, guides them along its scented trail to the food.

In the more advanced species of stingless bees the guidance is abbreviated. The forager indicates the distance by means of a sound code and the direction by means of its zigzag flight. In the honeybee the entire language has become symbolic. Instead of the zigzag flight it performs a wagging dance within the hive, representing the direction in terms of abstract geometry and gravity, with the vertical, symbolically pointing to the sun, as the reference line. The straight run of the dance, with the sun represented as to the right or to the left or ahead of the line of flight, simulates the actual flight to the food. The run also tells the

distance in symbolic terms, presumably making the duration of the emitted sound correspond to the distance.

There are variations—apparent throwbacks—in the behavior of honeybees that tend to support this evolutionary hypothesis. For instance, on a sunny day a honeybee forager will often revert to direct rather than symbolic guidance for its hivemates. It performs its wagging dance on a horizontal surface in front of the hive, pointing its run in the actual direction of the food site and buzzing its wings repeatedly as if to take off on a flight in that direction. Lindauer has observed that this kind of behavior belongs to a more primitive stage than the performance of the honeybee in the hive does. There is a dwarf bee (*Apis florea*), closely related to the European honeybee, that lives in the open, never in a hollow tree, cave or other dark place. This bee always performs its wagging dance on a horizontal surface and only if it can see the sky; deprived of a view of the sun's location, it stops dancing.

I found that, by eliminating the hive conditions that require the honeybee to resort to symbolic language, I could make the honeybee revert to the primi-

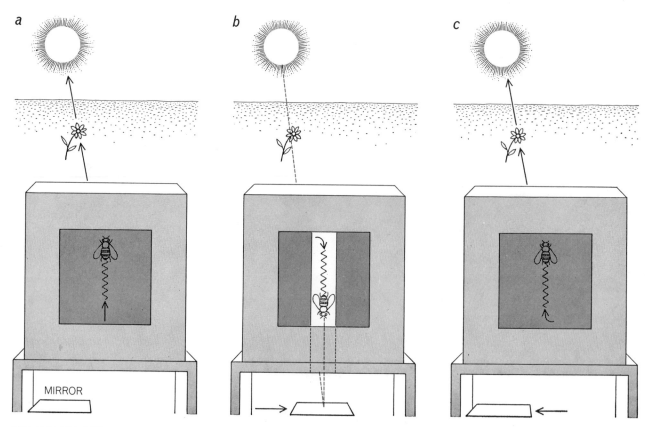

USE OF THE SUN as a direction indicator was induced experimentally in honeybees by the author. When food was placed along a line between hive and sun, a returning forager pointed the way to the food in the usual gravity-oriented manner by making runs straight up the face of the hive (*a*). The author then reflected sunlight into the bottom of the dark hive with a mirror (*b*). The forager stopped running upward and instead showed the way to the food by running toward the sun's image. With darkness restored (*c*), the forager resumed its upward runs. Turning the sun "on" and "off" caused repeated reversals and altered the tempo of the dance.

tive behavior of stingless bees. I laid the hive horizontally, so that there were no vertical surfaces on which the bees could dance, and then observed the dark hive under red light (which bees cannot see). In these circumstances returning foragers did not dance, presumably because in the dark the wagging-dance language requires a vertical, gravitational reference line to indicate direction. The scouts did, however, emit sound signals that told the distance to the food site [*see illustration above*]. In short, the honeybee under these conditions behaved very much like a *Melipona* stingless bee: no dance in the hive but a chatter of sound telling the hivemates that food had been found and how far away it was.

Experiments show that the honeybee prefers to use the sun, rather than the symbolic upward line in the hive, as the reference for indicating the direction of a food site to its hivemates. As we have noted, when the food source is in the direction of the sun, the forager makes its wagging run straight upward in the darkness of the hive. In some of my experiments I put a mirror at the bottom of the hive so that the sun's image appeared in the mirror. The dancer then turned about and made its run straight down toward the sun's image! That is to say, it gave up its artificial mode of representing the sun's direction and went for the sun itself. When I moved the mirror away, the dancer returned to its conventional upward wagging run [*see illustration on page 2418*].

(Incidentally, by turning the sun "on" and "off" rapidly in this way I caused the dancer to speed up the tempo of its dance greatly. The amount of wagging in each run remained the same, however.

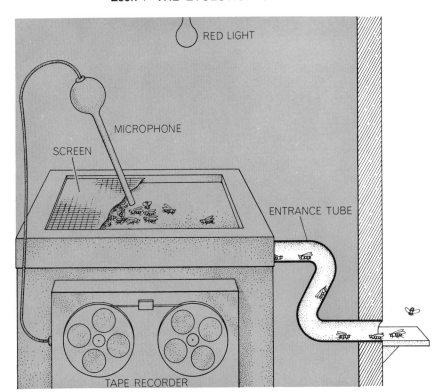

RED LIGHT

MICROPHONE

SCREEN

ENTRANCE TUBE

TAPE RECORDER

REVERSION to primitive behavior was forced on honeybees by an experiment in which the author tipped the vertical hive into a horizontal position and covered the formerly vertical face with screening so that the sounds made by returning foragers could be recorded. Coming back to a dark hive with no vertical surface to run on, the foragers did not dance. They did emit sounds indicating the distance to the food source, as stingless bee foragers do.

This experiment showed conclusively that the wagging time, rather than the number of runs per minute, is the significant indicator of the distance to the food site.)

Taken together, all the information gained from observation and experiment suggests that (1) the language of the bees had its origin in some automatic, rhythmic behavior of flying insects at the end of a flight; (2) at the most primitive stage of development the social bees obtained information primarily from sounds emitted by the foragers; (3) the language gradually evolved into the precise ritual of the honeybees' wagging dance and its accompaniment of sound. We plan to extend the research to many more species of bees, hoping to learn in detail just how the language developed.

The Author

HARALD ESCH is assistant professor of biology at the University of Notre Dame. He was born and educated in Germany, receiving a doctorate from the University of Würzburg in 1960. For some years he divided his interest between radiobiology and bees. In 1962 he joined the Radiation Research Institute at the University of Munich. He writes: "I had to devote most of my time to radiobiological research, but my contract contained a provision for me to have a sabbatical leave in 1964 to study the communicative behavior of Brazilian bees. Working full time on bees in Brazil, I realized that it was not a good idea to split my time between bees and radiation research." At Notre Dame his principal research is on bees.

Bibliography

COMMUNICATION AMONG SOCIAL BEES. Martin Lindauer. Harvard University Press, 1961.

SOUND: AN ELEMENT COMMON TO COMMUNICATION OF STINGLESS BEES AND TO DANCES OF THE HONEY BEE. Harald Esch and Warwick E. Kerr in *Science*, Vol. 149, No. 3681, pages 320–321; July 16, 1965.

SOUND PRODUCTION DURING THE WAGGLE DANCE OF THE HONEY BEE. A. M. Wenner in *Animal Behaviour*, Vol. 10, No. 1/2, pages 79–95; 1962.

TANZSPRACHE UND ORIENTIERUNG DER BIENEN. Karl von Frisch. Springer-Verlag, 1965.

SCIENTIFIC AMERICAN   May 1967, Vol. 216, No. 5, pp. 34-43

THE DIVING WOMEN OF KOREA AND JAPAN

by Suk Ki Hong and Hermann Rahn

Some 30,000 of these breath-holding divers, called ama, are employed in daily foraging for food on the bottom of the sea. Their performance is of particular interest to the physiologist.

Off the shores of Korea and southern Japan the ocean bottom is rich in shellfish and edible seaweeds. For at least 1,500 years these crops have been harvested by divers, mostly women, who support their families by daily foraging on the sea bottom. Using no special equipment other than goggles (or glass face masks), these breath-holding divers have become famous the world over for their performances. They sometimes descend to depths of 80 feet and can hold their breath for up to two minutes. Coming up only for brief rests and a few breaths of air, they dive repeatedly, and in warm weather they work four hours a day, with resting intervals of an hour or so away from the water. The Korean women dive even in winter, when the water temperature is 50 degrees Fahrenheit (but only for short periods under such conditions). For those who choose this occupation diving is a lifelong profession; they begin to work in shallow water at the age of 11 or 12 and sometimes continue to 65. Childbearing does not interrupt their work; a pregnant diving woman may work up to the day of delivery and nurse her baby afterward between diving shifts.

The divers are called ama. At present there are some 30,000 of them living and working along the seacoasts of Korea and Japan. About 11,000 ama dwell on the small, rocky island of Cheju off the southern tip of the Korean peninsula, which is believed to be the area where the diving practice originated. Archaeological remains indicate that the practice began before the fourth century. In times past the main objective of the divers may have been pearls, but today it is solely food. Up to the 17th century the ama of Korea included men as well as women; now they are all women. And in Japan, where many of the ama are male, women nevertheless predominate in the occupa-

tion. As we shall see, the female is better suited to this work than the male.

In recent years physiologists have found considerable interest in studying the capacities and physiological reactions of the ama, who are probably the most skillful natural divers in the world. What accounts for their remarkable adaptation to the aquatic environment, training or heredity or a combination of both? How do they compare with their nondiving compatriots? The ama themselves have readily cooperated with us in these studies.

We shall begin by describing the dive itself. Basically two different approaches are used. One is a simple system in which the diver operates alone; she is called *cachido* (unassisted diver). The other is a more sophisticated technique; this diver, called a *funado* (assisted diver), has a helper in a boat, usually her husband.

The *cachido* operates from a small float at the surface. She takes several deep breaths, then swims to the bottom, gathers what she can find and swims up to her float again. Because of the oxygen consumption required for her swimming effort she is restricted to comparatively shallow dives and a short time on the bottom. She may on occasion go as deep as 50 or 60 feet, but on the average she limits her foraging to a depth of 15 or 20 feet. Her average dive lasts about 30 seconds, of which 15 seconds is spent working on the bottom. When she surfaces, she hangs on to the float and rests for about 30 seconds, taking deep breaths, and then dives again. Thus the cycle takes about a minute, and the diver averages about 60 dives an hour.

The *funado* dispenses with swimming effort and uses aids that speed her descent and ascent. She carries a counterweight (of about 30 pounds) to pull her to the bottom, and at the end of her

dive a helper in a boat above pulls her up with a rope. These aids minimize her oxygen need and hasten her rate of descent and ascent, thereby enabling her to go to greater depths and spend more time on the bottom. The *funado* can work at depths of 60 to 80 feet and average 30 seconds in gathering on the bottom—twice as long as the *cachido*. However, since the total duration of each dive and resting period is twice that of the *cachido*, the *funado* makes only about 30 dives per hour instead of 60. Consequently her bottom time per hour is about the same as the *cachido*'s. Her advantage is that she can harvest deeper bottoms. In economic terms this advantage is partly offset by the fact that the *funado* requires a boat and an assistant.

There are variations, of course, on the two basic diving styles, almost as many variations as there are diving locations. Some divers use assistance to ascend but not to descend; some use only light weights to help in the descent, and so on.

By and large the divers wear minimal clothing, often only a loincloth, during their work in the water. Even in winter the Korean divers wear only cotton bathing suits. In Japan some ama have recently adopted foam-rubber suits, but most of the diving women cannot afford this luxury.

The use of goggles or face masks to improve vision in the water is a comparatively recent development—hardly a century old. It must have revolutionized the diving industry and greatly increased the number of divers and the size of the harvest. The unprotected human eye suffers a basic loss of visual acuity in water because the light passing through water undergoes relatively little refraction when it enters the tissue of the cornea, so that the focal point of the image is considerably behind the retina [see top

JAPANESE DIVING WOMAN was photographed by the Italian writer Fosco Maraini near the island of Hekura off the western coast of Japan. The ama's descent is assisted by a string of lead weights tied around her waist. At the time she was diving for aba- lone at a depth of about 30 feet. At the end of each dive a helper in a boat at the surface pulls the ama up by means of the long rope attached to her waist. The other rope belongs to another diver. The ama in this region wear only loincloths during their dives.

illustration on page 2427]. Sharp vision in air is due to the difference in the refractive index between air and the corneal tissue; this difference bends light sharply as it enters the eye and thereby helps to focus images on the retinal surface. (The lens serves for fine adjustments.) Goggles sharpen vision in the water by providing a layer of air at the interface with the eyeball.

Goggles create a hazard, however, when the diver descends below 10 feet in the water. The hydrostatic pressure on the body then increases the internal body pressures, including that of the blood, to a level substantially higher than the air pressure behind the goggles. As a result the blood vessels in the eyelid lining may burst. This conjunctival bleeding is well known to divers who have ventured too deep in the water with only simple goggles. When the Korean and Japanese divers began to use goggles, they soon learned that they must compensate for the pressure factor. Their solution was to attach air-filled, compressible bags (of rubber or thin animal hide) to the goggles. As the diver descends in the water the increasing water pressure compresses the bags, forcing more air into the goggle space and thus raising the air pressure there in proportion to the increase in hydrostatic pressure on the body. Nowadays, in place of goggles, most divers use a face mask covering the nose, so that air from the lungs instead of from external bags can serve to boost the air pressure in front of the eyes.

The ama evolved another technique that may or may not have biological value. During hyperventilation before their dives they purse their lips and emit a loud whistle with each expiration of breath. These whistles, which can be heard for long distances, have become the trademark of the ama. The basic reason for the whistling is quite mysterious. The ama say it makes them "feel better" and "protects the lungs." Various observers have suggested that it may prevent excessive hyperventilation (which can produce unconsciousness in a long dive) or may help by increasing the residual lung volume, but no evidence has been found to verify these hypotheses. Many of the Japanese divers, male and female, do not whistle before they dive.

Preparing for a dive, the ama hyperventilates for five to 10 seconds, takes a final deep breath and then makes the plunge. The hyperventilation serves to

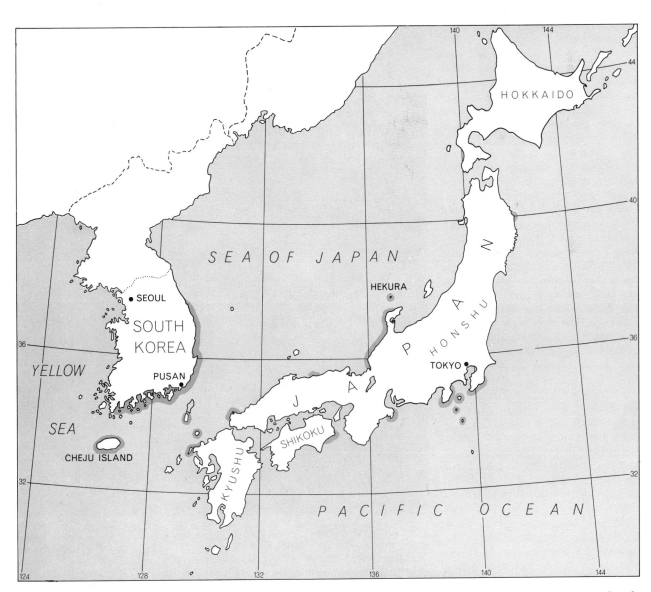

GEOGRAPHIC DISTRIBUTION of the ama divers along the seacoasts of South Korea and southern Japan is indicated by the colored areas. The diving practice is believed to have originated on the small island of Cheju off the southern tip of the Korean peninsula.

remove a considerable amount of carbon dioxide from the blood. The final breath, however, is not a full one but only about 85 percent of what the lungs can hold. Just why the ama limits this breath is not clear; perhaps she does so to avoid uncomfortable pressure in the lungs or to restrict the body's buoyancy in the water.

As the diver descends the water pressure compresses her chest and consequently her lung volume. The depth to which she can go is limited, of course, by the amount of lung compression she can tolerate. If she dives deeper than the level of maximum lung compression (her "residual lung volume"), she becomes subject to a painful lung squeeze; moreover, because the hydrostatic pressure in her blood vessels then exceeds the air pressure in her lungs, the pulmonary blood vessels may burst.

The diver, as we have noted, starts her dive with a lungful of air that is comparatively rich in oxygen and comparatively poor in carbon dioxide. What happens to the composition of this air in the lungs, and to the exchange with the blood, during the dive? In order to investigate this question we needed a means of obtaining samples of the diver's lung air under water without risk to the diver. Edward H. Lanphier and Richard A. Morin of our group (from the State University of New York at Buffalo) devised a simple apparatus into which the diver could blow her lung air and then reinhale most of it, leaving a small sample of air in the device. The divers were understandably reluctant at first to try this device, because it meant giving up their precious lung air deep under water with the possibility that they might not recover it, but they were eventually reassured by tests of the apparatus.

We took four samples of the diver's lung air: one before she entered the water, a second when she had hyperventilated her lungs at the surface and was about to dive, a third when she reached the bottom at a depth of 40 feet and a fourth after she had returned to the surface. In each sample we measured the concentrations and calculated the partial pressures of the principal gases: oxygen, carbon dioxide and nitrogen.

Normally, in a resting person out of the water, the air in the alveoli of the lungs is 14.3 percent oxygen, 5.2 percent carbon dioxide and 80.5 percent nitrogen (disregarding the rare gases and water vapor). We found that after hyperventilation the divers' alveolar air con-

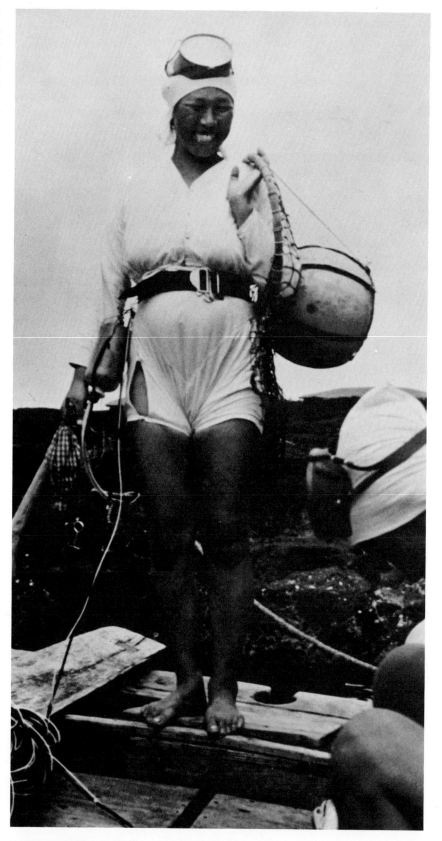

KOREAN DIVING WOMAN from Cheju Island cooperated with the authors in their study of the physiological reactions to breath-hold diving. The large ball slung over her left shoulder is a float that is left at the surface during the dive; attached to the float is a net for collecting the catch. The black belt was provided by the authors to carry a pressure-sensitive bottle and electrocardiograph wires for recording the heart rate. The ama holds an alveolar, or lung, gas sampler in her right hand. The Korean ama wear only light cotton bathing suits even in the winter, when the water temperature can be as low as 50 degrees Fahrenheit.

5 SECONDS   15 SECONDS   5 SECONDS

UNASSISTED DIVER, called a *cachido,* employs one of the two basic techniques of ama diving. The *cachido* operates from a small float at the surface. On an average dive she swims to a depth of about 15 to 20 feet; the dive lasts about 25 to 30 seconds, of which 15 seconds is spent working on the bottom. The entire diving cycle takes about a minute, and the diver averages 60 dives per hour.

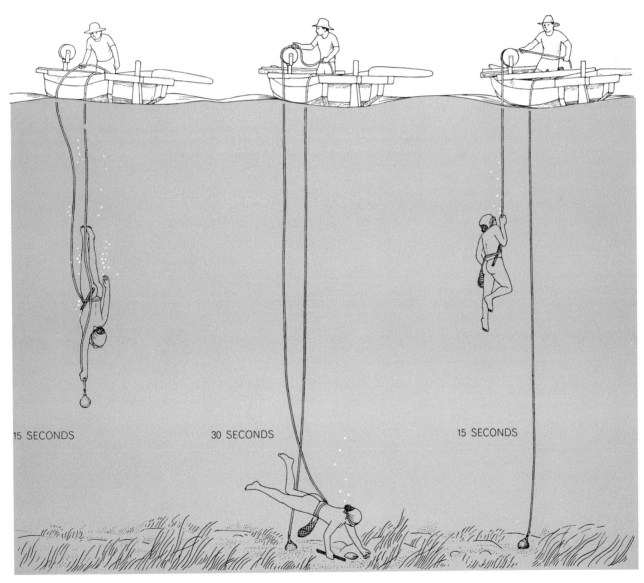

15 SECONDS   30 SECONDS   15 SECONDS

ASSISTED DIVER, called a *funado,* uses a counterweight to descend passively to a depth of 60 to 80 feet. She averages 30 seconds in gathering on the bottom but makes only about 30 dives per hour. At the end of each dive a helper in the boat pulls her up.

sists of 16.7 percent oxygen, 4 percent carbon dioxide and 79.3 percent nitrogen; translating these figures into partial pressures (in millimeters of mercury), the respective proportions are 120 millimeters for oxygen, 29 for carbon dioxide and 567 for nitrogen.

By the time the *cachido* (unassisted diver) reaches the bottom at a depth of 40 feet the oxygen concentration in her lungs is reduced to 11.1 percent, because of the uptake of oxygen by the blood. However, since at that depth the water pressure has compressed the lungs to somewhat more than half of their pre-dive volume, the oxygen pressure amounts to 149 millimeters of mercury— a greater pressure than before the dive. Consequently oxygen is still being transmitted to the blood at a substantial rate.

For the same reason the blood also takes up carbon dioxide during the dive. The carbon dioxide concentration in the lungs drops from 4 percent at the beginning of the dive to 3.2 percent at the bottom. This is somewhat paradoxical; when a person out of the water holds his breath, the carbon dioxide in his lungs increases. At a depth of 40 feet, however, the compression of the lung volume raises the carbon dioxide pressure to 42 millimeters of mercury, and this is greater than the carbon dioxide pressure in the venous blood. As a result the blood and tissues retain carbon dioxide and even absorb some from the lungs.

As the diver ascends from the bottom, the expansion of the lungs drastically reverses the situation. With the reduction of pressure in the lungs, carbon dioxide comes out of the blood rapidly. Much more important is the precipitous drop of the oxygen partial pressure in the lungs: within 30 seconds it falls from 149 to 41 millimeters of mercury. This is no greater than the partial pressure of oxygen in the venous blood; hence the blood cannot pick up oxygen, and Lanphier has shown that it may actually lose oxygen to the lungs. In all probability that fact explains many of the deaths that have occurred among sports divers returning to the surface after deep, lengthy dives. The cumulative oxygen deficiency in the tissues is sharply accentuated during the ascent.

Our research has also yielded a measure of the nitrogen danger in a long dive. We found that at a depth of 40 feet the nitrogen partial pressure in the compressed lungs is doubled (to 1,134 millimeters of mercury), and throughout the dive the nitrogen tension is sufficient to drive the gas into the blood. Lanphier has calculated that repeated dives to

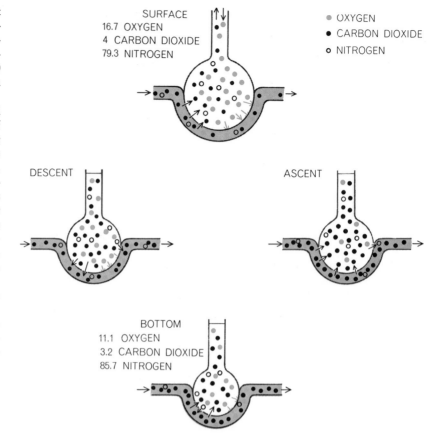

GASES EXCHANGED between a single alveolus, or lung sac, and the bloodstream are shown for four stages of a typical ama dive. The concentrations of three principal gases in the lung at the surface and at the bottom are given in percent. During descent water pressure on the lungs causes all gases to enter the blood. During ascent this situation is reversed.

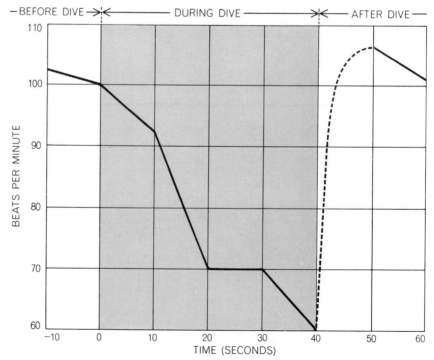

AVERAGE HEART RATE for a group of Korean ama was measured before, during and after their dives. All the dives were to a depth of about 15 feet. The average pattern shown here was substantially the same in the summer, when the water temperature was about 80 degrees Fahrenheit, as it was in winter, when water temperature was about 50 degrees F.

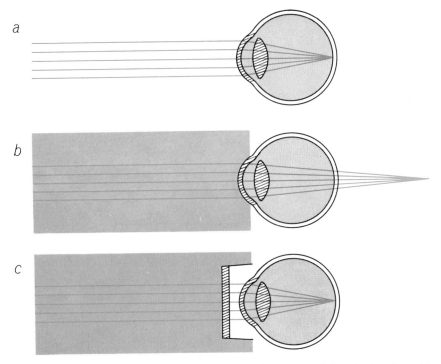

GOGGLES SHARPEN VISION under water by providing a layer of air at the interface with the eyeball (*c*). Vision is normally sharp in air because the difference in refractive index between air and the tissue of the cornea helps to focus images on the retinal surface (*a*). The small difference in the refractive index between water and corneal tissue causes the focal point to move considerably beyond the retina (*b*), reducing visual acuity under water.

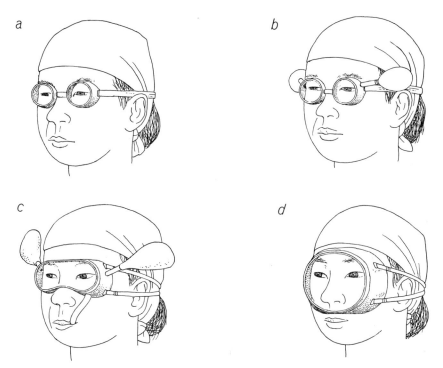

EVOLUTION OF GOGGLES has resulted in several solutions to the problem presented by the increase in hydrostatic pressure on the body during a dive. The earliest goggles (*a*) were uncompensated, and the difference in pressure between the blood vessels in the eyelid and the air behind the goggles could result in conjunctival bleeding. The problem was first solved by attaching air-filled, compressible bags to the goggles (*b*). During a dive the increasing water pressure compresses the bags, raising the air pressure behind the goggles in proportion to the increase in hydrostatic pressure on the body. In some cases (*c*) the lungs were used as an additional compensating gas chamber. With a modern face mask that covers the nose (*d*) the lungs provide the only source of compensating air pressure during a dive.

depths of 120 feet, such as are performed by male pearl divers in the Tuamotu Archipelago of the South Pacific, can result in enough accumulation of nitrogen in the blood to cause the bends on ascent. When these divers come to the surface they are sometimes stricken by fatal attacks, which they call *taravana*.

The ama of the Korean area are not so reckless. Long experience has taught them the limits of safety, and, although they undoubtedly have some slight anoxia at the end of each dive, they quickly recover from it. The diving women content themselves with comparatively short dives that they can perform again and again for extended periods without serious danger. They avoid excessive depletion of oxygen and excessive accumulation of nitrogen in their blood.

As far as we have been able to determine, the diving women possess no particular constitutional aptitudes of a hereditary kind. The daughters of Korean farmers can be trained to become just as capable divers as the daughters of divers. The training, however, is important. The most significant adaptation the trained diving women show is an unusually large "vital capacity," measured as the volume of air that can be drawn into the lungs in a single inspiration after a complete expiration. In this attribute the ama are substantially superior to nondiving Korean women. It appears that the divers acquire this capacity through development of the muscles involved in inspiration, which also serve to resist compression of the chest and lung volume in the water.

A large lung capacity, or oxygen intake, is one way to fortify the body for diving; another is conservation of the oxygen stored in the blood. It is now well known, thanks to the researches of P. F. Scholander of the Scripps Institution of Oceanography and other investigators, that certain diving mammals and birds have a built-in mechanism that minimizes their need for oxygen while they are under water [see "The Master Switch of Life," by P. F. Scholander; SCIENTIFIC AMERICAN Offprint 172]. This mechanism constricts the blood vessels supplying the kidneys and most of the body muscles so that the blood flow to these organs is drastically reduced; meanwhile a normal flow is maintained to the heart, brain and other organs that require an undiminished supply of oxygen. Thus the heart can slow down, the rate of removal of oxygen from the blood by tissues is reduced, and the animal can prolong its dive.

Several investigators have found recently that human subjects lying under water also slow their heart rate, although not as much as the diving animals do. We made a study of this matter in the ama during their dives. We attached electrodes (sealed from contact with the seawater) to the chests of the divers, and while they dived to the bottom, at the end of a 100-foot cable, an electrocardiograph in our boat recorded their heart rhythms. During their hyperventilation preparatory to diving the divers' heart rate averaged about 100 beats a minute. During the dive the rate fell until, at 20 seconds after submersion, it had dropped to 70 beats; after 30 seconds it dropped further to 60 beats a minute [*see bottom illustration on page 2426*]. When the divers returned to the surface, the heart rate jumped to slightly above normal and then rapidly recovered its usual beat.

Curiously, human subjects who hold their breath out of the water, even in an air pressure chamber, do not show the same degree of slowing of the heart. It was also noteworthy that in about 50 percent of the dives the ama showed some irregularity of heartbeat. These and other findings raise a number of puzzling questions. Nevertheless, one thing is quite clear: the automatic slowing of the heart is an important factor in the ability of human divers to extend their time under water.

In the last analysis the amount of time one can spend in the water, even without holding one's breath, is limited by the loss of body heat. For the working ama this is a critical factor, affecting the length of their working day both in summer and in winter. (They warm themselves at open fires after each long diving shift.) We investigated the effects of their cold exposure from several points of view, including measurements of the heat losses at various water temperatures and analysis of the defensive mechanisms brought into play.

For measuring the amount of the body's heat loss in the water there are two convenient indexes: (1) the increase of heat production by the body (through the exercise of swimming and shivering) and (2) the drop in the body's internal temperature. The body's heat production can be measured by examining its consumption of oxygen; this can be gauged from the oxygen content of the lungs at the end of a dive and during recovery. Our measurements were made on Korean diving women in Pusan harbor at two seasons of the year: in August,

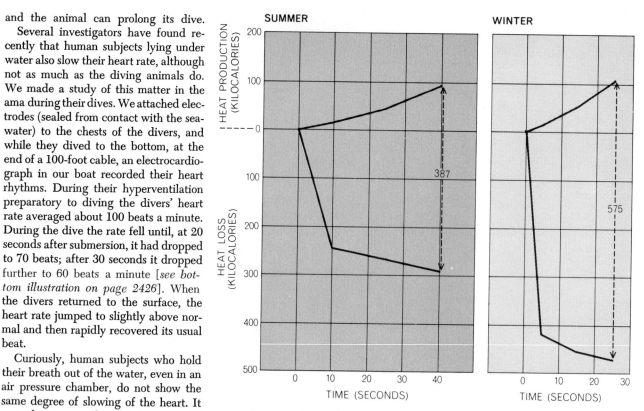

BODY HEAT lost by ama divers was found to be about 400 kilocalories in a summer shift (*left*) and about 600 kilocalories in a winter shift (*right*). The curves above the abscissa at zero kilocalories represent heat generated by swimming and shivering and were estimated by the rate of oxygen consumption. The curves below abscissa represent heat lost by the body to the water and were estimated by changes in rectal temperature and skin temperature.

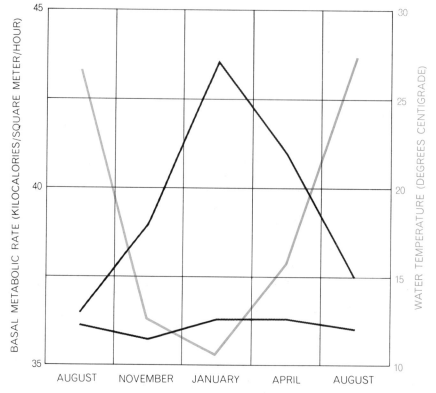

BASAL METABOLIC RATE of ama women (*top gray curve*) increases in winter and decreases in summer. In nondiving Korean women (*bottom gray curve*) basal metabolic rate is constant throughout the year. The colored curve shows the mean seawater temperatures in the diving area of Pusan harbor for the same period covered by the other measurements.

when the water temperature was 80.6 degrees F., and in January with the water temperature at 50 degrees.

In both seasons at the end of a single diving shift (40 minutes in the summer, 25 minutes in winter) the deep-body temperature was found to be reduced from the normal 98.6 degrees F. to 95 degrees or less. Combining this information with the measurements of oxygen consumption, we estimated that the ama's body-heat loss was about 400 kilocalories in a summer shift and about 600 kilocalories in a winter shift. On a daily basis, taking into consideration that the ama works in the water for three long shifts each day in summer and only one or two short shifts in winter, the day's total heat loss is estimated to be about the same in all seasons: approximately 1,000 kilocalories per day.

To compensate for this loss the Korean diving woman eats considerably more than her nondiving sisters. The ama's daily food consumption amounts to about 3,000 kilocalories, whereas the average for nondiving Korean women of comparable age is on the order of 2,000 kilocalories per day. Our various items of evidence suggest that the Korean diving woman subjects herself to a daily cold stress greater than that of any other group of human beings yet studied. Her extra food consumption goes entirely into coping with this stress. The Korean diving women are not heavy; on the contrary, they are unusually lean.

It is interesting now to examine whether or not the diving women have developed any special bodily defenses against cold. One such defense would be an elevated rate of basal metabolism, that is, an above-average basic rate of heat production. There was little reason, however, to expect to find the Korean women particularly well endowed in this respect. In the first place, populations of mankind the world over, in cold climates or warm, have been found to differ little in basal metabolism. In the second place, any elevation of the basal rate that might exist in the diving women would be too small to have much effect in offsetting the large heat losses in water.

Yet we found to our surprise that the diving women did show a significant elevation of the basal metabolic rate—but only in the winter months! In that season their basal rate is about 25 percent higher than that of nondiving women of the same community and the same economic background (who show no seasonal change in basal metabolism). Only one other population in the world has been found to have a basal metabolic rate as high as that of the Korean diving women in winter: the Alaskan Eskimos. The available evidence indicates that the warmly clothed Eskimos do not, however, experience consistently severe cold stresses; their elevated basal rate is believed to arise from an exceptionally large amount of protein in their diet. We found that the protein intake of Korean diving women is not particularly high. It therefore seems probable that their elevated basal metabolic rate in winter is a direct reflection of their severe exposure to cold in that season, and that this in turn indicates a latent human mechanism of adaptation to cold that is evoked only under extreme cold stresses such as the Korean divers experience. The response is too feeble to give the divers any significant amount of protection in the winter water. It does, however, raise an interesting physiological question that we are pursuing with further studies, namely the possibility that severe exposure to winter cold may, as a general rule, stimulate the human thyroid gland to a seasonal elevation of activity.

The production of body heat is one aspect of the defense against cold; another is the body's insulation for retaining heat. Here the most important factor (but not the only one) is the layer of fat

BETWEEN DIVES the ama were persuaded to expire air into a large plastic gas bag in order to measure the rate at which oxygen is consumed in swimming and diving to produce heat. The water temperature in Pusan harbor at the time (January) was 50 degrees F. One of the authors (Hong) assists. Data obtained in this way were used to construct the graph at the top of the preceding page.

under the skin. The heat conductivity of fatty tissue is only about half that of muscle tissue; in other words, it is twice as good an insulator. Whales and seals owe their ability to live in arctic and antarctic waters to their very thick layers of subcutaneous fat. Similarly, subcutaneous fat explains why women dominate the diving profession of Korea and Japan; they are more generously endowed with this protection than men are.

Donald W. Rennie of the State University of New York at Buffalo collaborated with one of the authors of this article (Hong) in detailed measurements of the body insulation of Korean women, comparing divers with nondivers. The thickness of the subcutaneous fat can easily be determined by measuring the thickness of folds of skin in various parts of the body. This does not, however, tell the whole story of the body's thermal insulation. To measure this insulation in functional terms, we had our subjects lie in a tank of water for three hours with only the face out of the water. From measurements of the reduction in deep-body temperature and the body's heat production we were then able to calculate the degree of the subject's overall thermal insulation. These studies revealed three particularly interesting facts. They showed, for one thing, that with the same thickness of subcutaneous fat, divers had less heat loss than nondivers. This was taken to indicate that the divers' fatty insulation is supplemented by some kind of vascular adaptation that restricts the loss of heat from the blood vessels to the skin, particularly in the arms and legs. Secondly, the observations disclosed that in winter the diving women lose about half of their subcutaneous fat (although nondivers do not). Presumably this means that during the winter the divers' heat loss is so great that their food intake does not compensate for it sufficiently; in any case, their vascular adaptation helps them to maintain insulation. Thirdly, we found that diving women could tolerate lower water temperatures than nondiving women without shivering. The divers did not shiver when they lay for three hours in water at 82.8 degrees F.; nondivers began to shiver at a temperature of 86 degrees. (Male nondivers shivered at 88 degrees.) It appears that the diving women's resistance to shivering arises from some hardening aspect of their training that inhibits shiver-triggering impulses from the skin. The inhibition of shivering is an advantage because shivering speeds up the emission of body heat. L. G. Pugh, a British physiologist

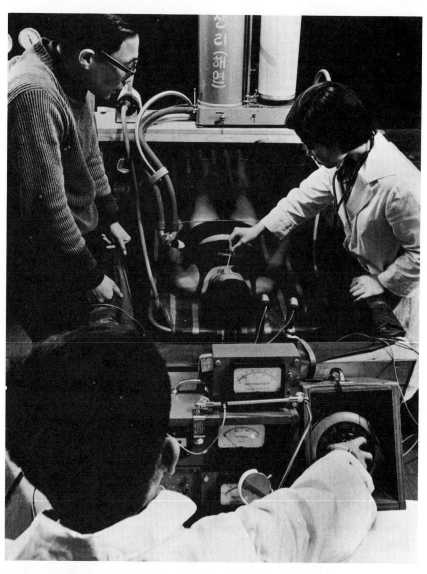

AMA'S THERMAL INSULATION (mainly fat) was measured by having the subjects lie in a tank of water for three hours. From measurements of the reduction of deep-body temperature and the body's heat production the authors were able to calculate the degree of the subject's overall thermal insulation. Once again Hong (left) keeps a close eye on the operation.

who has studied long-distance swimmers, discovered the interesting additional fact that swimmers, whether fat or thin, lose heat more rapidly while swimming than while lying motionless in the water. The whole subject of the body's thermal insulation is obviously a rather complicated one that will not be easy to unravel. As a general conclusion, however, it is very clearly established that women are far better insulated than men against cold.

As a concluding observation we should note that the 1,500-year-old diving occupation in Korea and Japan is now declining. The number of divers has dwindled during the past few decades, and by the end of this century the profession may disappear altogether, chiefly because more remunerative and less

arduous ways of making a living are arising. Nonetheless, for the 30,000 practitioners still active in the diving profession (at least in summer) diving remains a proud calling and necessary livelihood. By adopting scuba gear and other modern underwater equipment the divers could greatly increase their production; the present harvest could be obtained by not much more than a tenth of the present number of divers. This would raise havoc, however, with employment and the economy in the hundreds of small villages whose women daily go forth to seek their families' existence on the sea bottom. For that reason innovations are fiercely resisted. Indeed, many villages in Japan have outlawed the foam-rubber suit for divers to prevent too easy and too rapid harvesting of the local waters.

The Authors

SUK KI HONG and HERMANN RAHN are professors of physiology, Hong at the Yonsei University College of Medicine in Korea and Rahn at the State University of New York at Buffalo. Each is also chairman of the department of physiology at his institution. Hong was born and educated in Korea. He received the degree of M.D. at Severance Union Medical College (now part of Yonsei University) in 1949 and a Ph.D. from the University of Rochester in 1956. He then joined the faculty of the University of Buffalo School of Medicine (now the State University of New York at Buffalo). Before he left Buffalo in 1959 he and Rahn made plans for a long-term collaborative research program on physiological adaptations to diving. Rahn was graduated from Cornell University in 1933 and received a Ph.D. from the University of Rochester in 1938. He was a member of the department of physiology at Rochester until 1956, when he went to the State University of New York at Buffalo.

Bibliography

THE ISLAND OF THE FISHERWOMEN. Fosco Maraini. Harcourt, Brace & World, Inc., 1962.

KOREAN SEA WOMEN: A STUDY OF THEIR PHYSIOLOGY. The departments of physiology, Yonsei University College of Medicine, Seoul, and the State University of New York at Buffalo.

THE PHYSIOLOGICAL STRESSES OF THE AMA. Hermann Rahn in *Physiology of Breath-Hold Diving and the Ama of Japan.* Publication 1341, National Academy of Sciences–National Research Council, 1965.

SPECIAL NOTE TO TEACHERS: Each article in this volume, plus more than 660 others, is available as a separate, self-bound SCIENTIFIC AMERICAN Offprint. Offprints may be ordered in any combination and in any quantity. Teachers who want to adopt articles for their courses, therefore, can ensure that each student has his own set. Students' sets are collated by the publisher before shipment.

SCIENTIFIC
AMERICAN May 1967, Vol. 216, No. 5, pp. 44-52

OFFPRINT 1073

SMALL SYSTEMS OF NERVE CELLS

by Donald Kennedy

In some invertebrate animals complete behavioral functions may be controlled by a very few cells. This makes it possible to trace out the interactions of the cells and so to investigate nervous integration.

The nervous system of a man comprises between 10 billion and 100 billion cells, and the "lower" mammals men study in an effort to understand their own brains may have two or three billion nerve cells, Even specialized parts of vertebrate nervous systems have an awesome number of elements: the retina of the eye has about 130 million receptor cells and sends more than a million nerve fibers to the brain; a single segment of spinal cord controls the few muscles it operates through several thousand motoneurons, or motor nerve cells, which in turn receive instructions from a larger number of sensory elements.

These vast populations of cells present a formidable challenge to biologists trying to understand how the nervous system works. Since the system is made up of cells, one would like to understand it in terms of cellular activities, and by examining the activity of single nerve cells investigators have been able to learn a great deal about the nature of the nerve impulse and about the generation and transmission of the patterns of impulses that constitute nervous signals. The ultimate object must be, however, to understand not only the activities of single cells but also the rules of their interaction. Since one cannot expect to understand even the most restricted systems by predicting the possible interactions of an inadequately sampled population of cells, mammalian physiologists have devised ingenious ways of circumventing the superabundance of elements, involving particularly biochemical studies of regions of the brain and sophisticated computer analyses of brain waves. The trouble is that most of these methods treat cells as anonymous members of a population rather than as interacting individuals.

Some biologists are taking a different approach, one that retains the individual nerve cell as the focus of attention and yet attempts to deal with groups of them. This approach is made possible by the availability of animals that have fewer nerve cells than any vertebrate and that nonetheless display reasonably complex behavior. The claw-bearing limb of the shore crab, for example, shows impressive coordination and range of movement, made possible by six movable joints with pairs of muscles acting in opposition to each other. As a mechanical device it is in most ways the equal of a mammalian limb, yet the crab operates all this machinery with about two dozen motor nerve cells. A mammal of comparable size would employ several thousand for the analogous purpose.

Nor is such parsimony confined to the motor apparatus: in contrast to the several billion cells of the entire mammalian nervous system, the crab has only half a million or so. The real utility of such systems to the investigator becomes apparent only when one concentrates on the nerve cells belonging to one functional unit such as a reflex pathway, a special sense organ or a particular pattern of behavior. Indeed, the nervous systems of some of the higher invertebrate animals are so economically built that for certain functions one may hope to specify the activity of every individual cell.

This achievement would be a hollow one insofar as learning about mammalian nervous systems is concerned if the additional complexity of more "advanced" systems depended heavily on new capabilities of the individual cells comprising them. All the evidence, however, indicates that the performance limits of the single nerve cell are already reached in relatively simple animals.

The central nervous elements found in the lobster or the sluglike "sea hare" nearly equal those of mammals in size, quantity of input and structural complexity. The marvelous performance of the mammalian brain is, it appears, not so dependent on the individual capabilities of its cells as it is on their greater number and the resulting opportunities for permutation. Therefore an understanding of the connections underlying behavior in a simple system can lead to useful conclusions about the organization of much more complicated ones.

The difficulty lies in the choice of appropriate experimental objects. Ideally one needs a nervous system that produces a reasonably complex repertory of behavior and has only a few cells, each of which can be recognized and located time after time. In certain animals specialized giant cells offer this ready identifiability. The giant axons, or nerve fibers, of the squid and the lobster are an example, and biophysicists have long exploited them for experiments on the properties of nerve-cell membranes. A student of integrative processes in the nervous system needs more; he wants to specify individual properties for each cell in an entire functional assembly.

Two different kinds of nervous system seem particularly promising for this purpose: that of mollusks and that of arthropods. The most thoroughly studied mollusk is the sea hare Aplysia, a snail that has only a vestigial shell and leads a somewhat more mobile life than its relatives. Its nervous system is concentrated in a few large ganglia connected by nerve trunks. Several features of the cells are advantageous. The cell bodies are unusually large, some with a diameter of .8 millimeter and the rest well sorted in size below this maximum. They contain

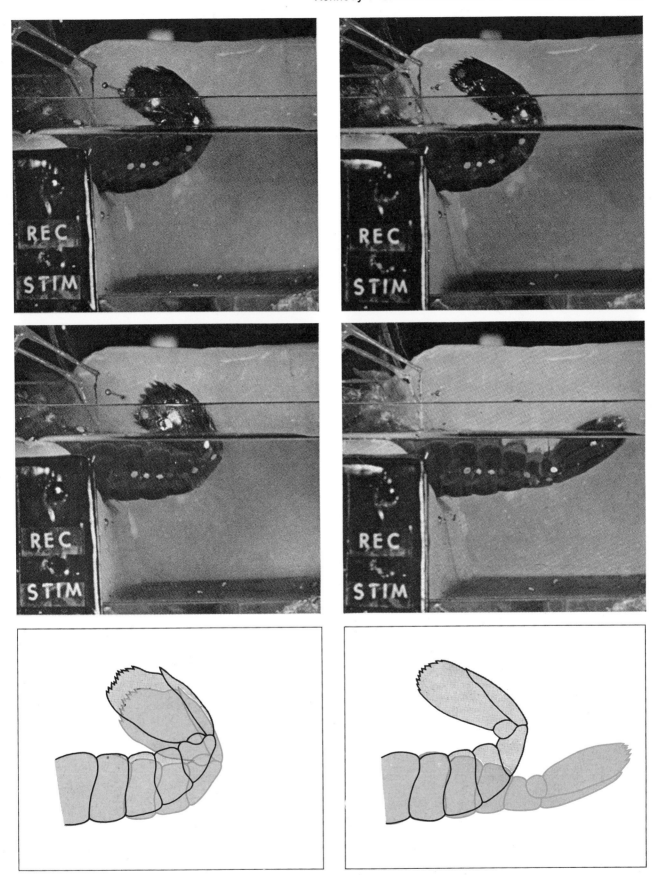

CRAYFISH ABDOMEN responds in complex and specific ways to stimulation of different single cells in the central nervous system. Frames from a motion-picture film made by Benjamin Dane in the author's laboratory record the effects of two different "command fibers"; the drawings specify the initial (gray) and the final (red) positions of the abdomen. One fiber evoked activity primarily in the forward segments (left); the other produced extension in all segments (right). Spots painted on the abdomen facilitated precise measurement of segment angles. Visible effects were confirmed by recording the activity of motor nerve fibers in the first segment.

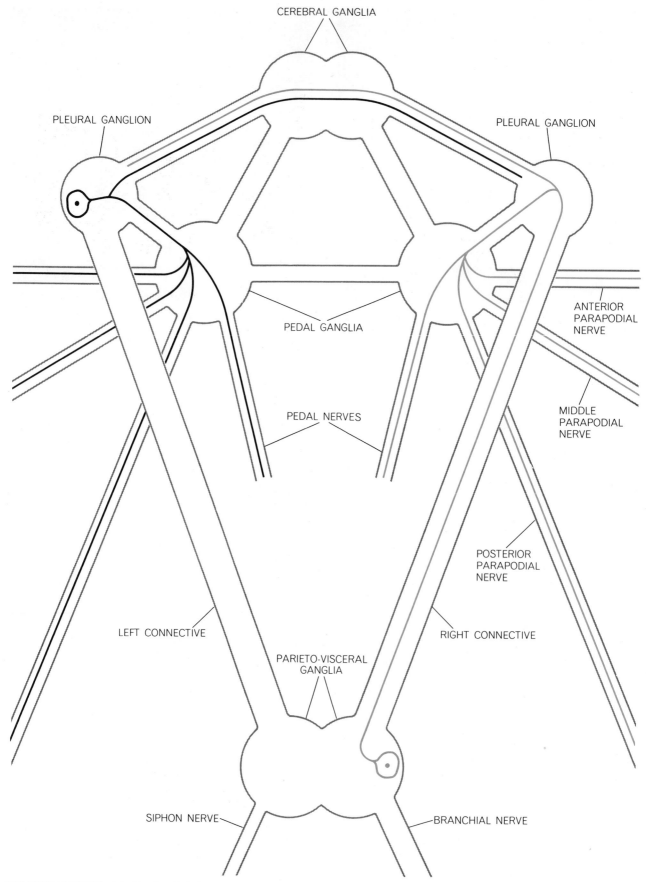

CEREBRAL GANGLIA

PLEURAL GANGLION

PLEURAL GANGLION

ANTERIOR
PARAPODIAL
NERVE

PEDAL GANGLIA

MIDDLE
PARAPODIAL
NERVE

PEDAL NERVES

POSTERIOR
PARAPODIAL
NERVE

LEFT CONNECTIVE

RIGHT CONNECTIVE

PARIETO-VISCERAL
GANGLIA

SIPHON NERVE

BRANCHIAL NERVE

NERVOUS SYSTEM of the "sea hare" *Aplysia*, a mollusk, lends itself to investigation because its cells are few, large and identifiable. Here the entire system is diagrammed and the paths of two nerve cells are shown in color. One of them (*red*) is cell No. 1 in the ganglion illustrated on the opposite page. The routes of a large number of *Aplysia* cells were worked out by L. Tauc of the Centre National de Recherche Scientifique in Paris and G. M. Hughes of Bristol University by recording from individual nerve cell bodies.

a variety of yellow and orange pigments in different proportions. Particular cells are consistent in position from one animal to the next. Several dozen cells can therefore be reliably recognized in different individuals by their size, color and position [*see illustrations on this page*].

Aplysia was first intensively studied in the late 1940's by A. Arvanitaki-Chalazonitis in her laboratory in Monaco. It has since attracted a number of investigators, notably L. Tauc of the Centre National de Recherche Scientifique in Paris, Eric R. Kandel of New York University and Felix Strumwasser of the California Institute of Technology. Tauc and his collaborators, notably G. M. Hughes of Bristol University, have constructed ingenious physiological maps of several *Aplysia* cells [*see illustration on opposite page*]. They accomplished this by inserting a glass microelectrode into a cell body and placing wire electrodes on all the nerve trunks connecting with the ganglion in which the cell body was located. If a particular nerve contained an axon of the cell in which the microelectrode was located, the microelectrode recorded an impulse when that nerve was stimulated with a brief electric shock. The branches of the axons may be arranged in an extremely complex way, but each cell is characterized by a constant arrangement of branches.

Other workers have demonstrated that the connections made in turn by such branches with other nerve cells are also constant. Microelectrodes were inserted in several identified cells, and one microelectrode was used to stimulate the cell it had penetrated while the others recorded impulse activity. A particular cell produced either of two kinds of effect in a nerve cell to which it was connected: an excitation, sometimes strong enough to evoke an impulse in the second cell, or an inhibition, which opposed the discharge of impulses. Strumwasser and Kandel have demonstrated that a single cell can directly excite some cells and inhibit others, and that a certain set of identifiable cells is always excited by a given cell and another set always inhibited.

The ganglia of *Aplysia* have been used in the investigation of two other important problems in nerve physiology: the cellular modifications that take place during "conditioning" and the origin of "discharge rhythms." To investigate the first, Kandel and Tauc recorded from an identifiable cell with a microelectrode while stimulating two nerve trunks containing nerve fibers that excited the recorded cell. A shock delivered to one of

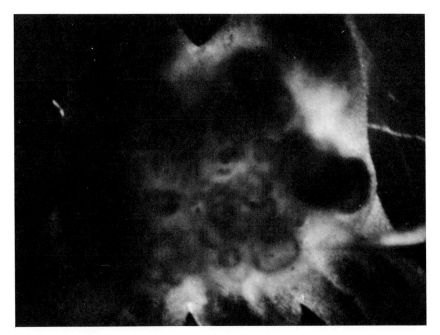

PARIETO-VISCERAL GANGLION of *Aplysia*, photographed unstained by Felix Strumwasser of the California Institute of Technology, measures about 2.5 millimeters across.

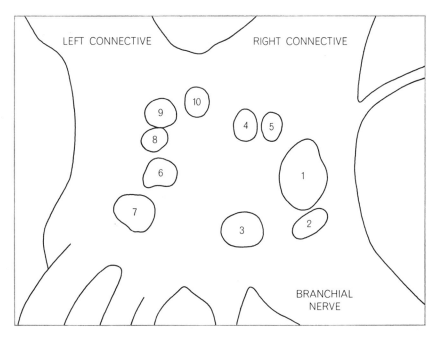

INDIVIDUAL CELLS that are consistently identifiable in the ganglion are diagrammed. Not all are clearly seen in the photograph, in which a microelectrode points to cell No. 3.

these nerves produced strong excitation, indicating that it was the more effective pathway; the other produced only a weak effect. If the shocks to the two pathways were repeatedly paired so that the weak followed the strong at a fixed, short interval, the response to the weak pathway became "conditioned" to the strong excitation; the response increased dramatically and stayed elevated for 15 minutes or more after the conditioning period. If the same number of shocks was delivered to both pathways for the same period but at random intervals, conditioning did not occur; the response to the weak pathway was not affected. Such systems promise that electrophysiological studies on learning may at last be brought down to the cellular level.

Nerve cells often discharge rhythmically, in bursts that last for a few seconds and are separated by longer intervals. Strumwasser discovered a particularly dramatic instance of rhythmicity

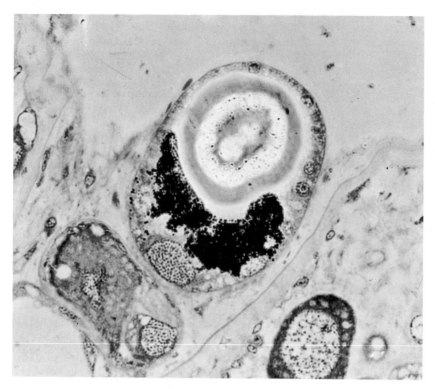

EYE OF *HERMISSENDA* is enlarged about 900 diameters in a photomicrograph made by the late John Barth at Stanford University. The longitudinal section shows the lens (*concentric rings*) and the retina below it. The granular gray structure just below and to the left of the black pigment screening the retina is the nucleus of one of the five receptor cells.

The remarkable feature of this miniature camera eye is that its retina consists of only five receptor cells, each one large enough to be penetrated with microelectrodes.

Barth found that cells exposed to light might respond in one of three ways: with an accelerated discharge, with a slower rate of firing followed by an "off" discharge (signaling the cessation of illumination) or with some complex mixture of the two. Dennis' experiments show clearly that this differentiation is not the result of separate classes of receptors. Both the excitatory response and the inhibitory one show similar peaks of sensitivity across the visible spectrum, indicating that they depend on the same light-absorbing pigment. When the activity of a pair (or a trio) of cells is recorded simultaneously, each impulse in one cell is followed by inhibition in the other (or the other two), indicating the presence of cross-connections among them [see *upper illustration on opposite page*]. Since this situation always holds, we conclude that the inhibitory network connects every cell with all four others.

We originally doubted that a mosaic of only five cells could actually form images as larger camera eyes do, but Dennis has demonstrated that the mosaic does indeed have the ability to detect the position of small light sources in the visual field. In one experiment a spot of light five degrees in diameter was moved from right to left and back again on a screen facing the eye [see *lower illustration on opposite page*]. Two of the five receptor cells were impaled with microelectrodes; one, whose activity is shown in the lower trace of each record, responded more strongly when the spot was moved to the left, and held its neighbor, whose activity is shown in the upper trace, under effective inhibitory check. When the light was at the right, the discharge ratio had been such that both cells were firing at almost the same frequency, and it returned to this former value when the spot was moved back to the right. Clearly the relative intensities impinging on the two cells must have been different for the two positions of the light. With the light at the left, the lower cell was more strongly illuminated and consequently fed a stronger inhibition to its neighbor; with the light at the right, the intensities were presumably nearly balanced. In addition, it may be that specific cells display individual personalities even under perfectly homogeneous illumination; those with comparatively little light-sensitive pigment or with relatively strong inhibitory input,

in a certain *Aplysia* cell whose activity—recorded over long periods of time in an isolated ganglion—exhibits a "circadian," or approximately 24-hour, rhythm. Its most active period is a few hours before what would be sunset on a normal light schedule. This inherent periodicity, like that of other biological clocks, is maintained even if such environmental variables as light and temperature are held constant. Strumwasser is now investigating the chemical changes that are correlated with the discharge cycle.

The large size and small number of nerve cells in certain mollusks makes them convenient systems in which to study a number of sensory phenomena. The mollusk *Hermissenda*, for example, has provided information on the nerve-cell interactions that underlie the processing of visual information in a simple "camera" eye: an eye in which a single lens focuses light on a retina of receptor cells. Vertebrate camera eyes have too many cells for such analysis, and so investigators have relied largely on simpler compound eyes, in which a number of independent elements, each with its own lens and sensory cells, send fibers to the central nervous system. Studies of such compound eyes, particularly in the horseshoe crab *Limulus*, revealed the

existence of one especially important process in visual systems: H. K. Hartline and his associates at the Rockefeller Institute found that when a given visual element is illuminated, it not only sends a train of impulses to the central nervous system along its own nerve fiber; it also inhibits the discharge of neighboring elements in the eye. This "lateral inhibition" decreases with distance from the visual element, and it functions to raise the level of contrast at boundaries of stimulus intensity [see "How Cells Receive Stimuli," by William H. Miller, Floyd Ratliff and H. K. Hartline; SCIENTIFIC AMERICAN Offprint 99].

Is lateral inhibition also an essential component of image-formation in other kinds of eye? What is the minimum number of light-receptor cells necessary to form a useful spatial representation of the visual field? What rules are followed in connecting them? These are among the questions investigated in our laboratory at Stanford University, first by the late John Barth and more recently by Michael Dennis, in the course of a study of the eye of *Hermissenda*. The eye measures less than .1 millimeter in its long dimension and consists of a lens, a cup of black pigment to ensure that light enters only from the right direction, and an underlying retina of receptor cells.

for example, would be particularly likely to respond in a predominantly inhibitory fashion and so would be characterized as "off" cells.

As the records show, there is a strong tendency for pairs of cells to fire at the same instant, even when their frequencies of discharge are quite different. This behavior cannot be accounted for on the basis of the inhibitory interaction alone, and it turns out that there is an additional kind of interaction of cells. It is of an excitatory nature, is very brief and is probably mediated by direct electrical connections between two cells. It promotes simultaneous discharge by acting as a trigger for the initiation of impulses in neighboring cells that are nearly ready to fire anyway. The resulting tendency to synchronize may be of value to the region of the brain that receives the visual messages.

These results indicate the technical advantage of small systems of nerve cells to the physiologist. In a larger sense

they illustrate how a few elements connected in simple ways can serve an organism remarkably well. It appears that with five receptor cells, a modest optical system and two types of interaction *Hermissenda* can build a crude image-forming system capable of enhancing contrast at boundaries and—at least theoretically—of measuring the speed and direction of moving objects.

The nerve cells of some crustaceans and insects are also easy to recognize individually, and there are relatively few of them. (They are not so spectacularly large as those in *Aplysia,* and instead of recording from the cells with microelectrodes most investigators dissect single axons from the connective nerves that run between central ganglia.) In such nervous systems a very few cells sometimes control a specific, anatomically restricted process. A network of this kind is found, for example, in the hearts of crabs and lobsters, where the beat is

triggered and spread by an assembly of only nine to 11 cells embedded in the heart muscle. Some of these cells are "pacemakers," which initiate impulses spontaneously at regular intervals; others are "followers" activated by the pacemakers. Connections among the follower cells marshal their responses into a burst of activity that grows and then subsides until the next pacemaker signals arrive. Activity from the followers also has a subtle feedback effect on the pacemaker frequency. With this system Theodore H. Bullock and his collaborators at the University of California at Los Angeles have pioneered in examining restricted ensembles of nerve cells to establish principles of nervous integration.

Can such analyses be expanded to deal with larger groups of nerve cells that control entire systems of muscles, or even control behavior complex enough to orient an animal in its environment or move the animal through it? They can, provided that the controlling cells are in-

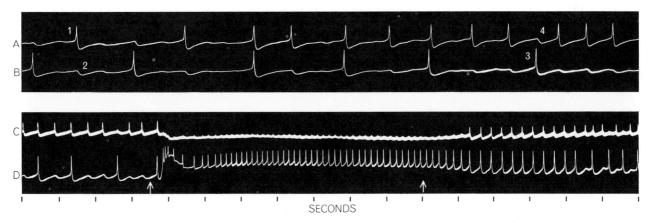

"ON" AND "OFF" responses are seen in records made simultaneously in two *Hermissenda* receptor cells. An impulse from either cell *A* or *B* (*1, 3*) produces an inhibitory hyperpolarization in the other cell (*2, 4*). The illumination of cell *D* (*interval between arrows*) makes it fire faster, inhibiting cell *C*. When the light is turned off, cell *C* is released from inhibition and discharges again.

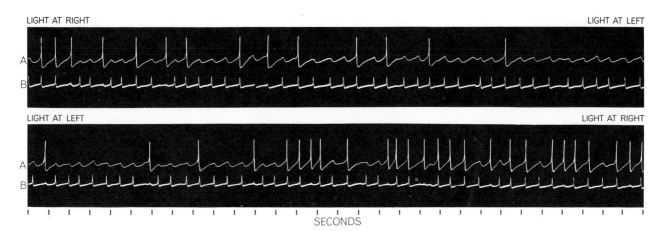

POSITION IS DETECTED by the differential responses of two receptor cells in *Hermissenda.* The discharge rates of cells *A* and *B* were about the same when a light was placed to the right of the field of view. As the light was moved to the left cell *B* discharged relatively more rapidly, effectively inhibiting cell *A.* When the light was moved back again, the former discharge ratio was reestablished.

dividually unique and are identifiable by the experimenter. The feasibility of such studies has been demonstrated primarily by C. A. G. Wiersma and his co-workers at the California Institute of Technology. In a series of investigations spanning the past three decades Wiersma has concerned himself with crustacean muscles and the motor-nerve axons that innervate them. The motor axons—which are remarkably few in number—can be distinguished from one another by their different electrical effects on the muscle and by the kinds of contraction they evoke. Some produce quick twitches by generating large, abrupt depolarizations (reductions in membrane potential that lead to excitation) in the muscle fibers; others make the muscle contract in a more sustained way by producing small and gradually augmenting depolarizations; still others prevent contraction. The number of nerve fibers serving any given muscle is small enough so that one can distinguish the impulses of each one in an electrical record from the entire nerve and correlate these impulses with events in the muscle.

Wiersma has exposed an even more remarkable differentiation of elements in the central nervous system of the crayfish. Single interneurons—nerve cells that collect information from a number of sensory fibers—can be isolated for electrical recording from a part of the central nervous system in the abdomen;

elsewhere such a cell runs its normal course, making connections by branching in each of several different ganglia. Wiersma has prepared maps that give the distribution over the animal's surface of the sensory receptors that will excite each such cell. He has shown that each interneuron is uniquely connected with a set of sensory-nerve fibers, so that a cell with a specific map is always found in the same anatomical location in the central nervous system.

A particular group of touch-sensitive hairs on the back of the fourth abdominal segment, for example, might connect with a dozen different central interneurons. Each interneuron, however, responds to some unique combination of that group of hair receptors and other groups. One interneuron, for instance, might be excited by the fourth-segment group alone; another might be activated by the corresponding group on segment No. 5 as well as by the hairs on segment No. 4; another by those on Nos. 6, 5 and 4; another by those on all segments on one side or on both sides, and so forth. Precise duplication of function is apparently absent; each element encodes a unique spatial combination of sensory inputs [see illustration below].

This specificity suggests that the position and connection pattern of each central nerve cell is precisely determined in the course of differentiation of the nervous system. The reliability of this

mechanism has been demonstrated impressively by Melvin J. Cohen and his colleagues at the University of Oregon, who have analyzed the organization of central ganglia in the cockroach. Cohen has located the cell bodies of specific motoneurons by taking advantage of a striking response shown by such cells when their axons are cut: If a motor nerve is severed at the periphery, even very near the muscle, each cell body supplying an axon in that nerve quickly develops a dense ring around its nucleus. This response, which can be detected with suitable stains, occurs within 12 hours [see illustration on page 2440]. New material comprising the ring has been identified as ribonucleic acid (RNA). Presumably it is required for the protein synthesis associated with regeneration; in any event, the ring provides an unambiguous label for associating a specific central cell with the peripheral destination of its axon.

By cutting individual motor nerves and locating their cell bodies in this way, Cohen has constructed a map that gives the positions for most of the motoneurons in a ganglion. The maps of ganglia from different individuals appear to be almost identical; indeed, specific cells are in nearly perfect register when sections of corresponding ganglia from several animals are superposed. Not only are the cell bodies of motoneurons that serve particular muscles precisely arrayed; they also appear to have rather specific biochemical personalities. Some motoneurons show the ring reaction especially strongly and others show it quite weakly, and these differences are consistently associated with particular cells—as judged by the position of the cell body and the peripheral destination of its axon.

In our own laboratory we have analyzed how the central nervous system of the crayfish deploys a limited array of identifiable nerve cells to control the posture of the abdomen. This structure consists of five segments with joints between them. Its shape is continuously and delicately varied by the action of thin sheets of muscle operating in antagonistic pairs—extensor and flexor—at each of the five joints. Both sets of muscles are symmetrical on each side of the abdomen. The extensors of each half-segment receive six nerve fibers, as do the flexors; the nerve fibers, like the muscles, are repeated almost identically in each segment.

Each individual motor nerve cell can be identified by the size of its impulses

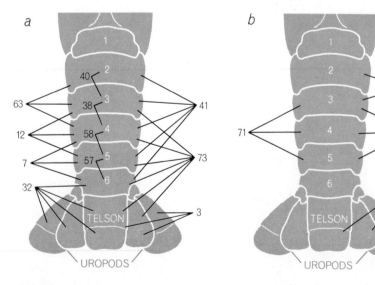

SPECIFIC GROUPS of touch-sensitive hairs on the segments of the crayfish abdomen excite specific interneurons located within the central nervous system. The receptive field of each interneuron listed here (*black numbers*) was mapped by C. A. G. Wiersma's group at Cal Tech. Each responds to stimulation of hair receptors on a unique combination of segments (*white numbers*), as shown by the pointers. The system is bilaterally symmetrical, with an interneuron No. 40, for instance, on each side. Neurons mapped at *a* respond to stimuli delivered to the same side of the animal. Of those mapped at *b*, those listed at the right respond to stimuli on the side opposite them; No. 71 responds to stimuli on either side.

in an electrical record obtained from the nerve bundles that run to flexor or extensor muscles. As one might expect, particular reflexes activate the nerves and muscles in rather stereotyped ways. If, for example, one forcibly flexes the abdomen of a crayfish while holding its thorax clamped and then releases it, the segments extend to approximately their former position. Howard Fields of our laboratory found that this action depends on a pair of receptors that span the dorsal joints in the abdomen. Flexion lengthens the muscle strands associated with these receptor cells, and the cells then discharge impulses that travel toward the central nervous system and activate motoneurons supplying the extensor muscles, which are thereby caused to contract against the imposed load. Such "resistance reflexes" are known in a variety of other systems, including the limbs of mammals and of crabs; in the crayfish they can be studied in a simplified situation, with a single receptor cell and six well-characterized motor cells constituting the entire neural equipment for the reflex loop.

Since only about 120 motoneurons are involved in the regulation of the entire abdomen's position, and since we were able to identify each of them, William H. Evoy and I decided to analyze the central control system for abdominal posture. While recording the motor discharge in several segments at once, we isolated and then stimulated single interneurons located within the central nervous system.

As we had anticipated, most cells had no effect on motor discharge, but we encountered some that regularly released intense, fully coordinated motor-output patterns when we stimulated them with a series of electric shocks. In every case the output was reciprocal: flexors were excited while extensors were inhibited, or vice versa, and the response was similar in several segments. Although equally complex behavior can be produced in many animals by localized stimulation of central nervous structures, it is likely that in most such cases many cells—perhaps thousands—are simultaneously activated by the comparatively gross stimulating procedure that is employed. In the crayfish abdomen, however, we have been able to demonstrate directly that a complete behavioral output can be the result of activity in a single central interneuron. Motor effects produced by stimulation of such central neurons in crayfish had been described earlier by Wiersma and K. Ikeda, who coined the term "command fiber" for those inter-

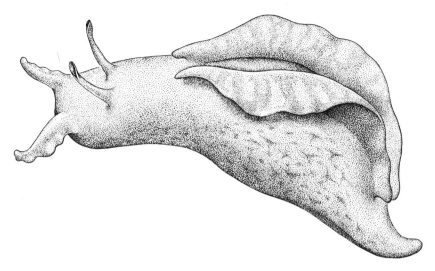

SEA HARE *APLYSIA* is a mollusk with a vestigial shell under the mantle between the winglike parapodia, which are used for locomotion. The animal is about 10 inches long.

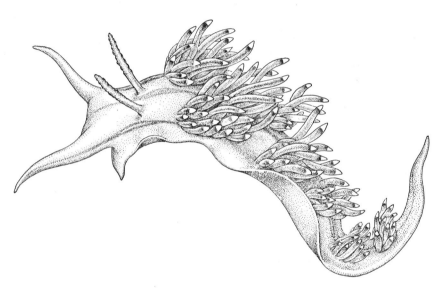

HERMISSENDA, another mollusk, is only one to three inches long. The "camera" eyes are embedded just behind the rhinophores, the two upright stalks near the left end of the animal.

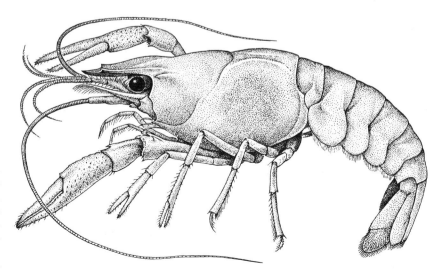

CRAYFISH *Procambarus*, the invertebrate in which complex motor effects produced by single cells are studied by Wiersma and by the author, is from three to five inches long.

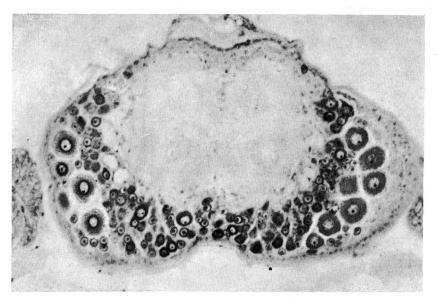

DENSE RINGS of ribonucleic acid surround the nuclei of the cells on one side (*left*) of a stained section of a cockroach ganglion about a millimeter across. Two days before the photograph was made by Melvin J. Cohen of the University of Oregon, all peripheral nerves from one side of this ganglion had been cut. The rings appear in the cells on that side.

neuron axons that produce stereotyped, complex motor effects.

When we compared, in single animals, a series of central nerve cells that produce extension, we found that each produced a special distribution of motor output in different segments. One strongly influenced the last two segments but had a weak effect on segments farther forward; another yielded an almost even balance of output; another activated the forward segments more strongly, and so on. This result led naturally to the inference that individual command elements might each code for a unique combination of segmental actions and thereby produce specific movements or positions. In collaboration with Benjamin Dane, who is now at Tufts University, we filmed the maneuvers of the abdomen that occurred when command fibers were stimulated, while simultaneously recording the discharge of motoneurons supplying muscles in one of the segments. This experiment confirmed the neurophysiological predictions: the films show that two command elements with a generally similar action affect the segments in different ratios and so produce unique abdominal postures [*see illustration on page 2433*].

These results indicate that the coordination of at least some behavior is based on the intrinsic "wiring" of a nervous center and can be released by single-cell triggers. Such a conclusion would have been more surprising a decade ago than it is now. It was once

thought that complex sequential behavior such as locomotion depended for its organization on a series of instructions fed back to the central nervous system from peripheral sensory cells. Each new act, according to this view, was initiated by proprioceptive sense organs that were excited by the animal's own movement and signaled that one response had been completed; the whole sequence was likened to a chain of reflexes successively activated by the continuous inflow of sensory signals from the periphery. In recent years biologists have become more convinced that the connections among interneurons at the nervous center, selected by evolution and precisely made during the developmental process, contain most of the organization inherent in such behavior, and that sense organs play a role that is more permissive than instructive.

One of the most convincing demonstrations of the importance of these central connections was provided by the experiments of Donald M. Wilson of the University of California at Berkeley on the flight of locusts. This behavior pattern consists of a sequence of actions in the muscles that elevate, depress and twist the wings. Since these muscles are served by only one or two motor nerve cells, one can obtain a record of the activity of each cell by inserting fine wires into the muscles of a relatively intact animal. In this way Wilson and Torkel Weis-Fogh were able to define the impulse sequences, along various motor nerves, characteristic of normal flight.

The pattern can be triggered in several ways. When the insect is stimulated by having air blown on its head, the motor activity characteristic of flight is frequently released, but Wilson has shown that the output pattern has no relation to the timing of the input. Indeed, when he stimulated one of the central connectives electrically at random intervals, the flight motor output still had its normal frequency and pattern.

Associated with the base of each wing of the locust there is a sensory-nerve cell that responds with single impulses or a short burst when the wing comes to the top of its upstroke. It had been supposed that these receptors might be providing phase information about the wingbeat cycle and perhaps initiating activity in the motor nerves controlling the downstroke. Wilson eliminated these receptors and found that although the frequency of flight motor output dropped somewhat, its repetitive character and the sequence of events within a single cycle were unimpaired. This showed that the stretch receptors, although they participate in a reflex that controls frequency, do not provide any information about the phase relations within a single cycle. Since the entire pattern of behavior can be produced by a central nervous system isolated from peripheral structures—as long as enough excitation of some kind is supplied—it must be concluded that all the information for the flight sequence is stored in a set of central connections.

At this point one can only assume that the sequential events of the flight pattern, like the motions that result in postural changes in the crayfish abdomen, are released by activity in central "command" elements. Some single interneurons are known to release similar complex, sequential behavior in the crayfish. One, for example, produces a sequence of flexions that ascends slowly from segment to segment until it reaches the forward end of the abdomen and then begins again at the back. Another causes an intricate series of movements in the appendages of the tail. We wonder how such central command neurons are activated during voluntary movements, whether they are organized entirely in parallel or in part as a hierarchy of related elements, and what kinds of sensory stimulus excite them. While it would be premature to assume that all these questions can be answered or that we can apply the results to other systems, it is the peculiar advantage of small networks of nerve cells that such a prospect does not seem hopeless.

The Author

DONALD KENNEDY is professor of biology and head of the department of biological sciences at Stanford University. He was graduated from Harvard College in 1952 and obtained a Ph.D. from Harvard four years later. After teaching at Syracuse University for four years he went to Stanford. He writes that he shares his interest in the subject matter of his article "with a small network of comparative neurophysiologists, most of them located on the West Coast." He adds: "I am especially anxious to acknowledge my gratitude to these friends, most of whom are mentioned in the article. They have provided substantial help in its preparation." Kennedy was the author of "Inhibition in Visual Systems" in the July 1963 issue of SCIENTIFIC AMERICAN.

Bibliography

HETEROSYNAPTIC FACILITATION IN NEURONS OF THE ABDOMINAL GANGLION OF APLYSIA DEPILANS. E. R. Kandel and L. Tauc in *Journal of Physiology* (London), Vol. 181, No. 1, pages 1–27; November, 1965.

ON THE FUNCTIONAL ANATOMY OF NEURONAL UNITS IN THE ABDOMINAL CORD OF THE CRAYFISH, PROCAMBARUS CLARKII (GIRARD). C. A. G. Wiersma and G. M. Hughes in *The Journal of Comparative Neurology*, Vol. 116, No. 2, pages 209–228; April, 1961.

RELEASE OF COORDINATED BEHAVIOR IN CRAYFISH BY SINGLE CENTRAL NEURONS. Donald Kennedy, W. H. Evoy and J. T. Hanawalt in *Science*, Vol. 154, No. 3751, pages 917–919; November 18, 1966.

TYPES OF INFORMATION STORED IN SINGLE NEURONS. Felix Strumwasser in *Invertebrate Nervous Systems: Their Significance for Mammalian Neurophysiology*, edited by Cornelius A. G. Wiersma. The University of Chicago Press, 1967.

SPECIAL NOTE TO TEACHERS: Each article in this volume, plus more than 660 others, is available as a separate, self-bound SCIENTIFIC AMERICAN Offprint. Offprints may be ordered in any combination and in any quantity. Teachers who want to adopt articles for their courses, therefore, can ensure that each student has his own set. Students' sets are collated by the publisher before shipment.